THE PHYSIOLOGY OF CRUSTACEA

VOLUME II
SENSE ORGANS, INTEGRATION, AND BEHAVIOR

THE PHYSIOLOGY OF CRUSTACEA

VOLUME I
METABOLISM AND GROWTH

VOLUME II
SENSE ORGANS, INTEGRATION, AND BEHAVIOR

THE PHYSIOLOGY
OF CRUSTACEA

EDITED BY

TALBOT H. WATERMAN
DEPARTMENT OF ZOOLOGY, YALE UNIVERSITY

VOLUME **II**

SENSE ORGANS,
INTEGRATION, AND BEHAVIOR

ACADEMIC PRESS, NEW YORK AND LONDON
1961

ACADEMIC PRESS INC.
111 Fifth Avenue, New York, New York 10003

United Kingdom Edition published by
ACADEMIC PRESS INC. (LONDON) LTD.
Berkeley Square House, London W.1

LIBRARY OF CONGRESS CATALOG CARD NUMBER: 59-7690

Second Printing, 1968

PRINTED IN THE UNITED STATES OF AMERICA

VOLUME I

METABOLISM AND GROWTH

1. GENERAL CRUSTACEAN BIOLOGY. *Talbot H. Waterman*, Department of Zoology, Yale University, New Haven, Connecticut, and *Fenner A. Chace, Jr.*, Division of Marine Invertebrates, U. S. National Museum, Washington, D. C.
2. RESPIRATION. *H. P. Wolvekamp*, Zoölogisch Laboratorium der Rijksuniversiteit te Leiden, Leiden, The Netherlands, and *Talbot H. Waterman*, Department of Zoology, Yale University, New Haven, Connecticut.
3. BIOCHEMISTRY OF PIGMENTS. *T. W. Goodwin*, Department of Biochemistry, The University of Liverpool, Liverpool, England.
4. BLOOD CHEMISTRY. *Marcel Florkin*, Laboratoires de Biochimie, l'Université de Liège, Liège, Belgium.
5. CIRCULATION AND HEART FUNCTION. *Donald M. Maynard*, Department of Zoology, University of Michigan, Ann Arbor, Michigan.
6. FEEDING AND NUTRITION. *S. M. Marshall and A. P. Orr*, Marine Station, Millport, Isle of Cumbrae, Scotland.
7. VITAMINS. *L. R. Fisher*, National Institute for Research in Dairying, University of Reading, Reading, England.
8. DIGESTION AND METABOLISM. *H. J. Vonk*, Laboratorium voor Vergelijkende Physiologie der Rijksuniversiteit, Utrecht, The Netherlands.
9. OSMOTIC AND IONIC REGULATION. *James D. Robertson*, Department of Zoology, The University, Glasgow, Scotland.
10. EXCRETION. *Gwyneth Parry*, Freshwater Fisheries Laboratory, Ministry of Agriculture, Fisheries and Food, London, England.
11. TERRESTRIAL ADAPTATIONS. *E. B. Edney*, Zoology Department, University College of Rhodesia and Nyasaland, Salisbury, Southern Rhodesia.
12. ECOLOGY AND METABOLISM. *Marcel Florkin*, Laboratoires de Biochimie, l'Université de Liège, Liège, Belgium.
13. SEX DETERMINATION. *Hélène Charniaux-Cotton*, Laboratoire de Génétique Évolutive et de Biométrie, Gif-sur-Yvette (Seine-et-Oise), France.
14. INTEGUMENT AND EXOSKELETON. *Ralph Dennell*, Department of Zoology, University of Manchester, Manchester, England.
15. MOLTING AND ITS CONTROL. *L. M. Passano*, Department of Zoology, Yale University, New Haven, Connecticut.
16. RELATIVE GROWTH. *Georges Teissier*, Laboratoire de Zoologie, Université de Paris, Paris, France.
17. AUTOTOMY AND REGENERATION. *Dorothy E. Bliss*, Department of Fishes and Aquatic Biology, American Museum of Natural History, New York, New York.

VOLUME II

SENSE ORGANS, INTEGRATION, AND BEHAVIOR

1. LIGHT SENSITIVITY AND VISION. *Talbot H. Waterman,* Department of Zoology, Yale University, New Haven, Connecticut.
2. MECHANORECEPTION. *Melvin J. Cohen,* Department of Biology, University of Oregon, Eugene, Oregon, and *Sven Dijkgraaf,* Laboratorium voor Vergelijkende Physiologie der Rijksuniversiteit, Utrecht, The Netherlands.
3. CHEMORECEPTION AND THERMORECEPTION. *Saul B. Barber,* Department of Biology, Lehigh University, Bethlehem, Pennsylvania.
4. PIGMENTARY EFFECTORS. *Lewis H. Kleinholz,* Department of Biology, Reed College, Portland, Oregon.
5. LIGHT PRODUCTION. *E. Newton Harvey,* formerly Department of Biology, Princeton University, Princeton, New Jersey.
6. THE NEUROMUSCULAR SYSTEM. *C. A. G. Wiersma,* Division of Biology, California Institute of Technology, Pasadena, California.
7. REFLEXES AND THE CENTRAL NERVOUS SYSTEM. *C. A. G. Wiersma,* Division of Biology, California Institute of Technology, Pasadena, California.
8. NEUROHUMORS AND NEUROSECRETION. *J. H. Welsh,* The Biological Laboratories, Harvard University, Cambridge, Massachusetts.
9. LOCOMOTION. *John H. Lochhead,* Department of Zoology, The University of Vermont, Burlington, Vermont.
10. KINETIC AND TACTIC RESPONSES. *L. Pardi,* Istituto e Museo di Zoologia, Università di Torino, Torino, Italy, and *F. Papi,* Istituto di Zoologia dell'Università, Pisa, Italy.
11. PHYSIOLOGICAL RHYTHMS. *Frank A. Brown, Jr.,* Department of Biological Sciences, Northwestern University, Evanston, Illinois.
12. MIGRATIONS. *Richard Bainbridge,* Department of Zoology, University of Cambridge, Cambridge, England.
13. COMPLEX BEHAVIOR. *Hermann Schöne,* Max-Planck-Institut für Verhaltensphysiologie, Seewiesen über Starnberg, Germany.
14. COMPARATIVE PHYSIOLOGY. *Talbot H. Waterman,* Department of Zoology, Yale University, New Haven, Connecticut.

PREFACE

A crustacean, like any other organism, is a living steady state system which must be capable of maintaining its essential integrity for a generation. To do this, external or internal changes which affect its functional organization have to be counteracted by appropriate adjustments holding the steady state within viable limits despite such perturbations. To some extent maintenance of the steady state is dependent on basic physical and chemical factors like the properties of water or on relationships like those underlying Le Chatelier's principle. But the homeostasis of many organismal characters depends on biological feedback loops connecting the perturbation with a compensating response. In eumetazoans the feedback loops generally consist of 1) sense organs which detect external or internal changes, 2) effector elements, which can do work, and 3) nervous or hormonal integrating systems which transform afferent information into efferent commands for effector responses which tend to preserve the steady state.

This volume reviews these three components of self regulation for the Crustacea and analyzes the behavior which emerges therefrom. Within the limits of these objectives the book is a coherent unit by itself. However, it is closely integrated with the first volume of the "Physiology of Crustacea" which deals mainly with their metabolism and growth. Both volumes together are intended to provide a broad review of the physiology of the Class Crustacea considered to some extent in terms of their special physiology but mainly from a comparative point of view. The latter is particularly emphasized in the final chapter of this volume which attempts to summarize the entire work.

The completion of Volume II six to eight months after the first one has aggravated the difficult problem of keeping the material strictly up to date. Most of the contributors have felt this pressure more or less strongly. However, rather extensive alterations in galleys and page proofs, which were checked by the authors late in 1959 or early in 1960, permitted the addition of important new findings and references. The constant need for revision is either disheartening because it proves the ephemeral nature of work such as ours, or it is pleasantly stimulating because it shows how lively current interest is in crustacean physiology!

For consistency the same classification of the Class Crustacea used in Volume I has been employed here. This is presented for reference at the beginning of the Systematic Index, which also indicates for all organisms mentioned their systematic position and their synonymy within the physiological literature cited. Determination of the correct name and synonymy is particularly important in comparative work where different animals known under the same name or the same animal known under different names can be especially troublesome. We are again most grateful for the expert collaboration of Dr. F. A. Chace, Jr., of the United States National Museum in preparing the classification used and in checking the correct names of all the hundreds of different species cited.

Hearty thanks are also due to the numerous others whose help has contributed greatly to the preparation of this book. In addition to the authors, many colleagues and friends of the Editor have helped very much in planning and executing various phases of the work. Particular mention should be made of Dietrich Bodenstein, John B. Buck, George Camougis, V. G. Dethier, Timothy H. Goldsmith, Earl D. Hanson, G. Evelyn Hutchinson, Rudolf Jander, Stephen W. Kuffler, Irwin C. Lieb, Ernst Mayr, Alvin Novick, C. Ladd Prosser, Charles L. Remington, A. G. Richards, Berta Scharrer, Hermann Schöne, John H. Welsh, and C. A. G. Wiersma. Elizabeth A. Livingston has continued to serve most effectively as the Editor's assistant in the arduous work of preparing manuscripts and proofs for the press. Jean Caldwell Kashgarian has also given able assistance in many ways, as has the staff of Academic Press.

Strong support for the Editor's over-all research program has been provided for a number of years by the Office of Naval Research and also, more recently, by the National Science Foundation. Indispensable basic facilities and support of many kinds have also been generously given by Yale University. The Editor's indebtedness to these many co-workers and institutions is great, and we may only hope that the end results repay the time and effort invested.

During the final stages of our book's preparation we suffered a serious loss in the death of Professor E. Newton Harvey. Fortunately he had already corrected the galley for his chapter in Volume II, and we are happy in publishing it to salute the memory of an outstanding comparative and general physiologist. His influence as a research worker, teacher, writer, and editor has been far-reaching and salubrious.

August, 1960   TALBOT H. WATERMAN
Honolulu, Hawaii

CONTENTS

Contributors and Chapter list, Volume I.................................... v
Contributors and Chapter list, Volume II................................. vi
Preface vii

Chapter 1. LIGHT SENSITIVITY AND VISION, *Talbot H. Waterman.*

   I. General Sensitivity 1
  II. Median Eyes 6
 III. Lateral Eyes 8
     A. Structural Pattern... 8
     B. Image Formation 17
     C. Functional Units 26
     D. Intensity Functions 30
     E. Time and Space Functions 35
     F. Wavelength Functions 42
     G. Polarized Light Sensitivity................................. 48
  IV. Summary and Conclusions.. 52
     References 53

Chapter 2. MECHANORECEPTION, *Melvin J. Cohen and Sven Dijkgraaf.*

   I. Introduction 65
  II. Methods of Study.. 66
 III. Touch 67
  IV. Proprioception 68
     A. Muscle Receptor Organ...................................... 69
     B. Limb Proprioceptors.. 74
     C. Comparative Aspects 77
   V. Equilibrium Receptors 77
     A. Receptor Structure and Distribution......................... 78
     B. Physiology 80
     C. Comparative Aspects 99
  VI. Hearing and Sound Production.................................... 100
     A. Hearing and Vibration Reception............................ 100
     B. Sound Production 101
 VII. Summary and Conclusions....................................... 102
     References 104

Chapter 3. CHEMORECEPTION AND THERMORECEPTION, *Saul B. Barber.*

I. Chemoreception 109
   A. Introduction 109
   B. The Receptor Organs 109
   C. Functional Properties 116
   D. Summary 125
II. Thermoreception 125
   A. Introduction 125
   B. Responses to Thermal Stimuli.. 126
   C. Summary 128
   References 128

Chapter 4. PIGMENTARY EFFECTORS, *Lewis H. Kleinholz.*

I. Introduction 133
   A. Chromatophores 133
   B. Retinal Pigments 134
II. Chromatophores 135
   A. Chromatophore Responses 135
   B. Mechanisms Regulating Chromatophores.................................. 136
III. Retinal Pigments 148
   A. General Morphology 148
   B. Normal Photomechanical Changes 150
   C. Regulation 151
IV. Comparisons with Other Animals.. 159
   A. Insect Color Changes 159
   B. Insect Retinal Pigments 161
   C. Vertebrate Color Changes.. 161
V. General Summary and Conclusions.. 163
   References 163

Chapter 5. LIGHT PRODUCTION, *E. Newton Harvey.*

I. Occurrence and Distribution of Luminescence.............................. 171
II. Types of Luminous Organs.. 174
   A. Ostracoda 174
   B. Copepoda 175
   C. Malacostraca 175
III. Physical Nature of the Light... 177
IV. Biochemistry of Light Production.. 178
   A. Miscellaneous Observations 178
   B. *Cypridina* Luciferin and Luciferase.................................. 180
V. Control of Luminescence.. 184
VI. Use of the Light.. 186
   References 187

Chapter 6. THE NEUROMUSCULAR SYSTEM, *C. A. G. Wiersma.*

I. Introduction 191
II. Efferent Nerve Fibers and Their Properties.............................. 193
III. Neuromuscular Connections 196
   A. Histology 196

B. Typical Responses to Efferent Stimulation........................ 198
C. Innervation Patterns in Different Crustacea...................... 202
IV. Electrophysiology of Nerve-Muscle Preparations.................... 206
A. Membrane Potential of Muscle Fibers........................... 206
B. Electrical Changes Caused by Motor Axon Stimulation............. 207
C. Membrane Potential and Inhibition............................ 210
D. Membrane Potential and Double Motor Innervation............... 213
E. Quadruple Motor Innervation.................................. 215
V. Processes Between Nerve Impulse and Contraction................... 216
VI. Properties of Muscle Fibers..................................... 219
A. Anatomy 219
B. Metabolism and Biochemistry 221
VII. Comparison of Different Innervation Systems...................... 222
A. Comparison of Slow Systems and Opener Systems................. 222
B. Comparison of Fast Systems.................................. 224
C. Comparison of Inhibitory Systems............................. 228
VIII. Effects of Drugs and Ions...................................... 231
A. Drugs 231
B. Ions 233
IX. Summary and Conclusions....................................... 235
References 236

Chapter 7. REFLEXES AND THE CENTRAL NERVOUS SYSTEM, C. A. G. Wiersma.

I. Introduction 241
II. Histology 242
A. Sensory Fibers 244
B. Efferent Fibers... 244
C. Interneurons 246
D. Synaptic Connections 250
III. Reflexes 251
A. Axon Reflexes.. 252
B. Simple Reflexes 253
C. Complex Reflexes 256
D. Effects of Surgical Interference............................... 257
IV. Spontaneous Activity.. 258
V. Physiology of Central Units..................................... 260
A. Giant Fiber System 260
B. Transmission from Giant Fibers to Motor Fibers................. 261
C. Other Central Fibers, Motor Aspect........................... 265
D. Other Central Fibers, Sensory Aspects......................... 267
VI. Pharmacology 273
VII. General Conclusions... 275
References 276

Chapter 8. NEUROHUMORS AND NEUROSECRETION, J. H. Welsh.

I. Introduction 281
II. Acetylcholine 282
A. Evidence for the Ach System in Crustaceans.................... 282
B. Function of Ach 286
III. Amines 289

IV. Factor I.. 290
V. Neurosecretory Systems................................. 291
    A. Sinus Gland System 291
    B. Postcommissural and Pericardial Organs............. 295
VI. Neurosecretory Substances.............................. 296
    A. Diversity and Chemical Nature..................... 296
    B. Storage and Release................................ 299
    C. Functions 303
VII. Comparisons and Conclusions........................... 303
    References 305

Chapter 9. LOCOMOTION, *John H. Lochhead.*

I. Introduction 313
II. General Features..................................... 314
    A. Biomechanics 314
    B. Integration and Control of Locomotion............. 316
III. Types of Locomotion................................. 322
    A. Walking and Running.............................. 322
    B. Climbing 332
    C. Plowing through Mud or Sand..................... 333
    D. Burrowing 334
    E. Jumping 335
    F. Swimming 335
    G. Escape Mechanisms 353
IV. Comparison with Other Animals....................... 354
V. Summary and Conclusions.............................. 354
    References 356

Chapter 10. KINETIC AND TACTIC RESPONSES, *L. Pardi and F. Papi.*

I. Introduction 365
II. Fundamental Mechanisms.............................. 366
    A. Kineses 366
    B. Taxes 367
III. Responses to Light.................................. 369
    A. Directional Responses to Light 369
    B. Photokineses 373
    C. Phototaxes 375
    D. Special Cases 380
IV. Responses to Chemical Stimuli........................ 383
V. Responses to Mechanical Stimuli....................... 387
    A. Rheotaxis and Anemotaxis........................ 387
    B. Thigmokinesis 388
    C. Geotaxis 389
VI. Responses to Thermal Stimuli........................ 390
VII. Responses to Electrical Stimuli...................... 391
VIII. Conclusions 391
IX. Summary 392
    References 393

Chapter 11. PHYSIOLOGICAL RHYTHMS, *Frank A. Brown, Jr.*

   I. General Introduction... 401
  II. Persistent Rhythms.. 402
     A. Chromatophores and Color Change............................ 402
     B. Retinal-Pigment Migration 405
     C. Spontaneous Motor Activity................................. 408
     D. Metabolic Rate 410
     E. Other Phenomena 414
  III. Properties of the Rhythmic Mechanism........................... 415
     A. Temperature Relations 415
     B. Relationships to Light 417
     C. Other Properties 421
  IV. The Nature of the Frequency-Regulating Mechanism................ 421
   V. General Conclusions and Summary................................ 425
     References 426

Chapter 12. MIGRATIONS, *Richard Bainbridge.*

   I. Introduction 431
  II. Pelagic Migrations... 431
     A. Vertical Migration 432
     B. Horizontal Migration 446
  III. Benthic and Terrestrial Migrations............................... 449
     A. Description 449
     B. Mechanisms 452
     C. Initiating and Controlling Factors........................... 452
     D. Value to the Animal....................................... 453
  IV. Conclusions 454
     References 455

Chapter 13. COMPLEX BEHAVIOR, *Hermann Schöne.*

   I. Introduction 465
  II. Behavior Types.. 466
     A. Individual Behavior 466
     B. Behavior Toward Others.................................... 473
  III. Analysis of Behavior... 487
     A. Components of Behavior.................................... 487
     B. Behavioral Changes in Ontogeny............................. 504
     C. Behavior and Evolution.................................... 512
  VI. Conclusions 514
     References 515

Chapter 14. COMPARATIVE PHYSIOLOGY, *Talbot H. Waterman.*

   I. Introduction 521
  II. The Comparative Process....................................... 523
  III. Descriptive Comparisons....................................... 528
     A. Within Individuals 528
     B. Between Individuals of a Species............................. 536
     C. Between Crustaceans 537
     D. Between Crustacea and Other Taxa.......................... 540

IV. Explanatory Comparisons... 554
A. Genetic 555
B. Developmental 558
C. Adaptive 560
D. Evolutionary 570
V. Conclusions 583
References 584

Author Index 595

Systematic Index (including synonymy)................................. 615

Subject Index 637

CHAPTER 1

TALBOT H. WATERMAN

LIGHT SENSITIVITY AND VISION

I. *GENERAL SENSITIVITY*

Sensitivity to electromagnetic energy at wavelengths extending from the ultraviolet (UV) to the infrared is a widespread and important adaptive function in crustaceans, as in most living things. According to the analysis of Viaud[185,186] such sensitivity is of two basic sorts: 1) generalized or dermal light sensitivity without any obvious receptor structures, and 2) specialized light reception dependent on differentiated eyes or eyespots. In the former case conspicuous photolabile pigments are not present; in the latter, visual pigments can often be observed in the retina, but they may in other cases be masked by photostable pigments or be too dilute to appear distinctly colored.

Certain crustacean light responses may fall into the first of these categories. The eyeless* isopod *Paragnathia*,[130] the blind cumacean *Leucon nasica*,[235] and *Cambarus ayersii*, with extremely degenerate eyes,[223] all respond to light. Similarly, photokinesis still occurs in *Daphnia* with the compound eyes extirpated;[78] blinded isopods may respond to light by chromatophore expansion,[2] blinded amphipods by light-oriented behavior;[229] the coconut crab (*Birgus latro*)[77] and perhaps the fish louse (*Argulus foliaceus*)[96] are photosensitive after the compound eyes are removed. In *Artemia*, however, careful removal of both the compound and naupliar eyes produces animals which do not respond at all to light.[119]

The untested influence of a persistent naupliar eye could have affected the decapods and branchiuran cited above, but such an organ

---

* Larval eyes are enormous but their only adult vestiges are diffuse masses of black pigment.

seems to be completely lacking in isopods and amphipods. The photo-kinesis of *Daphnia* without compound eyes could also have been evoked through the naupliar eye. Yet that alternative was apparently elim-inated in an earlier study[168] showing that *Daphnia* still avoid near UV light even after both median and compound eyes have been removed.*

This diffuse UV sensitivity has been explained merely as a general damaging effect of these short wavelengths on the animal. But this appears inadequate since two cladocerans, *Peracantha truncata* and *Scapholeberis mucronata*, among many negative species tested, are positively phototactic to UV.[143] However, the possible secondary in-fluence of tissue fluorescence was not controlled in this case.[125] Not only does *Daphnia*'s response to UV persist in completely blinded animals but the effect of λ on its photokinesis is curious. It is a sigmoid function decreasing from violet toward the red, which sug-gests a UV maximum[184] and is distinctly different from the action spectrum of phototactic orientation (Table 4).†

On this basis Viaud has hypothesized that a generalized dermal light sense is responsible for all but the axial orientation in *Daphnia*'s light responses. But the only other known arthropod photokinetic action spectrum (in the fresh-water mite *Unionicola*[208]) has its maxi-mum near 530 mμ and falls off sharply on either side of this λ, thus resembling the phototactic action spectrum for *Daphnia* rather than its photokinetic one[184] (Fig. 1). Localized stimulation shows that many general body areas of decapods are sensitive to light in certain forms with little integumentary pigment (e.g. *Alpheus armillatus*) and in others which are sensitive immediately after molting before such pig-ment has formed again.[101]

Possibly related to such structurally cryptic photosensitivity is the light response of the sixth abdominal ganglion of macrurans. This was discovered electrophysiologically in *Orconectes virilis*.[146] Behavioral studies confirmed its presence and demonstrated a similar caudal pho-toreceptor in *Procambarus clarkii*, *Panulirus argus*, and *P. guttatus* but not in various Natantia tested.[224] In the crayfish at least, the caudal photoreceptor increases pereiopod locomotor activity, either when stim-

---

* Similarly the influence of light on *Daphnia* heart rate does not appear to de-pend either on the compound or naupliar eyes (Chapter 5, Vol. I).

† Similar differences in spectral sensitivity appear in the compound eye move-ments induced by selective illumination of *Daphnia pulex*. Irradiation of the eyes alone has its maximal effect on this response near 520 mμ, whereas illuminating the body but not the eyes is most effective at the shortest wavelengths studied, 400–420 mμ.[162a]

ulated alone or with the compound eyes. Despite the absence of histologically demonstrated light-sensitive elements, this ganglion responds
to illumination with a barrage of neural discharges seemingly limited
to 2–4 active fibers. Long latencies of as much as 10 sec are typical
at threshold. With steady stimulation, impulses build up in frequency
for several seconds to a stable rate; at the end of any considerable
illumination an after-discharge persists for several seconds.

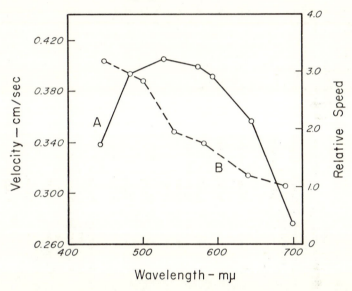

Fig. 1. Relation between photokinetic velocity of locomotion and wavelength in
(*A*) the fresh-water mite *Unionicola ypsilophorus* (redrawn from Waterman[208]), and
in (*B*) *Daphnia* (redrawn from Viaud[184]). These curves suggest that quite different
photosensitive systems are involved in these responses. The left ordinate applies to
A, the right to *B*.

Unlike the light-induced impulses from the compound eyes, on-
and off-effects are lacking in this system even though behavioral off-
effects occur at stimulus levels too low for other motor influences.[224]
In addition, the caudal light receptor has a higher threshold, responds
more slowly, and adapts less rapidly than the compound eye.[146] The
spectral sensitivity of this abdominal receptor extends from blue violet
to orange but excludes the red. Infrared is without effect and UV has
not been tested. In occasional individual crayfish a red pigment
(absorption λ max 500 mμ) is obvious in cell bodies and axons of the
sixth abdominal ganglion. Bleaching of this substance has not been
detected, and it cannot yet be identified as a visual pigment.[108]

TABLE 1

Types and Distribution of Eyes

Group	Median			Lateral*			
	Occurrence	Units	Special interest	Occurrence	Retinular cells	Cone segments	Special interest
Anostraca	Nauplius / Adult	—	Lenses only in *Artemia*	Adult (stalked)	5^{140}	—	—
Notostraca	Nauplius / Adult	—	—	Adult (sessile)	7^{227}	—	*Limnadia* Eye muscles and chamber
Conchostraca	Nauplius / Adult	—	—	Adult (sessile)	5	—	2 Eyes may partly fuse
Cladocera	Nauplius / Adult	—	—	Adult (sessile)	5^{28}†	5	Fused to 1 median; movable
Myodocopa	Nauplius / Adult	—	—	Adult Cypridinidae	7	2	*Gigantocypris*
Cladocopa	None	—	—	None	—	—	—
Podocopa	Nauplius / Adult	2–3	—	None	—	—	—
Platycopa	Nauplius ? / None in adult	—	—	None	—	—	—
Cephalocarida	Adult		—	None	—	—	—
Mystacocarida	Adult	One or more lateral pairs	—	None	—	—	—
Calanoida	Larvae / Adult	3 Usually	*Anomalocera* *Labidocera*	None	—	—	—
Harpacticoida	Larvae / Adult	—	*Macrosetella* *Miracia*	None	—	—	—
Cyclopoida	Larvae / Adult	—	*Corycaeus* *Copilia*	None	—	—	—
Notodelphyoida	Larvae / Adult	—	—	None	—	—	—
Monstrilloida	Larvae / Adult	—	—	None	—	—	—
Caligoida	Larvae / Adult	—	—	None	—	—	—
Lernaeopodoida	Larvae / Adult ?	—	—	None	—	—	—

	Naupliar eye		Compound eye			Remarks
Branchiura	Larva; Adults	3; No lenses	Larva; Adult (sessile)	4 + 1[121]	4	
Thoracica	Larvae; Adult	2–3 part; in adults may be 2 separate	Cypris	—	—	8–10 Ommas; degenerates at metamorphosis; 5 Ommas
Acrothoracica	Nauplius, Cypris, Adult ♂	—	Metanauplius; Cypris	—	—	
Ascothoracica	Absent in most	2; Laura	None; Not known	—	—	
Apoda	Not known	—	—	—	—	
Rhizocephala	Nauplius, Cypris	—	Not in cypris; Adult (stalked)	7	4	
Nebaliacea	Not known	—	Adult (sessile or stalked)	—	—	
Anaspidacea	Only in *Paranaspides lacustris*	—	Adult (stalked)	7 + 1[124]	2 (4 cells)	
Mysidacea	None	—	None	3[61]	—	Usually fused to 1 median unit
Thermosbaenacea	None	—	Adult (sessile)	—	—	
Cumacea	None	—	Adult (sessile)	7 (6)	2	
Tanaidacea	None	—	Praniza; Adult (sessile)	7[142] usual	—	14 Retinular cells *Oniscus*[39]
Isopoda	None	—	Adult (sessile)	5 (4 + 1)[175]	2	May be 1, 2, 3, 4, or 6 cells; No corneal facets usually; *Phronima*, Ampeliscidae
Amphipoda	None	—				
Euphausiacea	Larvae; Adult	—	Calyptopis (sessile); Furcilia on (stalked)	7[236]	—	*Stylocheiron*
Decapoda	Larvae; Adult	No lenses	Protozoea to adult (stalked); Antizoea (sessile)	7 + 1	4	
Stomatopoda	Larvae; Adult	—	Pseudozoea (sessile); Adults (stalked)	7 + 1	—	

* Superscript numbers indicate references.
† A formula of 5 + 2 has been reported for Cladocera, and Heberdey and Kupka[91] found 7 + 1 in *Daphnia pulex.*

Beyond this little is known of the functional properties, adaptive significance, or further occurrence of light-sensitive elements of this sort. Possibly comparable photoreception has been reported in apparently undifferentiated nervous structures of insects, echinoderms, hemichordates, and vertebrates. The far-reaching importance of such effects in the brain of teleosts, particularly in determining endocrine interrelationships,[150] should promote further interest in such systems. In this vein direct action of light on the central nervous system has been suggested in *Daphnia*[125] as an explanation of the UV responses of eyeless specimens.[168]

Turning from such structurally ill-defined light reception there are two types of eyes which are the main visual organs of Crustacea: 1) median simple eyes and 2) lateral compound eyes. In this respect the class resembles the Xiphosura, Eurypterida, and Insecta. Both eye types may be present together in crustaceans, or one or both may be absent. The median eye is typical of the basic larval type, the nauplius, but it is also the only adult eye in most ostracods and in all copepods, where the compound eyes may have been lost secondarily. On the other hand, no vestige of median eye is known either in the embryo or the adult of the mysid *Praunus flexuosus*.[124] They are similarly absent, except for *Paranaspides lacustris*, in all other Malacostraca except Eucarida and Hoplocarida.

Where present such median eyes persist along with well-developed compound eyes in the adults of many species. In Mystacocarida one or more pairs of ocellus-like structures are present laterally on the head, but they may merely be relocated median eye elements.[35] Table 1 summarizes the types and distribution of eyes in the various groups.

II. *MEDIAN EYES*

Median eyes of crustaceans consist usually of three or four simple ocelli. There may be one median with two lateral or two median (one dorsal and the other ventral) with two lateral. In each simple eye, two, or a few, neurosensory cells are partly surrounded by a cup of screening and reflecting pigments and are innervated by a median nerve from the forebrain. Lens-like structures may be present, but in Anostraca, except *Artemia*, most copepods, *Argulus*, and decapods with persistent median eyes there are none. A striking specialization of the lateral pair of median eyes occurs in certain bathypelagic copepods like *Sapphirina*.[43] Rhabdom-like structures, large cuticular or liquid-filled lenses, eye muscles, and various pigment layers may be developed.[154]

Little or nothing is known about the physiology of such special ocelli[62] although they have been thought to be related to directional light perception in bathypelagic species.[179a]

No direct study has been made of crustacean median eyes by electrophysiological means. However, light-evoked ocellar nerve impulses have been recorded in Xiphosura[211] and presumably in Insecta,[25,104,156] so that comparable normal sensory responses might be anticipated in Crustacea. Similarly, although ocelli are commonly referred to as "simple" eyes, some cases are known where such organs function in movement perception,[194] form discrimination,[47] and even orientation by polarized light in the sky[139,221] in various other animal groups, which suggests their potential versatility and importance in Crustacea.

Practically nothing is known of median eye function in crustaceans where both compound and ocellar elements occur at the same time. In *Artemia* certain visual responses, like the visual recognition of females by males, cannot be made by individuals having only their naupliar eyes intact. The latter seems in fact to duplicate in this form only some of the functions of the compound eyes.[119] Removal of the naupliar eye in *Daphnia* is reported on the one hand not to affect their light behavior[168] and on the other to be crucial for their sensitivity to UV and certain light-induced changes in their vertical migrations.[17] Further careful work will be required to explain such discrepancies. This limits presently available knowledge to animals where the only eyes are median ocelli. These would be nauplii of many groups, ostracods except Cypridinidae, copepods, and adult cirripeds.* But in none of these has the possible involvement of a generalized photosensitivity independent of any eyes[186] been eliminated.

Thus several visual functions have been quantitatively studied in adults of the barnacle *Balanus improvisus*.[190] A diffuse light sense appears to be present, but it is not known whether the rudimentary and internal median eyes[57] are involved in this. The withdrawal reflex in response to shading was used to measure the influence of various stimulus parameters. The threshold, in terms of per cent shading required to evoke the response, follows the Bunson-Roscoe law since the product of per cent shading multiplied by exposure time is nearly constant (Fig. 7). This simple relation does not hold for stimulus intensity and duration even though these are related by some sort of reciprocal function.

---

* Citations of the older literature in this field may be found in references.[100,122]

The Weber fraction $\Delta I/I$* is relatively stable only in the middle range of stimulus intensities. It has a minimum of about 2–4% between 100 and 1000 lux[†] rising sharply at both higher and lower I's. Adaptation curves can be obtained over I ranges of 4–5 log units, with dark adaptation generally resembling that typical of other forms. Light adaptation is peculiar since the sensitivity first decreases to a minimum, then rises to a steady value at higher adapting intensities. An extended period in the dark may eliminate responses to shadows for some time. Central factors are undoubtedly involved in certain of these visual responses, but they have not yet been analyzed. *Balanus* responds to light over a broad wavelength band from red to UV, but neither the precise spectral limits of sensitivity[‡] nor the effect of λ on relative brightness has been determined.

III. *LATERAL EYES*

As in the compound eye of other arthropods, the crustacean lateral eye is most succinctly characterized by its method of image formation. The dioptric system consists of a multiple array of optically more or less isolated lens doublets. Since their optic axes diverge, each of these surveys a somewhat different part of the total object space, and each of them projects an image of its bit of the visual field into a cluster of neurosensory cells, the retinula. A lens system with its retinula plus a characteristic group of pigment cells comprise an ommatidium. This is the elementary structural unit of the compound eye and is typically reduplicated hundreds or thousands of times in the whole organ (Figs. 2 and 3). To a degree the ommatidium along with its central neural connections is a functional as well as a structural unit of compound eyes. But the extent of its independence, composite activities, and neural integration are so poorly known that sweeping generalizations are quite unwarranted at present.

A. STRUCTURAL PATTERN

Crustacean lateral eyes, like those of several other major animal groups, exhibit great diversity of structural variations on a basic plan.

---

* The ratio of the just noticeable difference (jnd) in stimulus intensity (ΔI) to the prevailing intensity (I).

† Unit of illuminance, lumen/m²; roughly equivalent to about 0.1 millilambert, a unit of luminance.[106]

‡ Ocellar sensitivity to X-rays, in addition to UV, has been reported for *Daphnia*, but no details have been given.[17]

In general, however, two morphological eye types are distinguished. Apposition eyes (Figs. 2A, B, D, F; 3G–L; Chapter 4, Figs. 5, 6) are usually found in diurnal, littoral, and terrestrial forms; they are presumably specially adapted for photopic vision. Superposition eyes (Figs. 2C, 2E, 4), in contrast, are usually found in nocturnal, cre-puscular, deep sea, and subterranean species; they are believed to function scotopically. Intermediate types occur, and in numerous orders of the class lateral eyes show a wide range of development, being variously small or large, simple or complex, uniform or differ-entiated, standard or aberrant, specialized or degenerate, spheroidal or planiform, sessile or stalked. Although these features no doubt are cor-related with physiological, ecological, and evolutionary factors, most of our present ideas in this field are quite speculative. In the stalk-eyed crustaceans at least, these structures are well vascularized with branches of the ophthalmic artery supplying the subretinal region and more proximal parts of the optic tract (Fig. 2B).[123]

1. *Components.* Since the ommatidium is the morphological unit of compound eyes, their description may well begin at this level (Fig. 3). Thirteen or fourteen cells (exclusive of pigment cells) and their products comprise the ommatidium as it occurs most widely. Distally it is capped by a corneal lens whose outer surface, usually square or hexagonal, constitutes the externally visible facet. Beneath this trans-parent bit of exoskeleton are two corneagenous cells which secrete it and are presumably comparable to ordinary epidermal cells. Further proximal are the cells (four in decapods) which produce the second lens-like structure, the crystalline cone which is a cylindrical, or long tapering conical, axial element often retaining obvious evidence of its four-part origin.

Central to this is the retinula consisting of neurosensory cells radially arranged around the ommatidial axis. These are long in apposition eyes and extend from the crystalline cone to the basilar membrane which bounds the retina proximally and in decapods is a connective tissue meshwork supporting the central end of the retin-ulas.[13] In superposition eyes they usually are short, remote from the highly refractile part of the cone, and basally located in the omma-tidium. In many carefully examined cases, all but one of these retinular cells are alike and axially arranged in a symmetrical way. But the one extraordinary retinular cell is quite different in being shorter, having its nucleus at a different level, and sometimes in being distinctively placed along the ommatidial axis or in being quite eccentric relative to the rosette of ordinary retinular cells.[37] The number of the latter is consistently seven in a number of major groups. When such is the case and an extraordinary cell is present, the retinular formulas may be given as $7 + 1$, where the first number represents ordinary visual cells and the second, if present, the basal,

---

FIG. 2. Structure of decapod compound eyes.

A. Radial section from cornea to basilar membrane in an adult crab *Grapsus grapsus*. Most likely the thin vertical line just distal to the retinulas is an artifact. In the connective tissue separating the retinulas a number of nuclei can be seen near the basilar membrane. 20 μ section, bleached, then stained with azan, $\times$ 85.

B. Radial section of basilar membrane region in a mature mangrove crab *Goniopsis cruentata*. The primary optic nerve fibers originate proximally from the retinular cells as axons which penetrate the basilar membrane lateral to the retinula of their origin, and course in bundles to the lamina ganglionaris. The highly vascularized subretinal region is typical. 20 μ section, bleached, then stained with Mallory's triple, $\times$ 225.

C. Radial section of basilar membrane region in a juvenile spiny lobster *Panulirus argus*. The eye was fixed in the dark-adapted state so that the prominent dark proximal retinal pigment is withdrawn from the distal ends of the retinular cells and a considerable part of it has moved beneath the basilar membrane. Presumably the tapetal reflecting pigment was more distal than this, but since it was dissolved out by the histological procedure it cannot be seen here. 20 μ section, unbleached, stained with Mallory's triple, $\times$ 115.

D. Radial section of lamina ganglionaris region in the eyestalk of a mature *Goniopsis cruentata*. The ganglion itself forms a C-shaped figure with the chiasma externa at the right and bundles of primary optic fibers coming from the retina to the left and below. 20 μ section, bleached, then stained with Mallory's triple, $\times$ 115.

E. Tangential surface view of juvenile *Panulirus* eye cut just distal to the basilar membrane. The proximal ends of the retinular cells form a star-shaped figure for each ommatidium. This preparation was fixed briefly in formalin, bleached, and then photographed in reflected light. The proximal dark retinal pigment was removed by the bleaching, but the white reflecting pigment persisted and contrasts sharply with the retinular elements. $\times$ 225.

F. Tangential section of the retina in a mature *Goniopsis*. The regular widespaced pattern of retinulas, each with a central rhabdom surrounded by retinular cells, usually seven in number, is clearly shown. If the apparently single, rod-shaped rhabdom is the photoreceptor element, the question of whether individual retinular cells can be separately stimulated appears from these relations to be an acute one. 20 μ section, bleached, then stained with azan, $\times$ 380.

In A–D light would normally enter the eye from the left. According to Exner's analysis the eyes in A, B, D, and F are of the apposition type, while those in C and E are superposition. A–D and F were prepared with Mrs. Helen Hutchins, and E with Dr. R. A. Ellis. *a*, vacuole (probably artifact); *b*, basilar membrane, *c*, cornea; *e*, chiasma externa; *f*, primary optic fibers; *g*, cell bodies of lamina ganglionaris neurons; *h*, rhabdom; *n*, retinular cell nuclei; *o*, neurommatidia; *p*, bundles of primary optic nerve fibers; *r*, retinular cells; *s*, cone stalk; *t*, connective tissue; *v*, subretinal blood vessel; γ, crystalline cone.

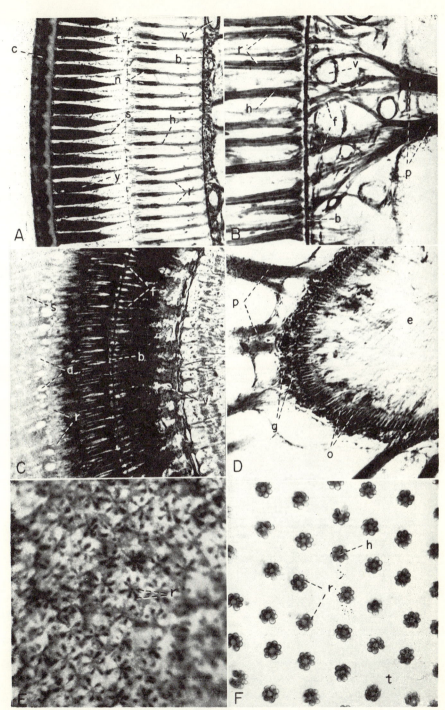

FIG. 2. See legend on opposite page.

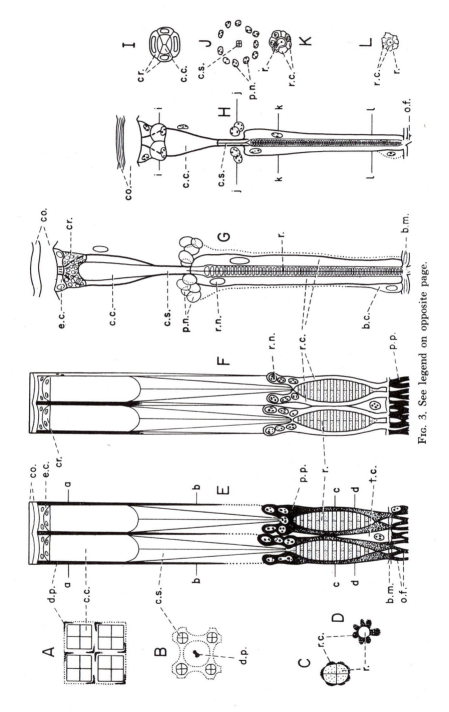

FIG. 3. See legend on opposite page.

eccentric, or otherwise special retinular cell. Some examples of retinular cell formulas are given in Table 1.

There are two points of particular interest here. One is that the
typical insect ommatidium in many orders also has seven or eight
retinular cells (often $6 + 1$ or $7 + 1$).[102,174] Whether the evolutionary
emphasis on this number in two quite distinct arthropod classes signi-
fies some special functional importance for it is uncertain. Even in
the human fovea a point source of light may illuminate a retinal
receptor surface consisting of seven cones.[178] The other point is that
if there is any physiological division of labor within one ommatidium,
then the observed variations in cell number should be directly correlated with the sensory capabilities of the animals concerned, such
as color vision (Section III,F,2) or polarized light perception (Section
III,G).

A peculiarly differentiated retinula is present in the isopod *Ligia*
where there are three cell types: 2 small, 5 large, and 1 eccentric,[157]
somewhat like the pattern observed in certain insects. Here again a
functional correlation may be expected from the addition of another
cell type to the one or two more usually present in a single retinula.

The rhabdom, a translucent refringent element located in the
ommatidial axis, is an important part of the retinula. Present almost
universally in compound eyes, it is apparently produced by, or part
of, the retinular cells.[18,37,136] Rhabdoms are commonly stated (e.g.
Mayrat[124]) to consist at least partly of chitin, but there seems to be
no good supporting evidence.[151] In Crustacea as in Insecta they have

---

FIG. 3. Structure of decapod ommatidia. *Astacus astacus* (redrawn from Bernhards[20]): A, B, C, D. Cross (tangential) sections of four (A, B) ommatidia or
one (C, D) ommatidium at the levels indicated in E by *aa, bb, cc,* and *dd,*
respectively. E. Radial (axial) section of two ommatidia showing the pigment in
the light-adapted condition providing maximum shielding of each single unit.
F. Similar view in the dark-adapted condition with a condition of minimum light
shielding by pigment. The facet diameter of such an eye is about 60 μ. The
crab *Macropodia rostrata* (redrawn from Bernard[18]): G. Radial section of a single
ommatidium as seen in a fresh preparation. H. The same after fixation in alcoholic
Bouin's, indicating the marked shrinkage and other changes. I, J, K, L. Cross
sections of an ommatidium at the levels indicated in H by *ii, jj, kk,* and *ll*
respectively. The facet diameter in such an eye is about 30 μ. *b.c.,* basal cell;
b.m., basilar membrane; *c.c.,* crystalline cone; *co.,* cornea; *cr.,* crystalline cone
cells; *c.s.,* crystalline cone stalk; *d.p.,* distal pigment; *e.c.,* corneagenous cells; *o.f.,*
optic nerve fibers (these are proximal axons of retinular cells); *p.p.,* proximal pigment; *p.n.,* pigment cell nuclei; *r.,* rhabdom; *r.c.,* retinular cells; *r.n.,* retinular
cell nucleus; *t.c.,* tapetal cell.

two main forms. One of these is a long rod-like unit made up of fused rhabdomeres, each produced by a retinular cell (usually the odd basal or eccentric cell does not contribute to the rhabdom)[12] (Fig. 2F). Distally such rhabdoms touch the inner end of the crystalline cone, proximally they approach the basilar membrane (Fig. 2A, B; 3G).

This rhabdom type is characteristic of ommatidia in apposition eyes and probably is the primitive kind.[18] On the other hand, superposition eyes, whose optical distinctions from the former type are considered below (pages 23–26), normally have rhabdoms which are fusiform, shorter, and remote in position from the crystalline cone (e.g. *Palaemon, Astacus, Galathea*) (Fig. 3E, F). In addition, they often appear to be composed of a stack of 5–35 plates,[124,149] or to have transverse or longitudinal folds.[37] The rhabdom of *Procambarus* apparently consists of alternate layers of lipid and protein.[72] The rod-shaped or filiform rhabdoms in apposition eyes may also comprise stacks of tiny platelets[24,28] (Fig. 3G, H), but more frequently they seem homogeneous.

Electron micrographs of the rhabdomeres in the apposition eyes of a variety of other arthropods[64,127,233] have shown them to consist of a great many microvilli or rods lying close-packed and perpendicular to the surface of the contiguous retinular cell. Preliminary data indicate a similar rhabdom structure in *Callinectes*.[128] These obviously recall the "Stiftchensäume" bordering the rhabdom as described in many arthropods by the earlier histologists (e.g. Max Schultze[167]).

Although the previous section has discussed ommatidia as if they could be neatly divided into two basic types in terms of the shape and relations of the rhabdom, many intermediate and modified types exist, a fact which was already obvious to Exner.[59] The double rhabdoms of the mysid *Praunus* and the crab *Dromia* are pertinent examples, suggesting a dual function.[124,155] Also the depth of the retinular cell layer, as well as the length of the rhabdom, may be quite different in various crustacean eyes which seem nevertheless, on the evidence of basally localized rhabdoms, all to be of the superposition type.[236]

In some crustacean compound eyes the rhabdom apparently is either lacking or quite atypical. This is true, for instance, in Cumacea,[61] in Palinuridae[140] (Fig. 2C, E), in Penaeidae,[149] as well as in the deep sea caridean *Hymenodora glacialis*,[225] and the burrowing macruran *Callianassa subterranea*,[163] which have reduced eyes. On the other hand, hypertrophied rhabdoms may be present in ommatidia which otherwise seem reduced (deep sea amphipods;[75] various decapods[18]). Since the rhabdom may likely be the photoreceptor element of the compound eye (pages 26–27) the importance of studying the functional significance of such morphological variance is obvious.

2. *The eye as a whole.* The lateral eye, of course, consists of a number of component ommatidia. These vary from a few (20–25, *Armadillidium*[95]) to a few hundred (272, *Triops*[227]) to a few thousand (3000, *Squilla*[48]). In the eye of a 30-cm *Homarus*, 14,000 are estimated to be present.[13] In its simplest and most regular form such an eye comprises a nearly spherical aggregate of identical contiguous ommatidia resting on a concentric spheroidal basilar membrane (Fig. 2). The optic axes of the ommatidia are perpendicular to both the corneal surface and the supporting membrane. If extended centrally, the ommatidial axes would all meet at a point where they would subtend equal angles. Such a geometrically simple, diagrammatic kind of organization for the whole eye is, in fact, approached by the superposition eyes of many Eucarida like *Palaemon* or *Panulirus*. It is reasonably closely followed by small central retinal areas in the majority of Crustacea.

However, even the most regularly structured eyes show deviations from the simple symmetrical pattern. Thus the radii of corneal curvature may vary from one eye region to another; also they tend to be different in different planes; the ommatidia of various areas are often not the same size and shape; the subspherical basilar membrane may have a lesser curvature than the cornea; the ommatidial axes do not always meet at a point; the angles between them frequently do not subtend equal areas of the visual field, nor are the axes always normal to the corneal surface.

Such deviations from a simple regular plan are marked in the widely occurring apposition eyes of many crustacean groups. Some or all of the features listed above may be quite irregular, especially in the eyes of certain deep sea and troglodytic forms.[18,28,55] Particularly in relation to the many distinctions between superposition and apposition eyes, the Crustacea show close parallels with the Insecta.[41] Clearly, such structural and geometrical variants must be functionally important, especially for physiological optics (Section III,B).

Departures from regularity frequently result in areal specialization in crustacean eyes. In mild form this may involve a gradual change in ommatidial pattern from one eye region to another. Thus facet size and other ommatidial parameters can vary conspicuously in the same eye, as for example in the stomatopod *Squilla*.[148] Behavioral data on other crustaceans (e.g. *Artemia*[169] and *Carcinus*[193]) also imply functional specialization of retinal regions, but response pattern may also be dependent on central nervous factors.[1] In extreme cases of areal specialization whole eye regions different from the rest may become more or less isolated from the main retina. Thus accessory eyes, comprising small patches of ommatidia near the rest of the compound eye, occur in the deep sea shrimps *Acanthephyra eximia* and *Meningodora vesca*.[13] The eye shows partial division into two parts in some deep water mysids. Still other Crustacea have the functional retina separated into two distinct sections looking in quite different directions.

Such double eyes occur independently in carnivorous Cladocera,[28] various bathypelagic Amphipoda,[175] Mysidacea,[176] Euphausiacea,[236] and some deep water sergestid Decapoda. Most frequently one part of the double eye looks upward with numerous (e.g. 1000) large, elongate, nearly parallel ommatidia while the other section surveys other diverse parts of the visual field with fewer (e.g. 300), smaller, shorter, more divergent units. In mysids and euphausiids both eye areas are superposition in structure. Double eyes are usually assumed to be adaptations for pelagic predation in dim light,[28] but this has yet to be proved.[182]

In addition to specialization practically all groups show a repeated tendency toward degeneration and even complete loss of eyes. This trend is usually correlated with parasitic, sessile, subphotic zone, or cavernicolous habits, but such habits apparently do not require a reduction, because all species living under seemingly similar conditions do not have equal eye degeneration, and some may show specialization.[53,55] As a result homologies may be difficult to establish in highly aberrant visual structures. Thus in Amphipoda the ommatidia are not contiguous but are separated by epidermal cells and corneal areas between facets. Hence these organs have sometimes been considered not to be strictly compound eyes at all.[18] In terms of close contiguity of units *Artemia, Daphnia, Argulus,* and *Nebalia* also have atypical eyes, since these, too, have considerable space between facets.[91,96,137] Cumacea are even more of a problem because their eyes consist of one to eleven ocellus-like, loosely aggregated units.[235]

Equally ambiguous, but in a different way, are the divided and modified eyes of the bottom-living ampeliscid amphipods.[175] These individual eyes, of which there are two large and one small pair, comprise a number of retinulas for all of which there is only a single large corneal lens, as in a camera-type eye. A somewhat comparable trend toward an ocellus-like structure is suggested in several bathypelagic prawns where an open chamber separates the crystalline cones from the retina, and marginal ommatidia may lack both cones and corneal lenses.[13,28,149] The pseudo-ocelli of the nocturnal forms of doryline ants are apparently a convergent type of similar eye development.[228] In the Conchostraca, Cladocera, and Cumacea the lateral eyes may be partly or wholly fused into a single median cyclopean aggregate.

Such comparative data suggest questions on the origin and evolution of crustacean lateral eyes. Movable stalked compound eyes appear to be characteristic of the class and probably were present during early stages of its evolution (Chapter 1, Vol. I). The close similarity in many general and specific ways between the faceted eyes of the higher crustaceans and those of the pterygote insects is a striking fact. Whether this results from a common evolutionary origin of their compound eyes or more likely represents a strong convergence is uncertain. At present our knowledge of early arthropod phylogeny is too vague to provide a clear decision.

B. IMAGE FORMATION

Since the presence of multiple dioptric systems is undoubtedly the most important diagnostic feature of crustacean lateral eyes, the image-forming properties of each unit will be the basic determinant of the whole eye's physiological optics. According to the simplest version of Johannes Müller's[131] theory of mosaic vision, each ommatidium contributes to the total image perceived a small elementary area like one tile in a mosaic. The object seen therefore forms an image comprised of contiguous bits contributed by all the ommatidia present. Thus the idealized spherical eye postulated in Section III,A would form a reduced erect convex image with an undistorted point-for-point correspondence to the visual field. Obviously, with few optic units the correspondence would be coarse, becoming progressively finer the more ommatidia there are surveying a given field.

On the other hand, the greater the departures from a geometrically regular type of eye, the less perfectly would the image directly match the object seen. Since such departures are the rule and may be extreme, the actual image formed will be rather special for each kind of eye. Thus corneal curvature differences in various planes will introduce astigmatism, which is quite different for a cylindrical retina than for a spheroidal or a nearly flat one. Changes in radius of curvature in different retinal regions will further affect the image like a bent mirror, with ommatidial size influencing light-collecting power and ultimate resolution, while axial divergence between ommatidia will determine coarseness of the resulting mosaic and the total extent of the visual field.

Basic to this kind of image formation is the assumption that each ommatidium looks out on its own bit of visual space which is bordered by that of its neighbors but not shared by them. In this case each facet and its underlying retinula would receive a small pencil of light from points lying on or near the outward extension of its optic axis. Theoretically this restriction to near-axial rays could be established by the geometrical optics of the lens system relative to the photosensitive region and the masking effect of various screening and reflecting pigments typically present. Physical processes of refraction, reflection, and absorption would be fundamental here.

1. *Ommatidial optics.* As in their morphology, the optics of compound eyes must be considered at two levels: once in terms of the eye's component units, and then in terms of the organ as a whole. The classic work in this field for all the arthropods is that of Exner,[59] which in spite of its pioneer nature is still the best available.* Unfortunately, the physiological optics of crustacean eyes is particularly difficult because of the gelatinous or semifluid nature of key structures, so that even Exner was unable to learn much about it.

a. *Refraction.* As mentioned above, the main refracting elements are the corneal lens and the crystalline cone. The former is usually only slightly convex in stalk-eyed crustaceans, so that its refractive effect is not great, particularly in aquatic forms. In stomatopods[12] the corneal facets appear to be partitioned from one another by highly refringent layers which would reduce the opportunity for light, which enters one lens obliquely, from straying into its neighbors. A similar dioptric isolating device is known in insects.[174]

The crystalline cone is a strongly refractile structure which was shown by Exner to function in insects as a lens cylinder having different refractive indexes in its various parts. The refractive index is maximum axially and decreases radially, a condition which would tend to funnel near-axial rays to the retinula and refract out those which are more oblique. A somewhat similar waveguide effect has been attributed to the rods and cones of the vertebrate retina[138] and in fact may be demonstrated in a gelatin lens model made to fit Exner's

---

* For details the original monograph should be consulted. Where this is not accessible, key figures and their explanation are reproduced by Wigglesworth[231] and Dethier.[48]

specifications for the arthropod eye.[103] Interestingly enough, a lens cylinder functions nearly independently of the medium in which it is immersed, quite unlike ordinary lenses where surface refraction is the primary effect.[59]

Although mainly derived from insect data, the presumptive extension of Exner's idea of lens cylinders to Crustacea is supported by the reduction in refractive power shown by euphausiid[236] and sergestid[28] crystalline cones decreasing from their axes toward their periphery.* However, the occurrence of two types of lens cylinders, corresponding to those typical respectively of superposition and apposition eyes in insects, has not been optically proven in crustaceans, even though it is generally assumed.

In apposition eyes the axial length of the lens cylinder is equal to or slightly shorter than its focal length; a small inverted and reversed image is formed at or near the inner surface of the crystalline cone. Such have been reported for stomatopods[12] and have been seen in the author's laboratory in fresh frozen sections of various decapod eyes.

In superposition eyes the lens cylinder differs, according to Exner, by being twice as long as its focal length. This fact, combined with an appropriate variation of refractive index, causes rays to leave the inner surface of such lenses at the same emergent angle and in the same axial half of the plane in which they entered its outer surface. Thus a single ommatidium projects a dim, erect and not reversed image of its object space onto its own retinula if the eye is light-adapted so that each ommatidium is effectively isolated by its sleeve of screening pigment. The superposition image which presumably appears when this pigment migrates into the dark-adapted state is discussed in Section III,B,2,b below.

No dioptric mechanism for accommodation is known in crustacean eyes although the extensive radial length of retinular cells and rhabdoms, particularly in apposition eyes, may itself allow for considerable changes in image position with various object distances. Also note that "depth of focus" is inversely related to the aperture of a lens, which of course is minute in the compound eye. But their very small diameter, favorable for this one factor, will at the same time adversely affect the system's light-collecting power since this varies inversely with the f number which equals the ratio of focal length to diameter, and image

---

* No refractive index gradients appear in fixed sections of *Palaemon serratus* cones examined with an interference microscope,[38] nor were such gradients observed with phase contrast in fresh crustacean eyes (Kuiper, J. W. 1959. *Program and Abstracts Biophys. Soc., Pittsburgh*).

brightness is inversely proportional to the square of the f value. Similarly the theoretical resolution of a lens system depends directly on its diameter, which may become limiting for visible λ's at dimensions not much smaller than existing facet diameters.[14]

Our present inadequate state of knowledge of ommatidial image formation may be summarized by saying that in apposition eyes a small image of each ommatidium's object space is projected onto the central part of the distal region of its retinula; a comparable but erect image or at least a corresponding spot of light is also directed onto its retinula by the corneal lens and crystalline cone of the superposition ommatidium.

Whether or not the rhabdom in turn has dioptric effects is even less certain. This composite organelle is usually described as clear and highly refractile but characteristically striated in appearance. One possible function widely held for it is to scatter the light received into the contiguous retinular cells, which in this case would presumably be the site of the photochemical receptor process.[18,124,135,136] Another possibility which now seems more likely is that the rhabdom itself is the actual photoreceptive structure containing visual pigment.[102,207] Striking parallels in the microstructure of rhabdoms in a variety of arthropods (pages 13–15) and some similarities to the outer segments in vertebrate rods,[45,46,105] coupled with the evidence on rhodopsin localization in both crustaceans and vertebrates, would definitely seem to favor this second alternative.

b. *Screening and reflection.* In addition to its dioptric elements each ommatidium usually has several screening and reflecting pigments which also affect the formation of the visual image. The chemistry of these substances is discussed in Chapter 3, Vol. I, and the factors relating to the control of their distribution, which usually changes with the eye's state of light or dark adaptation and with the time of day, in Chapters 4 and 11. Black or brown screening pigment is present ordinarily in the retinular cells and, at least in the light-adapted condition, restricts the entering light to the axial region including the rhabdom and sometimes the immediately adjacent parts of the retinular cells. This is the so-called proximal retinal pigment which would act to prevent stray light within the eye from having any effect on the photosensitive regions. The distal retinal pigment found in many forms, including mysids and eucaridans,[124,141] is contained in two or more pigment cells which form a partial or complete sleeve around the outer part of the ommatidium, including the crystalline cone. This screen in the light-adapted eye would presumably absorb light rays which may be refracted or scattered out of the axial dioptric system.

Clearly the proximal and distal pigments, in collaboration with the corneal lens and crystalline cone, should act as optical stops which restrict the beam of light rays reaching the corresponding retinula. Thus the visual field of a single ommatidium, as well as the amount of light it admits, are established. Although the visual field has been assumed quite generally to be as small as, or smaller than, the axial angle separating neighboring ommatidia,[49,102] there is optical evidence in various arthropods which indicates that it is in fact much larger, at least in a number of species.[191] Well-developed crustacean eyes in their areas of greatest acuity have ommatidia separated by axial angles of 2° or less, yet the visual field of each ommatidium apparently is 10–20° in diameter[12] (Ellis and Waterman, 1956, unpublished).

Comparable data have been obtained optically and electrophysiologically in *Limulus*[59,212] as well as in the insects *Locusta* and *Apis*.[25] These facts indicate that a hypothesis of a simple mosaic image composed of contiguous but not overlapping parts[131] is untenable for the compound eyes of arthropods where this factor has been studied. Obviously this is an important matter for visual acuity, movement perception, and other specific functions, as well as the over-all image formed by the eye. These are discussed further below.

So far the ommatidial visual image has been described only for the light-adapted state. In many species, particularly those with superposition eyes, during dark adaptation the proximal pigment withdraws toward or through the basilar membrane and the distal pigment sleeve contracts toward the cornea (illustrations and further references in Chapter 4). Both changes would tend to increase the light received by the rhabdom and retinula by reducing the screening of the visual unit and in effect decreasing its *f*-number. At the same time the superposition eye is believed to be so constituted that with the screening pigment withdrawn several lens systems collaborate to focus light on a single retinula[59] in a manner discussed in Section III,B,2,b below. These adaptive changes due to retinal pigment migration are supposed to lower the threshold and to lessen acuity, but present evidence supports only some of the effects expected (pages 25, 34). In bathypelagic and subterranean forms one or both of the screening pigments may be absent,[18,28] or only one or neither may respond to the diurnal rhythms or light stimuli which affect them in other cases (Chapters 4 and 11).

Reflecting pigment may be present in two places in the eye. In some apposition eyes, like those of the rock crab *Grapsus*, an iris tapetum[59] is present distally against the transparent cornea; it may function to deflect strongly oblique rays away from the ommatidia or may just be part of the superficial color pattern of the animal. In others, like those of *Gammarus*, the interstitial cells between ommatidia contain a white pigment. In addition many superposition eyes contain light-reflecting pigment basally. This may also migrate in response to hormonal or light stimuli[111,225,226] (Chapter 4). Functioning during dark adaptation when the black screening pigments are withdrawn, this white pigment should increase light utilization but decrease acuity by scattering and diminish contrast.[180]

Although usually considered a particular characteristic of superposition eyes, retinal pigment movements in response to light and dark adaptation occur as well in at least some apposition eyes [Isopoda: *Idotea*[142] (Chapter 4, Fig. 6), *Ligia;*[132] Amphipoda: *Gammarus*[192] Chapter 4, Fig. 7); Cumacea[61]]. Photomechanical reactions of unknown physiological significance also have been described in *Idotea*,[142] where the retinular cells change shape on adaptation. In insects such reflexes are known in both superposition and apposition eyes where the rhabdom,[161] retinular cells,[120] or retinular cell nuclei[179] have been reported to migrate in various species.

2. *Total image.* Although many of the image-forming properties of the whole compound eye may be hypothesized from ommatidial optics, there remain for discussion several important visual characteristics which emerge from interactions of ommatidia.

a. *Apposition eyes.* In these typically photopic diurnal eyes recent work has revived the old idea that marked overlap occurs in the visual fields of individual ommatidia. Accordingly a single object point may stimulate a considerable number of contiguous retinulas, depending on the ratio of their visual fields to their axial separation. The occurrence of such a circle of confusion was observed long ago by Exner,[59] who pointed out that it might improve movement perception (pages 39, 40).

A second possibility, which has not been seriously considered, is that there are definite gaps in the object space covered by sufficiently divergent neighboring ommatidia. In eyes where considerable space separates neighboring facets (page 16) there might be such a blind reticulum if the ommatidial aperture were strictly limited to axial rays. But since the latter restriction now seems unlikely, the simple geometry of the eye (e.g. in *Daphnia*[91]) does not suffice to predict this effect. Also in this cladoceran example the constant tremor of the eye produced by its muscles must also be taken into account.* Of course, independent visual fields are known to be present in the ocelli of insects and spiders, but accepting their occurrence in a compound eye requires proof.

Note also that the total visual mosaic in apposition eyes is complicated further by the inversion and reversal of the components contributed by each ommatidium as they are projected on the retinula despite the erect and nonreversed nature of the whole image. The importance of this depends mainly on whether or not the individual retinular cells resolve these ommatidial images into a corresponding pattern of seven or eight parts as some have suggested.[49,65] Even if they do so, appropriate peripheral and central nervous connections could prevent this from having any more effect for vision than the image inversion and reversal typical of all camera eyes. However, such image-forming properties of compound eyes should warn the physiologist from depending too much on his own subjective visual experience in reconstructing that of Crustacea.

b. *Superposition eyes.* According to Exner's analysis, the lens cylinders of these typically nocturnal, scotopic eyes have optical properties (pages 18–19) which should greatly increase the amount of light reaching the retina during dark adaptation.† This effect results from the superposition of light rays entering a whole cluster of 30 or so facets onto a single retinula.[59] Light from a point object would thus attain the corresponding retinula not only directly along its own ommatidial axis but also indirectly by the refractive effect of the lens cylinders of neighboring facets. Hence the effective light-collecting power of the eye is augmented by the number of lenses participating in any given case. If the facets are hexagonal and two more in each direction are involved in addition to the central one, eighteen times as much light then illuminates the retinula whose axis is directed toward the object point. Correspondingly more light would, of course, be collected when an even larger patch of ommatidia participates; the greater the separation between crystalline cones and retinulas, the larger this patch could be[236] (Fig. 4). The notably elongate ommatidia in super-

---

* Comparable eye tremor occurs in *Triops, Artemia,* and perhaps other crustaceans.[60] This might improve form vision by flickering objects in the visual field or increase the persistence of visual images as in the human eye.[153]

† The effects of pigment migration on the geometrical optics of superposition eyes have been frequently diagrammed; one of the best illustrations for insect eyes is in Weber.[220]

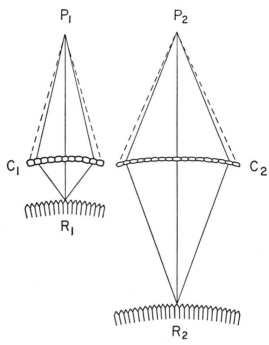

Fɪɢ. 4. Diagram illustrating the geometrical optics of superposition eyes (according to the hypotheses of Exner[59]) with different distances between the cornea (C_1, C_2) and the retina (R_1, R_2). According to this, wider separation between these elements allows more facets to transmit light from a single luminous point (P_1, P_2) onto a corresponding retinal point and hence augments the eyes' light-collecting power. The highly elongate ommatidia in the frontal eyes of certain bathypelagic crustaceans may be related to this. The central ray from the light source (P_1, P_2) as well as the marginal ones from the outermost lens cylinders capable of refracting the light back to the axial retinula are drawn as solid lines. The corresponding dioptric systems and all those included in the circular area between them contribute light from the object to the image. More deviant rays which are too divergent to contribute to the image point are shown as dashed lines. Note that such a mechanism requires that the tissues and tissue fluids between the crystalline cone and the retina have negligible optic effects. (Redrawn from Zimmer and Gruner.[236])

position eyes like those *Panulirus argus, Penaeus duorarum,* and the frontal part of the double eyes of bathypelagic crustaceans such as *Phronima* (page 16) may be causally related to this factor.

Of course, the superposition effect described for one image point applies to all points within the eye's whole visual field. Consequently the total image is erect and not reversed, having this complex multiple origin and its resultant increased brightness. Generally this gain in sensitivity has been believed to involve a loss in acuity, but this has either not been found at all[88] or only found in connection with proximal but not distal pigment migration.[38] However, the method used to test this may not have been ideal for the purpose. In any case, superposition image formation has never been demonstrated* in Crustacea although it is widely assumed to occur. As a result, depth of focus, resolution, and other important details are quite unknown.

The thick fusiform rhabdoms of superposition eyes (e.g. in Euphausiacea[236]) have been described as adaptations to the oblique incidence of the greater part of the illumination involved in superposition image formation; but as in much of the field under review, adequate supporting evidence is not at hand.

A possible complication for superposition image formation may result from the usual presence in the higher crustaceans (and in some insects) of a stalk-like tapering of the crystalline cone which connects it directly to the distal end of the rhabdom. This occurs in many eyes presumed to be superposition (Figs. 2C; 3B, E), as well as in supposed apposition (Figs. 2A; 3G, J), types.

Opinions differ on whether this acts as a light conductor and concentrator (in sergestids,[28] a mysid, and two carideans[38]) or has negligible dioptric effect because its refractive index is merely that of ordinary tissue.[13] The latter notion is supported by the appearance of the cone and cone stalk of *Panulirus argus* in teased preparations made with Dr. R. A. Ellis. These show the crystalline cone to be highly refractile in appearance and the cone stalk much less so. However, in further work undertaken with Professor R. F. Nunnemacher, fresh frozen eyes sliced open at the level of the cone stalk seem to concentrate light within this structure even though no sharp images have been observed there. If the cone stalk does in fact always act as a wave-

---

* A considerable series of littoral and bathypelagic crustacean eyes have been examined in fresh frozen preparations without any superposition images being detected (Ellis, Nunnemacher, and Waterman, 1956–1957, unpublished). Also an abstract reports absence of superposition images in the morphologically "superposition" eyes of *Homarus* and *Orconectes* and fails to confirm Exner's claim for the occurrence of such an image at the retinal level in the firefly (Nunnemacher, R. F. 1959. *Anat. Record* 134:618–619). Similarly another abstract reports lack of a superposition image in an unspecified crustacean eye as well as absence in its crystalline cone of the refractive index gradients required for Exner's lens cylinder function (Kuiper, J. W. 1959. *Program and Abstracts Biophys. Soc., Pittsburgh*). These data and some for insects[26a] suggest the importance of quantitatively re-examining the physiological optics of compound eyes.

guide for light,[38] superposition image formation in the classic sense of Exner could not take place.

C. FUNCTIONAL UNITS

The nature of the component physiological elements in compound eyes is uncertain. Opinion has mainly been divided between the ommatidia and individual retinular cells as the primary units. But in vertebrate visual systems the elements operating at the perceptual level[145] also include the central pathways and projections as well as retinal visual fields.[81,117] Consequently an ultimate understanding of visual mechanisms in Crustacea will most likely require adequate functional knowledge of the peripheral neurosensory components and of the optic ganglia in the eyestalk as well as their protocerebral connections.

1. *Peripheral.* Section III,B above has already shown that detailed quantitative information about image formation in crustacean eyes is lacking. This imposes a severe handicap on attempts to deduce the primary responding unit in a retina. Furthermore, the site of the initial photochemical process is not certain, which makes adequate analysis practically impossible. The latter problem can probably be reduced in apposition eyes to a choice between the axial region of the retinular cells and the rhabdom, although ill-supported speculation has at various times assigned the photoreceptive function to various other components ranging from the crystalline cone to regions below the basilar membrane. In superposition eyes also, either the retinular cells or the rhabdom are the most likely photoreceptor elements since electrophysiological evidence indicates that the generator potential for the electroretinogram (*ERG*) originates primarily at their level in the eyes of *Procambarus clarkii*[70] (Fig. 5) and *Panulirus japonicus*.[115]

As already mentioned (pages 13, 20) there had for some time been a fairly persuasive tendency to consider the rhabdom as a composite secreted product of the neurosensory cells making up a retinula and as a light-conducting, light-scattering element which diverts light into the contiguous receptor cells. Although this may still be plausible, recent electron micrographic and biochemical evidence (pages 14, 44) derived from both vertebrate and arthropod eyes makes a photoreceptive role for the rhabdom itself appear more likely.

Which of these two alternatives is correct is crucial for recognizing the compound eye's functional unit. If the retinular cytoplasm is the photosensitive region, then each of these usually seven or eight cells might be individually excited and relay visual information centrally via its own proximal axon. But if the rhabdom is photoreceptive, the retinula would more likely function as a whole in crustaceans, since their rhabdomeres usually appear fused into a single conjoined structure. In any case, independent rhabdomere activity is conceivable[90] and is certainly suggested in the eyes of some other arthropods, like dipterans, where rhabdomeres are quite independent rodlets each attached to its own retinular cell.[233] However, in insects even a single central rhabdom may show radial microstructure related to its compound origin.[64]

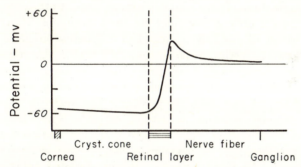

FIG. 5. Relation in a *Procambarus* compound eye between the peak potential of the electroretinogram in millivolts and the depth within the eye at which this function is measured relative to a remote reference electrode. The sharp reversal of potential observed in the retinular layer supports other evidence that the primary photochemical response and the ensuing generator potential occur in this layer, perhaps in the rhabdom. (Redrawn from Hanaoka.[70])

Decisive evidence on whether single retinular cells can independently give rise to optic nerve impulses might be sought in electrical recordings of primary optic nerve fiber activity. But nerve action potentials have not yet been found distal to the most peripheral optic ganglion [in *Procambarus* (T. Hanaoka, 1953, in lit.)], so there are no data now available. In insects, too,[5,19,25] spikes have not been observed distal to the medulla externa (the second optic ganglion from the retina). Similarly in *Limulus* it has not been possible to record action potentials in ordinary retinular cell axons or somata.[* 84,219] Apparently only the eccentric cells, which usually occur one to each ommatidium in these aberrant horseshoe crab eyes, and which are probably sec-

---

* A situation rather similar to these several arthropod cases is reported for vertebrate eyes, too, where generator potentials are found in the neurosensory layer but spikes are not. The latter appear only in the more proximal neural layers of the retina.[68]

ondary neurons rather than neurosensory cells, give rise to conducted responses in the optic nerve. It is these impulses which have for many years been called single photoreceptor unit responses by Hartline and his co-workers (e.g.[82,85]). Thus photosensory spikes have not yet been recorded in regular retinular cell axons of any arthropod, and in *Limulus* the ommatidium as a whole apparently constitutes the known visual unit.

Direct evidence for the site of the primary photochemical process in crustacean compound eyes would obviously be available if the nature and localization of the visual pigment itself were known. Unfortunately there are only a few clear-cut facts available. Many accounts have been given of reddish or purplish pigments observed either in fresh rhabdoms or retinular cells (e.g.[72,124,167,183]). In some of these cases bleaching comparable to that of visual pigments was reported, in others denied. However, a rhodopsin-retinene$_1$ system essentially like that in cephalopod and vertebrate retinas has recently been demonstrated in decapod crustaceans (pages 43–45). Since the technique employed for this in *Homarus* was like that used to isolate the photosensitive outer segments of vertebrate rods,[207] this work implies that the rhabdom is the photoreceptor site in decapod lateral eyes although direct proof of the rhodopsin localization remains to be given. This will be an important advance.

The identity of the eye's peripheral functional unit has sometimes been sought in measurements of optomotor responses, visual acuity, and movement perception. However, different techniques and functions studied in various Crustacea provide thresholds ranging from a small fraction of the axial angles between ommatidia to angles which would subtend the axes of a whole cluster of facets. These differences, in addition to species idiosyncracies, are due partly to the particular conditions of specific experiments and partly to the various additional, but usually unanalyzed, central factors included with the peripheral sensory ones in any behavioral response. Furthermore the marked overlap, apparently present in ommatidial visual fields, would completely vitiate any superficial assumptions concerning functional units based simply on facet geometry.

Thus it is uncertain whether the retinular cell can function as an independent unit in crustacean eyes. Since each is a cell and has its own private axonal connection with more central parts of the nervous system, the "common sense" assumption would be that it can, but the data for the *Limulus* eye should provide a caveat against unsupported hypotheses.

So far only the light-adapted eye has been considered in this discussion of functional units. Yet the dark adaptation of a superposition eye is thought to alter its physiological optical properties so greatly that its unitary organization may also be changed at the same time. Certainly in the vertebrate eye, light and dark adaptation have extensive effects on a number of levels, particularly, it seems, in relation to the neural organization of visual fields.[144] There is also some evidence for this in insects.[193]

2. *Optic tracts and central connections.* If the effects of adaptation in Crustacea are like those in other animals, they most likely alter the functional state of deeper-lying components as well as the peripheral ones. Even less is known about these more central factors than those already considered in the eye itself. Details of the neural pathways have not yet been adequately examined in crustaceans although they resemble in a general way the better-studied visual tracts of insects.[13,40]

In entomostracans there are two optic ganglia; in malacostracans there are three, and in stalk-eyed forms, four, if the medulla terminalis, which is part of the protocerebrum located in the eyestalk, is counted too.[74] No chiasmata are present in the nonmalacostracan subclasses, but the remainder of the Crustacea typically have two, an inner and an outer chiasma connecting the three distal ganglia. The fiber crossover in these two chiasmata may be either in the same plane (Macrura, some Anomura), or in perpendicular planes (Brachyura, some Anomura).

In various forms there is wide variation in the proportions and arrangement of the parts of the optic tract, particularly in bathypelagic, burrowing, or troglodytic species with modified eyes. Thus the optic fibers coming into the head from the peripheral visual elements usually comprise higher-order neurons of the optic peduncle (e.g. *Carcinus*), but may in aberrant forms consist of fibers of an elongate chiasma interna (anomurans *Hippa, Emerita*), or even of primary optic fibers (macruran, *Calocaris;* alpheoidan, *Athanas*).[76]

The primary optic fibers (Figs. 2B, D) in malacostracans run in bundles from the retina to the lamina ganglionaris where they synapse with secondary neurons whose cell bodies lie in the most distal layer of the ganglion (Fig. 2D) except in euphausiids.[236] In crepuscular and bathypelagic species particularly this synaptic layer of the lamina ganglionaris appears to be organized in structures called neurommatidia (Fig. 2D) because there is usually one, or occasionally two of them, for each retinal ommatidium.[18] Typically each neurommatidium is formed by a clustering of axons from six to eight primary fibers, which probably come from several ommatidia and synapse with one second-order neuron.

Note that the convergence here of about seven primary fibers per single secondary one is much less than the over-all average for the human retina of about 100:1. Although these neurommatidia have been observed by a number of careful workers, they have recently been claimed in dipteran insects[126] to be an artifact arising from axon clumping. This will be an important possibility to check when the much needed careful impregnation studies are made of crustacean optic tracts.

From the physiological point of view a summary of the remaining detailed neurology of the crustacean visual system would not seem worth while at present. However, it is clear that a highly integrated and differentiated pattern of visual nerve impulses is transmitted from the eyestalk to the brain. Single-fiber recordings from the optic peduncle of several decapods (Waterman and Wiersma, 1955, unpublished) show that the retinal field covered by one of these higher-order neurons includes a large number of ommatidia. Most of such units differentiate the stimulus into on- and off-responses. Clearly the analysis of the functional units in the visual system must be extended to include not only the peripheral components but also these more central ones, whose importance is obvious from the little already known. As in their morphology so in their function, these visual nervous pathways are rather better known in insects,[26b] but even in that class the optic tract's integrative action is just beginning to be studied.

D. Intensity Functions

The most elementary of the visual functions is the discrimination of light from dark. As already discussed (Section I) this does not require an eye or a conspicuous visual pigment, although at least one photon must be so absorbed that it activates a molecule which in turn triggers a more elaborate excitatory mechanism on the cellular level. Such light-sensitive systems are practically universal in living organisms and are obviously basic to the physiology of crustacean lateral eyes.

1. *Threshold.* No precise measurements of light threshold have been made in crustaceans. However, some bathypelagic carideans apparently respond to light by undertaking diurnal vertical migrations at depths of 800–1000 m; this implies that they perceive illumination at

intensities not more than about 10⁻¹⁰ that of full-noon sunlight.[30,218] Although the relation between the λ of maximum penetration and maximum sensitivity could make a large difference here,[44a] the light intensity in question probably is the order of magnitude of the human rod threshold.[205] This also agrees reasonably well with a crustacean threshold estimate of 10⁻⁵ to 10⁻⁶ lux cited in reference[217], and the threshold for distal pigment migration in the prawn *Palaemonetes*.[159]

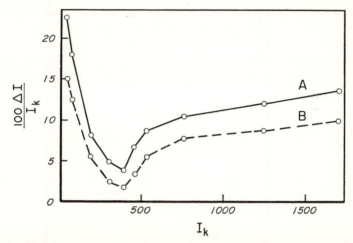

Fig. 6. Relation in *Daphnia* between intensity discrimination and light intensity. The abscissa represents the intensity of one fixed light source, while the ordinate is the just detectable percentage difference from this of a second variable source. Curve *A* connects points where the intensity differences are clearly discriminable; curve *B*, relative intensity differences which were just not detectable. Obviously the thresholds, for say 50% response, lie between these. (Redrawn from Heberdey and Kupka.[91])

2. Intensity discrimination. This function has been studied in *Daphnia* by phototactic choice experiments using two light stimuli with intensities between 40 and 1720 lux.[91] In absolute terms, the jnd in intensity is constant between 40 and 400 lux then rises linearly as far as the upper limit tested. The Weber fractions* are a complex function of I such that a minimum (i.e. best discrimination) occurs at 400 lux where the fraction averages 2.8% (Fig. 6). Behavioral studies of fresh-water Cladocera have disclosed effective Weber fractions of 1–10%.[17] By optomotor techniques, values between 1.2 and

---

* The ratio of the just noticeable difference (jnd) in stimulus intensity (ΔI) to the prevailing intensity (I).

4.2% have been found in the mangrove crab, *Goniopsis* (Barber and
Waterman, 1955, unpublished), 25% in *Apis*, and 150% in *Drosophila*.[93] Psychophysical measurements in man yield a threshold near
1%.[15]

Note, however, that, because of quite different methods used, the
functions measured in the four species may not be strictly the same.

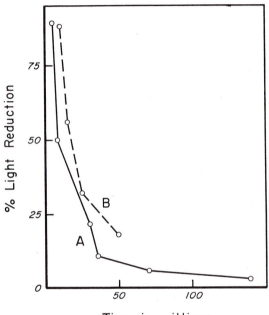

Time in millisec

Fig. 7. Relation in *Balanus improvisus* between threshold duration of light
reduction and the percentage decrease as measured by the animal's withdrawal
response to shadows. Curves *A* and *B* are data for two different specimens. These
functions follow the Bunson-Roscoe law reasonably well ($I \times T = k$). (Redrawn
from von Buddenbrock.[190])

The lowest *I* tested in *Daphnia* was far higher than the range where
human rods are the exclusive photoreceptor units (about 0.03 lux or
less). In evaluating complex intensity-discrimination curves like those
of *Daphnia*, the possibility should be considered that different parts of
the whole function are contributed by the median eyes, and perhaps
a dermal photoreceptor mechanism, as well as the compound eyes.
The comparable data for adult *Balanus improvisus* (Fig. 7), where
the minimum $\Delta I/I$ is between 2 and 4% (page 8), certainly do not

include compound eye influence since barnacles lose their lateral eyes at metamorphosis, but may relate to a generalized light sensitivity in addition to the persistent median eyes.

3. *Adaptation.* At any given instant sense organs ordinarily respond to a range of stimulus intensities which is but a fraction of their total capability. The latter only becomes fully accessible through shifts of as much as 40 db or more in the organ's operating range; such adaptation is regulated by ambient conditions, internal physiological factors, or both. In crustacean compound eyes, as in those of other animals, light and dark adaptation are complex processes occurring at several levels. These must include screening and reflecting pigment migration, changes in the steady state concentration of photoreceptor pigments, and central as well as retinal changes in receptor fields like those in insects[196] and vertebrates.[144] If adaptation is being estimated from behavioral responses, efferent pathways and peripheral effector systems may be involved, too. Before dealing with its components the over-all phenomenon will first be described.

Although adaptation in compound eyes may involve other factors like the change in image type which occurs in superposition eyes (page 23), the main effect is an alteration in sensitivity. Consequently the basic data needed are the quantitative effects of ambient light intensity on various threshold functions. Relatively little such information on crustaceans is at hand. Light adaptation measured in terms of minimum separable optomotor acuity takes 6–10 min in *Palaemon serratus* and *Praunus flexuosus*, while it requires only about 3 min in *Pandalus montagui*.[38] Adaptation has been studied to some extent in terms of its influence on the *ERG* in *Ligia*,[157] *Homarus*,[152] *Cambarus*,[71,134] and *Eriocheir*.[116] Dark adaptation takes from about 20 min to an hour or more, while light adaptation often is two or more times faster, taking only 3–5 min in *Ligia*, for example. Over the small range tested, the amplitude decrease in the *ERG* on-effect in the crayfish is proportional to the quantity of light $(I \times t)$* causing adaptation.[70] In *Homarus*,[152] *Cambarus*,[134] and *Eriocheir*[116] adaptation affects the various components of the *ERG* differently so that its shape changes with the state of adaptation.

In such decapods the *ERG* has two principal components, an initial fast peak and a subsequent slow plateau, as described by Hartline.[80]

---

* A similar effect has been observed behaviorally in *Artemia salina* whose light adaptation was studied in a two-light experiment. Rate of adaptation depends on the adapting I and for any particular degree of adaptation $\log I \times t = k$.[170]

These respond quite differently to dark adaptation, appearing together at medium I's. The initial fast peak becomes small or absent in strongly light-adapted eyes whereas it grows large on dark adaptation and the plateau disappears.[134] Thus the dark-adapted eye appears to respond only with an on-effect, the light-adapted eye with a sustained response. During the first 10–20 min dark adaptation the sustained response increases its amplitude moderately to a steady level, but after long periods (2–3 hours) in the dark, it declines to zero or nearly so. Meanwhile the quick peak grows in 20–60 min to a high amplitude which is maintained. The sources of these two ERG components are not known, but the balance of current evidence suggests that both are retinal in origin.

Although the maximum degree to which dark adaptation may alter the threshold in Crustacea is not known,* its effect in *Ligia* is small (3 $\times$ compared with 20,000 $\times$ in *Carausius*,[4] and 40,000 $\times$ in human rods) as it is in the so-called fast eyes (pages 36–37) of insects like *Calliphora*.[4] Thoroughly dark-adapted *Nototropis swammerdamii* (amphipod) has a phototactic sensitivity about 3000 $\times$ that of light-adapted specimens.[100] In dark-adapted *Daphnia* locomotor inhibition occurs at I's about 0.002 $\times$ those which produce a lively positive photokinesis in light-adapted animals.[100] In *Limulus*, adaptation, gauged by optic nerve impulses, extends over a range of about 130 $\times$.[83]

Of the several physiological changes involved in dark adaptation, pigment migrations, whose optical effects are discussed in Section III,B, have been studied the most (Chapters 4 and 11). Although they undoubtedly act like an iris diaphragm and otherwise regulate the amount of light reaching the photosensitive regions, few quantitative measurements of their influence on vision have been made. In *Cambarus* the light-adapted pigment position slightly decreases the critical fusion frequency (*cff*),[33] whereas in the prawns *Palaemon* and *Lysmata*, which like the crayfish have superposition eyes, no effect of adaptation on acuity could be demonstrated by optomotor tests.[88] Further work on *Palaemon serratus*, *Pandalus montagui*, and *Praunus flexuosus* indicates that minimum separable thresholds for acuity are affected by proximal retinal pigment migration but not by distal pigment movement. But as noted above this type of response is often

---

* No dark or light adaptation appears in the optomotor responses of *Pagurus bernhardus* to moving black and white stripes of equal width,[38] but in general such minimum separable thresholds are mainly independent of I (page 38).

insensitive to changes in illumination over a wide range and hence may not be a critical indicator of the effects of distal pigment position.

Studies of the pigment movements themselves provide some data of wider interest. In *Palaemonetes* for example, the distal retinal pigment migrates in response to illumination between 5×10^{-5} and 5 lux with the movement occurring mainly in the thousandfold range of I's between 10^{-3} and 1 lux.[159] Adequate correlation of this and similar information on the highly varied patterns of pigment migrations in crustaceans with their eyes' visual capabilities should provide a rich fund of knowledge. No changes in the neural organization of the retina as a result of adaptation[3] have been reported as yet in crustaceans, but collective functioning of seven ommatidia operating as a unit at low I's has been described in insects.[196] The prey-catching reflex of *Caprella liparotensis* probably involves nine ommatidia, but the effect of I on this collaboration is unknown.[229]

In various insects, as well as vertebrates, one effect of adaptation is to transpose the eye's spectral sensitivity from a maximum at one λ to another, the Purkinje shift.[160,166] Such a change has been observed in *Daphnia* where blue sensitivity remains about the same but the effectiveness of green and yellow wavelengths decreases to about one-third during dark adaptation.[90] In vertebrates such shifts are usually attributed to the duplex nature of the photoreceptor cell population in many eyes; this matter is discussed further in relation to crustacean color vision (pages 46–48).

Note, however, that the crustacean flicker fusion functions discussed below give no evidence for the presence of more than one light receptor population; in vertebrates the "scotopic" and "photopic" response systems contribute discrete segments to such curves. Human rod and cone components in various intensity discrimination and acuity functions are also discontinuous.[15] In this respect crustaceans are similar because somewhat comparable breaks appear in phototactic intensity discrimination curves for *Daphnia* (pages 46–47). These have been interpreted as evidence for three or more photoreceptor cell populations.[90]

E. TIME AND SPACE FUNCTIONS

In addition to their fundamental property of discriminating light from dark, photoreceptors usually have the further ability to resolve some temporal features of the stimulus; more versatile systems add spatial analysis to this so that movement and form perception become possible. Normally developed crustacean lateral eyes possess all these attributes although their image-perceiving abilities have yet to be demonstrated in detail.

1. *Flicker.* The temporal characteristics of several crustacean eyes have been studied by measuring the critical flicker fusion frequency (*cff*) determined with a visual field of moving vertical stripes whose visibility is gauged by some optomotor response such as eyestalk nystagmus. As in other eyes, the *cff* is strongly dependent on I. Plots of *cff* against log I for *Asellus*[34] and for *Cambarus*[32,33] (Fig. 8) give

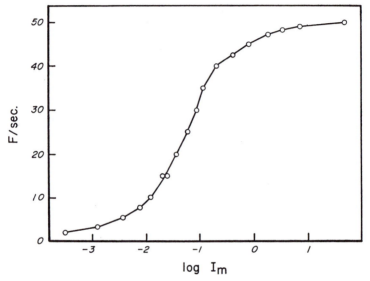

Fig. 8. Critical flicker fusion frequency in *Cambarus bartonii* as a function of log mean flash intensity (I_m measured in millilamberts). This was determined in terms of the threshold for optomotor walking in response to a rotating cylinder of vertical black and white stripes of equal width. (Redrawn from Crozier and Wolf.[32])

sigmoid curves, although in *Pagurus* the relationship is linear.[24] This function is an interesting one since in other animal groups where its correlates have been measured, *cff* is directly proportional to optic nerve spike frequency and in turn to apparent brightness.[67]

Maximum *cff*'s have been reported as shown in Table 2. According to Autrum and Stöcker's measurements,[8] insects have *ERG*'s which are either slow (e.g. *Tachycines*) or fast (e.g. *Calliphora*). The slow type with low maximum *cff*'s is monophasic and relatively simple in form, but has extensive adaptation, whereas the fast, with high maximum *cff*'s, shows a positive on-wave, a negative off-wave, and little adaptation.* Because of a high *cff* along with its almost trivial range of dark adaptation, *Ligia* has been thought to possess a fast eye type.[157] Its complex *ERG* is consistent with such an analysis.

However, the experimental isolation of the retina from the optic ganglia in *Ligia* was not found to simplify the *ERG* as it has been reported to do in insect fast eyes.[5] For this reason the complex *ERG*'s of *Ligia* are believed by Ruck and Jahn[157] to originate in the retina alone, which contains three retinular cell types. These authors believe, in opposition to Autrum, that in fast insect eyes, too, the *ERG*'s are entirely

TABLE 2
Maximum Flicker Fusion Frequencies

	Max. *cff*/sec
Crustacea:	
Asellus communis (?)[34,a]	51.6
Cambarus bartonii[32,33]	50.3
Ligia occidentalis[157]	120
Pagurus bernhardus[24]	56
Other groups:	
Apis[232,b]	55
Apis, Calliphora, and Vespa[8]	≥200
Periplaneta[8]	10
Tachycines (a cricket)[8]	5
Rana[22]	5
Columba (a pigeon)[54]	143

ᵃ Note that the statistical arguments used by Crozier to analyze the flicker curve for *Cambarus* in terms of that for *Asellus* are based on quite incorrect ommatidial number and arrangement assumed for the latter (compare reference[39]).

ᵇ Autrum and Stöcker[8] explain Wolf's low *cff* for the honeybee on the basis that he used rotating sectors in a disk as stimuli rather than vertical stripes in a cylinder.

retinal in origin. The latter maintains, in contrast, that an electrotonic influence of the closely contiguous lamina ganglionaris confers their high temporal resolution and their diphasic response on the fast insect eyes.[6] Thus the crustaceans have not helped to clarify the vexing question of *ERG* interpretation in insects.[48] However, the wide range of eye and optic ganglion morphology found in Crustacea may provide good comparative material with which to solve the relevant problems.

2. *Acuity.* Space perception is based on an ability to discriminate various parts of the visual field. Consequently at least a crude image

---

* In this connection note that in vertebrates the flicker *ERG* of rod eyes which have low fusion frequencies consists merely of monophasic positive waves, while that of cone eyes which have high *cff*'s possesses diphasic waves.[67]

is required on the retina. Minimum detectable objects (acuity is usually defined as the reciprocal of the angle in minutes of arc, subtended at the eye by the minimum detectable detail) are limited by two factors: the ratio of their retinal image size to effective retinal grain and the object's contrast relative to the minimum $\Delta I/I$. In crustacean lateral eyes the retinal grain will depend on whether the peripheral functional units are single retinular cells, whole ommatidia, or clusters of ommatidia. For technical reasons determinations of acuity depend on some behavioral response which can only arise if the object tested is discriminated. Thresholds obtained are, therefore, those for the behavioral reaction and not necessarily as low as the true sensory thresholds. The kind of object discriminated is critical also since minimum visible, minimum separable, vernier acuity, and so on all may be quite different numerically.[15] Naturally wavelength and intensity of the stimulus might also affect such thresholds in complex ways.

The commonest method of estimating arthropod visual acuity has been by means of optomotor responses. These have been tested mainly with moving fields of evenly spaced vertical black and white stripes of equal width or with wide-spaced or single narrow stripes. The end point for the evenly spaced stripes is related to the minimum separable threshold and the effective retinal grain; the wide-spaced or single stripe thresholds are instead related to the minimum visible line and minimum $\Delta I/I$.[199] In the first instance the threshold is largely independent of I, and in the second case it is directly dependent on I.

Visual acuities measured in crustaceans vary over a broad range, partly owing to the differences in technique used and end points observed (Table 3). Furthermore, available evidence indicates that even where comparable techniques are used there is no simple correlation between visual acuity and the angles separating the axes of neighboring ommatidia. This lack would be expected with optically overlapping visual fields (page 22) and also if there are neurologically overlapping receptor fields as there are in vertebrates.[117] Most of the minimum separable angles observed in crustaceans correspond to two or more ommatidia subtended, a fact which is perhaps related to the image movement involved in their determination (pages 39–41); on the other hand most of the minimum visible objects subtend far less than the ommatidial aperture implied by the axial separation of neighboring ommatidia. The latter varies widely from 1°, or somewhat less in well-developed eyes with many facets, to 40° in *Oniscus* and *Porcellio*[50] or 55° in *Daphnia*.[91] Yet the minimum visible may be 2.5′ or less (*Goniopsis*; Barber and Waterman, 1955, unpublished).

3. *Movement.* The detectable transposition of a retinal image from one place to another is the elementary basis of movement perception. Direction and rate are additional perceivable properties beyond mere detection. Both temporal and spatial factors are important for such sensory ability, which may be subdivided into 1) real movement vision, 2) kinematoscopic movement vision involving the perceptual fusion of successive discrete stimulus patterns into apparently continuous movement, and 3) induced movement vision where background

TABLE 3

Visual Acuity

Animal	Test object	Acuity
Lysmata[88]	Stripes (min. separable)	0.00128
Pandalus[38]	Stripes (min. separable)	.00163
Palaemon[88]	Stripes (min. separable)	.00192
Praunus[38]	Stripes (min. separable)	.00268
Palaemon[38]	Stripes (min. separable)	.00362
Pagurus[24]	Stripes (min. separable)	.00397
Uca[29]	Stripe (min. visible)	.00420
Goniopsis[a]	Stripes (min. separable)	.00476
Squilla[12]	Sphere (min. visible)	.0384
Pagurus[24]	Stripe (min. visible)	.0795
Goniopsis[a]	Stripes (min. visible)	.400
Apis[94]	Stripes (min. separable)	.017
Limulus[b]	Stripe (min. visible)	.0910
Man[92]	Stripe (min. visible)	120

[a] Barber and Waterman, 1955, unpublished.
[b] Gallagher and Waterman, 1954, unpublished.

motion makes an object appear to move.[202] The last type has an important variant in the behavioral response usually found when the induced movement is the result of the animal's own motion.[172,201]

Clearly the perceptual equivalence of the three different types of events seen must indicate the participation of complex peripheral and central components in movement perception and response. The most peripheral element would depend on the relation between image formation and retinal grain. As Exner[59] pointed out, marked overlap of visual fields of ommatidia should improve movement perception in two ways. For a given object displacement, the greater the number of ommatidia (up to some fairly large fraction of the total in the eye) responding to a single object point, the greater will be the retinal response in terms of changes in visual cell stimulation. Similarly a larger patch stimulated requires a smaller minimum displacement to alter the cellular pattern of excitation. Pari passu the minimum displacement required to change the patch of visual cells stimulated will vary similarly. Thus the problem of movement perception, like that of visual acuity, reduces to matters of minimum separable retinal image positions and optimum intensity discrimination (Sections III, D,2 and E,2).

The time course of unit visual processes is obviously important for movement perception both peripherally and centrally. The adaptive explanation for the fast eyes of certain insects has been based on the functional importance of good temporal resolution in rapidly flying species.[5] Whether comparable influences have affected crustacean eye evolution is not known. An interesting suggestion that movement detection might involve the temporal coding of the nerve impulses concerned has been made for *Squilla* because its primary optic fibers from different retinal areas vary in length by a factor of as much as four.[148]

Most of the data on movement perception in crustaceans have been obtained either with a "signal reaction" to a single object's displacement or with optomotor responses. In the former the antennae are directed toward the object seen (e.g. *Caprella*,[229] *Galathea*,[56] *Pagurus*[24]), while in the latter eyestalk nystagmus or whole body movements tend to stabilize the moving field's image on the retina.[21] An avoidance reaction to a single moving stripe is shown by *Uca* when the object subtends an angle of 4°, which is twice the minimum angle between neighboring ommatidia.[29] This might be interpreted as supporting the notion proposed for insects[97] that temporally asymmetrical stimulation of two visual fields is required at the threshold for direction perception; a somewhat similar unit comprising two ommatidia was hypothesized for a beetle on the basis of kinematoscopic movement responses.[87]

However, overlap of ommatidial visual fields was thought to interfere with this hypothesis in crustacean superposition eyes,[88] and quite likely marked overlap of ommatidial fields of view is general in compound eyes (pages 21, 39). Furthermore, direct electrical recordings show that in an insect compound eye (*Locusta*) where interaxial angles for centrally located ommatidia are about 1° and the visual fields of each are about 20°, nerve spikes are evoked by object displacement as small as 0.1°. Movement perception data obtained with optomotor responses are further complicated by the need of a horizontally extensive moving field to evoke the characteristic behavior and by some differences in the sensitivity of various retinal areas to the moving stimulus (*Car-*

cinus;[193] *Goniopsis*, Barber and Waterman, 1955, unpublished). Clearly further data and analysis are both required before these interactions can be understood.

Although the various types of movement vision, including movement after-images,[63] have been studied to some extent in insects, relatively little has been done in crustaceans. Kinematoscopic movement perception is absent in the prawns *Lysmata* and *Palaemon*, and its lack was attributed to the superposition type of their eyes.[88] It has been claimed on the basis of compensatory eyestalk movements during walking[195] that *Carcinus* cannot distinguish between true movement and apparent movement induced by its own locomotion. This claim was used by von Buddenbrock to attack the cybernetic explanation of such discriminatory ability in insects and other forms by the "Reafferenzprinzip" of von Holst and Mittelstaedt.[201] However, in *Palinurus*,[51] *Maja* and *Carcinus*,[52] the compensatory eyestalk movements evoked by their own locomotion are not mediated through visual stimuli. This reduces the cogency of von Buddenbrock's arguments against the "Reafferenzprinzip."

4. *Form discrimination.* Potentially an image-forming eye provides sensory information related to the shape of things seen. The degree to which this is used by various animals must ordinarily be studied by conditioning reflexes or more complex ethological methods. Compound eyes are commonly stated to be movement-perceiving rather than image-perceiving eyes. But certainly in insects the geometry of some visual stimuli can be discriminated and remembered.[98,177] In pagurid crabs size is predominant to form and color for selecting gastropod shells. Glass artificial shells are hesitated over for a long time unless an opaque ring is painted around their aperture rim.[147] One of the few cases where form discrimination by Crustacea is strongly implied is in the orientation of semiterrestrial amphipods and isopods with the help of celestial cues (Chapter 10). The fact that these species can determine compass directions from the sun's position in the sky or, if in the shade, from the pattern of sky polarization (Section III,G) indicates among other things a good ability for some kind of spatial localization in their lateral eyes.

5. *Depth perception.* The major cue for this ability is usually considered to be overlapping binocular visual fields. These occur in many stalk-eyed as well as sessile-eyed crustaceans, but practically nothing is known of their functional importance. Good depth perception might be predicted especially in carnivorous forms with raptorial

appendages like caprellids and stomatopods. In the latter group visual fixation of objects seen is particularly obvious. *Squilla mantis* has compound eyes so organized that in addition to binocular depth perception of vertical objects, monocular stereoscopic vision should be possible for horizontal objects.[42] This depends on its strongly astigmatic bilobed eyes, in each of which considerable numbers of ommatidial axes converge in a vertical plane.[162] Closer study of the mechanism of prey-catching in such forms should be as rewarding as it has been in insects[129] both from a sensory and a behavioral point of view.

F. Wavelength Functions

With light beams of equal energy, two different perceived effects can arise from changes in the λ of the stimulus. These of course

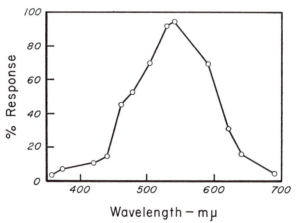

Fig. 9. Relative stimulating efficiency of various wavelengths in an equal energy spectrum for cypris larvae of *Balanus*. Phototactic responses were used as an index of sensitivity to the light. (Redrawn from Visscher and Luce.[189])

are 1) alterations in brightness related to the number of quanta effectively absorbed, and 2) alterations in hue related to the differential absorption of photons by more than one population of neurosensory units. The first of these is universal in light receptors, the second occurs only in systems specially differentiated to discriminate color.

1. *Spectral sensitivity and visual photochemistry.* The action spectrum of a visual system is properly defined by the effect of λ on some particular threshold function. Since physiological input-output relations are generally nonlinear, equal response thresholds must be de-

termined throughout. Much of the work on crustacean spectral sensitivity does not meet these criteria of adequacy since uncontrolled spectral energies were often used and various end points have been taken for different wavelengths. Thus there are many descriptions of the phototactic behavior of a great variety of crustaceans exposed to a spectrum. Positively phototactic forms including cladocerans, cirripeds (Fig. 9), amphipods, mysids, and decapods typically aggregate in the green and yellow-green wavelengths with fewer in the blue and violet, plus an even steeper drop off toward the red.[100,122]

TABLE 4
WAVELENGTH OF MAXIMUM SPECTRAL SENSITIVITY

Animal	Max. sensitivity (mμ)	Response
Daphnia pulex[162a] (dermal light sense)	<(?)400–420	Eye movement
Palaemon paucidens[133]	455–510	Distal pigment response
Paratya compressa[133]	455–510	Distal pigment response
Meganyctiphanes norvegica[59a]	460–465	Difference spectrum
Euphausia pacifica[107]	462	Difference spectrum
Palaemonetes sp.[230]	470–510	Phototaxis
Callinectes sapidus[23]	480	Pigment bleaching
Homarus americanus[207]	515	Difference spectrum
Daphnia pulex[162a] (visual sensitivity)	520	Eye movement
Nototropis swammerdamii[100]	520–540	Phototaxis
Daphnia pulex[184]	530–540	Phototaxis
Balanus amphitrite[189]	530–545	Phototaxis
Balanus improvisus[189]	530–545	Phototaxis
Procambarus clarkii[72]	550–560	Electroretinogram

More specific maximal sensitivities are listed in Table 4. The limits of spectral sensitivity in crustaceans are poorly known, but in *Daphnia* the curve resembles that for the honeybee in extending well into the UV but cutting off short of the red.[36,90] However, in *Artemia salina* the ventral light reflex determining its swimming orientation continues in dim red light and can be mediated by any one of the three eyes but not entirely without them (Chapter 9).[119]

Behaviorally measured spectral sensitivity may originate at several levels. Primarily, however, it is determined by the absorption spectrum of the photosensitive pigment in the retina. In man at least, where the most detailed comparisons have been made, the correspondence of the in vitro absorption spectrum of rhodopsin and psychophysically determined scotopic sensitivity is quite close down to wavelengths near 400 mμ where the α-absorption band with its peak near 500 mμ gives way to the β-band which has its maximum in the near UV between 300 and 400 mμ.[206] This divergence of absorption and sensitivity curves is due to the filtering action of the human cornea and lens which cuts off the short wavelengths. Such UV cut-off λ's are lower in some other vertebrates[44,109] and may generally be quite considerably so in arthropods since UV is a color at least for certain insects[36] and apparently also for *Daphnia*.[90]

Relatively little was known about the biochemistry of crustacean vision until the basic pattern in *Homarus* was shown by Wald and Hubbard to be like that in vertebrate rods and in cephalopod retinas.[207] As reviewed in Chapter 7, Vol. I, vitamin A had been found in large quantities in various crustacean eyes; retinene, which is vitamin A aldehyde and an end product of rhodopsin bleaching, as well as related carotenoid derivatives, had also been extracted. Yet earlier attempts to isolate photosensitive systems from these compound eyes were largely unsuccessful although some partial separations were made in *Callinectes*[23] and *Euphausia*.[107] However, application of the technique used to obtain relatively pure rhodopsin from the outer segments of vertebrate rods virtually eliminated the large amounts of masking photostable pigment present in crustacean eyes and finally demonstrated that a quite analogous rhodopsin system is present in *Homarus americanus* retinas, probably localized in the rhabdom[207] (Fig. 10). Similar findings have since been reported in *Nephrops norvegicus* (Chapter 7, Vol. I) and *Meganyctiphanes norvegica*.[59a]

The *Homarus* rhodopsin bleaches on exposure to light and, after a series of dark reactions, yields retinene$_1$ and opsin. From the difference spectrum of the photopigment one would predict that the lobster's maximum visual sensitivity is near 515 mμ, that its ability to see beyond 600 mμ (orange-red and red) is negligible, and that after a minimum at 420 mμ, its sensitivity increases slightly into the UV provided that the eye has no cut-off filters for this spectral region. The difference spectrum maximum for the *Meganyctiphanes* pigment[59a] is at 460–465 mμ, similar to that reported for another euphausiid, *Euphausia pacifica*.[107] This shift toward the blue may be an adaptation[59a] to deep-water illumination comparable to the smaller shift in the same direction reported for the visual pigments of some bathypelagic fishes.[44a] The extension of this work in the comparison of other crustaceans and arthropods will be most interesting.

The possibility that a chemically quite different kind of photo-sensitive system may also be active in compound eyes is implicit in biochemical work on insect eye pigments initiated by geneticists. Six or more fluorescent pterins, which are chemically close to purines, have

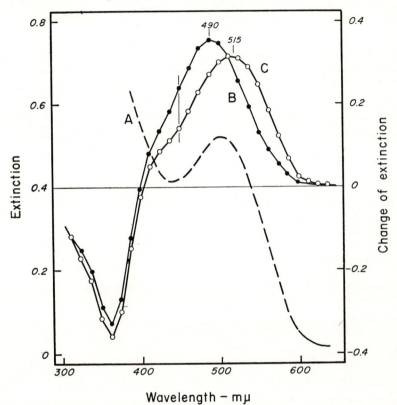

FIG. 10. Spectral characteristics of *Homarus americanus* rhodopsin. Curve *A*. Absorption spectrum of visual pigment extract determined in the dark. Curve *B*. Difference spectrum (max 490 mμ) of an early photoproduct of rhodopsin bleach-ing obtained by subtracting the absorption spectrum of the final bleaching product after treatment with hydroxylamine from that of the early photoproduct. Curve *C*. Difference spectrum (max 515 mμ) of rhodopsin itself obtained in a comparable manner. *B* and *C* so measured are virtually absorption spectra above a wavelength of 450 mμ, marked with a vertical line. The left ordinate applies to *A*, the right to *B* and *C*. (Redrawn from Wald and Hubbard.[207])

been extracted from the eye of the moth, *Anagasta kuhniella*.[187] Three similar substances also are present in *Astacus astacus* lateral eyes.[188] Since some pterins are photolabile,[7,234] their significance in crustacean as well as insect eye metabolism should be tested.

2. *Color discrimination.* Rather complex behavioral responses must be studied to prove this perceptual ability. Two difficulties must be overcome in establishing its presence or absence. First is the need to isolate λ differences from *I* changes or other possible secondary clues; second is the fact that lack of different specific behavior for different λ's cannot of itself deny color vision except for those particular experimental circumstances. In this instance electrophysiology does not always provide decisive data either. Thus optic fiber recordings in a number of nonprimate mammalian retinas give evidence for several populations of sensory units which respond differentially to λ yet there is no critical ethological evidence for color vision in these animals.[66] As a result of these difficulties, the color field has often been a controversial one, with the extended argument between von Frisch and von Hess over the occurrence of color vision in arthropods and fish being a classic example.

The first demonstration of λ discrimination in Crustacea was made by von Frisch and Kupelwieser[198] in moderately light-adapted *Daphnia magna, D. pulex,* and to some extent in *Artemia salina.* These entomostracans independently of a considerable intensity range are phototactically repelled by short λ's and attracted by long. This was confirmed by a number of later workers (e.g.[89]) and serial color contrast as well as complementary colors were demonstrated for *Daphnia.*[112,118] These behavior patterns have been restudied as "color dances" by Smith and Baylor[171] and extended to *Ceriodaphnia, Moina, Bosmina,* stomatopod larvae, and three copepods.[17] Their ecological significance has been attributed to an adaptive advantage for phytoplankton feeding. Further evidence from eye movements also indicates that *Daphnia* can distinguish long from short λ's.[198]

Phototactic intensity discrimination of two colored stimulating lights has been used to continue the analysis of λ discrimination by this cladoceran.[90] Different "scotopic" and "photopic" receptor systems are implied by the sharp breaks in the $\Delta I/I$ vs. log I curves at moderate I's (Fig. 11). Color vision is possible with the photopic system and perhaps with the scotopic.[91] The photopic responses suggest that three populations of differentially sensitive retinal units are operative at high light intensities. These have maximum sensitivities in the 1) UV, 2) blue-violet, and 3) yellow.*

Three hue-discriminating receptor types are consistent with the

---

* Presumably the effects attributed to long wavelengths[171,198] must be close to the limit of the spectral sensitivity curve which is near zero at 650 mμ.[184]

Young-Helmholtz trichromatic theory of color vision, and their apparent spectral positions in *Daphnia* are close to those described for *Apis* which also discriminates UV as a color.[36,99] The evidence for a multiple photoreceptor system in *Daphnia* would seem difficult to correlate with its reduced and peculiar compound eye. This is a cyclopean median unit comprising only 22 ommatidia, each with eight retinular

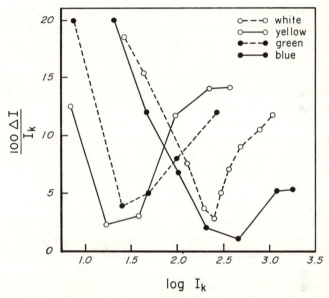

Fig. 11. Intensity discrimination in *Daphnia* as a function of log intensity in lights of various spectral composition. The data were obtained in a two-light experiment where one light source (I_k measured in lux) was constant and the other varied to determine the difference threshold (jnd). (Redrawn from Heberdey.[90])

cells, one of which is apparently different from the others on the evidence of its larger nerve fiber.[91]

Such a situation raises the question of functional units in acute form and recalls the suggestion that if single retinular cells can function independently, perhaps scotopic and photopic vision as well as hue discrimination might be encompassed in one ommatidium.[73,158] This notion is reminiscent in turn of the cluster hypothesis advocated to account for color discrimination in the human retina.[86,178] However, none of the above *Daphnia* experiments tested the possible influence of the naupliar eye. Furthermore, a dermal light sense may be responsible for part of the behavior reported.[184] Either of these sensory mechanisms could in fact quite possibly account for the blue-violet, or perhaps even the UV, components of the animal's color sensitivity.[17,162a] If such elements are involved, the cladoceran responses described obviously cannot be interpreted solely in terms of lateral eye physiology. Further quantitative experiments with adequate controls need to be done.

In the Malacostraca color vision has been found in a number of forms. The first case was established in *Crangon crangon* by Koller[113] using chromatophore responses mediated through the compound eyes. Adaptation is possible to yellow, orange, and red; yet the specific responses to these colors cannot be evoked by any shade of gray from white to black. Similarly the color changes of the amphipod *Caprella liparotensis* in response to various wavelengths are largely independent of I so that λ per se must be discriminated.[229] Optomotor techniques using alternating colored and gray stripes did not at first give evidence for color vision in decapods,[165] but when the effect of relative brightness was adequately controlled,* an ability to discriminate yellow and blue was proved in *Carcinus maenas*.[193] In similar experiments *Crangon crangon* and *Palaemon squilla* are also specifically color sensitive.[164]

Evidence that yellow and blue can be discriminated from all shades of gray by *Pagurus* was found by testing its choice of painted gastropod shells.[114] The modest sample of Branchiopoda and Decapoda which have been studied suggest that color discrimination is widespread in Crustacea; at present its behavioral importance appears related to feeding and cryptic coloration, although this subject has been little explored. Similarly the biochemical mechanism of color vision as well as its cellular basis in the retina await quantitative study.

G. POLARIZED LIGHT SENSITIVITY

While direct sunlight is not polarized a considerable fraction of all the scattered and reflected light in the atmosphere as well as in the hydrosphere is (review and references in[214,215,218]). Consequently the possibility that the eyes of some animals can detect this parameter of light is an intriguing one. While much of the current comparative

---

* In such experiments various shades of gray are alternated with a particular color until optomotor nystagmus is negligible or eliminated altogether. Such a pair is assumed to have equal brightness for the crab. Next various saturations of a second color are tested with the gray from the first pair until again the response becomes minimal or nil. Then the two colors both matching the same gray shade in brightness are alternated. If these evoke an optomotor response, perceived color difference must be the stimulus.

research in this field stems from von Frisch's work on the honeybee,[197] some early knowledge of it in the human eye dates from the discovery of Haidinger's brushes in 1844[69] and von Helmholtz's hypothesis explaining their origin.[200] Meanwhile many arthropods have been shown to respond to polarized light both in the field and in the laboratory.[174a] In Crustacea the first attempts to demonstrate polarized light behavior failed.[31] The terrestrial isopod, *Cylisticus convexus*, while negatively phototactic was found, in experiments using two opposed horizontal light beams, not to respond differently to vertically and horizontally polarized light. Similar and additional tests also did not then demonstrate polarized light sensitivity in insects.

However, Verkhovskaya[181] found by using pairs of horizontal light beams that *Daphnia magna* and *D. pulex* aggregate in linearly polarized light in preference to unpolarized light of the same *I*. For example, in one measurement series with two parallel beams, 70% of the *Daphnia* were found in the polarized zone, 15% in the unpolarized beam, with 15% intermediate. Equal numbers of individuals are attracted into both beams when the unpolarized beam has two to three times the *I* of the polarized one. If both beams are unpolarized, the brighter one attracts more cladocerans. This suggests that for *Daphnia* at least the apparent brightness of polarized light is greater than that for unpolarized light. A similar relation is implied by the *ERG* of insect compound eyes, because unpolarized light must be 16–36% more intense than linearly polarized light to produce on-waves of the same amplitude in the honeybee.[9]*

Oriented responses to vertical beams of linearly polarized light occur in *Daphnia* (Fig. 12) and a number of other cladocerans[16,58,79] as well as† in *Mysidium gracile*.[10] In general these crustaceans orient by swimming perpendicular to the plane of polarization. Apparently these responses are strongly influenced by the turbidity of the medium. In *Mysidium*, for example, significant responses to polarized light seemed to depend on the presence of a considerable amount of suspended matter in the water[11] (Fig. 13); a quantitative study of such effects will be essential for understanding the physiological mechanism of polarized light sensitivity.‡

---

* Other workers, however, report failure to confirm these measurements.[15b]

† The preliminary report of a polarized light response in *Pagurus*[110] seems questionable in the absence of adequate controls because the observed effect of the polarization plane could have arisen by reflection and refraction at the cylindrical surface of the experimental vessel, just as in the sporangiophore of *Phycomyces*.[27]

‡ Orientation to polarized light in clear water has now been described for *Mysidium* as well as for *Daphnia*.[216c]

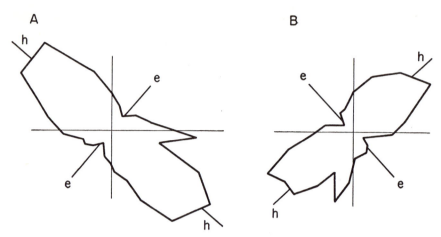

Fɪɢ. 12. Orientation of *Daphnia* to two vertical planes (*ee* in A and B) of linearly polarized light nearly at right angles to each other. Records compiled from a photographic record. (Redrawn from Eckert.[58])

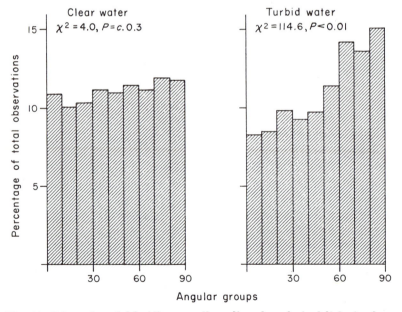

Fɪɢ. 13. Orientation of *Mysidium gracile* to linearly polarized light in clear and turbid water. The *e*-vector was at 0°. (From Bainbridge and Waterman.[11])

More complex behavioral responses to sky polarization are well known from the works of Pardi and Papi on the beach-living amphipod *Talitrus saltator* and the isopod *Tylos latreillei* (Chapter 10). These peracaridans, although they normally use the sun (or the moon) to determine compass direction, are not disoriented in the shade, provided the sky is clear. Controls with Polaroid filters indicate that the polarization of the blue sky is then being utilized by these crustaceans as in the case of many other orienting arthropods (review and references in[174a,216,216b]). Presumably the underlying sensory discrimination is the same here as in the simpler laboratory situations where an accurate time sense and visual pattern memory are not essential accessories as they are for direction finding in nature.

The question of the physiological mechanism of polarized light sensitivity cannot be answered unequivocally now, nor can that of the possible involvement of crustacean naupliar eyes in this function as in the case of insect ocelli.[222] Several plausible suggestions of mechanisms are current; one or more of them may turn out to be correct. Baylor and Smith[16,17] believe that a reflection-refraction mechanism is responsible for the polarized light detection of the *Daphnia* compound eye, a notion which derives some support from behavioral experiments on insects[173,204] and electrophysiological evidence in *Limulus*.[209,213] However, other arthropod data variously suggest a birefringent,[174,210] dichroic,[64] or Tyndall scattering[192] mechanism.

In any case good quantitative measurements which provide decisive information on this physiological mechanism are scanty for crustaceans as well as other arthropods. More specifically, several attempts to obtain such facts have produced only negative information. Thus Waterman and Wiersma (1955, unpublished) repeatedly recorded visual action potentials from single fibers in the optic peduncle of several marine decapods without finding any which were sensitive to the plane of polarization of the stimulating light. Similarly experiments designed to evoke optomotor responses in the crab, *Goniopsis*, by stimulating it with a pattern of stripes alternately polarized in two planes 90° apart gave no significant response (Barber and Waterman, 1955, unpublished). Closely parallel negative results have apparently been obtained in insects since bees do not respond to comparable polarized optomotor stimuli (Autrum, 1956, personal communication), and spikes in the visual tract of *Locusta* show no influence of the polarization plane of the light stimulus evoking them (Burtt and Catton, 1956, personal communication).

While inconclusive, this considerable body of data at least suggests that the physiological basis for polarized light sensitivity is for some reason an elusive function. In any case the nature of the functional unit in crustacean eyes is crucial here, as it is for understanding color vision. A primary question is whether the whole eye, a single ommatidium, or one retinular cell is the unit for polarization analysis. No information is available for crustaceans, but Autrum and Stumpf[9] hypothesized from the *ERG* data cited on page 49 that individual retinular cells in the honeybee are differentially sensitive to the plane of polarization, and Vowles[203] has shown in ants that the angular accuracy of polarized light orientation ($\pm 27°$) corresponds with the average angle subtended by one retinular cell in a seven-celled retinula. However, this correlation could be fortuitous since accuracy of orientation is strongly dependent on the exact experimental conditions and methods of measurement. In addition, individual retinular cell analysis cannot occur in *Limulus* since stimulation of an ommatidium activates only one optic nerve fiber.[84,210,219] Furthermore, turbidity of the medium[11,216a,216b,216c] and comparable extraocular factors[15a] may critically affect polarization responses. Nevertheless, current research reaffirms the conclusion that arthropods must see the *e*-vector of linearly polarized light (Jander and Waterman, 1960, unpublished).

IV. *SUMMARY AND CONCLUSIONS*

Light sensitivity and vision in Crustacea depend on the naupliar eye, on the compound lateral eyes, and probably on a generalized or dermal light sense. The capabilities and limitations of these three photoreceptor systems are poorly known although most information is attributed to the second mechanism, which is the most obvious when present. In spite of large bodies of behavioral data derived from phototactic, optomotor, and other responses, understanding of almost every function in crustacean visual physiology is sharply limited by the virtual lack of good quantitative measurements of the basic events starting with the photochemical trigger and continuing through the coded message of spikes in the optic tract. Detailed structural information derivable from electronmicrographs and neurological techniques are much needed, as are precise comparative studies of physiological optics.

While obvious comparisons may suggest that the compound eye even at its best is not as effective a visual organ in some ways as a well-developed camera eye, there are two points to consider before reaching any final conclusions. One is that our anthropomorphic preconceptions of the nature of crustacean visual perception may hinder an adequate comprehension of its capabilities. The other is the remarkable cellular and spatial economy represented in these eyes compared with the millions of units required in our own, for instance. When one considers that less than 200 neurosensory cells are involved, it surely is noteworthy that a minute *Daphnia* can execute visual avoidance responses, perceive colors, and analyze polarized light. This combination of cellular parsimony with functional versatility may be comparable to the relatively few efferent and internuncial neurons in crustacean nervous systems in general (Chapters 6, 7).

REFERENCES

1. Alverdes, F. 1930. Tierpsychologische Analyse der intracentralen Vorgänge, welche bei decapoden Krebsen die locomotorischen Reaktionen auf Helligkeit und Dunkelheit bestimmen. *Z. wiss. Zoöl.* **137**:403–475.
2. Amar, R. 1951. Formations endocrines cérébrales des isopodes marins et comportement chromatique d'*Idotea*. *Ann. fac. sci. Marseille* [Sér. 2], **20**:167–305.
3. Arden, G. B., and Weale, R. A. 1954. Nervous mechanisms and dark-adaptation. *J. Physiol. (London)* **125**:417–426.
4. Autrum, H. 1950. Die Belichtungspotentiale und das Sehen der Insekten (Untersuchungen an *Calliphora* und *Dixippus*). *Z. vergleich. Physiol.* **32**: 176–227.
5. Autrum, H., and Gallwitz, U. 1951. Zur Analyse der Belichtungspotentiale des Insektenauges. *Z. vergleich. Physiol.* **33**:407–435.
6. Autrum, H., and Hoffmann, E. 1957. Die Wirkung von Pikrotoxin und Nikotin auf das Retinogramm von Insekten. *Z. Naturforsch.* **12b**:752–757.
7. Autrum, H., and Langer, H. 1958. Photolabile Pterine im Auge von *Calliphora erythrocephala*. *Biol. Zentr.* **77**:196–201.
8. Autrum, H., and Stöcker, M. 1952. Über optische Verschmelzungsfrequenzen und stroboskopisches Sehen bei Insekten. *Biol. Zentr.* **71**:129–152.
9. Autrum, H., and Stumpf, H. 1950. Das Bienenauge als Analysator für polarisiertes Licht. *Z. Naturforsch.* **5b**:116–122.
10. Bainbridge, R., and Waterman, T. H. 1957. Polarized light and the orientation of two marine Crustacea. *J. Exptl. Biol.* **34**:342–364.
11. Bainbridge, R., and Waterman, T. H. 1958. Turbidity and the polarized light orientation of the crustacean, *Mysidium*. *J. Exptl. Biol.* **35**:487–493.
12. Balss, H. 1938. Stomatopoda. *In:* "Bronn's Tierreich," Bd. 5, Abt. 1, Bch. 6, Teil II, pp. 1–173. Akademische Verlagsges., Leipzig.
13. Balss, H. 1944. Decapoda. *In:* "Bronn's Tierreich," Bd. 5, Abt. 1, Bch. 7, Lfg. 1–5, pp. 1–669. Akademische Verlagsges., Leipzig.
14. Barlow, H. B. 1952. The size of ommatidia in apposition eyes. *J. Exptl. Biol.* **29**:667–674.
15. Bartley, S. H. 1951. The psychophysiology of vision. *In:* "Handbook of Experimental Psychology" (S. S. Stevens, ed.), pp. 921–984. Wiley, New York.
15a. Baylor, E. R. 1959. The responses of snails to polarized light. *J. Exptl. Biol.* **36**:369–376.

15b. Baylor, E. R., and Kennedy, D. 1958. Evidence against a polarizing analyzer in the bee eye. (Abstract.) *Anat. Record* **132**:411.

16. Baylor, E. R., and Smith, F. E. 1953. The orientation of Cladocera to polarized light. *Am. Naturalist* **87**:97–101.

17. Baylor, E. R., and Smith, F. E. 1957. Diurnal migration of plankton crustaceans. In: "Recent Advances in Invertebrate Physiology" (B. T. Scheer, ed.), pp. 21–35. University of Oregon Publications, Eugene.

18. Bernard, F. 1937. Recherches sur la morphogénèse des yeux composés d'arthropodes. *Bull. biol. de France* **23**, Suppl.: 1–162.

19. Bernhard, C. G. 1942. Isolation of retinal and optic ganglion response in the eye of *Dytiscus*. *J. Neurophysiol.* **5**:32–48.

20. Bernhards, H. 1916. Der Bau des Komplexauges von *Astacus fluviatilius* (*Potamobius astacus* L.). *Z. wiss. Zoöl.* **116**:649–707.

21. Bethe, A. 1898. Das Nervensystem von *Carcinus maenas*. Teil II. *Arch. mikroskop. Anat. u. Entwicklungsmech.* **51**:382–452.

22. Birukow, G. 1937. Untersuchungen über den optischen Drehnystagmus und über die Sehschärfe des Grasfrosches (*Rana temporaria*). *Z. vergleich. Physiol.* **25**:92–142.

23. Bliss, A. F. 1942. Derived photosensitive pigments from invertebrate eyes. *J. Gen. Physiol.* **26**:361–367.

24. Bröcker, H. 1935. Untersuchungen über das Sehvermögen der Einsiedlerkrebse. *Zool. Jahrb. Abt. Allgem. Zool. Physiol. Tiere* **55**:399–430.

25. Burtt, E. T., and Catton, W. T. 1954. Visual perception of movement in the locust. *J. Physiol.* (*London*) **125**:566–580.

26. Burtt, E. T., and Catton, W. T. 1956. Electrical responses to visual stimulation in the optic lobes of the locust and certain other insects. *J. Physiol.* (*London*) **133**:68–88.

26a. Burtt, E. T., and Catton, W. T. 1959a. Visual acuity of the compound eyes in three species of insects. *XV Intern. Congr. Zool. London, 1958, Proc.*, pp. 535–536.

26b. Burtt, E. T., and Catton, W. T. 1959b. Transmission of visual responses in the nervous system of the locust. *J. Physiol.* (*London*) **146**:492–515.

27. Castle, E. S. 1934. The phototropic effect of polarized light. *J. Gen. Physiol.* **17**:751–762.

28. Chun, C. 1896. Atlantis: Biologische Studien über pelagische Organismen. *Zoologica* (*Stuttgart*) **19**:1–260.

29. Clark, L. B. 1935. The visual acuity of the fiddler-crab, *Uca pugnax*. *J. Gen. Physiol.* **19**:311–319.

30. Clarke, G. L., and Wertheim, G. K. 1956. Measurements of illumination at great depths and at night in the Atlantic Ocean by means of a new bathyphotometer. *Deep-Sea Research* **3**:189–205.

31. Crozier, W. J., and Mangelsdorf, A. F. 1924. A note on the relative photosensory effect of polarized light. *J. Gen. Physiol.* **6**:703–709.

32. Crozier, W. J., and Wolf, E. 1939a. The flicker response contour for the crayfish. I. *J. Gen. Physiol.* **23**:1–10.

33. Crozier, W. J., and Wolf, E. 1939b. The flicker response curve of the crayfish. II. Retinal pigment and the theory of the asymmetry of the curve. *Biol. Bull.* **77**:126–134.

34. Crozier, W. J., Wolf, E., and Zerrahn-Wolf, G. 1939. The flicker response contour for the isopod *Asellus*. *J. Gen. Physiol.* **22**:451–462.

35. Dahl, E. 1952. Mystacocarida. *Lunds Univ. Årsskr.* [N.F.] Avd. 2, **48**(6):1–41.
36. Daumer, K. 1956. Reizmetrische Untersuchung des Farbensehens der Bienen. *Z. vergleich. Physiol.* **38**:413–478.
37. Debaisieux, P. 1944. Les yeux des Crustacés: structure, développement, réactions à l'éclairement. *La Cellule* **50**:5–122.
38. de Bruin, G. H. P., and Crisp, D. J. 1957. The influence of pigment migration on vision in higher Crustacea. *J. Exptl. Biol.* **34**:447–463.
39. de Lattin, G. 1939. Untersuchungen an Isopodenaugen. (Unter besonderer Berücksichtigung der blinden Arten.) *Zool. Jahrb. Abt. Anat. u. Ontog. Tiere* **65**:417–468.
40. del Cañizo, J. 1945. Investigaciones de Cajal sobre los ojos y las fibras musculares de algunas insectos. *Graellsia* **3**:73–89.
41. del Portillo, J. 1936. Beziehungen zwischen den Öffnungswinkeln der Ommatidien, Krümmung und Gestalt der Insekten Augen und ihrer funktionellen Aufgabe. *Z. vergleich. Physiol.* **23**:100–145.
42. Demoll, R. 1909. Über die Augen und die Augenstielreflexe von *Squilla mantis*. *Zool. Jahrb. Abt. Anat. u. Ontog. Tiere* **27**:171–212.
43. Demoll, R. 1917. "Die Sinnesorgane der Arthropoden ihr Bau und ihre Funktion," 243 pp. Vieweg, Braunschweig.
44. Denton, E. J. 1955. Absorption du crystallin de *Rana esculenta* et d'*Anguilla vulgaris*. *Bull. muséum natl. hist. nat. (Paris)* **27**:418–425.
44a. Denton, E. J., and Warren, F. J. 1957. The photosensitive pigments in the retinae of deep-sea fishes. *J. Marine Biol. Assoc. United Kingdom* **36**:651–662.
45. DeRobertis, E. 1956a. Electron microscope observations on the submicroscopic organization of the retinal rods. *J. Biophys. Biochem. Cytol.* **2**:319–330.
46. DeRobertis, E. 1956b. Morphogenesis of retinal rods, an electron microscope study. *J. Biophys. Biochem. Cytol.*, 2, Suppl: 209–218.
47. Dethier, V. G. 1943. The dioptric apparatus of lateral ocelli. II. Visual capacities of the ocellus. *J. Cellular Comp. Physiol.* **22**:115–126.
48. Dethier, V. G. 1953. Vision. *In:* "Insect Physiology" (K. D. Roeder, ed.), pp. 488–522. Wiley, New York.
49. de Vries, H. 1956. Physical aspects of the sense organs. *Progr. Biophys. and Biophys. Chem.* **6**:207–264.
50. Dietrich, W. 1931. Die lokomotorischen Reaktionen der Landasseln auf Licht and Dunkelheit. *Z. wiss. Zoöl.* **138**:187–232.
51. Dijkgraaf, S. 1956a. Ueber die kompensatorischen Augenstielbewegen bei Brachyuren. *Pubbl. staz. zool. Napoli* **28**:341–358.
52. Dijkgraaf, S. 1956b. Kompensatorische Augenstieldrehungen und ihre Auslösung bei der Languste (*Palinurus vulgaris*). *Z. vergleich. Physiol.* **38**:491–520.
53. Dobkiewicz, L. V. 1912. Über die Augen der Tiefseegalatheiden. *Z. wiss. Zoöl.* **99**:688–716.
54. Dodt, E. 1954. Ergebnisse der Flimmer-Elektroretinographie. *Experientia* **10**:331–333.
55. Doflein, F. 1903. Die Augen der Tiefseekrabben. *Biol. Zentr.* **23**:570–593.
56. Doflein, F. 1910. Lebensgewohnheiten und Anpassungen bei dekapoden Krebsen. "Festschrift zum 60 Geburtstag Richard Hertwigs," Vol. 3, pp. 215–292. Fischer, Jena.

57. Doochin, H. D. 1951. The morphology of *Balanus improvisus* Darwin and *Balanus amphitrite niveus* Darwin during initial attachment and metamorphosis. *Bull. Marine Sci. Gulf Carib.* 1:15–39.

58. Eckert, B. 1953. Orientující vliv polaisovaného světla no perloočky. *Českoslov. biol.* 2:76–80. [Abstract (G. Birukow), *Ber. wiss. Biol.* 89:198, 1954.]

59. Exner, S. 1891. "Die Physiologie der Facettirten Augen von Krebsen und Insecten," 206 pp. Deuticke, Leipzig and Vienna.

59a. Fisher, L. R., and Goldie, E. H. 1959. The eye pigments of a euphausiid crustacean, *Meganyctiphanes norvegica* (M. Sars). *XV Intern. Congr. Zool. London, 1958, Proc.*, pp. 533–535.

60. Fox, H. Munro, 1949. On *Apus:* Its rediscovery in Britain, nomenclature and habits. *Proc. Zool. Soc. London* 119:693–702.

61. Fricke, H. 1931. Die Komplexaugen von *Diastylis rathkei. Zool. Jahrb. Abt. Anat. u. Ontog. Tiere* 53:701–724.

62. Friedrich, H. 1931. Mitteilungen über vergleichende Untersuchungen über den Lichtsinn einiger mariner Copepoden. *Z. vergleich. Physiol.* 15:121–138.

63. Gaffron, M. 1934. Untersuchungen über das Bewegungsehen bei Libellen, Fliegen und Fischen. *Z. vergleich. Physiol.* 20:299–337.

64. Goldsmith, T. H., and Philpott, D. E. 1957. The microstructure of the compound eye of insects. *J. Biophys. Biochem. Cytol.* 3:429–440.

65. Gottsche, C. M. 1852. Beitrag zur Anatomie und Physiologie des Auges der Krebse und Fliegen. *Arch. Anat. u. Physiol. wiss. Medezin* 1852:483–492.

66. Granit, R. 1947. "Sensory Mechanisms of the Retina," 412 pp. Oxford Univ. Press, London and New York.

67. Granit, R. 1955. "Receptors and Sensory Perception," 366 pp. Yale Univ. Press, New Haven, Connecticut.

68. Grüsser, O.-J. 1957. Rezeptorpotentiale einzelner retinaler Zapfen der Katze. *Naturwissenschaften* 44:522.

69. Haidinger, W. 1844. Ueber das direkte Erkennen des polarisierten Lichts und der Lage der Polarisationsebene. *Ann. Physik. Chemie* 63:29–39.

70. Hanaoka, T. 1950a. Electric response in the unit receptors of the simple retina of cray-fish (*Cambarus*). (In Japanese.) *Seitai no Kagaku* 2:8–13.

71. Hanaoka, T. 1950b. Photo-tonus or effect of light adaptation upon the isolated electric response of the unit receptors in simple retina. (In Japanese.) *J. Physiol. Soc. Japan* 12:197–200.

72. Hanaoka, T., Suganuma, Y., Ikari, C., and Yasumi, Y. 1957. Light receptive organellae in visual cell and their function. II. Ultrastructure of the rhabdom of cray fish visual cells and the electric response correlated with its structure. (In Japanese with English summary.) *Symposium on Cytochemistry* 6:189–202.

73. Hanström, B. 1927. Über die Frage, ob funktionell verschiedene, zapfen- und stäbchenartige Sehzellen im Komplexauge der Arthropoden vorkommen. *Z. vergleich. Physiol.* 6:566–597.

74. Hanström, B. 1928. "Vergleichende Anatomie des Nervensystems der Wirbellosen Tiere," 628 pp. Springer, Berlin.

75. Hanström, B. 1933. Neue Untersuchungen über Sinnesorgane und Nervensystem der Crustaceen. II. *Zool. Jahrb. Abt. Anat. u. Ontog. Tiere* 56:387–520.

76. Hanström, B. 1948. The brain, the sense organs, and the incretory organs of the head in the Crustacea Malacostraca. *Bull. biol. France et Belg. Suppl.* 33:98–126.

77. Harms, J. W. 1932. Die Realisation von Genen und die consecutive Adaption. II. *Birgus latro* L. als Landkrebs und seine Beziehungen zu den Coenobiten. *Z. wiss. Zoöl.* 140:167–290.

78. Harris, J. E., and Mason, P. 1956. Vertical migration in eyeless *Daphnia*. *Proc. Roy. Soc.* B145:280–290.

79. Harris, J. E., and Wolfe, U. K. 1955. A laboratory study of vertical migration. *Proc. Roy. Soc.* B144:329–354.

80. Hartline, H. K. 1928. A quantitative and descriptive study of the electric response to illumination of the arthropod eye. *Am. J. Physiol.* 83:466–483.

81. Hartline, H. K. 1940. The receptive fields of optic nerve fibers. *Am. J. Physiol.* 130:690–699.

82. Hartline, H. K., and Graham, C. H. 1932. Nerve impulses from single receptors in the eye. *J. Cellular Comp. Physiol.* 1:277–295.

83. Hartline, H. K., and McDonald, P. R. 1947. Light and dark adaptations of single photoreceptor elements in the eye of *Limulus*. *J. Cellular Comp. Physiol.* 30:225–253.

84. Hartline, H. K., Wagner, H. G., and MacNichol, E. F., Jr. 1952. The peripheral origin of nervous activity in the visual system. *Cold Spring Harbor Symposia Quant. Biol.* 17:125–141.

85. Hartline, H. K., Wagner, H. G., and Ratliff, F. 1956. Inhibition in the eye of *Limulus*. *J. Gen. Physiol.* 39:651–673.

86. Hartridge, H. 1947. The visual perception of fine detail. *Phil. Trans. Roy. Soc. London* B232:519–671.

87. Hassenstein, B. 1951. Ommatidienraster und afferente Bewegungsintegration. (Versuche an dem Rüsselkäfer *Chlorophanus viridis*.) *Z. vergleich. Physiol.* 33:301–326.

88. Hassenstein, B. 1954. Über die Sehschärfe von Superpositionsaugen. (Versuche an *Lysmata seticaudata* und *Leander serratus*). *Pubbl. staz. zool. Napoli* 25:1–8.

89. Heberdey, R. F. 1936. Die Farbensinn helladaptierter Daphnien. *Biol. Zentr.* 56:207–216.

90. Heberdey, R. F. 1949. Das Unterscheidungsvermögen von *Daphnia* für Helligkeiten farbiger Lichter. *Z. vergleich Physiol.* 31:89–111.

91. Heberdey, R. F., and Kupka, E. 1942. Helligkeitsunterscheidensvermögen von *Daphnia pulex*. *Z. vergleich. Physiol.* 29:541–582.

92. Hecht, S., and Mintz, E. V. 1939. The visibility of single lines at various illuminations and the retinal basis for visual resolution. *J. Gen. Physiol.* 22:593–612.

93. Hecht, S., and Wald, G. 1934. The visual acuity and intensity discrimination of *Drosophila*. *J. Gen. Physiol.* 17:517–547.

94. Hecht, S., and Wolf, E. 1929. The visual acuity of the honeybee. *J. Gen. Physiol.* 12:727–760.

95. Henke, K. 1930. Die Lichtorientierung und die Bedingungen der Lichtstimmung bei der Rollassel *Armadillidium cinereum* Zenker. *Z. vergleich. Physiol.* 13:534–625.

96. Herter, K. 1927. Reizphysiologische Untersuchungen an der Karpfenlaus (*Argulus foliaceus* L.). *Z. vergleich. Physiol.* 5:283–370.

97. Hertz, M. 1934. Zur Physiologie der gesehenen Bewegung. *Biol. Zentr.* 54:250–264.

98. Hertz, M. 1935. Die Untersuchungen über den Formensinn der Honigbiene. *Naturwissenschaften* 36:618–624.

99. Hertz, M. 1939. New experiments on colour vision in bees. *J. Exptl. Biol.* **16**:1–8.

100. Hess, C. 1913. Gesichtsinn. *In:* "Handbuch der Vergleichenden Physiologie" (H. Winterstein, ed.), Vol. IV, pp. 555–840. Fischer, Jena.

101. Hess, W. N. 1940. Regional photosensitivity and photoreceptors of *Crangon armillatus* and the spiny lobster, *Panulirus argus*. *Papers Tortugas Lab.* **32**:153–161.

102. Hesse, R. 1908. "Das Sehen der niederen Tiere," 47 pp. Fischer, Jena.

103. Homann, H. 1924. Die Optik der Facettenaugen im Versuch. *Z. math. naturwiss. Unterr.* **63**:13–18.

104. Hoyle, G. 1955. Functioning of the insect ocellar nerve. *J. Exptl. Biol.* **32**:397–407.

105. Hubbard, R. 1954. The respiration of the isolated rod outer limb of the frog retina. *J. Gen. Physiol.* **37**:373–379.

106. Judd, D. B. 1951. Basic correlates of the visual stimulus. *In:* "Handbook of Experimental Psychology" (S. S. Stevens, ed.), pp. 811–867, Wiley, New York.

107. Kampa, E. M. 1955. Euphausiopsin, a new photosensitive pigment from the eyes of euphausiid crustaceans. *Nature* **175**:996–998.

108. Kennedy, D. 1957. Responses of a crustacean photoreceptor. (Abstract.) *Federation Proc.* **16**:71.

109. Kennedy, D., and Milkman, R. D. 1956. Selective light absorption by the lenses of lower vertebrates, and its influence on spectral sensitivity. *Biol. Bull.* **111**:375–386.

110. Kerz, M. 1950. Wahrnehmung polarisierten Lichtes durch *Eupagurus*. *Experientia* **6**:427.

111. Kleinholz, L. H. 1955. The nature of the reflecting pigment in the arthropod eye. *Biol. Bull.* **109**:362.

112. Koehler, O. 1924. Über das Forbensehen von *Daphnia magna* Strauss. *Z. vergleich. Physiol.* **1**:84–174.

113. Koller, G. 1927. Über Chromatophorensystem, Farbensinn und Farbwechsel bei *Crangon vulgaris*. *Z. vergleich. Physiol.* **5**:191–246.

114. Koller, G. 1928. Versuche über den Farbensinn der Eupaguriden. *Z. vergleich. Physiol.* **8**:337–353.

115. Konishi, J. 1955a. Retinal and optic nerve response of the compound eye of spiny lobster *Panulirus japonicus* (von Siebold). *Rept. Fac. Fisheries, Pref. Univ. Mie* **2**:138–144.

116. Konishi, J. 1955b. Electrical studies on the compound eyes of *Eriocheir japonicus* de Haan. *Rept. Fac. Fisheries, Pref. Univ. Mie* **2**:145–150.

117. Kuffler, S. W. 1953. Discharge patterns and functional organization of mammalian retina. *J. Neurophysiol.* **16**:37–68.

118. Kühn, A. 1929. Farbenunterschiedsvermögen der Tiere. *In:* "Handbuch der Normalen und Pathologischen Physiologie" (A. Bethe, ed.), Vol. XII (Heft 1), pp. 720–741. Springer, Berlin.

119. Lochhead, J. H., and Resner, R. 1959. Functions of the eyes and neurosecretion in Crustacea Anostraca. *XV Intern. Congr. Zool. London, 1958, Proc.*, pp. 397–399.

120. Lüdtke, H. 1951. Über retinomotorische Erscheinungen im Insektenauge. *Naturwissenschaften* **38**:285–286.

121. Martin, M. F. 1932. On the morphology and classification of *Argulus* (Crustacea). *Proc. Zool. Soc. London* 1932:771–806.
122. Mast, S. O. 1917. The relation between spectral colors and stimulation in the lower organisms. *J. Exptl. Zool.* 22:471–528.
123. Mauchline, J. 1958. The vascular system of crustacean compound eyes, especially those of the euphausid, *Meganyctiphanes norvegica*. *Quart. J. Microscop. Sci.* 99:89–93.
124. Mayrat, A. 1956. Oeil, centres optiques et glandes endocrines de *Praunus flexuosus* (O. F. Müller). *Arch. zool. exptl. et gén.* 93:319–353.
125. Merker, E. 1930. Sehen die Daphnien ultraviolettes Licht? *Zool. Jahrb. Abt. allgem. Zool. Physiol. Tiere* 48:277–348.
126. Meyer, G. F. 1955. Vergleichende Untersuchungen mit der supravitalen Methylenblaufärbung am Nervensystem wirbelloser Tiere. *Zool. Jahrb. Abt. Anat. u. Ontog. Tiere* 74:339–400.
127. Miller, W. H. 1957a. Morphology of the ommatidia of the compound eye of *Limulus*. *J. Biophys. Biochem. Cytol.* 3:421–428.
128. Miller, W. H. 1957b. Comparative study of fine structure of some invertebrate photoreceptors. (Abstract.) *Science* 126:1233–1234.
129. Mittelstaedt, H. 1956. Regelung und Steuerung bei der Orientierung der Lebewesen. *In:* "Regelungsvorgänge in der Biologie" (H. Mittelstaedt, ed.), pp. 87–101. Oldenbourg, Munich.
130. Monod, T. 1926. Les Gnathiidae (Essai monographique—Morphologie, Biologie, Systématique). *Mém. soc. sci. nat. Maroc* 13:1–667.
131. Müller, J. 1826. "Zur vergleichenden Physiologie des Gesichtssinnes," 462 pp. Cnobloch, Leipzig.
132. Nagano, T. 1949. Physiological studies on the pigmentary system of Crustacea. III. The color change of an isopod *Ligia exotica* (Roux). *Science Repts. Tôhoku Univ. Fourth Ser.* 18:167–175
133. Nagano, T. 1950. Physiological studies on the pigmentary system of Crustacea. VII. The effect of colored light on pigment migration of the compound eye of the shrimps. *Science Repts. Tôhoku Univ. Fourth Ser.* 18:453–459.
134. Naka, K., and Kuwabara, M. 1956. The component analysis of the ERG from the compound eye of *Cambarus*. *Mem. Fac. Sci. Kyushu Univ.* [Ser. E.] 2:75–86.
135. Nowikoff, M. 1931a. Das Modell des Rhabdoms von Komplexaugen. *Biol. Zentr.* 51:325–329.
136. Nowikoff, M. 1931b. Untersuchungen über die Komplexaugen von Lepidopteren nebst einigen Bemerkungen über die Rhabdome der Arthropoden im allgemeinen. *Z. wiss. Zoöl.* 138:1–67.
137. Nowikoff, M. 1937. Über den Parallelismus der Augenformen. *Anat. Anz.* 85:261–272.
138. O'Brien, B. 1951. Vision and resolution in the central retina. *J. Opt. Soc. Amer.* 41:882–894.
139. Papi, F. 1955. Richerche sull'orientamento astronomico di *Arctosa perita* (Latr.) (Araneae-Lycosidae). *Pubbl. staz. zool. Napoli* 27:80–107.
140. Parker, G. H. 1891. The compound eyes in crustaceans. *Bull. Mus. Comp. Zool. Harvard* 21:45–140.
141. Parker, G. H. 1948. "Animal Colour Changes and their Neurohumours," 377 pp. Cambridge Univ. Press, London and New York.

142. Peabody, E. B. 1939. Pigmentary responses in the isopod, *Idothea*. *J. Exptl. Zool.* **82**:47–83.

143. Peters, E. 1926. Vergleichende Untersuchungen über den Lichtsinn einheimischer Cladocerenarten. *Zool. Jahrbch. Abt. Allgem. Zool. Physiol. Tiere* **43**:1–40.

144. Pirenne, M. H., and Denton, E. J. 1952. Accuracy and sensitivity of the human eye. *Nature* **170**:1039–1042.

145. Polyak, S. 1957. "The Vertebrate Visual System" (H. Klüver, ed.), 1390 pp. University of Chicago Press, Chicago.

146. Prosser, C. L. 1934. Action potentials in the nervous system of the crayfish. II. Responses to illumination of the eye and caudal ganglia. *J. Cellular Comp. Physiol.* **4**:363–377.

147. Rabaud, E., and Verrier, M-L. 1940. Vision et comportement des Pagures et théorie d'Exner. *Compt. rend.* **211**:300–302.

148. Rádl, E. 1900. Untersuchungen über den Bau des Tractus opticus von *Squilla mantis* und von anderen Crustaceen. *Z. wiss. Zoöl.* **67**:551–598.

149. Ramadan, M. M. 1952. Contribution to our knowledge of the structure of the compound eyes of decapod Crustacea. *Lunds Univ. Årsskr.* [N. F.] Avd. 2, **48**(3):1–20.

150. Rasquin, P., and Rosenbloom, L. 1954. Endocrine imbalance and tissue hyperplasia in teleosts maintained in darkness. *Bull. Am. Museum Nat. Hist.* **104**: 359–426.

151. Richards, A. G. 1951. "The Integument of Arthropods," 411 pp. University of Minnesota, Minneapolis.

152. Riedel, A. H. 1918. Ein Beitrag zur Kenntnis der photoelektrischen Reaktion des Hummerauges. *Z. Biol.* **69**:125–140.

153. Riggs, L. A., Ratliff, F., Cornsweet, J. C., and Cornsweet, T. N. 1953. The disappearance of steadily fixated visual test objects. *J. Opt. Soc. Amer.* **43**:495–501.

154. Rose, M., and Vaissière, R. 1952. Le complexe oculaire des Sapphirines (Copépodes pélagiques). *Arch. zool. exptl. et gén.* **88**:205–221.

155. Rosenstadt, B. 1896. Beiträge zur Kenntniss des Baues der zusammengesetzten Augen bei den Dekapoden. *Arch. mikroskop. Anat. u. Entwicklungsmech.* **47**:748–770.

156. Ruck, P. 1957. The electrical responses of dorsal ocelli in cockroaches and grasshoppers. *J. Insect Physiol.* **1**:109–123.

157. Ruck, P., and Jahn, T. L. 1954. Electrical studies on the compound eye of *Ligia occidentalis* Dana (Crustacea: Isopoda). *J. Gen. Physiol.* **37**:825–849.

158. Sánchez y Sánchez, D. 1923. Action spécifique des batonnets rétiniens des insectes. *Trabajos lab. invest. biol., Univ. Madrid* **21**:143–167.

159. Sandeen, M. I., and Brown, F. A., Jr. 1952. Responses of the distal retinal pigment of *Palaemonetes* to illumination. *Physiol. Zoöl.* **25**:222–230.

160. Sander, W. 1933. Phototaktische Reaktionen der Bienen auf Lichter verschiedener Wellenlänge. *Z. vergleich. Physiol.* **20**:267–286.

161. Sato, S., Kato, M., and Toriumi, M. 1957. Structural changes of the compound eye of *Culex pipiens* var. *pallens* Coquillet in the process of dark adaptation. *Science Repts. Tôhoku Univ., Fourth Ser.* **23**:91–99.

162. Schaller, F. 1953. Verhaltens- und sinnesphysiologische Beobachtungen an *Squilla mantis*. *Z. Tierpsychol.* **10**:1–12.

162a. Scheffer, D., Robert, P., and Médioni, J. 1958. Réactions oculo-motrices de la Daphnie (*Daphnia pulex* De Geer) en réponse à des lumières monochromatiques d'égale énergie. Sensibilité visuelle et sensibilité dermatoptique. *Compt. rend. soc. biol.* 152:1000–1003.

163. Scheuring, L. 1923. Die Augen von *Gebia* und *Callianassa*. (Ein Beitrag zur Kenntnis des rückgebildeten Facettenauges). *Zool. Jahrb. Abt. Anat. u. Ontog. Tiere* 44:389–436.

164. Schlechtendal, A. 1934. Beitrag zum Farbensinn der Arthropoden. *Z. vergleich. Physiol.* 20:545–581.

165. Schlieper, C. 1927. Farbensinn der Tiere und optomotorische Reaktionen. *Z. vergleich. Physiol.* 6:453–472.

166. Schneider, G. 1956. Zur Spektralempfindlichkeit des Komplexauges von *Calliphora*. *Z. vergleich. Physiol.* 39:1–20.

167. Schultze, M. 1868. "Untersuchungen über die Zusammengesetzten Augen der Krebse und Insecten," 32 pp. Cohen, Bonn.

168. Schulz, H. 1928. Über die Bedeutung des Lichtes im Leben niederer Krebse. *Z. vergleich. Physiol.* 7:488–552.

169. Seifert, R. 1932. Raumorientierung und Phototaxis der anostraken Euphyllopoden. (Versuche an *Chirocephalus* und *Artemia*). *Z. vergleich. Physiol.* 16:111–184.

170. Seifert, R. 1934. Über den Verlauf der Helladaption bei *Artemia salina*. *Zool. Anz.* 7 Suppl.: 224–228.

171. Smith, F. E., and Baylor, E. R. 1953. Color responses in the Cladocera and their ecological significance. *Am. Naturalist* 87:49–55.

172. Sperry, R. W. 1950. Neural basis of the spontaneous optokinetic response produced by visual inversion. *J. Comp. and Physiol. Psychol.* 43:482–489.

173. Stephens, G. C., Fingerman, M., and Brown, F. A., Jr. 1953. The orientation of *Drosophila* to plane polarized light. *Ann. Entomol. Soc. Amer.* 46:75–83.

174. Stockhammer, K. 1956. Zur Wahrnehmung der Schwingungsrichtung linear polarisierten Lichtes bei Insekten. *Z. vergleich. Physiol.* 38:30–83.

174a. Stockhammer, K. 1959. Die Orientierung nach der Schwingungsrichtung linear polarisierten Lichtes und ihre sinnesphysiologischen Grundlagen. *Ergeb. Biol.* 21:23–56.

175. Strauss, E. 1909. Das Gammaridenauge. *Wiss. Ergeb. Deut. Tiefsee Expedition* 20, Pt. 1:1–84.

176. Tattersall, W. M., and Tattersall, O. S. 1951. "British Mysidacea," 460 pp. Ray Society, London.

177. Tinbergen, N., and Kruyt, W. 1938. Über die Orientierung des Bienenwolfes (*Philanthus triangulum* Fabr.). III. Die Bevorzugung bestimmter Wegmarken. *Z. vergleich. Physiol.* 25:292–334.

178. Tonner, F. 1943. Die Grösse der Empfindungsfläche eines Lichtpunktes und der Zapfenraster. *Arch. ges. Physiol. Pflügers* 247:168–182.

179. Umbach, W. 1934. Entwicklung und Bau des Komplexauges der Mehlmotte *Ephestia kühniella* Zeller nebst einigen Bemerkungen über die Entstehung der optischen Ganglien. *Z. Morphol. Ökol. Tiere* 28:561–594.

179a. Vaissière, R. 1958. Morphologie et Histologie Comparées des Yeux des Crustacés Copépodes. Thesis, University of Paris.

180. van Essen, J. 1938. Zur Funktion des Tapetum lucidum zugleich ein Beitrag zur Sinnesphysiologie selbstleuchtender Tiere. *Z. Sinnesphysiol.* 67:245–257.

181. Verkhovskaya, I. N. 1940. The influence of polarized light on the phototaxis of certain organisms. (In Russian with French summary and figure legends.) *Bull. Moscow Nat. Hist. Soc., Biol. Sect.* **49**:101–113.

182. Verrier, M-L. 1942. Recherches sur les yeux et la vision des Arthropodes. II. Le dédoublement des yeux et le problème des réductions oculaires à propos du Diptère *Bibio marci* L. *Bull. biol. France et Belg.* **76**:1–3.

183. Viallanes, M. H. 1892. Contribution à l'histologie du système nerveux des Invertébrés—La lame ganglionnaire de la langouste. *Ann. sci. nat.* Ser. 7, **13**:385–397.

184. Viaud, G. 1938. Recherches expérimentales sur le phototropisme des Daphnies. *Publs. fac. lettres Strasbourg* **84**:1–196.

185. Viaud, G. 1948. Le phototropisme et les deux modes de la photoreception. *Experientia* **4**:81–88.

186. Viaud, G. 1951. Le phototropisme chez les Cladocères, les Rotifères et les Planaires. *Année biol.* **27**:365–378.

187. Viscontini, M., Kühn, A., and Egelhaaf, A. 1956. Isolierung fluorescierender Stoffe aus *Ephestia kühniella. Z. Naturforsch.* **11b**:501–504.

188. Viscontini, M., Schmid, H., and Hadorn, E. 1955. Isolierung fluorescierender Stoffe aus *Astacus fluviatilis. Experientia* **11**:390–392.

189. Visscher, J. P., and Luce, R. H. 1928. Reactions of the cyprid larvae of barnacles to light with special reference to spectral colors. *Biol. Bull.* **54**:336–350.

190. von Buddenbrock, W. 1930. Untersuchungen über den Schattenreflex. *Z. vergleich. Physiol.* **13**:164–213.

191. von Buddenbrock, W. 1935. Versuche über die Wahrnehmungsgrenze des Insektenauges. *Naturwissenschaften* **23**:154–157.

192. von Buddenbrock, W. 1952. Sinnesphysiologie. *In:* "Vergleichende Physiologie," Vol. 1, 504 pp. Birkhäuser, Basel.

193. von Buddenbrock, W., and Friedrich, H. 1933. Neue Beobachtung über die kompensatorischen Augenbewegungen und den Farbensinn der Taschenkrabben (*Carcinus maenas*). *Z. vergleich. Physiol.* **19**:747–761.

194. von Buddenbrock, W., and Moller-Racke, I. 1953a. Über den Lichtsinn von *Pecten. Pubbl. staz. zool. Napoli* **24**:218–246.

195. von Buddenbrock, W., and Moller-Racke, I. 1953b. Über das Wesen der optomotorischen Reaktionen. *Experientia* **9**:191–193.

196. von Buddenbrock, W., and Schulz, E. 1933. Beiträge zur Kenntnis der Lichtkompassbewegung und der Adaptation des Insektenauges. *Zool. Jahrb. Abt. Allgem. Zool. Physiol. Tiere* **52**:513–536.

197. von Frisch, K. 1948. Gelöste und ungelöste Rätsel der Bienensprache. *Naturwissenschaften* **35**:38–43.

198. von Frisch, K., and Kupelwieser, H. 1913. Über den Einfluss der Lichtfarbe auf die phototaktischen Reaktionen niederer Krebse. *Biol. Zentr.* **33**:517–552.

199. von Gavel, L. 1939. Die "kritische Streifenbreite" als Mass der Sehschärfe bei *Drosophila melanogaster. Z. vergleich. Physiol.* **27**:80–135.

200. von Helmholtz, H. 1896. "Handbuch der Physiologischen Optik," 1334 pp. Voss, Hamburg.

201. von Holst, E., and Mittelstaedt, H. 1950. Das Reafferenzprinzip (Wechselwirkungen zwischen Zentralnervensystem und Peripherie). *Naturwissenschaften* **37**:464–476.

202. von Schiller, P. 1937. Vergleichende Untersuchungen über Bewegungssehen. *Biol. Revs. Cambridge Phil. Soc.* **12**:116–153.

203. Vowles, D. M. 1954. The orientation of ants. II. Orientation to light, gravity and polarized light. *J. Exptl. Biol.* **31**:356–375.
204. Vowles, D. M. 1955. The foraging of ants. *Brit. J. Animal Behaviour* **3**:1–13.
205. Wald, G. 1938. Area and visual threshold. *J. Gen. Physiol.* **21**:269–287.
206. Wald, G. 1952. Alleged effects of the near ultra-violet on human vision. *J. Opt. Soc. Amer.* **42**:171–177.
207. Wald, G., and Hubbard, R. 1957. Visual pigment of a decapod crustacean: the lobster. *Nature* **180**:278–280.
208. Waterman, T. H. 1937. The relative effectiveness of various wavelengths for the photokinesis of *Unionicola*. *J. Cellular Comp. Physiol.* **9**:453–467.
209. Waterman, T. H. 1950. A light polarization analyzer in the compound eye of *Limulus*. *Science* **111**:252–254.
210. Waterman, T. H. 1951. Polarized light navigation by arthropods. *Trans. N. Y. Acad. Sci.* **14**:11–14.
211. Waterman, T. H. 1953. Action potentials from an arthropod ocellus: the median eye of *Limulus*. *Proc. Natl. Acad. Sci. U. S.* **39**:687–694.
212. Waterman, T. H. 1954a. Directional sensitivity of single ommatidia in the compound eye of *Limulus*. *Proc. Natl. Acad. Sci. U. S.* **40**:252–257.
213. Waterman, T. H. 1954b. Polarized light and angle of stimulus incidence in the compound eye of *Limulus*. *Proc. Natl. Acad. Sci. U. S.* **40**:258–262.
214. Waterman, T. H. 1954c. Polarization patterns in submarine illumination. *Science* **120**:927–932.
215. Waterman, T. H. 1955. Polarization of scattered sunlight in deep water. *Deep-Sea Research* **3** Suppl.: 426–434.
216. Waterman, T. H. 1958. Polarized light and plankton navigation. *In:* "Perspectives in Marine Biology" (A. A. Buzzati-Traverso, ed.), pp. 429–450. University of California Press, Berkeley.
216a. Waterman, T. H. 1959a. The problem of polarized light sensitivity. (Abstract.) *XV Intern. Congr. Zool. London, 1958, Proc.*, pp. 537–539.
216b. Waterman, T. H. 1959b. Animal navigation in the sea. *Gunma J. Med. Sci. (Japan)* **8**:243–262.
216c. Waterman, T. H. 1960. Interaction of polarized light and turbidity in the orientation of *Daphnia* and *Mysidium*. *Z. vergleich. Physiol.* **43**:149–172.
217. Waterman, T. H., Nunnemacher, R. F., Chace, F. A., Jr., and Clarke, G. L. 1939. Diurnal vertical migrations of deepwater plankton. *Biol. Bull.* **76**:256–279.
218. Waterman, T. H., and Westell, W. E. 1956. Quantitative effect of the sun's position on submarine light polarization. *J. Marine Research (Sears Foundation)* **15**:149–169.
219. Waterman, T. H., and Wiersma, C. A. G. 1954. The functional relation between retinal cells and optic nerve in *Limulus*. *J. Exptl. Zool.* **126**:59–86.
220. Weber, H. 1933. "Lehrbuch der Entomologie," 726 pp. Fischer, Jena.
221. Wellington, W. G. 1953. Motor responses evoked by the dorsal ocelli of *Sarcophaga aldrichi* Parker, and the orientation of the fly to plane polarized light. *Nature* **172**:1177–1179.
222. Wellington, W. G. 1955. Solar heat and plane polarized light versus the light compass reaction in the orientation of insects on the ground. *Ann. Entomol. Soc. Amer.* **48**:67–76.
223. Wells, P. H. 1952. Response to light by the eyeless white cave crayfish, *Cambarus ayersii*. (Abstract.) *Anat. Record* **113**:613.

224. Welsh, J. H. 1934. The caudal photoreceptor and responses of the crayfish to light. *J. Cellular Comp. Physiol.* **4**:379–388.

225. Welsh, J. H., and Chace, F. A., Jr. 1937. Eyes of deep sea crustaceans. I. Acanthephyridae. *Biol. Bull.* **72**:57–74.

226. Welsh, J. H., and Chace, F. A., Jr. 1938. Eyes of deep-sea crustaceans. II. Sergestidae. *Biol. Bull.* **74**:364–375.

227. Wenke, W. 1908. Die Augen von *Apus productus*. *Z. wiss. Zoöl.* **96**:236–265.

228. Werringloer, A. 1932. Die Sehorgane und Sehzentren der Dorylinen nebst Untersuchungen über die Facettenaugen der Formiciden. *Z. wiss. Zoöl.* **141**: 432–524.

229. Wetzel, A. 1933. Studien über die Biologie der Caprelliden. II. Raumorientierung, Farbanpassung, und Farbwechsel. *Z. wiss. Zoöl.* **143**:77–125.

230. White, G. M. 1924. Reactions of the larvae of the shrimp *Palaemonetes vulgaris* and the squid *Loligo pealii* to monochromatic light. *Biol. Bull.* **47**:265–273.

231. Wigglesworth, V. B. 1950. "The Principles of Insect Physiology," 4th ed., 544 pp. Methuen, London.

232. Wolf, E. 1933. Critical frequency of flicker as a function of intensity of illumination for the eye of the bee. *J. Gen. Physiol.* **17**:7–19.

233. Wolken, J. J., Capenos, J., and Turano, A. 1957. Photoreceptor structures. III. *Drosophila melanogaster*. *J. Biophys. Biochem. Cytol.* **3**:441–448.

234. Ziegler-Günder, I. 1956. Pterine: Pigmente und Wirkstoffe im Tierreich. *Biol. Revs. Cambridge Phil. Soc.* **31**:313–348.

235. Zimmer, C. 1941. Cumacea. *In:* "Bronn's Tierreich," Bd. 5, Abt. 1, Bch. 4, pp. 1–222. Akademische Verlagsges., Leipzig.

236. Zimmer, C., and Gruner, H.-E. 1956. Euphausiacea. *In:* "Bronn's Tierreich," Bd. 5, Abt. 1, Bch. 6, Pt. 3, pp. 1–281. Akademische Verlagsges., Leipzig.

CHAPTER 2

MELVIN J. COHEN

SVEN DIJKGRAAF

MECHANORECEPTION

I. *INTRODUCTION*

A rigid exoskeleton is one of the primary morphological features of all Arthropoda and provides a key for understanding many of their physiological characteristics (Chapter 14, Vol. I). In most of these animals, and particularly in the Crustacea, a major means of contact between the enclosed sensitive tissues and the surrounding environment is achieved by the development of fine hollow extensions of the exoskeleton in the form of setae or "hairs" which communicate with the interior via a channel in the integument. The so-called tactile hair* or seta of crustaceans consists of a chitinous shaft with fringing setules which articulates with the skeleton or special chitinous substrate by means of a dilated base termed the ampulla. The shaft is relatively rigid over its length and any bending usually occurs at the hair base. The hairs are innervated by distal processes of bipolar sensory neurons whose cell bodies usually lie within 0.5 mm of the hair base. A central process extends from the peripherally located cell body to the central nervous system (CNS).

The details of the innervation of crustacean sensory hairs have been in controversy for well over one hundred years. The questions of primary interest from a functional standpoint are 1) how many neurons innervate a single hair, and 2) do the nerve fibers continue out into the shaft, or do they terminate in the basal region? A definitive gen-

---

* Note that these hairs are termed tactile largely on the basis of their morphological appearance and location.

eral statement cannot yet be made; however, the sensory hairs found in decapod statocysts appear to receive only one sensory neuron per hair and the neuron terminates at some point in the basal region (Fig. 10).[39,47,63]

Another major consequence of the rigid exoskeleton is the need to provide mobility with flexible articulations in the segmented body and in the jointed appendages. To function efficiently, the position and movement of such articulated parts must be accurately detected and communicated to the CNS. Receptors fulfilling this need for proprioception form the second major type of mechanoreceptor in Crustacea and consist of groups of sense cells with their terminal processes embedded in various types of connective tissue membranes, specialized muscle cells, or epithelial cells. The organs fall into three broad categories: muscle receptor organs, scolopophorous or chordotonal-like organs, and groups of bipolar sense cells with nerve endings terminating in connective tissue strands.

II. *METHODS OF STUDY*

Effective stimulation of any receptor may give rise to the following detectable events: changes within the receptor itself, afferent nerve impulses, processes within the CNS and, finally, effector activity. In the study of crustacean mechanoreceptors, the recording of afferent nerve impulses (electrophysiological method) and motor reactions (behavioral method) have been the main types of responses measured thus far.

Electrophysiological studies provide direct evidence about the effectiveness of stimuli for the receptor organ or even for single receptor units or sensory cells. The method is particularly suited for analytical purposes. By means of single-fiber preparations the properties of the different receptor units may be studied and the pattern of messages passing from receptor to CNS in response to effective stimulation may be analyzed. In addition, this approach may yield information concerning the transducing mechanism whereby an environmental change is translated into an excitatory process leading to a propagated action potential. However, this method obviously does not demonstrate the central and efferent effects of the sensory messages.

The behavioral experiment, on the other hand, includes such effects of sensory stimulation because it involves the animal as a whole. Whether one considers only reflex movements or the composite behavioral responses of the entire animal, the CNS is always inserted between receptor and effector so that the outcome is an integrated result of sensory stimulation. This method is therefore essentially synthetic and serves two purposes. First, it may provide complementary information about the physiology of the peripheral receptor proper; and second, it may show the biological function of the receptor under investigation.

Surgical elimination and isolation of receptors and nerve fibers have been used successfully in connection with both methods.

III. *TOUCH*

There is a widespread sensitivity among Crustacea to external changes in mechanical force brought about by direct contact with solids or, in some cases, by fluid movement. Three different groups of receptors may be involved: 1) tactile hairs, especially important in animals with part or all of the body covered by a rigid exoskeleton; 2) free nerve endings in soft-skinned species or in joints; and 3) proprioceptors, if the externally applied stimulus leads to movement or stress of the body or its appendages.

In contrast to the ubiquity and apparent biological importance of tactile hair receptors in Crustacea, little experimental evidence is available concerning their physiology. Action potentials recorded in the crayfish CNS, evoked by movement of hairs on various walking legs and body segments, demonstrate that the hairs are sensitive only to actual movement and not to contact alone.[68] The tactile nature of hairs on the body and a variety of appendages has been further demonstrated by recording evoked action potentials in the circumesophageal commissures of the crayfish.[86] As early as 1910 the possibility of a proprioceptive function of tactile hairs ("Stellungshaare" or position hairs) located near articulations had been put forward.[36] In several cases exceptionally delicate and flexible hair structures have been described and usually either the detection of water currents or of vibrations and sound has been suggested as their function.[43,52] However, all this is merely conjecture based upon morphology.

Many behavioral observations point to the importance of tactile stimuli. Detection of enemies, prey, sex partners, and obstacles generally requires the participation of touch, particularly by the antennae (Fig. 1). In pagurids, discrimination of shells on the basis of structural features has been observed.[14] Furthermore, tactile stimuli may contribute to the regulation of body posture and spatial orientation. The compensatory eye and limb reflexes induced by tilting a suspended crayfish (*Astacus astacus*) are reversed when a solid substrate is placed in contact with the limbs on the elevated side.[51] The eyestalks in a blinded and statocyst-less *Palinurus elephas* lose and regain their oriented posture immediately with respective loss and re-establishment of contact between the legs and a solid substrate.[33]

In *Carcinus maenas*, receptors which are sensitive to water currents have been demonstrated on the antennules;[15] they permit rheotactic

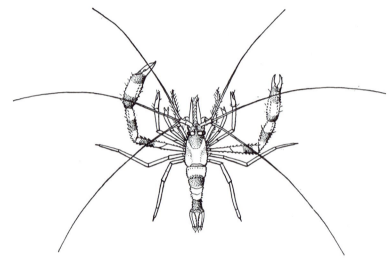

Fig. 1. Dorsal view of the natantian *Stenopus hispidus* showing the highly developed uniramous antennules and biramous antennae which, among other sense organs, bear numerous tactile receptors. (Redrawn from Brooks and Herrick.[16])

orientation in a hungry animal.[59] The ability of blinded *Carcinus* to detect moving objects at some distance ("distant touch") may also be due to antennular current sensitivity.[13]

IV. *PROPRIOCEPTION*

The original designation of proprioceptors by Sherrington in 1906[75] as receptors which receive their stimulus from the organism itself has been modified in recent years to include primarily receptors in muscles or tendons which serve to detect muscular tension or relative position of jointed body parts. Movement of the limbs in many crustaceans is accompanied by bursts of impulses in sensory leg nerves.[8] Action potentials have also been recorded in the CNS of the crayfish in response to movement of the limbs.[68] In a blinded spiny lobster, rotation of the cephalothorax, relative to the legs, about a vertical axis causes compensatory eyestalk reflexes.[33] After fixation of one eyestalk in an abnormal position, blinded *Squilla mantis* performed spiral swimming movements.[27] Although no receptor organ was identified in any of the above cases, certain structures have been described in recent years which appear morphologically likely to be involved in proprioception. In certain instances their function has been experimentally demonstrated.

A. MUSCLE RECEPTOR ORGAN

1. *Structure.* This organ (MRO), first described in 1951 by Alexandrowicz, is present in stomatopods as well as all Natantia and Anomura examined.[1,2,3] The following description applies primarily to the MRO's of *Homarus gammarus*.[1,2] A pair of modified muscle fibers (RM1 and RM2) occurs on both sides of the dorsal musculature in each of the six abdominal segments and in the extensor muscles of the seventh and eighth thoracic segments. Near the middle of each RM the muscle tissue is replaced by a region of connective tissue into which dendrites of the associated sensory neurons penetrate.

The cell body of a large multipolar neuron lies adjacent to each RM and sends several dendrites into its substance (Fig. 2). A central process is given off from the neuron soma and joins the nerve supplying the other muscles of the segment. In *Homarus* the dendrites are entirely confined to the region of the RM occupied by the intercalated connective tissue.

Two main motor fibers supply each MRO. Each fiber bifurcates just before entering the muscle, and the branches run along the RM to end among the myofibrils (Fig. 2). The number of motor fibers in addition to these is not known, but both morphological[1,2] and physiological[49] evidence indicates that there are relatively few.

Accessory nerve fibers form the third nervous component of the MRO. In *Homarus* there is a thick and thin accessory fiber for each MRO; their distribution to its various elements is shown in Fig. 2. In the crayfish, only one accessory fiber innervates both receptor muscles of each MRO.[40]

2. *Physiology.* The initial functional study of muscle receptor organs[85] demonstrated that flexion of the crayfish tail evokes action potentials in two nerve fibers of each MRO. One fiber, identified as the sensory neuron connected to RM1, adapts slowly and continues to

discharge during constant stretch for as long as one hour. The other fiber was identified as the sensory neuron of RM2 and gives rise to a response which adapts to zero within one minute during constant stretch. Stimulation of the motor nerves causes contractions of the receptor muscles and also gives rise to action potentials in the sensory neurons.

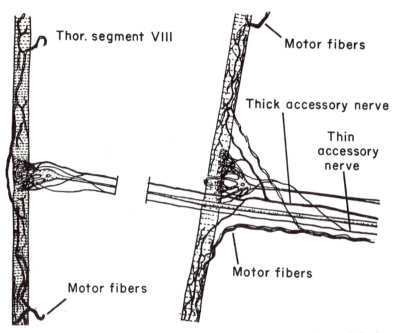

FIG. 2. Diagram of receptor muscles on the right side of the eighth thoracic segment in *Homarus gammarus*. The element on the right is more lateral and designated as RM1, while the more medial muscle is termed RM2. (From Alexandrowicz.[2])

The two receptor muscles behave differently during contraction.[49] The larger muscle (RM2) shows a relatively rapid contraction lasting 60–100 msec and hence is referred to as the fast receptor. The smaller receptor muscle (RM1) has a contraction lasting much longer and is termed the slow receptor.

The sensory neurons fire at a frequency which is dependent upon the amount of stretch applied to their dendritic terminals.[37,38] Stretch can be applied to the latter either by flexion of the abdominal musculature or by contraction of the receptor muscles due to stimulation by their motor fibers. These two factors interact to govern the discharge frequency of the sensory neurons[49] so that the sensory response to a standard motor stimulus varies according to the initial tension applied to the receptor (Fig. 3).

Intracellular recordings from the somas of the sensory neurons show that in the slow nerve cell the 60–70-mv resting potential can

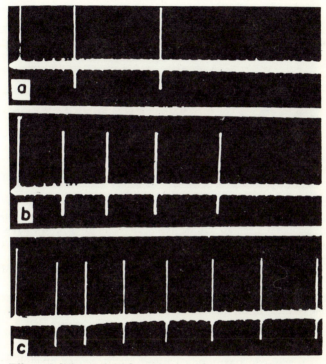

FIG. 3. Effect of different initial tensions on the sensory response to motor stimulation in the slow muscle receptor of the lobster *Homarus americanus*. a. A single stimulus evokes two afferent discharges. b, c. The same stimulus at higher initial tensions elicits a greater number of afferent discharges. (From Kuffler.[49])

be reduced in a graded manner by 6–7 mv before causing a propagated action potential. The fast cell requires more stretch, and the membrane potential may be reduced in a graded manner by 15–22 mv before a spike is evoked. Only the dendrites are affected by stretch since the cell body can be moved without causing an action potential. The depolarization set up in the dendritic terminals and spreading electrotonically to the soma is the generator potential; its amplitude is directly related to the degree of stretch applied to the dendritic terminals. Within the soma, the generator potential gives rise to a local secondary prepotential which, when it reaches the critical level of depolarization, elicits the propagated action potential (Fig. 4).[37,38]

Following every impulse during maintained stretch, there are two opposing factors acting on the membrane potential: 1) a recovery process in the soma tending to repolarize the membrane to its resting equilibrium level, and 2) the persisting generator potential in the terminals which tends to depolarize the soma membrane. During maintained suprathreshold stretch the generator potential can prevent complete repolarization by initiating the secondary depolarizing prepotential before the soma's resting level is reached (Fig. 4c). The

Fig. 4. The effect of different levels of stretch on the firing threshold and frequency in a slow nerve cell of a muscle receptor organ. Intracellular recording, resting potential near 70 mv. a. Near threshold stretch, discharge frequency about 5/sec. b. Greater steady stretch gives rise to more regularly maintained activity at 16/sec. c. Stretch further increased, discharge rate 40/sec. Note that the firing level is similar in a and b, but in c it is about 7 mv higher. At the higher tension of c, note that the rate of rise of the prepotential is increased and that the repolarization phase is less complete. The second beam of the oscilloscope is in the same position in all records, several millivolts below firing level (point of inflection between prepotential and spikes). (From Eyzaguirre and Kuffler.[37])

increase in discharge frequency caused by increased stretch appears to be due to the greater rate of rise of the prepotential and the decrease in the extent of repolarization (Fig. 4).[37]

The accessory fibers which terminate among the dendrites have proved to exert an inhibitory influence on the activity of the sensory neuron.[50] This work was carried out in the crayfish where only one accessory fiber innervates both sensory cells of each MRO.[40] Repetitive stimulation of the accessory fiber can stop a continuous discharge set up in the sensory neuron, apparently by restoring the membrane potential to an equilibrium level inadequate to initiate spikes (Fig. 5). The level toward which the inhibitory impulses drive the soma membrane potential is usually not the full resting value, but 5–6 mv of depolarization relative to the resting level.

The inhibitory impulses act on the generator potential in the dendritic terminals. Thus in a slightly stretched sensory cell the inhibitory impulses reduce the generator potential and permit a repolarization of the soma membrane to a subthreshold level. Because

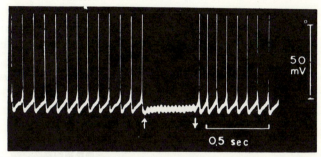

Fig. 5. Intracellular recording from a slowly adapting neuron of a muscle receptor organ. The regular train of afferent discharges set up by maintained stretch is interrupted (between arrows) by stimulation (at 34/sec) of the inhibitory axon (accessory fiber). Small deflections are inhibitory potentials. (From Kuffler and Eyzaguirre.[50])

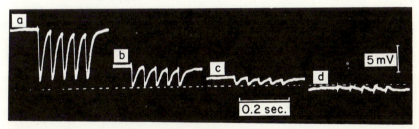

Fig. 6. Effect of inhibitory impulses at different membrane potential levels recorded intracellularly from the fast receptor cell of a muscle receptor organ. Trains of inhibitory impulses delivered at 20 per second. a. Cell stretched, causing initial maintained depolarization of 16.5 mv. Each inhibitory impulse causes a repolarization (downward deflection). b, c. Initial stretch is progressively decreased, resulting in higher maintained membrane potentials. d. Still further relaxation of stretch results in a maintained resting potential which is below the inhibitory equilibrium level. Here the inhibitory impulse sign is reversed and an initial depolarization follows each inhibitory stimulus. (From Kuffler and Eyzaguirre.[50])

this repolarization tends to approach the inhibitory equilibrium level, the absolute amount of repolarization caused by inhibition will depend upon the existing level of the generator potential (Fig. 6). In the completely relaxed cell where the membrane potential is at the resting value, a depolarization is evoked by the inhibitory stimuli so that the membrane potential is in fact decreased to reach the inhibitory equilibrium level.

The full significance of the muscle receptor organs in the behavior of Crustacea is not yet fully understood. The activity of the slowly adapting neuron may provide information about maintained postural positions while the fast receptor may signal phasic changes.[49,85] The sensory axons from these receptors continue through the cord, apparently as primary sensory fibers ending in the brain. This indicates their importance in the integration of motor patterns (see Chapter 7).

B. LIMB PROPRIOCEPTORS

A great diversity of receptors has been described in crustacean appendages.[4,5,9,18,77,84] Most have in common the presence of bipolar sensory neurons with peripherally located cell bodies in contrast to the multipolar neurons of the muscle receptor organs previously described. A type of receptor resembling the muscle receptor organ occurs in the coxal region of several decapods. Adjacent to the coxal muscular receptors there occurs a system of innervated elastic strands. Both of these receptors are unusual because their associated sensory nerve cell bodies apparently lie within the CNS.[4,5] The latter receptor should be distinguished from the elastic receptor, which has bipolar sensory neurons located peripherally and whose physiological properties have been studied.

1. *Elastic receptors.* This type of organ was first described by Burke[18] for the most distal joint of the walking leg in *Carcinus maenas*. It has since been described for most joints of the walking legs in many Macrura, Anomura, and Brachyura[5] (also, C. A. G. Wiersma and E. G. Boettiger, 1958, personal communication). In the propodite-dactylopodite joint the organ consists of a connective tissue strand spanning the joint; its proximal attachment is to the tendon of the flexor muscle, and the distal portion joins a small protuberance on the wall of the next more distal segment (Fig. 7). A group of nerve cells are attached to the tendon and send their proximal processes into the main nerve trunk of the limb, while their distal processes pass into the elastic strand.[18] By recording from the proximal nerve processes of this organ in *Carcinus*, a resting discharge can be observed in small-amplitude units (Fig. 8). This discharge varies with the position of the joint and seems relatively nonadapting. High-amplitude spikes are observed during movement of the joint and increase in frequency with

greater rate of movement. The large-amplitude fibers also respond to vibration conducted through solid substrate.[18]

By unit analysis of the nerve bundle, Wiersma and Boettiger (1958, personal communication) have found four main types of sensory axons

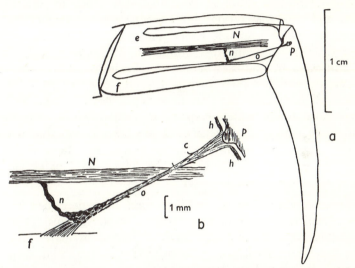

Fig. 7. Sketch of a limb proprioceptor organ spanning the protopodite-dactyl joint in *Carcinus maenas*. a. Joint in the flexed position. b. Enlarged view of organ. *h*, Epidermis; *N*, main leg nerve bundle; *n*, nerve bundle to organ; *o*, organ; *p*, distal attachment to protuberance; *e*, apodeme of extensor muscle; *f*, apodeme of flexor muscle; *c*, small connective tissue attachment. (From Burke.[18])

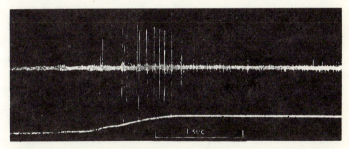

Fig. 8. Response of protopodite-dactyl proprioceptor recorded from nerve in meropodite. Lower beam indicates flexion of the dactyl. (From Burke.[18])

in the elastic receptor. 1) Fibers which discharge during extension only. Several of these occur in the receptor nerve bundle and each fiber has a different threshold. The smallest and most sensitive fiber responds to movements as slow as 1° per second. 2) Fibers which discharge during flexion only. Again several are present with varying thresholds. The most sensitive one has about half the sensitivity of fiber type 1. 3) Position fibers which respond only in extended positions. Some of these do not respond at all during movement, and all have slow adaptation rates. 4) Position fibers which respond to flexed positions and otherwise do not differ from those in category 3.

Unidirectional movement fibers and position fibers occur in the PD (protopodite-dactylopodite) organs of *Maja, Homarus, Pagurus,* and *Palinurus.* In joints where two elastic receptors are present (carpo-protopodite and mero-carpopodite) the organs CP1, CP2, MC1, and MC2 all may have the four fiber types, but CP2 and MC2 seem to have more fibers which respond to flexion while their partners respond more readily to extension. It has been shown that the larger cell bodies which are more proximally located are those of the fibers responding to movement and that the flexion and extension fibers are grouped on one side of the organ or the other.

2. *Myochordotonal organs.* These have been described by Barth[9] in great detail and occur in most major decapod groups. Their structure resembles the chordotonal organ of insects in many ways, and, because they are almost always associated with muscular tissue, they have been called myochordotonal organs.

One of these organs is found in the lumen of the meropodite of each walking leg, ventrally located at the proximal end of the segment. A thin connective tissue membrane spans the area between the small accessory flexor muscle and the inner ventral surface of the meropodite wall. The sensory portion of the organ consists of a large number of bipolar neurons whose cell bodies are embedded in the membrane. The distal nerve processes join together in several strands to run free across the lumen and attach to the ventral chitinous wall at several anchor points. The proximal processes of the neurons join the main trunk of the limb nerve. The region of the distal nerve termination shows the sheath cells and the rod or scolopale characteristic of chordotonal organs in insects.[76]

An attempt to study the effect of destruction of this organ on locomotion in several decapods was largely unsuccessful because it was not possible to avoid damaging the related muscles. The morphology of the myochordotonal organ strongly suggests a proprioceptive function connected with movement of the associated flexor muscle, and its function awaits investigation with modern electrophysiological techniques.

C. Comparative Aspects

The types of proprioceptors present in Crustacea resemble in many ways those of vertebrates. But whereas in vertebrates the sense organs are located within muscles, tendons, or internal joint membranes, in Crustacea the organs are always outside the main muscles. There is a striking similarity between the vertebrate muscle spindle and the crustacean MRO. The presence in both structures of efferent control exerted by the CNS permits the adjustment of sensitivity appropriate to the fluctuating activity of surrounding skeletal muscle.

The connection of the elastic receptors to the tendon of the muscle and the wall or joint membrane of the next segment enables one organ to detect both movement and position as well as possibly to serve as an active muscle-tension indicator. This latter aspect has been investigated only for the PD organ of *Carcinus*,[18] in which the signal during an isometric contraction was shown to differ from that obtained when the same position is passively achieved.

The elastic organs appear to split into two different groups, one located internally for movement reception and a more external organ responding primarily to maintained position (Wiersma and Boettiger, 1958, personal communication). It may be possible therefore to trace the cutaneous proprioceptors of insects[64] to the crustacean elastic organs by way of Barth's organ and the proprioceptors of *Limulus*[67] and other chelicerates.[66]

V. *EQUILIBRIUM RECEPTORS*

The ability to carry out rapid coordinated locomotion is frequently dependent upon two sensory capabilities: 1) a capacity to detect spatial position, i.e. position of the major planes of symmetry relative to the direction of gravitational force; and 2) the ability to detect the rate and direction of linear and angular displacement. Receptors concerned specifically with these parameters may be termed equilibrium receptors and are to be distinguished from other sensory systems such as vision, touch, and proprioception which may also participate in equilibration but whose major biological functions lie within other modalities.

In a large number of Crustacea, and particularly in highly developed forms such as the Decapoda, equilibrium organs occur which are in many respects analogous to the vertebrate labyrinth. During the nineteenth century these structures were generally considered to be organs of hearing and consequently designated as otocysts. The work of Delage in 1887[26] first pointed to their role in equilibration when elimination of the organs in *Mysis* and in several decapods was shown to cause "désorientation locomotrice." The similarity of the latter with symptoms following labyrinthectomy suggested that the animal's motions induce movements of the fluid or of the otoliths within the cyst, thus stimulating the nerve endings in its wall. In 1893 the spectacular iron-filing experiments of Kreidl[48] focused attention on the liths and the influence of gravity in directing static orientation; hence our present terms "statolith" and "statocyst." The less easily demonstrable influence of fluid movements has been somewhat neglected. But in recent studies the importance of this latter aspect of statocyst function has become clear, thus confirming the correctness of Delage's initial suppositions.

A. RECEPTOR STRUCTURE AND DISTRIBUTION

The occurrence of statocysts among the Crustacea is restricted to the highest subclass, the Malacostraca. They appear in some species of the orders Anaspidacea, Isopoda, Amphipoda, and in nearly all Mysidacea and Decapoda.[7,43,52] The organs are located either at the anterior end of the animal (within the head or the basal antennular segment), or posteriorly in the abdomen, uropods, or telson (Fig. 9). In several lower forms the statocysts show structural peculiarities which suggest interesting physiological properties.[54] Mysidacea and Decapoda have been used almost exclusively in the study of statocyst physiology, and our description is therefore largely restricted to these groups.[12,45,47,63]

Morphologically the statocyst represents a local invagination of the body wall. The hidden, fluid-filled ectodermal sac thus formed is never completely closed, although in some species the opening may become slit-like and the cavity functionally closed. In other species, on the contrary, the opening remains permanently rather large. In all cases the ectodermal inner chitinous lining and the contents of the statocyst (fluid, sensory hairs, and statoliths) are cast off during molting and then renewed. In most crabs the statocyst wall has a complicated shape due to deep invaginations which in some species cause a more or less pronounced division of the interior into two cavities oriented perpendicular to each other.[45,74]

The statolith may be a single, spherical body formed by the animal (Mysidacea[12]) (Fig. 9), or it may consist of sand grains usually cemented loosely together by a glandular secretion of the cyst wall

(Decapoda) (Figs. 9 and 15). A permanent, complete absence of statoliths is reported in some cases; however such statements must be accepted with caution. The statocyst of *Carcinus*, for example, has been described for nearly a century by a number of serious investigators as being completely devoid of statoliths.[13,45,63,72] Nevertheless, in

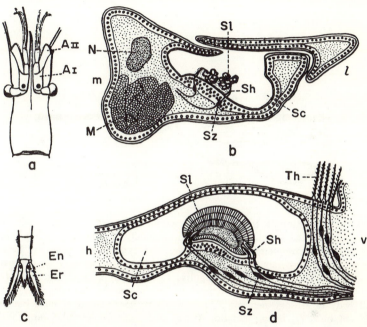

FIG. 9. Statocyst location and structure in various Crustacea. a. Location of statocysts in *Palaemon* indicated by black spots. b. Cross section through right basal antennular segment in *Palaemon* showing statocyst. Note lateral inclination of statocyst floor by about 30° from the horizontal. c. Location of statocysts in uropods of *Mysis*. d. Longitudinal section through tail fan of *Mysis* showing a statocyst. *AI*, antennule; *AII*, antenna; *En*, endopodite; *Er*, exopodite; *M*, muscle; *N*, nerve; *Sc*, statocyst; *Sh*, statolith hairs; *Sl*, statoliths; *Sz*, sense cells; *Th*, tactile hairs; *m*, median; *l*, lateral; *h*, caudal; *v*, rostral. (From Claus, Grobben, and Kühn.[20])

adult *Carcinus* and other crabs a typical cluster of statoliths (small sand grains) recently has been discovered[35] (Figs. 20 and 21).

In crabs and certain other decapods like the lobster, the sensory hairs can be divided into "statolith hairs," which have continuous or intermittent contact with the statoliths, and free sensory hairs like the "thread hairs" in which this contact never occurs (Figs. 15, 21, and 22).[22,35] The coarser and often hook-like statolith hairs are stimulated by movements of the statoliths, while the typical free sensory hairs are stimulated by fluid movements resulting within the statocyst from angular acceleration. Thus a statocyst with these two hair types contains both position and rotation receptors.

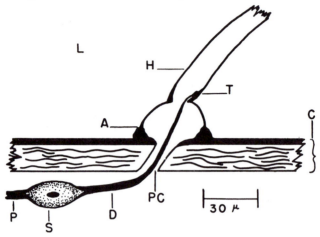

Fig. 10. Diagram of the base of a macruran statocyst sensory hair which is in contact with the statolith. Drawn approximately to scale except that the distal nerve process is frequently much longer. The region and mode of termination of the neuron in the hair is still uncertain; the drawing represents an approximation from the evidence available. *A*, ampulla; *C*, chitinous floor of statocyst; *D*, distal process of sensory neuron; *P*, proximal process of sensory neuron; *PC*, pore canal; *S*, cell body of sensory neuron; *T*, region where nerve terminal joins hair, usually on side of hair, *H*, facing statolith. (Combined from Cohen, 1957, unpublished results, and Kinzig.[47])

B. Physiology

1. *Position reception*

a. *General properties.* The classic iron-filing experiments suggested by Exner and performed by Kreidl[48] provide the first conclusive evidence that statocyst receptors are sensitive to maintained spatial position. By inducing a freshly molted shrimp (*Palaemon*) to put iron filings instead of sand grains in its statocysts, and then moving a strong magnet near the iron statolith, the animal could be made to assume and maintain different positions about its long axis. A simple force analysis showed that the final position is regulated by the resultant of the gravitational and magnetic forces acting on the iron statolith. The force exerted by the statolith on the sensory hair and dependent on the position of the animal within the gravitation field is therefore proven to be the adequate normal stimulus for this sensory function.

Further study has been devoted to reflex movements, especially compensatory eyestalk reflexes, elicited by angular displacement about horizontal axes.[13,19,42,51,60,63,83] Although the earlier work contains much useful data, not all of it is reliable and some of it is conflicting. The influence of visual and other stimuli on these reflexes was not always adequately controlled. Furthermore, important factors such as the functional difference between removal of the statoliths and destruction of the receptor cells, or central compensation of stimulus deficiency after unilateral operations, were either unknown or not taken

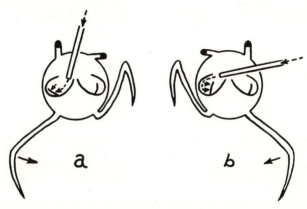

Fig. 11. Compensatory eyestalk and limb reflexes evoked in *Astacus astacus* by bending statocyst hairs in opposite directions with a fine water jet (statoliths removed). a. Bending the hairs laterally. b. Bending the hairs medially. (From Schöne.[71])

into account. The recent work of Schöne[72,73a] establishes a solid foundation for this field and explains several of the earlier apparently contradictory results.

Direct stimulation of the exposed statolith hairs in *Astacus astacus* by bending them laterally evokes the same reflex movements as rotation of the intact animal about its longitudinal axis toward the side of the statocyst involved (Fig. 11a). Bending the hairs in the opposite direction produces the reciprocal reflex movements (Fig. 11b). Thus each statocyst responds to angular displacement about the animal's longitudinal axis in either direction. This agrees with the conclusion drawn by earlier investigators with one apparent exception[51,82] (see below).

Blinded shrimps (*Palaemonetes*) in which one statolith was removed were rotated to the left 360° about their longitudinal axis,
and the compensatory deviation of the eyestalks was measured at
positions 30° apart (Fig. 12b). With the right statolith removed, the
maximum deviation is reached at a displacement of 60°. In this
position the floor of the left statocyst is oriented vertically (Fig. 9)
and the lateral bending of its sensory hairs must be maximal. Since

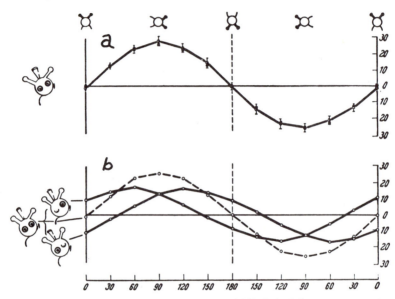

Fig. 12. Compensatory eyestalk reflexes of blinded *Palaemonetes varians* in
various positions during rotation about the longitudinal axis to the left. Abscissa:
degrees of angular displacement. Ordinate: eyestalk deviation in degrees, measured
as the angle between the animal's vertical axis and the line bisecting the angle
between both eyestalks. a. Normal animals. b. Continuous curves from unilaterally
statocystless animals. Broken curve derived from addition of two continuous curves.
(From Schöne.[72])

such bending by movements of the statolith parallel to the cyst wall
("Scherung") depends on the sine of the angle of displacement, the
sinusoidal form of the whole response curve demonstrates a linear
relation between hair bending and eyestalk deviation. Experiments
done by rotating shrimps about their transverse axis lead to a similar
conclusion.[73] In the former case (right statolith removed), addition of
this curve with the response curve from animals with the left statolith
removed (Fig. 12b) results in the same curve as that derived from
rotation of animals with both statocysts intact (Fig. 12a). This indi-

cates that when both statocysts are intact, their afferent influxes simply add algebraically within the CNS.

From elaborate studies of compensatory movements and reflexes evoked in different maintained positions about the longitudinal axis after unilateral elimination of either the statolith alone or statolith

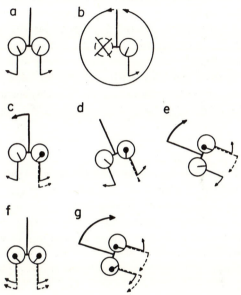

Fig. 13. Rotational tendencies about the longitudinal axis in decapods caused 1) "spontaneously" by the statolith hair receptor cells (small lower arrows in a–g), and 2) "reflexly" by lateral or medial pull of the statoliths (broken arrows in c–g). Heavy arrows on top in c, e, and g indicate direction of over-all rotational tendency of the animal and angle in which this tendency persists. (From Schöne.[71])

plus receptors, a clear picture of the statocyst mechanism has emerged. The main conclusions may be summarized as follows:

1) The receptor cells of each statocyst continuously generate impulses which cause a turning movement or tendency to rotate toward the contralateral side. This "spontaneous" afferent influx is independent of the presence or absence of statoliths and of the animal's position in space. The spontaneous rotational tendencies caused by the two statocysts counteract each other and become apparent only after unilateral destruction of the receptor cells (Figs. 13a and b). Then the animal shows constant rotation toward the injured side.

2) The statolith stimulates the receptor cells when a force, usually gravity, acts to move it either laterally or medially parallel to

the statocyst floor. This causes a turning movement whose magnitude and direction are dependent on the animal's position about its longitudinal axis. When the statocyst floor is horizontal there is no statolith-induced tendency to rotate (Fig. 13d); with the statocyst floor in a vertical position, stimulation of this sort reaches its maximum. When the statolith exerts a laterally directed force, the resulting rotational tendency is in the same direction as the spontaneous tendency within the statocyst concerned, i.e. toward the contralateral side (Fig. 13c); when the force is directed medially the evoked rotation is in the opposite direction (Fig. 13e).

3) In the normal resting position (dorsal side upward), both statoliths generate opposite rotational tendencies because the floor of each statocyst is laterally inclined by about 30° (Figs. 9 and 13f). This becomes apparent after unilateral removal of a statolith (Fig. 13c) when the animal comes to rest in a position which deviates about 30° toward the injured side (Fig. 13c). In other positions, the rotational tendency evoked by both statoliths is in the same direction (Fig. 13g).

The asymmetrical posture and movements which are caused by unilateral elimination of either the statolith or the receptor cells do not remain at a constant level, but decrease and may disappear in the course of some days after the operation. This is due to the development of a compensatory influence within the CNS which restores central symmetry for the normal position (see Chapter 13). This phenomenon is of biological importance because the weight of the right and the left statoliths is often unequal when new ones are acquired after molting.

If a decapod is rotated about the transverse axis until its longitudinal axis is vertical, the statoliths exert a force in a rostral or caudal direction parallel to the cyst wall. Such stimuli evoke corresponding eyestalk reflexes in the sagittal plane. But there is no lateral or medial pull of the statolith in these positions. For this reason animals with one statolith removed, and in which central symmetry in the normal position has been restored, begin to rotate about their anteroposterior axis toward the intact side if they are placed with this axis vertical. In the latter position central symmetry is destroyed because the statolith-induced turning moment is reduced to zero, whereas the central compensatory influence, which is independent of the animal's position in space, remains unchanged. Some of the apparently controversial older data regarding statocyst function in Astacus[51,81] can easily be explained in a similar way.

The principles of statocyst function mentioned above seem to be of quite general validity since similar behavioral responses have been observed in all species investigated (*Crangon, Palaemonetes, Astacus,* and *Homarus*). Even *Carcinus* shows essentially similar behavior. Although the statolith in crabs like *Carcinus* and *Maja verrucosa* is extremely small (Figs. 20 and 21), selective cutting of the nerve fibers innervating the few statolith hairs in these animals results in a complete loss of all static compensatory eyestalk reflexes.[35] After unilateral elimination of the statolith hairs or removal of one entire statocyst, these reflexes are usually less vigorous (Dijkgraaf, 1956, unpublished observations, and references[13,19,60]). Moreover, a marked difference between the two eyes is often observed. In some cases the ipsilateral eyestalk seems to be affected much more[19,42] (also, Dijkgraaf, 1956, unpublished observations), while in others this has been reported for the contralateral eye,[13,72] or no such difference between both eyes has been observed.[19,60]

There is a good correlation between the behavioral results of Schöne and the data of Cohen[22] obtained by recording action potentials from primary afferent neurons in the statocyst of *Homarus americanus*. Location and structure of the statocyst in this animal are shown in Figs. 14 and 15. There are several rows of statolith hairs along a crescent-shaped elevation termed the sensory cushion, and one row of thread hairs which float free in the cyst fluid (Fig. 15). The statolith is composed of many sand grains cemented together and flexibly joined to the cyst floor by a secretion from the tegumental glands.[53]

In the normal resting orientation (dorsal side upward), a continuous arrhythmic discharge is recorded from most statocyst receptors. Removal of the statolith does not noticeably affect this resting discharge. If the cyst is drained of fluid, the sensory cushion hairs can be observed to flatten medially against the cyst floor, and this is accompanied by a decrease of the spontaneous activity in most of the afferent neurons. Refilling the cyst with fluid causes the sensory hairs to float toward a vertical position, and this is accompanied by a return of the spontaneous activity to its previous level. If the tips of the flattened hairs of the drained cyst are lifted upward with a glass needle, bursts of activity are recorded from the sensory neurons. Thus movement of the sensory cushion hairs medially toward the horizontal decreases the frequency of discharge in most of the afferent neurons, while displacement toward the vertical results in an increased rate of discharge.

When these results are compared with the behavioral responses described by Schöne, it seems that a decrease in afferent impulse frequency, relative to the resting level, may evoke a coordinated compensatory reflex which is opposite to that caused by an increase in discharge frequency in the same sensory neuron. By moving statocyst hairs while recording from the oculomotor nerve in *Homarus*, the importance of a drop in steady background frequency from statocyst receptors has been further indicated. Displacing the hairs in a direction

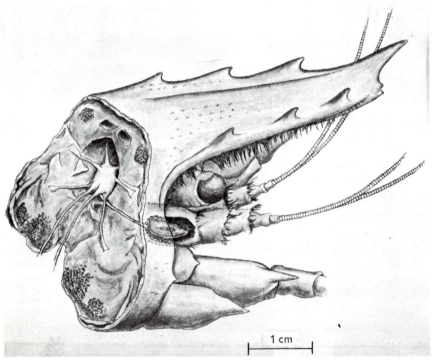

Fig. 14. Anterior cephalothoracic region of the lobster *Homarus americanus*. The statocyst is exposed in the basal segment of the right antennule. The nerve seen coursing from brain to the statocyst is the combined statocyst and antennular nerve. (From Cohen.[22])

usually associated with a decrease in sensory discharge frequency often evoked bursts of impulses in oculomotor neurons.[23]

b. *Receptor types.* By recording action potentials from statocyst neurons of *Homarus* while rotating the isolated anterior cephalothorax about the major horizontal axes, two types of position receptors have been observed by Cohen.[22] Both may have a spontaneous resting activity, even when outside the position-sensitive range, and this persists after statolith removal. Absence of the statolith abolishes position

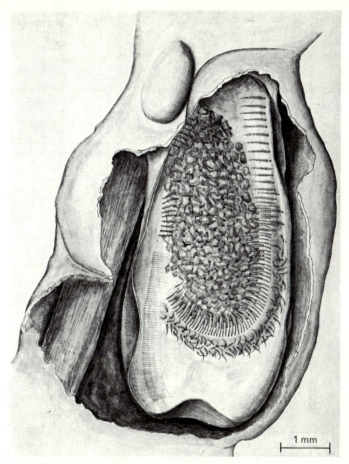

Fig. 15. Right statocyst of *Homarus americanus* as seen in situ from above. The dorsal region of the basal antennular segment and the dorsal cyst wall have been removed to expose the lumen contents. Anterior is toward the top of the page, lateral is to the right. Note the crescentic sensory cushion with its four hair rows. The statolith is in contact with the inner three rows. The fine medial thread hairs project horizontally into the lumen from the posterior region of the medial wall. The cyst opening is seen anteromedially. (From Cohen.[22])

sensitivity and indicates that most of these receptors are located on the sensory cushion and in contact with the lith.

i. *Type I position receptor.* This shows a specific non-adapting discharge frequency for each maintained position within a certain range about the transverse axis (Fig. 16). The receptor

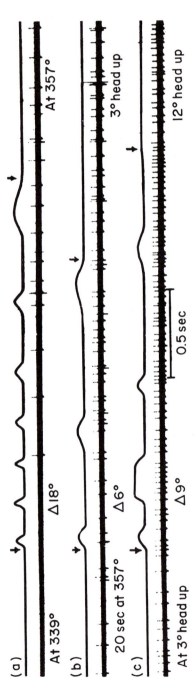

FIG. 16. Response of two or three Type I statocyst position receptors in *Homarus* to different positions about the transverse axis. Upper beam indicates displacement; one deflection every 3°. Arrows mark onset and termination of movement. Rotation is rostrum-up about the transverse axis. (From Cohen.[22])

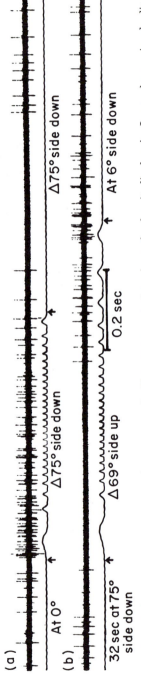

FIG. 17. Response of statocyst rotation receptors in *Homarus* to rotation about the longitudinal axis. Lower beam signals displacement; one deflection every 3°. Arrows indicate onset and end of movement. a. Side-down rotation. b. The reciprocal side-up rotation. In general, reciprocal movements elicit reversed response patterns. (From Cohen.[22])

threshold appears to be less than 6° of angular displacement (compare Figs. 16b and c). Figure 18 shows the response of a single Type I position receptor to continuous slow rotation in opposite directions about the transverse axis. The receptor responds to changes in position within a range of about 180°. Beyond this sensitive range it remains spontaneously active at a relatively low constant frequency. The displacement of the response curve caused by rotation in the opposite

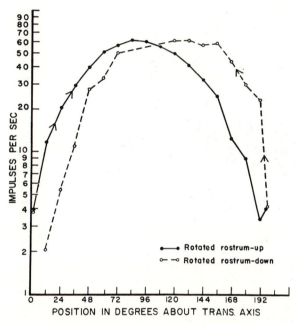

FIG. 18. Response of a single Type I statocyst position receptor in *Homarus* to continuous rotation in opposite directions about the transverse axis. Solid curve to be read from left to right; broken curve to be read from right to left. Each point represents average frequency over a 12° interval. Note dependence of the response curve upon direction of rotation. (From Cohen.[22])

direction would seem to be a source of ambiguity in detecting absolute position during slow rotation. However, the adapted frequency in the new position is independent of the direction from which the position was approached.

A greater source of ambiguity in this receptor type would seem to be due to the bell-shaped nature of the response curve. Any single Type I position receptor will reach a given specific frequency at two different positions in space (except in the region of peak response), and an individual receptor cannot distinguish between these two points. It appears that the response range of the various receptors differs from one to another so that overlap occurs at the extremes, but the point of peak response is separate for each receptor. Thus at any single position the composite input pattern from many different receptors will be characteristic for that position. This may be an explanation for the large number of statolith hair receptors in *Homarus* when there appears to be only a relatively small number of position receptor types.

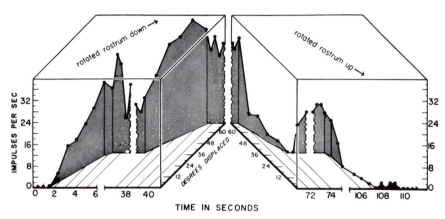

FIG. 19. Response of a 3- or 4-unit preparation of Type II statocyst position receptors in *Homarus* subjected to a series of interrupted displacements about the transverse axis; each new position was maintained for 33 sec before moving on. The frequency reached after the time break in each new position is the adapted level. Note the difference in response with displacement in opposite directions over the same region. The adapted response appears to be independent of the direction of approach. (From Cohen.[22])

No Type I position receptors have been found which respond to positional changes about the longitudinal axis.

ii. *Type II position receptor.* This is capable of signaling absolute position about the transverse axis, as is the Type I receptor. There is, in addition, a well-differentiated dynamic response consisting of a gradual frequency increase during movement toward positions of maximum static response, and an abrupt frequency decrease during movement away from such orientations (Fig. 19). This combined response pattern seems capable of signaling not only absolute position, but also the direction from which a given position is approached. The Type II receptor has also been observed to respond to rotation about the anteroposterior axis and usually reaches its maximum adapted frequency in the 45–90° side-down position. Single Type II receptors which respond to movement and static position about the transverse axis are usually not responsive to such stimuli about the longitudinal axis. Similarly, receptors responsive to turning about the anteroposterior axis do not respond to rotation or maintained position about the transverse axis.

It is significant that both types of position receptors appear slightly sensitive to stimuli other than absolute position, namely direction and velocity of rotation. In the Type I position receptor, a given frequency is reached earlier during a fast rotation than during a slow one. Slight adaptation does occur with maintained position; it may be that during faster rotations the shorter time lapse from one point to the next allows less adaptation, thereby resulting in a higher initial frequency for any given position. This receptor type can therefore be considered as imperfect since different environmental situations may evoke identical signals.

The dual sensibility of the Type II position receptor appears to be of a different nature. Two stimulus parameters are dealt with by one receptor, but the receptor output consists of different signals for each parameter rather than one integrated output. Two different stimuli, 1) displacement direction, and 2) absolute position, elicit distinct signals from a single receptor. This implies that central interpretation of an instantaneous frequency may depend upon the recent history of the unit involved. Hence a response pattern integrated over a relatively long period of time is important.

2. *Rotation reception.* Several investigators have observed compensatory locomotor and eyestalk reflexes (including nystagmus) evoked in blinded decapods by rotation around the vertical axis. This has been found in *Palaemon*,[48] *Astacus*,[60] *Carcinus*,[13,32,72,83] and *Maja*,[32] but not* in *Palinurus*,[33] *Pagurus* (Dijkgraaf, 1956, unpublished observations), or *Uca*.[60] The reactions are evoked only by angular acceleration or deceleration and are abolished after removal of both statocysts. Further behavioral evidence concerning the structure and function of rotation receptors in the statocyst of crabs has been recently presented by Dijkgraaf.[32,35]

Blinded, legless crabs (*Carcinus maenas* and *Maja verrucosa*) are placed on a turntable for rotation around the vertical axis. At the

---

* This is true only if movement of the body relative to the legs is avoided to prevent stimulation of certain proprioceptors at the leg-thorax joints.

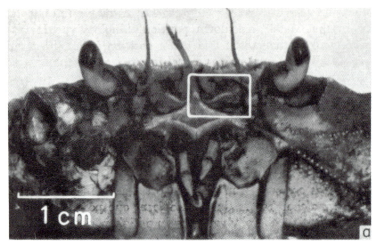

FRONTAL   LATERAL

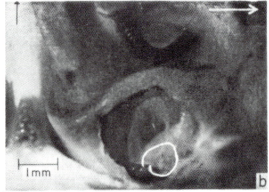

TH

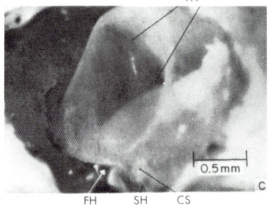

FH   SH   CS

See legend on opposite page.

onset of rotation to the right, for example, both eyestalks move to the left until they reach their maximum deviation. In most cases one or more jerky nystagmus movements in the opposite direction are observed during rotation. However, the eyes generally remain deviated opposite to the direction of rotation for several revolutions of the turntable (angular velocity 180–360° per second). Only during continuous constant velocity rotation do the eyestalks return slowly to their symmetrical position.

A sudden arrest of the turntable causes typical aftereffects. The eyes move promptly to the right (at about the same velocity as they moved to the left at the onset of rotation) until their maximum deviation toward this side is reached. After a quick jerk in the opposite direction (after-nystagmus) the eyes continue their movement to the right, and in this way sometimes up to three or more after-nystagmus jerks occur with decreasing intensity. Finally, the eyestalks slowly return to their symmetrical position. Such aftereffects may last many seconds and resemble closely the well-known aftereffects caused in vertebrates by fluid movements and elasticity of the cupulae within the semicircular canals of the labyrinth. This suggests that rotatory stimulation in the crab statocyst occurs in a similar manner, notwithstanding its minute dimensions (in *Carcinus*, 1–2 mm, see Fig. 20).

All reflexes and aftereffects due to horizontal rotation are abolished in a blinded *Maja* after bilateral elimination of the so-called thread hairs by their denervation or by cauterization of the hair bases. These extremely delicate and relatively long sensory hairs are arranged in a slightly curved row on top of a medioventral invagination of the statocyst wall. They extend more or less perpendicular to the wall free into the cyst fluid (Figs. 20–22). In fresh preparations of the opened cyst these hairs can be seen to follow the slightest movements of the surrounding fluid, swaying around their point of attachment in any direction, although they are apparently most readily moved perpendic-

---

Fig. 20. Location and structure of statocyst in *Carcinus maenas*. a. Head region (ventral view, slightly frontal). Rectangle indicates left antennule. b. Left antennule, enlarged. Basal segment opened ventrally, with statocyst in situ. See Fig. 21 for details of area outlined in white. c. Same statocyst, still more enlarged. *TH*, row of thread hairs attached on top of oval invagination of statocyst wall which projects dorsally into the lumen; points of hair attachment visible as small white spots; *CS*, cluster of statoliths; *SH*, region of statolith hairs; *FH*, region of free hook hairs (the *FH*-field is approximately vertical and consequently not visible from this side); compare Fig. 21. (From Dijkgraaf[35] and 1956 unpublished observations.)

ularly to the direction of the row. After displacement, all hairs return slowly to their normal perpendicular position regardless of the cyst's orientation. In *Eriocheir sinensis* marked deviation of the thread hairs and their slow return to the resting position after prolonged rotation can be seen by direct observation of the basal part of the hairs through the somewhat transparent wall of the intact statocyst (Dijkgraaf, 1956, unpublished observations).

There is little doubt that the adequate stimulus for the rotation receptors consists of fluid movement within the statocyst caused by angular acceleration and deceleration. The acceleration response is evoked by fluid movement in a direction opposite to that of the rotation; deceleration responses and aftereffects are caused by fluid movement in the same direction as the rotation. Apart from all fluid movements, the elasticity of the thread hairs will constantly tend to return these hairs to their resting position and thus function in restoring the undisturbed condition.

Bilateral elimination of the thread hairs does not affect the performance of position reflexes evoked by maintained angular displacement about horizontal axes in blinded *Maja*. But whereas the eyestalks in the animal with intact statocysts react immediately, in the thread-hairless crab the eyes hold their symmetrical position at the onset of rotation and start their compensatory movement only after rotation has begun or even at the end of rotation and after the animal has reached a new position. Furthermore, the velocity of this compensatory movement seems to be independent of the rate of angular acceleration or deceleration. The delayed nature of the response may be due to lack of rotation sensitivity about both horizontal axes as a result of thread hair elimination. That the thread hairs are indeed sensitive to rotation about all three major body axes is shown by the following observations.

Bilateral elimination of the statolith hairs (position receptors) by selective nerve cutting does not affect the animal's response to rotation around the vertical axis (Figs. 20–22). If such operated crabs are subjected to angular acceleration or deceleration about either horizontal axis, compensatory eyestalk reflexes and corresponding aftereffects occur. The aftereffects may be long lasting and complicated, particularly during the first 12–24 hours following statolith hair elimination. After fixation of the animal in any inclined position the eyestalks always return to their symmetrical posture, although complete return may require several minutes. Following bilateral elimination of the thread hairs as well as the statolith hairs, all these rotation reflexes and after-

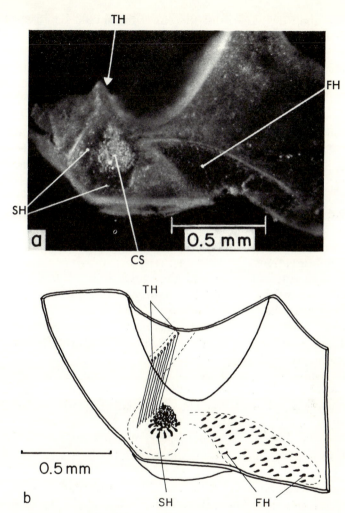

FIG. 21. Inside of isolated ventrocaudal corner of left statocyst of *Carcinus maenas* (region outlined in white in Fig. 20b), seen from dorsofrontal. a. Photograph of same statocyst as used in Fig. 20 focused on statolith level. b. Location of sense hairs in this region. Hair fields surrounded by interrupted lines are clearly transparent in contrast to rest of statocyst wall. *TH*, caudal end of thread hair row; *CS*, cluster of statoliths (sand grains); *SH*, statolith (hook) hairs touching liths with their tips; *FH*, free hook hairs with tips directed laterally. (From Dijkgraaf[35] and 1956 unpublished observations.)

effects are abolished. In crabs, therefore, the thread hair receptors are sensitive to rotation about all three major body axes.

After unilateral elimination of the thread hairs or removal of one entire statocyst in a blinded *Maja*, both eyes still react to rotation around the vertical axis, though with somewhat decreased magnitude. As a rule, there is no marked difference between the effect of ipsilateral and contralateral rotation and both eyes move to the same extent. Following bilateral elimination of the statolith hairs and unilateral elimination of the thread hairs, responses to acceleration and deceleration occur in both directions about the longitudinal and transverse axes. However, with rotation about the longitudinal axis, movement toward the intact side evokes a somewhat stronger response. With rotation about both axes, it is mainly the eyestalk on the unaltered side which responds. In freshly operated animals, the eye movements are performed after remarkable delays and quite slowly (Dijkgraaf, 1956, unpublished observations).

Besides the thread hairs and the statolith hairs there is a third group of sensory hairs within the statocyst of crabs. They have been called "free hook hairs" because most of them are bent, like the statolith-bearing hook hairs, yet none have any contact with statoliths.[35] These hairs stand close together on a shallow invagination of the caudal statocyst wall (Figs. 20–22) and their tips point more or less parallel toward the statolith region. In fresh preparations, these hairs can be seen to move under the influence of fluid currents (*Maja*), but their excursions are much less extensive than those of the thread hairs (*Carcinus*) and they return more quickly to their normal position. Some evidence indicates that the free hook hairs may act as auxiliary rotation receptors which inhibit and regulate the reflexes evoked by stimulation of the thread hairs during angular acceleration or deceleration about horizontal axes. Although this is uncertain, it seems fairly sure that the free hook hairs, if they are really rotation receptors at all, function in the detection of coarser fluid movements than those normally detected by the thread hairs. Model experiments show that accelerated rotation causes an intensified fluid flow along the surface of an invagination like that on which the thread hairs are inserted, while a whirlpool appears at the trailing border on deceleration (Dijkgraaf, 1956, unpublished observations). A study of the fluid movements within the intact statocyst during rotation would certainly be instructive.

Whether the so-called group hairs within the statocyst of crabs have any sensory or other physiological significance is unknown. In fresh preparations no movements of these coarse hairs can be detected, even with considerable currents in the surrounding fluid. They are lacking in larval stages where thread hairs and statolith hairs are already present.[45,47,63]

Only one crustacean, *Astacus*, has been reported to be sensitive to linear acceleration and deceleration. However, there is no convincing evidence that the statocysts are involved in this phenomenon.[28]

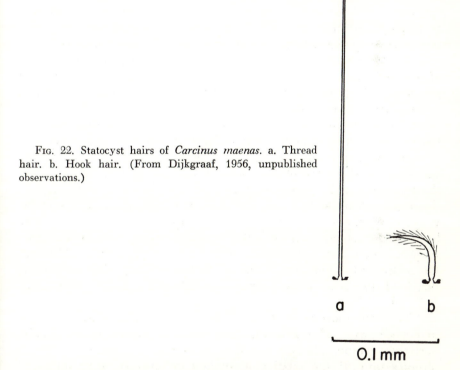

Fig. 22. Statocyst hairs of *Carcinus maenas*. a. Thread hair. b. Hook hair. (From Dijkgraaf, 1956, unpublished observations.)

a   b

0.1 mm

Apart from crabs, rotation receptors have been demonstrated by Cohen[21,22] in the statocyst of the lobster *Homarus americanus* by recording from the primary afferent neurons innervating the thread hair receptors (Fig. 15). These receptors respond only to angular acceleration and deceleration and are not sensitive to maintained position. They are spontaneously active at the same average frequency with the animal oriented in any static position. The response to rotation is superimposed upon the spontaneous background and consists of a coded sequence of frequency increases and decreases. As seen in Fig. 17, side-down rotation about the longitudinal axis evokes a burst of activity during acceleration associated with the onset of movement. Then there follows an abrupt decrease in frequency during the deceleration occurring at the end of movement. Side-up rotation evokes the reciprocal response pattern. The mean spontaneous frequency common to all resting positions is reached within one second after rotation stops.

During rotation about the transverse axis, rostrum-down rotation causes a burst of activity at the onset of movement and a depression in frequency at its termination. Rostrum-up rotation yields the reciprocal response. Rotation on a horizontal turntable about the vertical axis, with the preparation mounted in its normal position, also evokes a similar response pattern. Contralateral rotation (statocyst-trailing) causes a burst at the start of movement and a drop in frequency at the end of rotation. Ipsilateral rotation (statocyst-leading) causes the reciprocal response. When these results are compared to the observations mentioned above in crabs after unilateral statocyst ablation, it is again apparent that a decrease of spontaneous activity in statocyst receptors may have an important function in regulating behavioral responses.

Several factors indicate that angular acceleration is the adequate stimulus for these receptors. Constant velocity rotation about either the transverse or longitudinal axis is accompanied by a return toward the resting level within 0.5 sec after reaching a constant angular velocity. This, and the fact that the response pattern is evoked during horizontal rotation, where gravity could not play a role, indicate that the force due to angular acceleration is the adequate stimulus. Although the arrhythmic spontaneous activity creates difficulty in determining threshold, the latter apparently ranges between angular accelerations of 5 and $15°/sec^2$.

The same receptor unit responds to acceleration about all three major body axes. Thus rostrum-down, side-down, and statocyst-trailing horizontal rotation always elicit the same response pattern from a single receptor unit. If the relative movement between statocyst fluid and sensory hair provides the necessary stimulus, as in the semicircular canals of vertebrates, then the bending of the hair in either a posterior or a dorsal direction seems to be associated with an increase in the frequency of sensory nerve impulses, whereas bending in either an anterior or a ventral direction decreases receptor activity.

Any given rotation receptor therefore appears capable of differentiating rotation in opposite directions about the same axis by differences in the sequence of the burst-depression response. In *Homarus* one receptor unit of this type cannot alone specifically signal the axis about which the displacement is occurring. However, behavioral experiments with crabs showed that stimulation of the entire thread hair row provides these animals somehow with sufficient spatial information. Even after elimination of the position receptors, rotation about all three major body axes evokes compensatory reactions which are still fairly well adjusted to the plane of rotation (Dijkgraaf, 1956, unpublished observations).

C. Comparative Aspects

The function of statocyst receptors shows a remarkable resemblance to analogous receptors in the vertebrate nonacoustic labyrinth.[22,29,56] Both organs utilize spontaneous activity as a background on which to build their response patterns. Such a resting discharge permits a single receptor to detect a stimulus change in either of two directions. Among Crustacea, spontaneous activity from statocyst receptors also appears to function in the maintenance of muscular tone, as demonstrated by the quiescence and general muscular weakness observed after statocyst ablation.[13,42,60]

Although no labyrinthine counterpart to the statocyst Type II position receptor has been demonstrated, the general mechanism of position reception is essentially the same in Crustacea and vertebrates. The Type I statocyst position receptors not only show the same kind of bell-shaped response curve as labyrinthine position receptors, but even share with the vertebrate receptor the slight sensitivity to displacement direction during slow constant-velocity rotations.[57] A single Type I position receptor responds only to rotation about one major horizontal body axis, unlike the single vertebrate position receptor which is sensitive to displacement about both horizontal axes.[57] Although the threshold for vertebrate position receptors is not stated, the available data[57] indicate that it is probably higher than the $6°$-threshold of *Homarus* position receptors. Thus from the standpoint of absence of ambiguity in the afferent signal and of sensitivity, the position receptors of the lobster statocyst appear to be more functional than those of the vertebrate labyrinth.

The general mechanism of the statocyst rotation receptors and the semicircular canals is likewise almost identical. However, a single statocyst receptor in *Homarus* responds to displacement about all three major body axes, in contrast to the vertebrate rotation receptor[58] in which a single unit responds only to rotation in one given plane. In this instance the vertebrate receptors seem more discriminatory.

VI. *HEARING AND SOUND PRODUCTION*

A. Hearing and Vibration Reception

The question whether or not Crustacea are able to "hear" depends primarily on the definition of hearing. Contrary to a recent proposal in which sound and hearing are defined quite arbitrarily,[69] we prefer to ascribe the ability of hearing only to those animals which 1) are sensitive to air- or water-borne sound, i.e. to a succession of pressure waves conducted with a characteristic velocity through the medium involved, and which 2) detect these stimuli with sound receptors, i.e. sense organs or sensory endings especially developed and primarily used for this purpose. If the second condition is not fulfilled we may merely speak of sound reception. Sensitivity to sound or vibrations reaching the animal through the solid substrate, including high-amplitude, strongly damped pressure waves (like those caused by tapping against an aquarium wall) will be termed vibration reception and the sense organs involved called vibration receptors if they are especially adapted to this task.

According to these definitions, hearing has not yet been demonstrated in any crustacean. Sound reception has been observed with some probability in a few instances,[31,45,55] whereas vibration reception seems to be rather common since responses to stimuli of this kind have been reported by several authors for Mysidacea,[10,11,45] Caridea,[11,45,63] Paguridea,[44] and Brachyura.[44,63] Vibrational stimuli in general evoke only flight reactions or reflex-like jumps directed away from the source of vibration.[63] As in fishes,[30] immersion in water to which a trace of strychnine sulfate has been added raises the vibration sensitivity of Crustacea considerably, and the slightest tap evokes a vigorous jumping response.[45,63] In land-living forms all air-borne sounds, including intense noises, fail to evoke reactions even though the statocyst in terrestrial species shows several peculiar structural specializations.[44] However, "biological" sound stimuli, as opposed to artificial ones, seem never to have been tested.

With regard to the location of sound and vibration receptors, removal of both statocysts has generally been found to decrease the magnitude of the reactions somewhat, but does not seriously impair them. However, removal of both pairs of antennae in some cases reduces vibration sensitivity considerably.[63] This may be due to the presence of delicate hairs on these appendages; several other apparently adequate structures for the reception of vibrational stimuli have also been described.[45] Typical vibration receptors have been identified electrophysiologically within the statocyst of two species of lobster, *Panulirus*[24] and *Homarus*.[22] The receptors concerned respond exclusively to relatively high-intensity and low-frequency vibrations (tapping) conducted through the solid substrate supporting the preparation. Water- or air-borne vibrations are ineffective, as are position or rotation stimuli. Vibration receptors have also been demonstrated in certain elastic organs spanning walking-leg joints in *Carcinus maenas*.[18]

B. Sound Production

There are numerous sound-producing decapods distributed irregularly through the entire order. They comprise deep-sea animals as well as shore- and land-inhabiting species. With regard to the sound-producing structures, three different types can be distinguished:

1) In the snapping shrimps (*Alpheus, Crangon*) a loud click is produced by a vigorous closure of the enlarged snapping-claw. The finger of the claw has a smooth patch or disc which sticks like a sucker to a corresponding patch on the claw when fully opened.[46] During contraction of the closer muscle this connection is suddenly broken. The clicks are rather loud and are produced whenever an animal is disturbed spatially. Snapping evidently has a warning or threatening function. It has been suggested that the violent jet of water directed toward the obtruder by such a rapid closing of the claw may be of importance rather than the click itself.[78] Convincing experimental evidence is lacking with regard to both suppositions.

2) Most palinurids of both sexes produce rather loud noises when they are disturbed or when struggling with each other.[31] The basal segment of the antenna bears medially a specialized pad which is rubbed over a corresponding surface of the rostral skeleton. The sound is produced only while the antenna is being lifted and moved posteriorly under pressure against the skeleton, but never during the forward recovery movement. In *Palinurus elephas* the noise sounds like the creaking of leather[31]; in *Panulirus argus* it has been described as the sound of filing a saw,[17] and in *P. interruptus* as scraping.[55] It apparently has a threatening significance. In several cases responses to this noise have been observed which do not seem to be affected by removal of both antennules together with the statocysts.[31] In *P. argus* a slow rattle is characteristic of lobsters gathered in groups, whereas a rasp is a usual component of defensive behavior.[61]

3) In several Anomura and Brachyura sound production by stridulation has been observed. As in crickets and grasshoppers, a cre-

nated ridge on the exoskeleton is rubbed perpendicularly against a smooth ridge elsewhere on the body surface. In the pagurid *Coenobita* the stridulation sounds like a loud chirp[6]; in the marine crab *Matuta* it has been compared with the noise produced when a nail is moved to and fro along a file.[43] In the shore- and land-dwelling crabs of the Genus *Ocypode*, descriptions range from a fine filing noise[44] and twittering squeaks[25] to croaking[62] and the low buzz of a double-bass.[43] These sounds apparently seem higher pitched and louder if the animals stridulate from within their holes. The stridulation serves to warn trespassers that a burrow is occupied.[25] Usually both sexes produce these sounds. In a number of crabs, however, sexual dimorphism exists, and the stridulation apparatus is either better developed or exclusively present in the male. Actual sound production has not yet been described in those latter cases.[6]

VII. *SUMMARY AND CONCLUSIONS*

There are only two major morphological types of mechanoreceptors in Crustacea, the hair receptor and the sensory neuron with its distal terminal embedded either in muscle or in connective tissue membrane. The question arises as to how the functional specificity required for the several different modalities which these receptors serve is achieved. The problem of peripheral receptor specificity resolves into questions of threshold differences and frequency discrimination. The latter is demonstrated by comparing statocyst hair receptors, which are relatively nonadapting and respond to different steady levels of maintained force, and the rotation receptors of the same organ, which respond primarily to a transient change of force. In these instances the functional differences seem to be based on the physical properties of nonnervous accessory elements such as statoliths, the statocyst fluid, or the elasticity of the chitinous hair shaft. However, in the sensory neurons of the muscle receptor organ there appear to be differences in the nerve terminals themselves that cause one neuron to respond to the phasic aspect and another to the static component of the stimulus.

Mechanoreception plays an important role in the life of Crustacea. Notwithstanding the rigid skeleton this applies even to the sense of touch. However, the physiology of individual tactile hair receptors is still mainly unexplored and awaits further application of electrophysiological techniques.

A growing number of proprioceptors have been discovered and described. There are interesting physiological similarities between the vertebrate muscle spindle and the crustacean muscle receptor organ. However, proprioceptive organization within the limbs of insects and crustaceans seems to be fundamentally different, but see page 576.

Special equilibrium receptors have apparently evolved from the simple tactile hair in many of the more highly organized crustaceans, particularly decapods. These statocysts possess the clearly demonstrated ability to signal the animal's position with respect to gravity. There is a striking resemblance between the basic mechanisms of position reception in the crustacean statocyst and in the vertebrate labyrinth. The functional similarity between statocyst and labyrinth goes even further in crustaceans with highly specialized statocysts, such as most crabs and the lobster *Homarus*. Certain elements within the statocysts of these animals have been shown to be sensitive rotation receptors, responding to fluid movements caused by angular acceleration or deceleration about all three major body axes. They thus represent an interesting counterpart to the semicircular canals in vertebrates. In the possession of statocysts, Crustacea stand in striking contrast to insects since such receptors are lacking in nearly all of the latter animals.

It is curious that crustacean proprioceptors and equilibrium receptors should be so similar functionally to those of vertebrates and so dissimilar to analogous insect receptors. This may be a consequence of the unstable postural and locomotor equilibrium shared by many Crustacea and most vertebrates in contrast to the mechanical stability of the insect, both at rest and during locomotion. In the two former groups, spatial orientation must be maintained against physical forces tending to upset equilibrium, while in insects the low center of gravity and greater relative weight contribute to a mechanically more stable condition even during flight.[41] Among insects the Diptera are exceptional since they have the halteres which function in flight as gyroscopic sense organs to detect rotational movements and initiate counteracting reflex responses.[65] Furthermore, air-inhabiting animals like insects may have better opportunity in general to orient by skylight than marine crustaceans living at some depth, although many Crustacea, especially those naturally devoid of statoreceptors, have a dorsal light reflex.[73a,79,80] In some of the latter animals active equilibrium maintenance and normal orientation during swimming have been observed even after blinding, but the sensory basis of this ability is still obscure.[70]

A second biological task which the statocysts share with other receptors (visual, tactile, proprioceptive) is the initiation of compensatory eyestalk reflexes. In all Crustacea with well-developed eyes it is apparently of crucial importance during displacement about any axis to reduce the shift of the visual field across the retina to a minimum.[33,34] Remarkably enough, special organs of hearing are apparently lacking in Crustacea. In a few instances reactions to real sound stimuli have been observed, but the receptors involved were not identified and might be unspecific. On the other hand, a great number of decapods are known to produce characteristic sounds by means of special rubbing or stridulating mechanisms. The behavioral significance of such sounds offers a promising area for future research.

This chapter was prepared while one of us (M. J. C.) was a member of The Biological Laboratories, Harvard University.

REFERENCES

1. Alexandrowicz, J. S. 1951. Muscle receptor organs in the abdomen of *Homarus vulgaris* and *Palinurus vulgaris*. *Quart. J. Microscop. Sci.* **92**:163–199.
2. Alexandrowicz, J. S. 1952a. Receptor elements in the thoracic muscles of *Homarus vulgaris* and *Palinurus vulgaris*. *Quart. J. Microscop. Sci.* **93**:315–346.
3. Alexandrowicz, J. S. 1952b. Muscle receptor organs in the Paguridae. *J. Marine Biol. Assoc. United Kingdom* **31**:277–286.
4. Alexandrowicz, J. S. 1958. Further observations on proprioceptors in Crustacea and a hypothesis about their function. *J. Marine Biol. Assoc. United Kingdom* **37**:379–396.
5. Alexandrowicz, J. S., and Whitear, M. 1957. Receptor elements in the coxal region of Decapoda Crustacea. *J. Marine Biol. Assoc. United Kingdom* **36**:603–628.
6. Balss, H. 1921. Über Stridulationsorgane bei dekapoden Crustaceen. *Naturw. Wochschr.* [N.F.] **20**:697–701.
7. Balss, H. 1944. Decapoda. *In:* "Bronn's Tierreich," Bd. 5, Abt. 1, Bch. 7, pp 321–480. Akademische Verlagsges., Leipzig.
8. Barnes, T. C. 1932. Responses in the isolated limbs of Crustacea and associated nervous discharges. *Am. J. Physiol.* **99**:321–331.
9. Barth, G. 1934. Untersuchungen über Myochordotonalorgane bei dekapoden Crustaceen. *Z. wiss. Zoöl.* **145**:576–624.
10. Bauer, V. 1908. Über die reflektorische Regulierung der Schwimmbewegungen bei den Mysiden mit besonderer Berücksichtigung der doppelsinnigen Reizbarkeit der Augen. *Z. allgem. Physiol.* **8**:343–370.
11. Beer, T. 1898. Vergleichend-physiologische Studien zur Statocystenfunction. *Arch. ges. Physiol. Pflügers* **73**:1–41.
12. Bethe, A. 1895. Die Otocyste von *Mysis*. *Zool. Jahrb. Abt. Anat. u. Ontog. Tiere* **8**:544–564.
13. Bethe, A. 1897. Das Nervensystem von *Carcinus maenas*. *Arch. mikroskop. Anat. u. Entwicklungsmech.* **50**:460–546.
14. Brock, F. 1927. Das Verhalten des Einsiedlerkrebses *Pagurus arrosor* Herbst während des Aufsuchens, Ablösens und Aufpflanzens seiner Seerose *Sagartia parasitica* Gosse. *Wilhelm Roux' Arch. Entwicklungsmech. Organ.* **112**:204–238.

15. Brock, F. 1930. Das Verhalten der ersten Antennen von Brachyuren und Ano-
    muren in bezug auf das umgebende Medium. *Z. vergleich. Physiol.* **11**:774–790.
16. Brooks, W. K., and Herrick, F. H. 1891. The embryology and metamorphosis
    of the Macroura. *Mem. Natl. Acad. Sci.* **5**:321–576.
17. Brown, G. G. 1878. The voices of crustaceans. *Proc. U. S. Natl. Museum* **1**:7–8.
18. Burke, W. 1954. An organ for proprioception and vibration sense in *Carcinus
    maenas. J. Exptl. Biol.* **31**:127–138.
19. Clark, G. P. 1896. On the relation of the otocysts to equilibrium phenomena in
    Gelasimus pugilator and *Platyonichus ocellatus. J. Physiol. (London)* **19**:327–
    343.
20. Claus, C., Grobben, K., and Kühn, A. 1932. "Lehrbuch der Zoologie," 10th ed.,
    1118 pp. Springer, Berlin.
21. Cohen, M. J. 1953. Oscillographic analysis of an invertebrate equilibrium
    organ. *Biol. Bull.* **105**:363.
22. Cohen, M. J. 1955. The function of receptors in the statocyst of the lobster
    Homarus americanus. J. Physiol. (London) **130**:9–34.
23. Cohen, M. J. 1956. Sensory and motor relationships of a crustacean central
    ganglion. *Biol. Bull.* **111**:318.
24. Cohen, M. J., Katsuki, Y., and Bullock, T. H. 1953. Oscillographic analysis of
    equilibrium receptors in Crustacea. *Experientia* **9**:434–435.
25. Crane, J. 1941. On the growth and ecology of brachyuran crabs of the Genus
    Ocypode. Zoologica **26**:297–310.
26. Delage, Y. 1887. Sur une function nouvelle des otocystes comme organes d'ori-
    entation locomotrice. *Arch. zool. exptl. et gén.* **5**:1–26.
27. Demoll, R. 1909. Über die Augen und die Augenstielreflexe von *Squilla mantis.
    Zool. Jahrb. Abt. Morphol.* **27**:171–212.
28. Demoll, R. 1917. "Die Sinnesorgane der Arthropoden, ihr Bau und ihre Funk-
    tion," 243 pp. Vieweg, Braunschweig.
29. Dijkgraaf, S. 1952a. Bau und Funktionen der Seitenorgane und des Ohrlaby-
    rinths bei Fischen. *Experientia* **8**:205–216.
30. Dijkgraaf, S. 1952b. Über die Schallwahrnehmung bei Meeresfischen. *Z. ver-
    gleich. Physiol.* **34**:104–122.
31. Dijkgraaf, S. 1955a. Lauterzeugung und Schallwahrnehmung bei der Languste
    (*Palinurus vulgaris*). *Experientia* **11**:330–331.
32. Dijkgraaf, S. 1955b. Rotationssinn nach dem Bogengangsprinzip bei Crustaceen.
    Experientia **11**:407–409.
33. Dijkgraaf, S. 1956a. Kompensatorische Augenstieldrehungen und ihre Auslösung
    bei der Languste (*Palinurus vulgaris*). *Z. vergleich. Physiol.* **38**:491–520.
34. Dijkgraaf, S. 1956b. Über die kompensatorischen Augenstielbewegungen bei
    Brachyuren. *Pubbl. staz. zool. Napoli* **28**:341–350.
35. Dijkgraaf, S. 1956c. Structure and functions of the statocyst in crabs. *Experi-
    entia* **12**:394–396.
36. Doflein, F. 1910. Lebensgewohnheiten und Anpassungen bei dekapoden Krebsen.
    "Festschrift zum 60. *Geburtstag* Richard Hertwigs," Vol. 3, pp. 215–292. Fischer,
    Jena.
37. Eyzaguirre, C., and Kuffler, S. 1955a. Processes of excitation in the dendrites
    and in the soma of single isolated sensory nerve cells of the lobster and cray-
    fish. *J. Gen. Physiol.* **39**:87–119.

38. Eyzaguirre, C., and Kuffler, S. 1955b. Further study of soma dendrite and axon excitation in single neurons. *J. Gen. Physiol.* **39**:121–153.
39. Farre, A. 1843. On the organ of hearing in Crustacea. *Phil. Trans. Roy. Soc. London* **B133**:233–242.
40. Florey, E., and Florey, E. 1955. Microanatomy of the abdominal stretch receptors of the crayfish (*Astacus fluviatilis* L.). *J. Gen. Physiol.* **39**:69–85.
41. Fraenkel, G. S., and Gunn, D. L. 1940. "The Orientation of Animals," 352 pp. Oxford Univ. Press, London and New York.
42. Fröhlich, A. 1904. Studien über die Statocysten wirbelloser Tiere. II Mitt.: Versuche an Krebsen. *Arch. ges. Physiol. Pflügers* **103**:149–168.
43. Gerstaecker, A., and Ortmann, A. E. 1901. Malacostraca. *In:* "Bronn's Tierreich," Bd. 5. Abt. 2. Hälfte 2, pp. 1–1319. Akademische Verlagsges., Leipzig.
44. Harms, J. W. 1929; 1932. Die Realisation von Genen und die consecutive Adaption. I and II. *Z. wiss. Zoöl.* **133**:211–397; **140**:167–290.
45. Hensen, V. 1863. Studien über das Gehörorgan der Decapoden. *Z. wiss. Zoöl.* **13**:319–412.
46. Johnson, M. W., Everest, F. A., and Young, R. W. 1947. The role of the snapping shrimp (*Crangon* and *Synalpheus*) in the production of underwater noise in the sea. *Biol. Bull.* **93**:122–138.
47. Kinzig, H. 1921. Untersuchungen über den Bau der Statocysten einiger dekapoder Crustaceen. *Verhandl. naturhist.-med. Ver. Heidelberg* [N.F.] **14**:1–90.
48. Kreidl, A. 1893. Weitere Beitrage zur Physiologie des Ohrlabyrinthes (II. Mitth.) Versuche an Krebsen. *Sitzber. Akad. Wiss. Wien Math-naturw. Kl. Abt. III* **102**:149–174.
49. Kuffler, S. W. 1954. Mechanisms of activation and motor control of stretch receptors of lobster and crayfish. *J. Neurophysiol.* **17**:558–574.
50. Kuffler, S. W., and Eyzaguirre, C. 1955. Synaptic inhibition in an isolated nerve cell. *J. Gen. Physiol.* **39**:155–184.
51. Kühn, A. 1914. Die reflektorische Erhaltung des Gleichgewichtes bei Krebsen. *Verhandl. deut. zool. Ges.* **24**:262–277.
52. Kükenthal, W., and Krumbach, T. 1926. Crustacea. *In:* "Handbuch der Zoologie," Bd. 3, Hälfte 1, pp. 277–1074. de Gruyter, Berlin.
53. Lang, D., and Yonge, C. M. 1935. The function of the tegmental glands in the statocyst of *Homarus vulgaris*. *J. Marine Biol. Assoc. United Kingdom* **20**: 333–339.
54. Langenbuch, R. 1928. Über die Statocysten einiger Crustaceen. *Zool. Jahrb. Abt. Allgem. Zool. Physiol. Tiere* **44**:575–622.
55. Lindberg, R. G. 1955. Growth, population dynamics and field behavior in the spiny lobster, *Panulirus interruptus* (Randall). *Univ. Calif. (Berkeley) Publs. Zoöl.* **59**:157–248.
56. Lowenstein, O. 1950. Labyrinth and equilibrium. *Symposia Soc. Exptl. Biol. No.* 4:60–82.
57. Lowenstein, O., and Roberts, T. D. M. 1950. The equilibrium function of the otolith organ of the thornback ray (*Raja clavata*). *J. Physiol. (London)* **110**: 392–415.
58. Lowenstein, O., and Sand, A. 1940. The mechanism of the semicircular canal. A study of the responses of single-fiber preparations to angular accelerations and to rotation at constant speed. *Phil. Trans. Roy. Soc. London* **B120**:256–275.

59. Luther, W. 1930. Versuche über die Chemorezeption der Brachyuren. *Z. vergleich. Physiol.* **12**:177–205.

60. Lyon, E. P. 1900. A contribution to the comparative physiology of compensatory motions. *Am. J. Physiol.* **3**:86–114.

61. Moulton, J. W. 1957. Sound production in the spiny lobster *Panulirus argus* (Latreille). *Biol. Bull.* **113**:286–295.

62. Peters, H. M. 1955. Die Winkgebärde von *Uca* und *Minuca* (Brachyura) in vergleichend-ethologischer, -ökologischer und -morphologisch-anatomischer Betrachtung. *Z. Morphol. Ökol. Tiere* **43**:425–500.

63. Prentiss, C. W. 1901. The otocyst of decapod Crustacea. *Bull. Mus. Comp. Zool. Harvard* **36**:167–254.

64. Pringle, J. W. S. 1938. Proprioception in insects. II. The action of the campaniform sensilla on the legs. *J. Exptl. Biol.* **15**:114–131.

65. Pringle, J. W. S. 1948. The gyroscopic mechanism of the halteres of Diptera. *Phil. Trans. Roy. Soc. London* **B233**:347–384.

66. Pringle, J. W. S. 1955. The function of the lyriform organs of arachnids. *J. Exptl. Biol.* **32**:270–278.

67. Pringle, J. W. S. 1956. Proprioception in *Limulus*. *J. Exptl. Biol.* **33**:658–667.

68. Prosser, C. L. 1935. Action potentials in the nervous system of the crayfish. III. Central responses to proprioceptive and tactile stimuli. *J. Comp. Neurol.* **62**:495–505.

69. Pumphrey, R. J. 1950. Hearing. *Symposia Soc. Exptl. Biol. No.* **4**:3–18.

70. Schaller, F. 1953. Verhaltens- und sinnesphysiologische Beobachtungen an *Squilla mantis*. *Z. Tierpsychol.* **10**:1–12.

71. Schöne, H. 1951. Die statische Gleichgewichtsorientierung dekapoder Crustaceen. *Verhandl. deut. zool. Ges.* **16**:157–162.

72. Schöne, H. 1954. Statocystenfunktion und statische Lageorientierung bei dekapoden Krebsen. *Z. vergleich. Physiol.* **36**:241–260.

73. Schöne, H. 1957. Kurssteuerung mittels der Statocysten (Messungen an Krebsen). *Z. vergleich. Physiol.* **39**:235–240.

73a. Schöne, H. 1959. Die Lageorientierung mit Statolithenorganen und Augen. *Ergeb. Biol.* **21**:161–209.

74. Sesar, M. 1927. "Die Statocysten der Brachyuren," 30 pp. Thesis, Munich.

75. Sherrington, C. 1906. "The Integrative Action of the Nervous System," 433 pp. Cambridge Univ. Press, London and New York.

76. Snodgrass, R. E. 1935. "Principles of Insect Morphology," 667 pp. McGraw-Hill, New York.

77. Tonner, F. 1933. Ein Beitrag zur Anatomie und Physiologie des peripheren Nervensystems von *Astacus fluviatilis*. *Zool. Jahrbch. Abt. Allgem. Zool. Physiol. Tiere* **53**:101–152.

78. Volz, P. 1938. Studien über das "Knallen" der Alpheiden. *Z. Morphol. Ökol. Tiere* **34**:272–316.

79. von Buddenbrock, W. 1914. Über die Orientierung der Krebse im Raum. *Zool. Jahrbch. Abt. Allgem. Zool. Physiol. Tiere* **34**:479–514.

80. von Buddenbrock, W. 1952a. Der Lichtrückenreflex. *In:* "Vergleichende Physiologie," Sinnesphysiologie, Vol. I, pp. 71–74. Birkhäuser, Basel.

81. von Buddenbrock, W. 1952b. Der statische Sinn. *In:* "Vergleichende Physiologie," Sinnesphysiologie, Vol. I, pp. 269–330. Birkhäuser, Basel.

82. von Buddenbrock, W. 1945–1954. Physiologie der Decapoden. *In:* "Bronn's Tierreich," Bd. 5, Abt. 1, Bch. 7, pp. 863–1283. Akademische Verlagsges., Leipzig.
83. von Buddenbrock, W., and Friedrich, H. 1933. Neue Beobachtungen über die kompensatorischen Augenbewegungen und den Farbensinn der Taschenkrabben (*Carcinus maenas*). *Z. vergleich. Physiol.* **19**:747–761.
84. Wetzel, A. 1935. Das Chordotonalorgan in der erste Antenne der Caprelliden. *Zool. Jahrbch. Abt. Anat. u. Ontog. Tiere* **59**:355–382.
85. Wiersma, C. A. G., Furshpan, E., and Florey, E. 1953. Physiological and pharmacological observations on muscle receptor organs of the crayfish, *Cambarus clarkii* Girard. *J. Exptl. Biol.* **30**:136–150.
86. Wiersma, C. A. G., Ripley, S. H., and Christensen, E. 1955. The central representation of sensory stimulation in the crayfish. *J. Cellular Comp. Physiol.* **46**: 307–326.

CHAPTER 3

SAUL B. BARBER

CHEMORECEPTION AND THERMORECEPTION

I. *CHEMORECEPTION*

A. INTRODUCTION

The physiology of chemoreception is being actively studied in the vertebrates and invertebrates. Recent results in the mammals and insects especially have contributed much toward preliminary analysis of chemoreceptor mechanisms at the molecular level.[23] However work on Crustacea has not kept pace with these advances. Significantly the most recent reviews on crustacean chemoreception[56,57] perforce deal primarily with material published twenty or more years ago. Some promising preliminary electrophysiological results on crustacean chemoreceptors[34,34a] are now available but otherwise similar limitations of knowledge are still current. It is hoped that the present review will aid in stimulating a renewed interest in the study of crustacean chemoreceptors. The advances in technique and information that have increased our functional understanding of these sense organs in other animal groups should be applicable to similar problems in the Crustacea.

B. THE RECEPTOR ORGANS

1. *Structure.* A variety of different elements have been designated as chemoreceptors in Crustacea on the basis of their structural appearance, correlated, in most instances, with behavioral observations. These include aesthetascs (canals or tubules of Leydig), funnel canals, pores, and structures superficially similar to the basiconic sensilla of insects. None of these structures has been conclusively demonstrated to func-

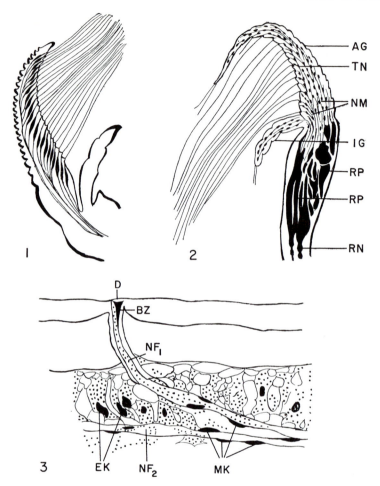

FIG. 1. Terminal portion of the antennule of the deep-sea brachyuran crab, *Geryon affinis*. Aesthetascs appear as long, thin hairs, each underlaid by a separate cluster of sense cells ("olfactory spindles"). The latter appear only as a group of darkly stained nuclei. A terminal strand from each cluster may be seen to reach the base of the corresponding aesthetasc. Nerve fibers from the sense cell clusters aggregate centrally into a sensory component ("olfactory nerve") of the antennular nerve. (Redrawn from Hanström.[27])

FIG. 2. Terminal portion of the antennule of the deep-sea brachyuran crab, *Physachaeus ctenurus*. Aesthetascs appear on the outer flagellum (*AG*) as in Fig. 1. Sense cell clusters (*RP*) are, in this species, displaced proximally to form a lobus osphradicus. Terminal strands (*TN*) innervating each aesthetasc are visible at the base of each hair. A sensory nerve (*RN*) is formed by the central aggregation of fibers from the lobus osphradicus. Nuclei of neurilemma cells (*NM*) are abundant. The inner flagellum (*IG*) is almost devoid of sensory hairs. (Redrawn from

tion as chemoreceptors. Proof of their function awaits more direct experimental evidence than has been available. Typical aesthetascs, as they are described in aquatic decapods,[4] are long, thin, cylindrical sensory hairs that occur most often in transverse rows on the outer flagellum of the antennules. Species differences in the number of hairs are considerable. Up to 1500 per antennular flagellum have been estimated for one deep sea form. Generally there occurs at the base of each such hair a group of bipolar primary sense cells, the dendrites of which form a terminal strand which penetrates the lumen of the hair to its extremity (Fig. 1). In some Brachyura and Anomura these sense cell groups may be displaced proximally and coalesced, to a greater or lesser degree, to form a ganglion, the lobus osphradicus.[27] This arrangement apparently has arisen independently within a number of crustacean groups (Fig. 2).

In terrestrial decapods the aesthetasc hairs are replaced by platelike structures which have a blunt, rounded, free end.[4] These are innervated like the hairs but also have underlying groups of glandular cells which keep the lumen of the plates filled with a fluid. The developmental transformation of the hair structures found in zoea-larvae to the plate structures of adults has been observed. Aesthetascs have also been described in most of the other crustacean orders. Sexual dimorphism has been reported in the quantitative distribution of these hairs in Cladocera, Ostracoda, Copepoda, Cumacea, Tanaidacea, and Amphipoda. In addition to the antennular location they are present on the antennae of some Ostracoda and Leptostraca and on the mouth parts of certain Decapoda and Anaspidacea.[40]

The funnel canals described in *Carcinus maenas*[43] are simple perforations of the cuticle, each containing the distal process of a peripheral ganglion cell (Fig. 3). The individual ganglion cells supplying the canals are usually so closely packed that they are not separately distinguishable. Peripherally the canal widens to a small funnel. Here the nerve fiber runs along the wall where it ends directly at the surface. The outer end of the funnel is covered by a thin cap which is usually broken in histological preparations. These organs

---

Hanström.[27])

FIG. 3. Section through a funnel canal from the tip of a *Carcinus maenas* walking leg. NF_1, nerve process from the sensory cell groups (not shown) innervating the canals of the general area. NF_2, nerve fiber of another funnel canal (not shown); MK, nucleus of neurilemma cell; D, covering of canal; EK, nucleus of epithelial cell; BZ, "structural" cell of canal cover. Magnification × 660. (Redrawn from Luther.[43])

occur on the legs, chelae, and mouth parts, not only in *Carcinus* but also in the spider crab, *Hyas*, and the hermit crab, *Pagurus*.

The pores described in *Astacus*[56] are found on the lateral wall of the gill chamber. They are about 4 μ in diameter and open into a wider chamber into which protrudes a small papilla. A group of free nerve endings passes through an opening in the epithelium and ends, entangled, in the papilla. The sensory cells of these endings are not described. Peg sensilla, superficially similar to chemically sensitive basiconic sensilla of millipedes, found on the terminal antennal segments of isopods, have been designated as chemoreceptors.[15]

2. *Evidence of chemical sensitivity.* The experimental evidence supporting the chemosensory functions of the sensilla described is entirely indirect. Attention has been naturally concentrated on those sensilla which seem morphologically likely to be chemically sensitive. In addition, the behavioral evidence depends largely on the correlation of demonstrable chemical sensitivity of particular body areas with the distribution of a specific kind of receptor structure. Electrophysiological records of invertebrate chemoreceptor responses have only been obtained quite recently, and relatively little data are yet available for Crustacea. The behavioral work contains abundant evidence for the chemical sensitivity of both pairs of antennae, mouth parts, and thoracic appendages, although disagreements over specific parts are found. This material will be considered here only briefly. A more complete discussion, especially of the early work, is available in von Buddenbrock's reviews.[56,57]

Only a few attempts to identify the chemoreceptors or even their location by physiological experiments have been reported in crustacean orders other than the Decapoda. Evidence indicating that the maxillae and swimming appendages are chemosensitive has been found for *Triops cancriformis*.[53] Gelatin is handled by these appendages in significantly different ways depending upon whether it is pure, or mixed with common sapid substances like sugar, salt, acetic acid, and quinine.

The presence of contact chemoreceptors has been indicated in the terminal antennal segments of the isopod *Oniscus asellus*.[15] This animal aggregates on filter paper soaked with distilled water in preference to that soaked in 1% or 2% sucrose solution. The response is abolished by amputating or covering the terminal segments of the antennae, but not by similar treatment of other suspected areas. Because of their structure and location, basiconic-like sensilla have been suggested as the receptors mediating this response. These receptors do not mediate the humidity response of the same organisms.

A similar antennal function may be suspected in another isopod, *Ligia occidentalis*, since testing of the water with the antennae has been observed when these organisms approach a tide pool.[1] On the other hand in the littoral isopod, *Ligia baudiniana*, a sensitivity to ions and water seems to be present on the legs.[7,8] Individuals collect on one side or the other of a dish which has a filter paper bottom with each half of the paper soaked with a different solution. In such tests the organisms can differentiate distilled water from sea water and from various pure salt solutions.

In the isopods *Porcellio scaber*, *Oniscus asellus*, and *Armadillidium vulgare* the receptors responsible for the humidity responses of these organisms have not been found.[15,26,58] The head and abdomen were eliminated as possible sites for these sense organs, and it was suggested that either internal receptors responding to osmotic changes in body fluids, receptors on the thoracic appendages, or a general dehydration effect is responsible.

Among the Decapoda in general it has been fairly conclusively demonstrated that the antennules, antennae, mouth parts, and thoracic legs bear chemoreceptors.[56,57] A few representative observations are described below.

In shrimps, *Palaemon serratus* and *Crangon crangon* have been studied by different methods and have yielded some similar results. Blinded *Palaemon* respond to filter paper soaked in meat juice when it touches the thoracic legs or mouth parts.[3] The response is a fast grasping reflex and does not occur when the general carapace surface is similarly stimulated. Other experiments involving the finding of food by blinded animals prove the chemosensory function of both pairs of antennae. In *Crangon*, on the other hand, specific chemicals such as vanillin, acetic acid, quinine, sucrose, NaCl, and others were used as stimulating agents.[54] A technique was used whereby the outer flagellum of the antennule alone could be stimulated under water. Under these conditions the animal responds to both sapid and odorous chemicals. The response criterion in this case is an initiation of, or increase in, movements of body parts such as both pairs of antennae, head, and chelae.

Reaction time for the feeding reflex in *Cambarus* has been used as a quantitative criterion of function.[36] When food is held close to, but not touching, individual body parts and the time for seizure and eating determined, the outer rami of the antennules are found to be most sensitive. After these are amputated the inner ramus is also effective. When the antennules are removed the sensitivity of the antennae and, similarly, the mouth parts and chelae, can be demonstrated.

The chemoreceptor function of the antennular inner flagellum, chelae and first two pairs of walking legs of *Cambarus bartonii sciotensis* has recently been confirmed by electrophysiological methods[34,34a] (also Hodgson, 1958, personal communication) (Figs. 4 and 5). This

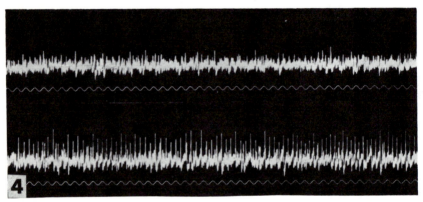

FIG. 4. Action potentials recorded from a single chemosensory hair on the tip of the first walking leg of the crayfish, *Cambarus bartonii sciotensis*. Upper record shows that stimulating with pond water does not induce activity which is significantly distinguishable from the noise level of the recording system. Lower record shows a repetitive discharge of action potentials when stimulating with 0.25M glycine in pond water. This activity is predominantly the response of a single peripheral neuron. Spike amplitude (lower record): 50 to 60 microvolts. Time base: 100 cycles/sec. (From Hodgson, 1958, personal communication.)

technique utilizes a fluid-filled capillary micropipette as both stimulating agent and recording electrode. When the pipette filled with pond water is placed over the tip of the entire antennular medial flagellum a "resting" level of action potential discharge is recorded. If the pond water in the pipette is replaced by a suitable sapid substance, the sensory spike frequency discharge is significantly higher (Fig. 5). The multiple nature of the discharge indicates that the activity of more than one receptor unit is recording under these conditions.

A more favorable preparation lies in the tufts of hair sensilla distributed over the chelae and first two pairs of walking legs of *C. bartonii sciotensis*. Here a micropipette electrode can be placed over a single hair sensillum so that the response is predominantly in the form of a regular, repetitive, spike discharge from a single receptor unit (Fig. 4). Thus the first electrophysiological observations in crustacean chemoreceptors confirm the chemical sensitivity of the antennules and thoracic appendages. They also indicate that hair sensilla are among the specific receptors mediating this sensitivity.

Sensitivity to an osmotic pressure different from that of normal sea water (e.g. four-fifths sea water) has been demonstrated in the spiny lobster *Jasus lalandei* by more conventional electrophysiological

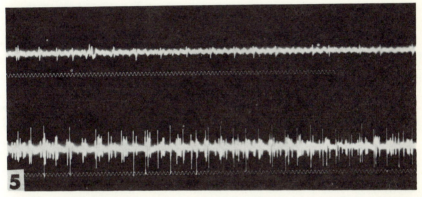

Fig. 5. Action potentials recorded from the medial branch of the antennule of *Cambarus bartonii sciotensis*. Upper record shows a low-level "resting" discharge of unknown origin while stimulating with pond water. Lower record shows a repetitive discharge of action potentials from several cells in response to stimulation with 0.25 *M* glutamic acid in pond water. Spike amplitude: small—30 microvolts, large —40 to 60 microvolts. Time base: 100 cycles/sec. (From Hodgson, 1958, personal communication.)

methods.[39] Action potential activity of a small, abdominal motor nerve occurs in response to osmotic stimulation of the antennular tips. These spikes are undoubtedly part of the efferent component of the vigorous escape reflexes which result from osmotic stimulation of the antennules and are mediated by the abdominal musculature.

Behavioral observations similar to some of those discussed have also indicated the existence of chemoreceptors on the mouth parts, chelae, and walking legs of *Carcinus maenas*.[43] Specific grasping and feeding reactions occur when these parts are stimulated individually. The sensitivity of the walking legs to chemicals can be demonstrated in a particularly striking way if crabs are caused to run, in air, on wet blotting paper. Searching, grasping, and feeding movements are initiated only after one of the walking legs touches a piece of the blotting paper which has been soaked in meat juice. Since the distribution of the funnel canals parallels that of the chemical sensitivity shown by *Carcinus*, these structures have been proposed as the chemoreceptors mediating the observed reflexes.[43]

Further experiments show that additional chemoreceptors are present somewhere in the field of the respiratory water current.[43] A piece of paper soaked in meat juice and placed close to the respiratory intake opening elicits grasping movements in a posterior direction by the last pair of walking legs. The pores found on the lateral wall of the gill chamber have been suggested as the receptors involved in this response.[56]

Antennular sensitivity to pH change has been demonstrated in the fresh-water crab, *Eriocheir sinensis*.[55] Exposure of these animals to a pH of approximately 6.5 invariably elicits an immediate decrease in the frequency of scaphognathite beats. Since antennular amputation abolishes this pH effect, whereas antennal removal does not, it may be concluded that chemoreceptors on the antennule mediate this reflex.

The chemical sensitivity of the antennule of brachyurans has also been confirmed electrophysiologically (Hodgson, 1958, personal communication), using the same technique as with *Cambarus*. Action-potential records from an entire antennule show a significant increase in spike activity when a stimulating substance is added to the pipette fluid.

C. FUNCTIONAL PROPERTIES

1. *Modalities.* The obvious classification of chemoreceptors into olfactory receptors which are stimulated by gaseous molecules and gustatory receptors which are stimulated by molecules in solution is a concept which appears to break down in the lower aquatic vertebrates and even more so in the invertebrates where receptor and nervous system homologies to the mammals do not pertain. For strictly terrestrial insects, however, there are receptors which may be called olfactory since they react to very low concentrations of compounds that are volatile at ordinary temperatures.[24] Similarly there is a class of receptors in these organisms which reacts to higher concentrations of substances in aqueous solution and which are, therefore, analogous to taste receptors.

For amphibious or aquatic organisms the situation is complicated by the lack of separation of the stimuli in two physical states. However, in the amphibious beetle, *Laccophilus maculosus*, there exists a group of receptors on the antennae which responds to the same substances, whether present in gaseous or aqueous solutions.[32] The thresholds of these receptors to the stimulating substances used were lower than those of the chemoreceptors located on the maxillary and labial palpi. This threshold difference apparently is not due to the presence of a larger number of sensilla on the antenna but to specialization in individual organs, although obvious morphological distinctions have not been reported. Thus any attempt to distinguish between smell and taste merely on the basis of the physical state of the stimulating substances is clearly inadvisable.

It has been proposed[24,37,48] that taste and smell may be discriminated in aquatic organisms on the basis of receptor sensitivity and behavior of the whole animal. Threshold concentrations of substances stimulating olfactory receptors in air-dwelling vertebrates are, in general, much lower than thresholds of gustatory substances. Although there is some overlap with the most stimulating sapid substances and the least effective odorous substances, this does not invalidate the general concept. This appears to be valid not only for man and other mammals but also for aquatic vertebrates, terrestrial insects, and for the amphibious insect discussed above. Likewise, olfactory stimuli usually elicit behavioral patterns in the nature of taxes or kineses (Chapter 10). That is, the organism responds as if the source of stimulating molecules is at some distance. On the other hand, behavioral responses to sapid substances are generally oriented to the immediate environment. Thus, the organism exhibits feeding reactions such as chewing, grasping and carrying objects to the mouth or, in other cases, shows specialized activity like oviposition or mating movements.

These are certainly not absolute criteria, but the existence of receptors analogous to vertebrate and insect olfactory and gustatory sense organs may be at least suspected in those Crustacea which respond to chemical stimulation with one or both of these behavior patterns. However, senses of taste and smell analogous to those of vertebrates and insects have been denied in Crustacea on the grounds that all of the known chemically receptive fields in Crustacea respond to both odorous and sapid substances.[57] Nevertheless, there may be more than one kind of receptor, perhaps analogous to taste and smell, located within the same sensory field. And recall that the physical state of stimulating substances does not provide a valid distinction between olfaction and gustation. Furthermore, there are abundant behavioral observations on Crustacea which do suggest at least partly independent olfactory and gustatory chemoreception.[56,57]

Illustrative of this kind of observation are those on *Crangon cran-*

gon.[54] When the antennules are stimulated under water without affecting any other part of the body, only awakening or alarm reactions result. These contrast with the food-seeking and feeding movements evoked by similar stimulation of other areas of the body. The methods used do not reveal a threshold difference between the antennules and the rest of the body, but this may be due to the existence of olfactory receptors on other body parts as well. There are, however, wide threshold differences between substances that generally stimulate olfactory receptors and those that normally are considered odorless but are effective stimuli for taste receptors. Thus, threshold concentrations of cumarin and vanillin were 0.0001–0.00005%, while that of acetic acid was 0.01%; saccharin, 0.5–0.1%; NaCl, 1.3–7.15%; and quinine chloride, 0.001–0.0005%.

Nevertheless, it has been maintained that taste and smell are not differentiated in *Crangon* because both odorous and sapid substances stimulate the antennules and because extirpation of the latter does not alter the threshold.[54] Support for this notion is sought in the failure to find more than one morphological type of chemoreceptor on the antennule. However, morphologically indistinguishable receptors may indeed have widely different response properties.[32] Thus the results on *Crangon* mentioned above and on other decapods[56,57] are sufficiently suggestive to warrant a reappraisal of these concepts in Crustacea.

In view of the foregoing uncertainties it is not surprising that there is no evidence for the presence of specific receptors corresponding to the four taste modalities of mammals. However, there are some data suggesting a functional differentiation of what may be provisionally designated as taste receptors. There is also some evidence for the existence in Crustacea of the so-called common chemical sense.[24,48] Experiments with *Orconectes limosus*[10] show that high concentrations of several substances (acetic acid 10%, HCl 1%, NaCl 36%, and sugar 40%) evoke movements of the body when the solutions, colored with eosin or carmine, reach the exoskeleton. However, the existence of a common chemical sense in the animal kingdom has been questioned on several grounds.[56,57] Whether or not the concept is a valid one, the data for Crustacea do not help to resolve the matter.

Behavioral experiments indicate that five different kinds of "taste" receptors may be present on the cirriped, *Balanus balanoides*.[19,20] Under normal conditions in running sea water the cirri of most of a given population of barnacles exhibit a constant rhythmic movement. Introduction of chemicals to the flowing sea water in threshold concentrations results in a change in the rate or character, or both, of the cirral movements. Stronger stimulation results in withdrawal of the cirri and closure of the valves. In a population of individuals it is possible to determine the percentage of animals closed by a predetermined exposure to a chemical of known concentration. Such measurements make it possible to compare quantitatively the stimulating effectiveness of various chemicals or different concentrations of the same chemical.

When organic and inorganic acids, such as HCl, H_2SO_4, HNO_3, and the low-carbon aliphatic acids were used as stimulating agents, the stimulating effectiveness of any one acid increased sharply with rise in hydrogen ion concentration $[H^+]$.[19] A plot of per cent closure against log $[H^+]$ for each acid yielded a compound sigmoid curve. If a single population of receptors had been stimulated, a single sigmoid curve should have resulted. If, however, more than one group of receptors had been responding, compound curves would have resulted and the number of groups responding should have appeared in the number of sigmoid curves summated. In order to determine the number of summated curves in each case the differential of each compound sigmoid curve was plotted against log $[H^+]$, and a series of trimodal distribution curves resulted. Thus the closing response in the population appears to be mediated by three groups of chemoreceptors which differ in their quantitative response characteristics. It is not possible from the data to determine whether the three groups of receptors are each present on the same individual or whether there existed in the population three groups of individuals differing in their kind of chemoreceptors.

Another type of barnacle response occurs when populations are stimulated by the sodium and potassium salts of the mineral acids and by the nonelectrolytes urea, glucose, and glycerol.[20] These chemicals initiated the common closing effect already described but, when used in concentrations below closure threshold, they caused an opening response. In each population of barnacles it was observed that a significant and constant percentage of the animals were closed prior to chemical stimulation. A closure effect was, therefore, observed as an increase, and an opening effect as a decrease, in this number. For each of the substances tested there were thus two thresholds: a lower threshold below which neither an opening or closing response was obtained and above which opening was observed within a narrow range of concentrations; at the upper end of the latter range was the threshold for the closure effect above which only closure occurs.

When per cent of animals open is plotted against concentration for each substance, similar-shaped curves are obtained. The symmetry of the curves and their similarity indicates that one group of receptors mediates the closing response and another group the opening response to all of the salts and nonelectrolytes tested. The opening effect is not produced by acids and it is not possible to say whether the receptor groups mediating closure to acids are the same as the group mediating closure to salts and nonelectrolytes. However, five groups of receptors may be present on a single individual. These obviously cannot be considered analogous to the taste modalities of mammals. But recall that the taste modalities of lower vertebrates and insects also do not correspond to those of mammals.[23] In insects two taste modalities, acceptable and unacceptable, have been distinguished. Additional work may permit their further subdivision, but it is unlikely that a correspondence with the mammalian categories will result.

2. *Thresholds.* Threshold concentrations of stimulating substances measured by behavioral experiments vary widely with the methods used, and the values are not usually directly comparable. Thus, von Buddenbrock[56] compared the results obtained by three investigators from three different organisms. Values obtained with *Crangon* for "odorous substances," cumarin and vanillin, are in the range of 10^{-4} to $10^{-5}\%$ and, for sapid substances such as acetic acid, saccharin, and NaCl, from just under 10% to $10^{-2}\%$. On the other hand, thresholds lower than these by a factor of 1000 have been obtained with *Carcinus*. These results were obtained by observing the kinds of behavioral reactions described above. In *Pagurus*, however, training experiments yield thresholds comparable to those of *Carcinus*, whereas the thresholds for untrained animals are closer to those of *Crangon*.

Of particular interest are experiments comparing threshold concentrations of homologous series of compounds. This approach has been exploited, particularly in insects,[21] to determine the relationship between stimulating effectiveness and chemical properties, and thus provide some clue as to the nature of the stimulatory process. Although many factors unrelated to the events occurring at the receptor surface may modify the response being observed, certain homologous series of compounds have allowed the demonstration of a correlation between stimulating effectiveness and such molecular properties as boiling point, oil-water distribution coefficient, vapor pressure, and others.[21] The behavioral criteria used are usually complex ones. For example, Dethier and his co-workers measured the concentration of aliphatic compounds needed to suppress a feeding response to a given concentration of sugar when the two solutions are applied at the same time to the tarsal chemoreceptors of flies. Similar correlations have been obtained in an aquatic insect.[31]

The data for Crustacea are not extensive enough to compare directly with those for insects. There are enough figures, however, to suggest that further investigation would be fruitful. It has been shown in insects[21-23] that, within the homologous series of certain aliphatic substances, stimulating efficiency increases logarithmically with increase in carbon chain length. Data from *Balanus* using aliphatic alcohols indicate that the same general rule may apply to Crustacea, too.[18] Experiments with *Daphnia* and copepods are also consistent with this idea.[42] This similarity of responses to aliphatic alcohols is illustrated in Table 1. The *Balanus* thresholds are given as concentrations needed to elicit a recognizable change in cirral beating rhythm. Those for *Daphnia* and copepods represent concentrations required to reverse a positive phototaxis. No special significance can be assigned to the wide threshold differences exhibited among the forms represented in Table 1, since the techniques of measurement

TABLE 1

Comparison of Chemoreceptor Thresholds for Normal Aliphatic Alcohols in Crustaceans and Insects (*Laccophilus* and *Phormia*)

Alcohol	*Balanus*[18]	*Daphnia*[42]	Copepods[42]	*Laccophilus*[31]	*Phormia*[24]
Methyl	0.06[a]	—	—	3.6	11.3
Ethyl	0.017	0.2	0.19	4.3	3.2
Propyl	0.0067	0.05–0.1	0.054	3.2	1.3
Butyl	0.0027	0.04	0.019	0.046	0.64
Amyl	—	—	0.011	0.0073	0.10
Hexyl	—	—	—	0.0011	0.012

[a] All concentrations are molar.

varied so greatly. On the other hand, the similarity of the results with respect to carbon chain length suggests that there may be a mechanism in the stimulatory process common to all of them.

Acid stimulation of *Balanus* chemoreceptors has yielded results similar to those observed on insects and mammals. For example, in all three groups the hydrogen ion is a major constituent of the stimulus by organic acids, but, in addition, the anion or undissociated molecule contributes significantly to the response.[19,21,23] The contribution of the anion is proportional to carbon chain length, although some exceptions to this appear in the crustacean data.

It should be possible to obtain absolute threshold values electrophysiologically by finding the lowest concentration of a substance which will elicit a measurable electrical response from a single receptor unit. This has been done for one compound, the amino acid glycine, in *Limulus polyphemus*, a chelicerate arthropod (Fig. 6).[5,6] Correlation of stimulating effectiveness, measured electrophysiologically, with chemical properties would provide helpful comparisons with similar correlations made with thresholds determined behaviorally.

3. *Discrimination.* There is abundant evidence that Crustacea discriminate among a variety of different chemicals. For example, some of the entomostracan Crustacea, such as Cladocera, Copepoda, Ostracoda, and Anostraca, have been observed to accept some food particles and reject others or to handle different particles in different ways.[11,49,53]

Isopods have developed a specific sensitivity to moisture which they appear to distinguish from all other stimuli. *Porcellio scaber* typically aggregates at the moist end of a humidity gradient by virtue of hygrokinetic and hygrotactic behavior, as does the myrmecophilous species, *Platyarthus hoffmannseggi*.[12] The head and abdomen have apparently been eliminated in *Porcellio* as possible sites for the receptors involved, but this was not possible in the case of the thorax without physically impeding locomotion. Similar responses occur in *Oniscus asellus* and *Armadillidium vulgare* also. It has been suggested that the receptor mechanism might be internal and sensitive to increased osmotic pressure of body fluids concentrated by evaporation.[15,58] The isopod *Ligia occidentalis* follows the tide in and out, as do other related species.[1] This suggests that an optimum humidity is being selected through the tidal cycle.

The littoral isopod, *Ligia baudiniana*, appears to distinguish distilled water from sea water, NaCl, KCl, $CaCl_2$, and LiCl.[7,8] Thresholds for this discrimination were determined for NaCl to be between 0.3 and 0.47 M; for KCl, between 0.03 and 0.06 M. *Ligia* can also distinguish isotonic solutions of $CaCl_2$ from NaCl, but not $CaCl_2$ from LiCl. The stimulation seems to occur in the legs since the animals respond when they merely run over filter paper soaked with the appropriate substances. *Platyarthus hoffmannseggi* is attracted to formic acid but is indifferent to acetic acid and repelled by propionic acid.[12]

In the Cirripedia, as mentioned above, acids appear to be discriminated from all other kinds of chemical stimuli, since acids do not

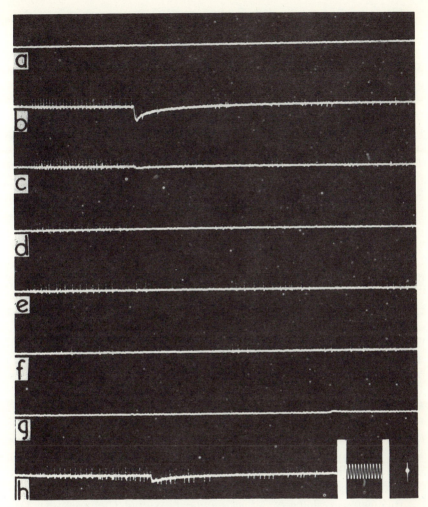

Fig. 6. Electrophysiological responses of *Limulus* chemoreceptors. Measurement of threshold to glycine. Receptors stimulated are located on coxal gnathobase spines of *Limulus* walking legs. Recordings made from a fine bundle of the gnathobase nerve. Large deflections of base line in "b" and "h" are mechanical artifacts. a. No response to sea water. b. Intermittent bursts of action potentials from two receptor units when spines were stimulated with the juice from minced clams. c. Response of a single unit to 0.5 *M* glycine in sea water is similar to the response from minced clams. d. Response of the same unit to 0.1 *M* glycine shows a lower action potential frequency than the previous response. e. and f. Responses of the same unit to 0.05 and 0.01 *M* glycine, respectively, exhibit a progressive decline in impulse frequency. g. No response to 0.001 *M* glycine. Threshold lies between 0.01 and 0.001 *M* glycine. h. Response, as in "b," of the same two fibers to minced clam juice. Calibration: time, 60 cycles/sec sine wave; voltage 500 microvolt deflection.

stimulate the receptors that mediate the opening response. On the other hand, a great variety of substances bring about the closing response.[16-20]

In *Carcinus* chemical stimulation of the antennules or thoracic appendages elicits similar behavioral responses regardless of the nature of the stimulating substances. Thus *Carcinus* reacts to filter paper soaked with stimulating chemicals by bringing it to the mouth for feeding. Only then are attractant and repellent stimuli distinguished. For example, paper soaked with meat juice is eaten, whereas that soaked with acetic acid is rejected, after contact with mouth parts. The receptors mediating the feeding responses are designated as belonging to the "outer" chemical sense. Those responsible for discrimination belong to the "inner" chemical sense.[43] As von Buddenbrock[56] has pointed out, however, substances are accepted or rejected in part at least on the basis of the animal's condition. Hungry animals will eat paper soaked in chemicals that are rejected by animals that have just fed. Nevertheless, this is not to deny that discrimination does occur.

However, other observations on *Carcinus*, under different conditions of stimulation, have shown that the chemoreceptors of the legs and chelae can differentiate a number of substances from each other.[43] On repeated stimulation with one substance, such as cumarin, the animal finally ceases to react to it. Then, when another substance is offered, it will be grasped if it can be distinguished from the cumarin. In this way, it has been shown that *Carcinus* does not distinguish cumarin and vanillin from each other but does distinguish them from typical sapid substances. Among the latter, it can be shown that *Carcinus* can differentiate sugar from acetic acid and NaCl from acetic acid by similar experimental procedures. These observations imply that discrimination may be mediated by the outer chemical sense under certain conditions of stimulation but not under others.

In electrophysiological experiments individual chemosensory hairs on the chelae and legs of *Cambarus* respond with increased action potential discharges to stimulation by solutions of amino acids but not to similar concentrations of sucrose, ethyl alcohol, or NaCl.[34] Similarly in *Limulus* certain receptor units respond to glycine but not to alanine and other amino acids.[5,6] Thus peripheral mechanisms for discrimination are evident in the electrical studies.

In the crab *Dissodactylus mellitae*, which is a commensal of the sand dollar *Mellita quinquiesperforata*, stimulation and orientation are effected by a substance produced by the host.[38] However, little is yet known of the chemoreceptor mechanisms involved here.

D. SUMMARY

It is clear that chemoreception must play a significant role in the normal behavior of Crustacea. Chemical stimuli may be the dominant initiating and directing influence in such activities as food seeking, feeding, mating, and migration. Now that the difficulties of electrophysiological recording in invertebrates are being overcome, more precise information on the contribution of chemoreceptor stimulation to specific behavior patterns than has hitherto been available should become known. Data such as absolute thresholds, latencies, and magnitude of responses of single receptor units may be forthcoming. From such data the afferent information being supplied the central nervous system by a single receptor or sensory field may be quantitatively assayed and its influence on particular behavior patterns more closely analyzed. So far, behavior patterns have been our main clue to chemoreceptor activities in invertebrates, and much useful information has been obtained in this way. Even though their predominant position in the field may now be reversed, behavioral techniques should prove even more valuable than before when supplemented by the more direct method of study.

Significant progress has been made in analyzing the mechanism of chemoreception at the molecular level, and data from insect receptors have been particularly helpful in the analysis.[23] Such studies may well serve as a stimulus and model for those interested in chemoreceptor functions in Crustacea, especially since several functional similarities between the receptors from the two groups are already apparent.

II. *THERMORECEPTION*

A. INTRODUCTION

This is probably the most neglected area of crustacean sensory physiology. However, significant advances have been made in the study of vertebrate thermal receptors,[14,28] and occasional progress has been reported among some invertebrate groups.[50] Since there is evidence that Crustacea aggregate or respond with kineses or taxes to temperature gradients, as well as exhibit temperature acclimation, one or more forms of temperature-sensitive devices may be presumed to mediate such responses.

Behavioral effects of temperature, such as orientation or acclimation, may be due to one or more of several different mechanisms (Chapters 2 and 12, Vol. I). Temperature may serve not only as a stimulus for specific end organs but also for centers in the central nervous system; in addition, temperature may affect the total metabolism of the body, the metabolism of specific central nerve centers or of peripheral receptors sensitive to other stimulus modalities. One or more nonspecific effects are believed to operate in some vertebrates and insects.[13,25,33,50] On the other hand, specific thermal receptors have been conclusively demonstrated in several vertebrate classes and invertebrate phyla.[25,28,50]

The mere presence of a temperature-compensating mechanism in an animal may be adequate evidence for the existence of specialized temperature receptors.[13] These might be absolute, nonadapting temperature receptors, in contrast with receptors which register only change in temperature. Any neural element which registers specific impulse frequencies at given temperature levels might conceivably function in this way. Consequently, this function could be served by receptors ordinarily believed to be concerned solely with other stimulus modalities, or by certain regions of the central nervous system which faithfully register temperature.

Primary chemoreceptors of insects display two types of temperature sensitivity in electrophysiological studies.[33,35] Some preparations respond to warming of the entire preparation by more rapid action potential frequencies, whereas others yield a decrease in the impulse frequency. These changes are observed during constant chemical stimulation of the single receptor but cannot be evoked by temperature changes applied by warming the stimulating chemical solution. Therefore, the temperature effects are mediated in the neuron at a site other than that concerned with chemoreception. This constitutes direct evidence that the modulation of the response of a receptor unit to other stimuli may provide a mechanism for temperature reception.[33]

B. RESPONSES TO THERMAL STIMULI

In arthropods, in general, it is believed that the antennae and other appendages are especially sensitive to temperature changes. There are few observations to establish this in Crustacea. Land isopods such as *Oniscus asellus* and *Porcellio scaber* have been observed to react from a distance to a warmed glass rod and to lose this reaction upon amputation of the antennae.[29] On the other hand, crayfish do not appear to react to much more intense thermal stimuli. Other aquatic decapods have failed to react to warming of the water until it reached a level of 40°C.[29] Members of some other crustacean orders have been observed to behave in relation to thermal stimuli as if they have thermal receptors, but these observations are not supported by any evidence on the anatomical site of the sensitivity.

In Cladocera *Daphnia pulex* orients toward the cooler end of a total thermal gradient as shallow as 1°C.[59] This reaction might have been entirely an orthokinetic or klinokinetic type of response and, therefore, possibly mediated by other than specific thermal receptors, but this cannot be determined from the brief description given. On the other hand, more direct orienting behavior of *Daphnia longispina* to abrupt temperature changes has been described.[51] These stimuli cause changes in vertical disposition of groups of individuals. Rapid temperature rise (actual values not given) results in a rapid and direct movement downward, whereas a similar fall in temperature causes a less rapid movement upward. The response to temperature rise as described suggests a tactic type of orienting behavior.

Aggregation of the anostracan, *Eubranchipus serratus*, in a preferred thermal zone has been observed.[44] In a gradient ranging from 8°C to 30°C the majority of the organisms at any time were present in the zone between 14 and 17°C. An aggregative effect of temperature has also been observed in the parasitic "carp louse," *Argulus foliaceus* (Order Branchiura), which lives on the skin of fresh-water fish.[30] It aggregates in the 29–30°C zone in a gradient ranging from 18.5 to 34.5°C. This thermal effect is superimposed on a gravity response which tends to keep the individuals at a lower level in the container. Such behavior is observable during a free-swimming stage in the life history.

Isopod aggregations are also affected by temperature changes.[2] Land isopods (*Oniscus asellus* and *Cylisticus convexus*) aggregate in bunches, or disperse, in response to changes in the water content of the substratum. But sudden changes in temperature (10°–20°C) cause bunches to scatter or scattered animals to group together. This kind of reaction may very well depend on the effect of the temperature change on general metabolism or on the nervous system as a whole.

Larval crustaceans have been observed to orient relative to thermal gradients. Zoeas of an undesignated species moved away from a high-temperature zone with lively swimming movements. The entire thermal gradient was 18 to 30°C. The description of their behavior suggests a tactic orientation.[52] Seasonal and diurnal migrations of planktonic crustaceans (Chapter 12) may be partly or wholly determined by temperature gradients and variations.[29,41,45,46,49,52] Temperature changes have been reported to reverse the sign of orientation to other stimuli such as light and gravity.[9,11,47] As in isopod aggregation, these effects may be due to metabolic changes, although the intervention of specific thermal receptors has not been ruled out.

Temperature-compensating mechanisms are widespread in various crustaceans (Chapter 12, Vol. I) so that the presence of a nonadapting temperature receiving system in many members of the class is indicated.[13] As yet, however, there is no evidence available for localizing and identifying such a mechanism.

C. Summary

The importance of Crustacea in the economy of marine and fresh-water environments should be a compelling stimulus for more thorough analyses of their thermal receiving mechanisms. Appropriate behavioral techniques are available and, at least for the larger forms, suitable analytical electrophysiological methods can be applied. In view of the theoretical and practical interest of the whole problem, it is to be hoped that significant progress in this field can be made in the near future.

Acknowledgment

Aided by a grant (B1389) from the National Institute for Neurological Diseases and Blindness, Bethesda, Maryland.

References

1. Abbott, C. H. 1939. Shore isopods; niches occupied, and degrees of transition toward land life with special reference to the family Ligydidae. *Proc. 7th Pacific Sci. Congr.* 3:505–511.
2. Allee, W. C. 1931. "Animal Aggregations," 431 pp. University of Chicago Press, Chicago.
3. Balss, H. 1913. Über die Chemorezeption bei Garneelen. *Biol. Zentr.* 33:508–512.
4. Balss, H. 1944. Decapoda. *In:* "Bronn's Tierreich," Bd. 5, Abt. 1, Bch. 7, Lfg. 3, pp. 363–369. Akademische Verlagsges., Leipzig.
5. Barber, S. B. 1954. Chemoreception in *Limulus polyphemus* (L.). 111 pp. Ph.D. Thesis, Yale University, New Haven, Connecticut.
6. Barber, S. B. 1956. Chemoreception and proprioception in *Limulus. J. Exptl. Zool.* 131:51–73.
7. Barnes, T. C. 1939. Experiments on *Ligia* in Bermuda. VI. Reactions to common cations. *Biol. Bull.* 76:121–126.
8. Barnes, T. C. 1940. Experiments on *Ligia* in Bermuda. VII. Further effects of sodium, ammonium and magnesium. *Biol. Bull.* 78:35–41.
9. Baylor, E. R., and Smith, F. E. 1957. Diurnal migration of plankton crustaceans. *In:* "Recent Advances in Invertebrate Physiology" (B. T. Scheer, ed.), pp. 21–35. University of Oregon Publications, Eugene.
10. Bell, J. C. 1906. The reactions of crayfish to chemical stimuli. *J. Comp. Neurol.* 16:299–326.

11. Birge, E. A. 1918. The water fleas (Cladocera). *In:* "Fresh-Water Biology" (H. B. Ward and G. C. Whipple, eds.), pp. 676–688. Wiley, New York.
12. Brooks, J. L. 1942. Notes on the ecology and the occurrence in America of the myrmecophilous sawbug, *Platyarthus hoffmannseggi* Brandt. *Ecology* 23:427–437.
13. Bullock, T. H. 1955. Compensation for temperature in the metabolism and activity of poikilotherms. *Biol. Revs. Cambridge Phil. Soc.* 30:311–342.
14. Bullock, T. H., and Diecke, F. P. J. 1956. Properties of an infra-red receptor. *J. Physiol. (London)* 134:47–87.
15. Cloudsley-Thompson, J. L. 1956. Studies in diurnal rhythms. VII. Humidity responses and nocturnal activity in woodlice (Isopoda). *J. Exptl. Biol.* 33:576–582.
16. Cole, W. H. 1932a. The sensitivity of the cirri and the variability of their movements in the barnacles *Balanus tintinabulum* and *B. balanoides*. *J. Exptl. Zool.* 63:143–153.
17. Cole, W. H. 1932b. Stimulation by the salts of the normal aliphatic acids in the rock barnacle *Balanus balanoides*. *J. Gen. Physiol.* 15:611–620.
18. Cole, W. H., and Allison, J. B. 1930. Chemical stimulation by alcohols in the barnacle, the frog and planaria. *J. Gen. Physiol.* 14:71–86.
19. Cole, W. H., and Allison, J. B. 1933. Stimulation by mineral and fatty acids in the barnacle *Balanus balanoides*. *J. Gen. Physiol.* 16:895–903.
20. Cole, W. H., and Allison, J. B. 1937. Responses of the barnacle to some strong electrolytes and to urea, glucose, and glycerol. *Physiol. Zoöl.* 10:405–411.
21. Dethier, V. G. 1953. Chemoreception. *In:* "Insect Physiology" (K. D. Roeder, ed.), pp. 544–576. Wiley, New York.
22. Dethier, V. G. 1955. The physiology and histology of the contact chemoreceptors of the blow-fly. *Quart. Rev. Biol.* 30:348–371.
23. Dethier, V. G. 1956. Chemoreceptor mechanisms. *In:* "Molecular Structure and Functional Activity of Nerve Cells" (R. G. Grenell and L. J. Mullins, eds.), pp. 1–33. American Institute of Biological Sciences, Washington, D.C.
24. Dethier, V. G., and Chadwick, L. E. 1948. Chemoreception in insects. *Physiol. Revs.* 28:220–254.
25. Fraenkel, G. S., and Gunn, D. L. 1940. "The Orientation of Animals," 352 pp. Clarendon Press, Oxford.
26. Gunn, D. L. 1937. The humidity reactions of the woodlouse, *Porcellio scaber* (Latreille). *J. Exptl. Biol.* 14:178–186.
27. Hanström, B. 1928. "Vergleichende Anatomie des Nervensystems der wirbellosen Tiere," 628 pp. Springer, Berlin.
28. Hensel, H. 1952. Physiologie der Thermorezeption. *Ergeb. Physiol. biol. Chem. u. exptl. Pharmakol.* 47:166–368.
29. Herter, K. 1925. "Tastsinn, Strömungssinn und Temperatursinn der Tiere und die diesen Sinnen zugeordneten Reaktionen," 182 pp. Borntraeger, Berlin.
30. Herter, K. 1927. Reizphysiologische Untersuchungen an der Karpfenlaus (*Argulus foliaceus* L.). *Z. vergleich. Physiol.* 5:283–370.
31. Hodgson, E. S. 1951. Reaction thresholds of an aquatic beetle, *Laccophilus maculosus* Germ., to salts and alcohols. *Physiol. Zoöl.* 24:131–140.
32. Hodgson, E. S. 1953. A study of chemoreception in aqueous and gas phases. *Biol. Bull.* 105:115–127.
33. Hodgson, E. S. 1956. Temperature sensitivity of primary chemoreceptors of insects. *Anat. Record* 125:560–561.

34. Hodgson, E. S. 1957. A comparative electrophysiological analysis of chemoreceptors in arthropods. *Anat. Record* **128:**565–566.

34a.Hodgson, E. S. 1958. Electrophysiological studies of arthropod chemoreception.
III. Chemoreceptors of terrestrial and fresh-water arthropods. *Biol. Bull.* **115:**114–
125.

35. Hodgson, E. S., and Roeder, K. D. 1956. Electrophysiological studies of arthropod chemoreception. I. General properties of the labellar chemoreceptors of
Diptera. *J. Cellular Comp. Physiol.* **48:**51–75.

36. Holmes, S. J., and Homuth, E. S. 1910. The seat of smell in the crayfish. *Biol.
Bull.* **18:**155–160.

37. Jahn, T. L., and Wulff, V. J. 1950. Chemoreception. *In:* "Comparative Animal
Physiology" (C. L. Prosser, ed.), pp. 447–470. Saunders, Philadelphia.

38. Johnson, I. S. 1952. The demonstration of host factor in commensal crabs.
Trans. Kansas Acad. Sci. **55:**458–464.

39. Krijgsman, B. J., and Krijgsman, N. E. 1954. Osmorezeption in *Jasus lalandii.*
Z. vergleich. Physiol. **37:**78–81.

40. Kükenthal, W., and Krumbach, T. (eds.) 1926. "Handbuch der Zoologie.
Crustacea," Bd. 3, Hälfte 1, 1158 pp. de Gruyter, Berlin.

41. Lloyd, A. J., and Yonge, C. M. 1947. The biology of *Crangon vulgaris* L. in the
Bristol Channel and Severn Estuary. *J. Marine Biol. Assoc. United Kingdom*
26:626–661.

42. Loeb, J. 1918. "Forced Movements, Tropisms, and Animal Conduct," 209 pp.
Lippincott, Philadelphia.

43. Luther, W. 1930. Versuche über die Chemorezeption der Brachyuren. *Z.
vergleich. Physiol.* **12:**177–205.

44. McGinnis, M. O. 1911. Reactions of *Branchipus serratus* to light, heat and
gravity. *J. Exptl. Zool.* **10:**227–240.

45. Marsh, C. D. 1918. Copepoda. *In:* "Fresh-Water Biology" (H. B. Ward and
G. C. Whipple, eds.), pp. 741–755. Wiley, New York.

46. Marshall, S. M., and Orr, A. P. 1955. "Biology of a Marine Copepod," 188 pp.
Oliver and Boyd, London.

47. Parker, G. H. 1901. Reactions of copepods to various stimuli and the bearing of
this on daily depth migrations. *Bull. U. S. Fish Comm.* **21:**103–123.

48. Parker, G. H. 1922. "Smell, Taste, and Allied Senses in the Vertebrates," 192
pp. Lippincott, Philadelphia.

49. Pennak, R. W. 1953. "Fresh-Water Invertebrates of the United States," 769
pp. Randall Press, New York.

50. Prosser, C. L. 1950. Temperature: metabolic aspects and perception. *In:* "Comparative Animal Physiology" (C. L. Prosser, ed.), pp. 341–380. Saunders,
Philadelphia.

51. Rose, M. 1910. Sur quelques tropismes. *Compt. rend.* **150:**1543–1545.

52. Schmid, B. 1911. Ein Versuch über die Wärmeempfindlichkeit von Zoea-Larven.
Biol. Zentr. **31:**538.

53. Seifert, R. 1930. Sinnesphysiologische Untersuchungen am Kiemenfuss (*Triops
cancriformis* Bosc). *Z. vergleich. Physiol.* **11:**386–436.

54. Spiegel, A. 1927. Über die Chemorezeption von *Crangon vulgaris* Fabr. *Z.
vergleich. Physiol.* **6:**688–730.

55. Van Heerdt, P. F., and Krijgsman, B. J. 1939. Die Regulierung der Atmung
bei *Eriocheir sinensis* Milne Edwards. *Z. vergleich. Physiol.* **27:**20–40.

56. von Buddenbrock, W. 1945. Physiologie der Decapoden. *In:* "Bronn's Tierreich," Bd. 5, Abt. 1, Bch. 7, Lfg. 7, pp. 913–921. Akademische Verlagsges., Leipzig.
57. von Buddenbrock, W. 1952. Sinnesphysiologie. *In:* "Vergleichende Physiologie," Bd. 1, 504 pp. Birkhäuser, Basel.
58. Waloff, N. 1941. The mechanisms of humidity reactions of terrestrial isopods. *J. Exptl. Biol.* **18:**115–135.
59. Yerkes, R. M. 1903. Reactions of *Daphnia pulex* to light and heat. *In:* "Mark Anniversary Volume" (G. H. Parker, ed.), pp. 359–377. Holt, New York.

CHAPTER 4

LEWIS H. KLEINHOLZ

PIGMENTARY EFFECTORS

I. *INTRODUCTION*

A. CHROMATOPHORES

Two types of pigmentary effectors occur in crustaceans: the chromatophores, found chiefly in the integument underlying the exoskeleton, and the pigments of the compound eye. These will be described briefly in the introductory section, but their physiology will be considered in greater detail under separate headings.

Chromatophores have been classified by several features. Histologically, the distinction can be made between unicellular chromatophores and those which are multicellular or syncytial. A second distinction depends on whether granules of only one pigment (monochromatic) or of two (dichromatic) or more (polychromatic) pigments are included in the cytoplasm of the chromatophore. The most commonly used classification is based on the color of the chromatophore's pigment, whence the terms melanophores (containing dark brown or black pigment), xanthophores (yellow), erythrophores (red), and guanophores (white). Not much is known of the chemical nature of the pigment in various chromatophore types, but there is little basis for believing that chromatophore behavior depends on the nature of the contained pigment; thus their color names are merely descriptive. In recent studies more detailed specification of the chromatophore types has been found desirable.

The chromatophore system of a species is characterized not only by the particular types of chromatophores in its integument but also by their specific patterns of distribution; moreover, within a species

133

like *Palaemon serratus* these patterns may show enough geographic variation that individuals from different parts of the range can be distinguished from each other.[34] Also within a single species, chromatophores of a given color type may differ in their chromatic behavior depending on their location on the body.[23,33,80]

The formation and destruction of pigment in a crustacean results in a morphological color change[17,52]; such changes are relatively slow in occurrence, and little is known of the mechanisms effecting them. The much more commonly investigated crustacean metachrosis deals with physiological changes that occur relatively rapidly, within a matter of minutes or hours. They are brought about by a centrifugal or centripetal streaming of the cytoplasm bearing the pigment granules within the arborescent processes that extend from the central body of the chromatophore into the adjacent tissues. The dark or strongly colored phase results when the pigment is maximally dispersed through these chromatophore processes, and the light phase when the pigment withdraws into a concentrated mass near the center of the cell body. In the latter situation the pigment appears as small dots and the chromatophores are then described as punctate. Intermediate conditions between maximum dispersion and complete concentration occur normally. The degree of pigment expansion or contraction has frequently been indicated by an arbitrary series of numbered stages, a method introduced by Hogben and his collaborators[61] in studies of color change in amphibians. This method has also been extended to include the duration of chromatophore response in quantitative studies.

Physiological color changes due to movements of chromatophoral pigments have been reported only in the malacostracans, and most recent experimental studies of color change have been restricted to the decapod macrurans and brachyurans. Few color-changing species are known among entomostracans; the metachrosis which occurs in some copepods has been reported to be due to iridescence caused by microcrystals in the integument, rather than by chromatophores.

B. Retinal Pigments

The principal photoreceptors of higher crustaceans are sessile or stalked compound eyes whose structural unit is the ommatidium (Chapter 1). Although their number and morphological detail may vary considerably in different species, all ommatidia are of the same basic general structure. Each possesses a corneal lens, a crystalline cone, and a rhabdom surrounded by a cluster of retinular cells. Each ommatidium also has three sets of pigments, conveniently distinguished in the recent literature as distal, proximal, and reflecting, in contrast with a more varied synonomy found in the older papers. The cells containing these pigments may respond to changes in illumination by photomechanical movements, but such ability may vary substantially with different species. Thus in *Palaemonetes* all three retinal pigments show photomechanical movements; in *Pacifastacus trowbridgii* the reflecting pigment is fixed in position, while the distal and the proximal elements move in response to light and to darkness; in *Homarus americanus* only the proximal retinal pigment shows such changes.

The mechanisms of these movements have not been thoroughly studied, but two general types have been described for the distal pigment. In one, as seen in *Palaemonetes*, the distal pigment cells, which form a sheath around the distal portion of the central refractive apparatus, move as a whole along the ommatidial axis, probably through the action of contractile fibrils.[119] In the other type as seen in *Cambarus*,[121] the main body of the distal pigment cell is located at the level of the crystalline cone, and the pigment granules move, supposedly by protoplasmic streaming, within processes which extend from the distal cell bodies toward the basal portion of the retina. Even less is known about the mechanism of movement in the other two sets of pigments, but protoplasmic streaming and ameboid movement have been suggested.

II. *CHROMATOPHORES*

A. CHROMATOPHORE RESPONSES

1. *To illuminated backgrounds.* Crustaceans differ in their chromatophore responses to illuminated backgrounds. In one group including the caridean prawns *Palaemonetes* and *Crangon* the abundance and distribution of the polychromatic chromatophores permit adaptive changes to background color.[18,19,83] In a second group including the isopods and brachyurans the predominance of monochromatic chromatophores restricts their metachrosis mainly to darkening and lightening. Thus in isopods,[51,66,92,110,114] where the melanophore is the chief component of the pigmentary system, the animal changes its shade in response to illuminated black or white backgrounds, but does not appreciably change its color through the activity of the lesser chromatophoral components. Similarly in brachyurans the deposits of extrachromatophoral pigment in the exoskeleton and epidermis coupled with the dominance of guanophores apparently prevent striking color

changes even though various background colors may evoke a full range of chromatophore responses from complete dispersion to full contraction.[1,60]

A third group includes the fiddler crab, *Uca*, whose dominant melanophores show a great range between pigment dispersion and concentration in a diurnal-nocturnal periodicity[2,30] but the melanophore response is insignificant with respect to backgrounds.[27] *Uca pugilator*, however, also possesses erythrophores that respond strongly to black and to white backgrounds.[21]

2. *To darkness and to light.* In darkness the erythrophores of most color-changing Natantia are in the concentrated state. A similar contraction of melanophores at night or in darkness is reported for some Reptantia[2,38] and Isopoda,[51,66,114] although in some of these the response may be complicated by the persistent diurnal rhythm of chromatophores (Chapter 11). Direct responses of chromatophores to light and to darkness have been reported for a number of species[26,74-76,78] (Fig. 1), but the evidence that they act as independent effectors is incomplete in some of these cases.

B. Mechanisms Regulating Chromatophores

1. *Historical background.* During the latter part of the nineteenth century and the first two decades of the present century the chromatophores were thought to be directly innervated and regulated by the nervous system. This conclusion was suggested largely by the observation that the normal color change of the animal ceased after removal of the eyestalks. But the more direct test of chromatophore innervation by sectioning the ventral nerve cord usually failed to support this view.

The first indication of a possible humoral agent in chromatophore activity was made by Koller,[82,83] who showed that blood from *Crangon*, adapted to a black background, caused melanophore dispersion in animals adapted to a white background; the converse experiment, transfer of blood from white-adapted to black-adapted *Crangon*, was without effect. Blood from individuals adapted to a yellow background also dispersed the xanthophores in white-adapted individuals. At about the same time Perkins[104] investigated the physiology of color changes in *Palaemonetes*. He found that, although cutting the ventral nerve cord had no effect on background adaptation, occluding the blood supply to a region of the body resulted in erythrophore dispersion in that region; when blood flow was restored, the region became pale like the rest of the body. Injection of sea-water extracts of various parts of the body into *Palaemonetes* revealed that the eyestalks contained a substance causing concentration of the erythrophores and xanthophores. This blanching hormone was soon confirmed in *Crangon* and evidence was presented for an additional darkening hormone that originated in

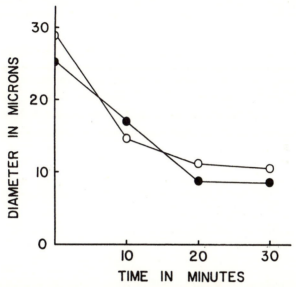

Fig. 1. Movement of white pigment within guanophores when *Palaemon squilla* is transferred from illuminated white to black backgrounds. The behavior in normal animals (O) is contrasted with that in sinus-glandless animals (●). Observations at 10-min intervals recorded as diameters of pigment masses in microns; each point is the mean diameter of single guanophores in five animals. Guanophore pigment is dispersed on an illuminated white background and is concentrated both on an illuminated black background and in darkness. Eyestalk removal results in loss of the background response, the guanophores being dispersed; in darkness, however, the guanophores of eyestalkless animals become concentrated. Injection of eyestalk extract into eyestalkless animals causes concentration of guanophore pigment, but extract of sinus glands only is without effect on dispersed guanophores. These results indicate the complexity of the physiological mechanism controlling these pigment cells, for, in addition to possible response as independent effectors, the guanophores appear to be regulated by a hormone originating outside the sinus gland. (Modified from Knowles.[78])

the rostral region.[84] Thus, two hormones were postulated at this time, a "contractin" and an "expantin."

2. *Hormonal mechanisms*

a. *Number of hormones involved.* After these initial discoveries in the regulation of crustacean color change, two main trends of investigation developed, one concerned with the number of hormones involved in metachrosis, and the other with localizing their origin. The latter will be discussed in the next section.

Study of *Palaemonetes* on variously colored backgrounds showed that the chromatophore types behaved independently. Since this independence persisted in denervated areas, several hormones were postulated as regulating the responses in question.[18,19] The rediscovery[36,37] that brachyuran crustaceans differed from most Caridea in their color response to eyestalk removal,[90] becoming pale where most prawns darkened, and Koller's report of a concentrating and a dispersing hormone for *Crangon*, stimulated new interest. This led to an examination of the comparative effects of eyestalk removal and of interspecific reciprocal injections of eyestalk extracts between *Palaemonetes, Uca pugilator, Uca pugnax,* and *Crangon.*[8] The qualitative responses of the various chromatophores were found identical with those produced when each test species was injected with extract of its own eyestalks. Two alternative working hypotheses were therefore proposed: 1) the unitary hypothesis, according to which one eyestalk hormone, common to all crustaceans, produces a diversity of responses in various species because of the specific organization of their chromatophores; 2) the multiple hormone hypothesis, which postulates a number of different eyestalk hormones, each of which specifically either disperses or concentrates one type of chromatophore pigment and is ineffective on the remaining chromatophore pigments of the species.

Although these two interpretations served as working hypotheses to aid in planning research, they were, however, premature for several reasons as explanations of the physiology of crustacean color change. For one, a number of investigators could not confirm, in the same and closely related species of *Crangon*, Koller's experimental evidence[84] for a melanophore-dispersing principle, expantin, in the blood and in the rostral region.[38,67,85,105] Another reason was that the classical criteria employed in endocrine research could not be adequately applied because the gland producing these hormones in the eyestalk was not yet fully known.

    b. *Hormone source within the eyestalk.* Perkins' demonstration in *Palaemonetes* that a blood-borne substance, apparently originating in the eyestalk, controlled chromatophores, stimulated attempts to locate the endocrine gland concerned. As a result[36-38,56,111] two possible sources of chromatophorotropic secretion were found: 1) the X-organ, consisting presumably of transformed sensory cells of a rudimentary eye papilla,[58] and 2) the sinus gland, commonly located between the two middle optic ganglia. To test the actual chromatophorotropic activity of these structures extracts of appropriate isolated eyestalk regions were injected into *Palaemonetes* and into *Uca* and any induced color changes noted. The evidence from such experiments pointed to the sinus gland rather than the X-organ as the source of chromatophorotropic activity.

Subsequent investigations described in Chapter 8 and in Chapter 15, Vol. I showed that the X-organ referred to in these later studies[35] was different from the one described by Hanström. This new X-organ is connected with the sinus gland by axons that constitute the so-called sinus gland nerve.[12,50,101,102] The anatomy of the complex so formed was shown to be even more elaborate when axons from neurosecretory cells at various locations in the central nervous system were also found to communicate with the sinus gland.[11] It has been suggested[79] that such clusters of neurosecretory cells in the central nervous system be called ganglionic X-organs and thus distinguished from Hanström's structure for which the terms sensory pore X-organ or sensory papilla X-organ are proposed.

Comparison of extracts prepared from isolated sinus glands with those from entire eyestalks and from eyestalks intact except for the sinus glands which had been previously removed were thought to indicate that most if not all the chromatophorotropic activity originated in the sinus gland.[20] On the same basis, activity in the remainder of the eyestalk was attributed to the escape of material from the sinus gland occurring naturally or induced by the surgical manipulation.

c. *Hormones from the central nervous system.* Early observations had demonstrated that chromatophorotropic activity was present in extracts prepared from the ventral nerve cord.[16,62] Many recent studies of crustacean color change have also demonstrated chromatophorotropically active substances in central nervous tissues by injection methods. These have been presented as evidence for the multiple hormone hypothesis of pigment cell control. Such active substances were found within the eyestalk ganglia,[15,21,108] as well as within the ventral nerve cord. Thus, extracts made from the isolated lamina ganglionaris, medulla terminalis, medulla externa, and medulla interna of the crab, *Hemigrapsus*, cause considerable melanophore dispersion, although not as much as that produced by extracts of sinus gland; weaker melanophore responses suggested that chromatophorotropins are also present in supraesophageal and in thoracic ganglia. A quantitative assessment of the relative activity of such extracts is difficult. According to current hypotheses[11,101,102] such comparisons, based on the volume of tissue extracted, are being made between secretory products accumulating in the terminal sinus gland and nervous tissue in which the proportion of neurosecretory cells and their neurosecretory product may be quite low. However, measurements of melanophore response to a series of extract dilutions show

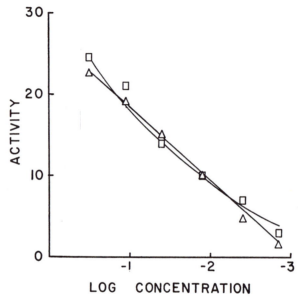

LOG   CONCENTRATION

Fig. 2. Comparison of chromatophorotropic activity of a series of dilutions of extract prepared from sinus gland ($\triangle$) and from optic ganglia ($\square$) in *Uca*. The vertical axis expresses activity in arbitrary units of degree and duration of melanophore response. (Modified from Sandeen.[108])

(Fig. 2) that extract prepared from sinus-glandless eyestalks or from the four optic ganglia is as active as extract prepared from sinus glands alone[108]; a similar relation was also shown for the erythrophores.[21]

In addition to the topographic distribution described above, qualitatively different chromatophorotropins have been reported.[22,80] On the basis of differential solubilities in ethanol and the responses of particular types of chromatophores in several crustacean species, Brown and his collaborators distinguish a number of different substances; three of these come from the sinus gland: a concentrator of the erythrophores of *Palaemonetes;* a disperser of melanophores of *Uca;* and a concentrator of the melanophores in the telson and uropods of *Crangon.* Two additional chromatophorotropins from the central nervous system of a variety of crustaceans are a disperser of melanophores of body and "tail" of *Crangon,* and a concentrator of the body melanophores of *Crangon* inactive in the tail. Evidence has also been presented for two chromatophorotropins having antagonistic action on the guanophores and melanophores of *Uca.*[108] Some attempt has been made to identify these and other chromatophorotropins with materials separated by paper electrophoresis from various portions of the central nervous system,[79,80] but in view of the great variety of such substances and the possibility of artifacts arising during the preparation of extracts, this remains a difficult and uncompleted undertaking.

d. *Present status.* Critical evidence proving the endocrine regulation of crustacean color change in the classic way was delayed until localization experiments made such study possible. Up to that time the best evidence came from injection experiments. Surgical removal of the sinus glands with no apparent disturbance to the rest of the eyestalk was first performed in *Palaemonetes.*[24] If the sinus gland is the exclusive physiological source of chromatophore-concentrating hormone, the erythrophores of such operated *Palaemonetes* should become dispersed and the animal unable to adapt itself to white backgrounds. In fact about one-third of such operated animals remained permanently dark when tested on an illuminated white background, another third showed weak concentration of erythrophores, and the remainder strong concentration. To test the completeness of sinus gland removal, eyestalks from each of these three groups were extracted and their chromatophorotropic activity assayed by injection into *Palaemonetes* and *Uca.* The results indicate that the degree of color response was inversely related to the completeness of the sinus gland extirpation.

More successful surgical removal of the sinus glands is possible in *Palaemon* in which 33–50% have failed to show any white-background response.[77,97] In these experiments the success of the operation can be checked by inspection after the subsequent molt when any remaining fragment of the sinus gland is readily visible.

These results of sinus gland removal supplement the evidence from injection experiments in pointing to this organ as the source of chromatophorotropic hormone. It is questionable whether similar surgical experiments are technically feasible to test for hormone sources in the central nervous system. Even without such evidence, however, there is doubt that secretion of chromatophorotropins from the central nervous system does occur as a normal physiological process in color change. If it did, the experiments described above where sinus glands were successfully removed without damaging the retina or optic pathways would have yielded different results. If indeed the central nervous system did secrete significant amounts of color-control hormones, the operated animals would have concentrated their erythrophores in adaptation to a white background. Yet we have seen that whatever adaptability was present could be explained as due to incomplete removal of the sinus glands. Thus, while there is some evidence, chiefly from injection experiments but also from chromatophore behavior under other experimental conditions, for sources of chromatophorotropins outside the sinus gland or the eyestalk, there is little to indicate the participation of these chromatophorotropins in the normal physiology of color change.

e. *Hormone properties.* One of the major obstacles to chemical studies of the pigment-activating substances in crustaceans has been the difficulty in obtaining adequate amounts of material for extraction and analysis. As a consequence, little is known of the chemical nature of the pigmentary hormones. Some recent studies[96] involving chromatographic techniques have implicated certain classes of compounds, but this matter requires further investigation.

Carlson[37] was among the first to undertake a systematic characterization of the hormone causing erythrophore concentration in *Palaemonetes.* In addition to some of the solubility properties (Table 1) he reported that eyestalks dried for a long period yield extracts as effective as those prepared from fresh material, that the active principle diffuses through cellophane, and that the activity of extracts is not destroyed by boiling for 5 minutes in 1 N HCl or NaOH. However, the effect of boiling on extract activity seems to have had disparate results in the hands of different investigators. Increased chromatophorotropic potency in boiled sea-water extracts has been reported by some;[56,105] whereas others[31] found only slight differences of questionable significance.

Extracts of sinus gland homogenates made in isotonic solutions cause little dispersion of *Uca* melanophores. However, similar homogenates, initially extracted with distilled water and then made isotonic prior to injection, show greatly increased chromatophorotropic activity.[103a] This difference in activity is believed to be physiological evidence for the presence within the sinus gland of hormone-containing granules, each bounded by a semipermeable membrane.[60a]

Comparison of the solubilities and chromatophorotropic activity of extracts from various eyestalks tested against different chromatophores (Table 1) also shows divergences between the reports of the several investigators. Some of the differences may lie in the inadequate assay

TABLE 1

SOLUBILITIES AND CHROMATOPHOROTROPIC ACTIVITIES OF EYESTALK EXTRACTS

Eyestalk source	Test chromatophore[a]	Solvent	Solubility
Palaemonetes sp.[31,37]	*Palaemonetes:* E	Ether	0; Absolutely inactive
	Palaemonetes: E	Pure alcohol	100% (activity of original extract)
	Palaemonetes: E	100% Ethanol	Approx. 40% of whole eyestalk
	Uca: M	100% Ethanol	Approx. 15% of whole eyestalk
Uca pugilator[6]	*Uca:* M	100% Ethanol	45%
	Uca: M	95% Ethanol	60%
	Uca: M	100% Acetone	0
	Uca: M	90% Acetone	20
	Uca: M	Ethyl ether	0
	Uca: M	Petroleum ether	1
Pandalus borealis[96]	*Palaemon:* E	100% Acetone	Used to extract eyestalks
	Palaemon: E	80% Ethanol	Nearly 100% activity in elution from aluminum oxide
	Carcinus: M	80% Ethanol	0 (?); Few animals tested
Astacus astacus[63]	*Astacus:* E, X	86% Ethanol	Active on both chromatophores; no activity in alcohol-insoluble residue
	Astacus: E, X	Ether[b]	No activity
	Astacus: E, X	Acetone[b]	Active on E
	Astacus: E, X	Butanol[b]	Active, particularly on E
Crangon crangon[63]	*Astacus:* E, X	87% Alcohol	Active on both

[a] E, erythrophore; M, melanophore; X, xanthophore.
[b] After extraction with 86% ethanol.

methods or in the fact that one group[6] extracted whole eyestalks whereas another[31] extracted only dissected sinus glands. However, some of the solubility data may have a more physiological significance. Thus, two principles have been separated from sinus glands on the basis of differential solubility in absolute ethanol.[31] Similarly, use of chromatographic methods on extracts of *Pandalus* eyestalks yielded 80% ethanol eluates effective on the erythrophores of *Palaemon squilla* but inactive on the melanophores of *Carcinus* and *Portunus*.[96] Since tests were few with the latter two genera and desirable controls assaying the original crude extracts with the two test chromatophores were not performed, separation of two hormonal principles must be viewed with reserve until additional information is available.

Recent studies[80] present evidence for a large precursor hormone molecule, chromatophorotropically active, which is transformed in vitro into smaller molecules with different electrophoretic and physiological properties (Fig. 3). Two substances, differing in their electrophoretic mobility, can be obtained from freshly dissected sinus glands. One compound (the A-substance) effects a strong concentration of pigment in both the large and the small erythrophores of *Palaemon serratus*. The other material (alpha-substance), electrophoretically occurring in two bands, causes only partial concentration of the small erythrophores. If, instead of testing the freshly removed sinus glands, distilled water extracts are made and allowed to stand for 12 hr at 18°C before application to the paper strip, the electrophoretic pattern shows two bands (Fig. 3); eluates of these produce strong concentration of small erythrophores only. Dialysis experiments indicate the A-substance is a larger molecule than the alpha-substance.

The possible polypeptide nature of crustacean pigmentary hormones is also indicated by observations that extracts of hepatopancreas,[103a,113a] chymotrypsin,[103a] trypsin,[81] and papain[113a] inactivate in vitro chromatophorotropins from *Palaemon* and from *Uca*. These studies, plus reports that extracts of epidermis[38a] and green gland[113a] are similarly effective, point to a possible enzymatic degradation of chromatophorotropic hormones after they have been secreted into the blood.

Electrophoretic separation from the sinus gland of *Uca pugilator* of three distinct peaks of melanophore-dispersing activity has been briefly reported. There are, in addition, one uncertain area of melanophore-concentrating activity, one peak of dispersing and one peak of concentrating activity for the erythrophores and xanthophores, as well as two peaks of guanophore-concentrating activity.[113] Separation by paper electrophoresis of chromatophorotropins from *Cambarellus*[51a] and from *Palaemonetes*[51c] has also been reported.

Attempts have been made to purify the chromatophorotropic hormones of the crustacean eyestalk.[5,96] One method using the melanophore of *Uca* for a standardized test object gives a 100- to 200-fold increase in purity, with a maximum activity of 200,000 to 400,000 *Uca* units per milligram. Such concentrates retain about 10–20% of the total original activity.[2,5,6]

Östlund and Fänge, using batches of 100–500 gm of eyestalks of *Pandalus borealis* in every preparation, tested fractions on dispersed

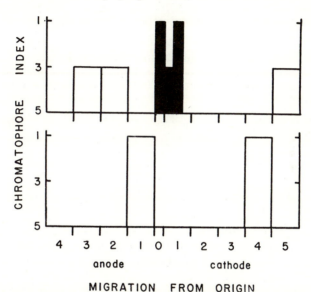

FIG. 3. Results of injection of sinus gland extract into *Palaemon* after paper electrophoresis. The horizontal axis represents the length of the paper strip that has been subdivided into numbered portions on each side of 0, the point of application of sinus gland extract; the vertical axis represents the chromatophore index 60 min after eyestalkless, test *Palaemon* were injected with eluates from the corresponding portions of the paper. Stage 5 indicates fully dispersed erythrophores; stage 1 represents their maximal concentration. The upper diagram shows the electrophoretic separation from sinus glands (immediately applied at 0) of a substance in the −1 range that strongly concentrated pigment in the small and in the large erythrophores, and of substances at about +2 and −5 that concentrated only the small erythrophores of the test *Palaemon*. In the lower diagram, sinus gland extract was kept at room temperature for some hours before application to the paper; after electrophoretic separation substances at about +1 and −4 produced strong concentration of the small erythrophores only. (Modified from Knowles, Carlisle, and Dupont-Raabe.[80])

erythrophore pigment of *Palaemon squilla*. Crude acetone extracts of ground eyestalks after application to filter paper were developed by ascending chromatography in butanol-HCl solvent. Sections of the filter paper were subsequently extracted with sea water and the eluates tested by injection into *Palaemon*. The distribution of the erythrophore-concentrating activity on such a chromatogram is shown in Fig. 4. Serial chromatography on columns of aluminum oxide yielded a product with an activity of about 100,000 units per milligram dry weight. Paper chromatography of this fraction gave an R_f for activity at 0.56–0.61, eluates of the active region showing an absorption spectrum with a maximum at 2700 A. Injection of the purified extract concentrated the erythrophores of *Palaemon* but had no effect on the melanophores of *Carcinus* and *Portunus* in the few cases tried.

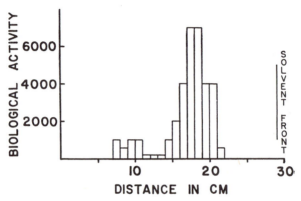

Fig. 4. Paper chromatogram showing distribution of chromatophorotropic activity of crude acetone extract of eyestalks of *Pandalus borealis*. Butanol-HCl solvent, ascending time 23 hr at 12°C. Sections of the paper were eluted with sea water and bioassayed on eyestalkless *Palaemon*. Vertical axis shows activity in terms of so-called "Leander units." Maximum chromatophorotropic activity has an R_f of 0.62. (Modified from Östlund and Fänge.[96])

f. *Response specificity*. Various extraneous substances have been tested for their chromatophorotropic activity. Injection of distilled water into eyestalkless *Uca* causes melanophore expansion which is quantitatively different from that produced by eyestalk extract; sucrose isosmotic with sea water (0.95 M) produces a slight melanophore dispersion, but sucrose believed isosmotic with the blood of *Uca* (1.3 M) does not; solutions of NaCl, $MgCl_2$, $CaCl_2$, Na_2HSO_4, and LiCl, in concentrations isosmotic with sea water cause slight melanophore dispersion.[6]

Sea-water solutions of sixteen drugs, in 100-μg doses, are without effect on the dispersed melanophores of *Uca*; acetylcholine, cocaine HCl, curare, strychnine sulfate, guanidine, chlorobutanol, caffeine, and nicotine bring about slight melanophore dispersion when injected into eyestalkless *Uca*, while hyoscine hydrobromide produces a more marked response; adrenaline (epinephrine) in dilutions of 1:1000 to

1:10,000 elicits a slight dispersion in eyestalkless animals only with the stronger doses.[6] In *Crangon crangon* adrenaline and noradrenaline in diluted solutions produce melanophore dispersion; ephedrine, Veritol, and Sympatol are effective only in high concentrations. Acetylcholine elicits melanophore dispersion in *Crangon*, but the cholinesterase-blocking drugs, physostigmine and prostigmine, do not. The acetylcholine-blocking agents, tubocurarine, atropine, and scopolamine do not prevent melanophore dispersion in response to an illuminated black background.[53] Injection of DDT in sublethal doses (0.01%–0.0001%) and of Ryanodine, an insecticide, in nonparalyzing doses, into pale eyestalkless *Uca* causes full melanophore dispersion within 1 hr; estradiol, sodium taurocholate, and soap solution, all in unspecified doses, disperse the melanophores in eyestalkless *Uca*.[49] Erythrophore dispersion in *Palaemon squilla* is induced by 5-μg doses of adrenaline, noradrenaline, and 5-hydroxytryptamine.[96]

Intermedin has been tested on a number of crustacean species, with variable effects. Melanophore dispersion has been reported in *Crangon*[14] and in *Uca*.[4] Variable effects of intermedin on the erythrophores of *Palaemonetes*[4] and of *Palaemon*[57,96] could be observed by others, although marked dispersion of chromatophores (erythrophores?) of *Paratya* resulted from injections of commercial preparations of anterior lobe and posterior lobe extracts of the pituitary gland.[94]

Evaluating the chromatophoral responses to various drugs is difficult because neither their mechanism of action on the chromatophores nor that of the crustacean chromatophorotropic hormones themselves is known. Injection of drugs or other substances may effect a chromatophore change similar to that occurring in normal metachrosis, but this change may be brought about by one of several different pathways: 1) The drug or extract may act pharmacologically on the secretory structure, the sinus gland, to inhibit or stimulate release of hormone. 2) The injected substance may act directly on one or more components of the pigmentary system, calling into action the mechanism normally in operation at the chromatophoral level. Somewhat more insight may be provided if such experiments are performed with eyestalkless animals, but even then the substance being tested may release chromatophorotropins previously synthesized and stored in the central nervous system. Some distinction may be possible among those several mechanisms by testing the activity of such extracts also on isolated chromatophores in vitro; however, establishing critical experimental conditions when the whole animal is used as a test object may still pose great technical difficulties.

III. *RETINAL PIGMENTS*

A. GENERAL MORPHOLOGY

To understand the physiology of retinal pigment movements in crustaceans effectively, some review of compound eye morphology is desirable. For details reference should be made to Chapter 1 and to

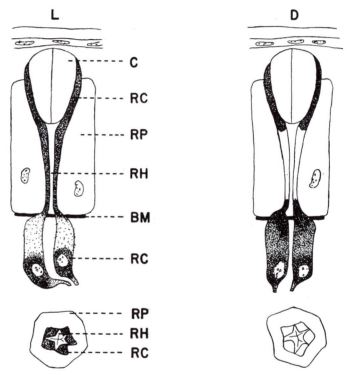

FIG. 5. Ommatidia from the eyes of light-adapted and dark-adapted *Gammarus*. The upper figures are longitudinal sections; the lower ones are transverse sections through the rhabdom. L, from light-adapted retina; D, from dark-adapted retina; C, cone; RC, retinular cell; RP, reflecting pigment cell; RH, rhabdom; BM, basement membrane. (Modified from Parker.[99])

Debaisieux's monograph.[42] The structure of an ommatidium in the sessile eye of *Gammarus* is shown in Fig. 5. Masses of black pigment granules lie within the five retinular cells that surround a rhabdom, and move from one part of the retinular cell to another in response to light and to darkness. The spaces between ommatidia are filled with reflecting pigment.

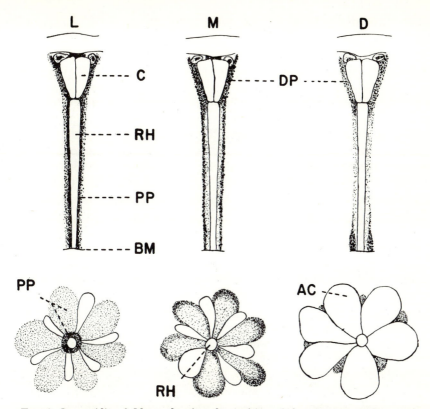

Fig. 6. Ommatidia of *Idotea* showing the position of the pigments under varying conditions of light and darkness. Upper figures are longitudinal sections; lower figures are transverse sections through the rhabdom at approximately comparable stages of light- or dark-adaptation as the corresponding longitudinal section. L, light-adapted; pigment forms a sheath about the rhabdom; in the transverse section the accessory cells alternate with the retinular cells. M, dark-adapted for ½ hr; the pigment has migrated laterally in the proximal cell and no longer forms a sheath about the rhabdom; the accessory cells are beginning to increase in size. D, dark-adapted for 2 hr; the proximal pigment has now migrated proximally where it causes bulging of the cells at the basement membrane; in the transverse section the accessory cells have increased greatly in size. *C*, cone; *DP*, distal pigment cells, *RH*, rhabdom; *PP*, retinular cells; *BM*, basement membrane; *AC*, accessory cell. (Modified from Peabody.[103])

An ommatidium from the sessile compound eye of *Idotea* shows a number of differences in structure[103] (Fig. 6). Distal pigment cells form a sheath around the cone. The retinular cells, of which there are usually six (and occasionally a seventh rudimentary one), contain black pigment. They are contiguous with the distal pigment cells and continue proximally to taper into optic nerve fibers. Elongated accessory cells extend from the base of the cone to the basement membrane and are alternately disposed with the retinular cells. The function of these accessory cells is unknown. Differences in their cross-sectional area in dark-adapted and light-adapted eyes indicate that the accessory cells undergo photomechanical changes. No reflecting pigment has been described in the retina of *Idotea*, but quite probably such pigment was dissolved from the accessory cells by the usual preservative and histological procedures (see Table 2), particularly since the eye of *Ligia*, also an isopod, does contain reflecting pigment.[92]

Retinal pigments from stalked compound eyes, as illustrated by *Palaemonetes*, show some structural elaboration over those in sessile compound eyes. There are three sets of pigment. Distal pigment cells enclose the axial crystalline cone; from the body of each pigment cell two processes extend, one distally to the cornea, and the other, rather thicker, proximally to the retinular cells. Three or four fibrils, contained within each distal pigment cell and probably responsible for its movement, extend from the distal region of the cell bodies through the cell's proximal process to terminate close to the nuclei of the retinular cells. Seven or eight of the latter, containing black pigment, enclose the rhabdom and extend proximally through the basement membrane, shortly below which they continue as primary optic axons to synapses in the optic ganglia. Interommatidial reflecting pigment cells have been described filling the space between the proximal ends of adjacent ommatidia. The fact that the outer ends of the distal pigment cells in some species of prawns have caps of reflecting pigment from which processes extend well below the basement membrane, suggests that present knowledge of these cells is incomplete.

The chemical nature of these retinal pigments is not yet well known (Chapter 3, Vol. I). The black pigments of the distal and retinular cells are apparently melanins in some forms but ommochromes in others; in most species specific chemical investigation has not been made. The reflecting pigment has been called guanine, by analogy with the tapetal pigment in the eyes of some vertebrates, but a comparative study of the nature of reflecting pigments in the crustacean retina[71,71b,72] indicates that they are mixtures of purines and pteridines, among which guanine is not evident.

B. NORMAL PHOTOMECHANICAL CHANGES

As has already been briefly mentioned (Section I,B), the photomechanical movements of these retinal pigments vary in different

Crustacea from the relatively simple migration of the black pigment to and from the proximal portions of the retinular cells of *Gammarus* to the more elaborate movements of the three sets of retinal pigments found in *Palaemonetes*. Nevertheless, the chief function of such movement appears to be the same, namely to screen the sensory component of the ommatidium, the rhabdom, in bright light, and to uncover the rhabdom in darkness or in light of low intensity. Thus, in bright illumination the distal pigment of *Palaemonetes* moves centrally away from the cone and the proximal pigment moves above the basement membrane so that these two sets of pigment form a screening collar around the rhabdom; in this condition, presumably only those light rays parallel to the ommatidial axis will stimulate the rhabdom; light rays that enter the eye obliquely to the ommatidial axes will be screened out by the collar of black pigment. On the other hand, in dim light or in darkness the distal and the proximal pigments move away from the rhabdom to leave it unscreened, so that light rays entering the eye may pass readily through several adjacent ommatidia to stimulate the rhabdoms of several units; this is believed to lower the eye's threshold by increasing the fraction of light absorbed by the photosensitive system (Chapter 1). In species where the reflecting pigment is fixed in position, the pigment is invariably located above the basement membrane; in other species, where the reflecting pigment migrates, it lies predominantly below the basement membrane in the light-adapted retina, and above it in the dark-adapted eye. Presumably, the latter condition scatters the light within the eye and increases the amount reaching the rhabdoms. The simultaneous withdrawal of the proximal and distal screening pigments permits maximum freedom of light paths in the dark-adapted eye. Despite these general relations, very few precise measurements of threshold and acuity have been made under the various conditions of pigment distribution[43] (Chapter 1).

C. REGULATION

1. *Early studies*

a. *Interrelationship of the eyes.* Early work on the mechanisms regulating retinal pigment migration in crustaceans was greatly influenced by the late-nineteenth century studies of retinal pigment movement in the lower vertebrates. There the controversial question was whether the movement was the direct response of independent effectors to light and to darkness or whether it was a reflex response. The crucial experiment, when applied to *Palaemonetes*, consisted of comparing the reactions of one illuminated eye while the other was covered. Such experiments first showed[98] that the three pigments in the covered eye of an otherwise illuminated animal approach more or less completely the condition characteristic of the dark-adapted eye. Because no innervation of the distal and reflecting pigments could be demonstrated and because photomechanical responses of the three pigments could be obtained in excised eyestalks and retinas, Parker believed the pigments behave as independent effectors. Von Frisch,[116] however, could obtain no decisive results in similar experiments with *Palaemon*. Castle[39] later repeated Parker's experiment, but from observations only on the proximal pigment agreed that an illuminated eye does not affect the position of the proximal pigment in the covered eye. Still further study[9] indicated that such translucent animals as *Palaemonetes* and *Palaemon* are not suited for experiments where the eye must be completely screened from outside light.

With *Cambarus, Carcinus, Libinia, Cancer,* and *Homarus,* whose opaque exoskeleton would prevent stimulation of the retina by any but direct light, Bennitt's observations[8,9] on the proximal pigment differed from those reported by Parker and by Castle. In a few cases, this pigment was in the dark-adapted position in the covered eye, while the illuminated eye was light-adapted; this left open the possibility that the proximal pigment is an independent effector. But in the great majority of cases illumination of the exposed retina led to light adaptation of the proximal pigment in the unexposed, dark-adapted retina. Such responses were thought to be mediated by a nerve reflex, although serious reservations were expressed on how such a mechanism could be brought into play.

b. *Temperature, anesthesia, oxygen deficiency, nerves.*   Shortly after the turn of the present century, the effects on retinal pigments of a variety of experimental and environmental conditions were studied. The influence of temperature on pigment migration was investigated in amphipods[8] and in decapods.[40] The effect of temperature on the rate of pigment migration in amphipods[8] suggests that the process involved is a thermochemical rather than a photochemical or physical one. This work also indicates that migration of the proximal retinal pigment is an all-or-nothing reaction. Chloretone anesthesia of the beach flea, *Talorchestia,*[8] and of the prawn, *Macrobrachium,*[120] induces the light-adapted position of the retinal pigments, while oxygen deficiency, brought about by a variety of methods in *Cambarus,*[10] has a similar effect on the proximal pigment. Ligation of the base of the eyestalk in *Macrobrachium*[120] so as to interrupt the flow of blood to the retina, results in the light-adapted position of the distal pigment.

The above observations indicate that retinal pigment movement is influenced by other factors than their own independent effector activity. The first, and most obvious, factor to be considered is the nervous system. No innervation of the distal and of the reflecting pigments has been demonstrated histologically in the decapod retina. Furthermore, the retinular cells, which contain the proximal pigment, do indeed terminate proximally as fibers of the optic nerve, in which they presumably serve a sensory function. To suppose that they also serve as efferent fibers regulating the proximal pigment is contrary to the generally accepted view of the polarity of the reflex arc.

c. *Eyestalk extracts.* The discovery that the compound eyestalks are endocrine organs involved in chromatophoral regulation,[104] coupled with the unsatisfactory evidence for nervous regulation of the retinal pigments and some evidence for their vascular control,[9,120] stimulated a series of studies presenting evidence for a hormonal factor in retinal pigment migration. The first of these[64,65] reported that injection of extracts prepared from the eyestalks of a variety of crustacean species into dark-adapted *Palaemonetes* results in movement of the distal and the reflecting pigments into the light-adapted position (Fig. 7); the proximal pigment is unaffected by such extracts. Converse experiments, where eyestalk extracts are injected into light-adapted *Palaemonetes*, are ineffective in moving the distal retinal pigment to the dark-adapted position. Light-adaptation of the distal retinal pigment results from injection of eyestalk extracts in *Cambarus*[121] and in the fresh-water prawn, *Paratya*.[91] Eyestalk extracts of brachyuran crustaceans[112] cause the complete or nearly complete disappearance of the "glow" observable at night in dark-adapted *Hemigrapsus* and *Pachygrapsus* eyes; this effect is presumably brought about hormonally by movement of retinal pigments so as to mask the reflecting pigment. Which of the retinal pigments is involved here was not indicated in the original report.

2. Mechanisms

a. *For distal pigment.* Additional data, also largely from injection experiments, suggest the hormonal regulation of the distal pigment. In attempting to localize the source of the retinal pigment hormone, extracts of the sinus gland and of the medulla terminalis of the eyestalk were found effective on *Cambarus*, but those of the cerebral ganglia were not.[122] The activity of medulla terminalis extracts could be explained as possibly due to residual tissue from the sinus gland or to material that had escaped from the sinus gland during its removal. If so, the sinus gland would be the source of this hormone.

However, in a number of crustaceans, substantial activity, like that of the light-adapting distal retinal pigment hormone, arises from components of the eyestalk other than the sinus gland, and also from other

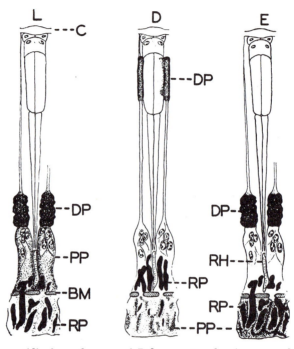

Fig. 7. Ommatidia from the eyes of *Palaemonetes*, showing general structure and the position of the three retinal pigments under various conditions. L, from a light-adapted eye; D, from a dark-adapted eye; E, from the eye of a dark-adapted animal that was injected with eyestalk extract. *C*, cornea; *DP*, distal pigment; *PP*, proximal pigment; *BM*, basement membrane; *RP*, reflecting pigment; *RH*, rhabdom. (From Kleinholz.[65])

ganglia of the nervous system.[71a] These results with extracts are in agreement with the hypothesis of neurosecretion.[11,101,102] But extracts of the sinus glands of some brachyuran crustaceans show insignificant retinal pigment activity, while similar extracts from two macruran species yield marked retinal pigment responses. Unpublished observations indicate that this distinction may not hold for all macrurans. The lack of light-adapting activity in sinus gland extracts from some brachyurans may be evidence for differences in neurosecretory storage and release. It also emphasizes that little is known of the regulatory mechanism for retinal pigments in brachyurans. Two groups of investigators[73,109] found that movement of the distal retinal pigment in *Palaemon* and in *Palaemonetes* is not an all-or-nothing response to illumination as it had been described in amphipods,[8] but that the amount of its movement could be graded between the extremes of light- and of dark-adaptation by regulating the intensity of illumination. Since various concentrations of injected eyestalk extract produce similar graded migration of the distal pigment in *Palaemon*,[67] this implies that the normal pigment movements may be mediated by the amount of hormone released into the circulation.

The effects of sinus gland removal on retinal pigment positions add support to the suggested humoral regulation of the distal pigment. Thus, in sinus-glandless *Palaemon* the distal pigment moves to the night position and the occurrence of retinal glow from reflecting pigment indicates that the other retinal pigments apparently are in their dark-adapted positions, too.[97] More detailed study[77,78] shows that in *Palaemon* 10 days after sinus gland removal the distal pigment remains in the maximally dark-adapted position even when usually the animals are kept for several hours under bright illumination. In some cases the distal pigment undergoes a slight proximal migration toward light-adaptation. Probably these are due either to slight surgical injury to the optic ganglia, which produces varying degrees of light-adaptation in the retina of crabs, or to release of active hormonal substances from other portions of the central nervous system.[112] It thus seems reasonably certain that a hormone from the sinus gland is responsible for the migration of the distal retinal pigment into the light-adapted position.

Brown and his collaborators have recently proposed[25,28,32] that an antagonistic hormone may cause dark-adaptation of this same system in *Palaemonetes*. Two kinds of observations form the basis for this hypothesis. One is that prawns from which one eyestalk has been removed show less light-adaptation of the distal pigment than do normal animals, while no significant difference is apparent in rate of dark-adaptation of the distal pigment between one-eyed and two-eyed animals. The other kind of observation comes from studying the distal pigment's rate and degree of light- and of dark-adaptation in animals that had been successively dark-adapted for varying periods, given a light stimulus, and then returned to darkness. In prawns maintained in darkness for 40, 60, 120, and 240 min before being given the light stimulus, the longer the stay in darkness before the light stimulus, the greater is the degree of light-adaptation of the distal pigment and the more rapid its rate of readaptation to darkness following the light stimulus. These results were interpreted as supporting the hypothesis for a dark-adapting hormone in addition to the light-adapting one.

Experimental support for this hypothesis was sought by examining the kinetics of readaptation to darkness in previously dark-adapted animals given a light stimulus and injected with various extracts. Compared with sea-water controls, extracts of the eyestalk and of the central nervous system not only supplement the degree of light-adaptation evoked by the light stimulus, but also produce faster rates of readaptation to darkness; injection of extracts of tritocerebral commissure induces less light-adaptation than do sea-water controls. These results were interpreted as indicating that the commissure extract contains only dark-adapting hormone and no light-adapting hormone, thus effecting a faster rate of readaptation to darkness than sea-water controls, while extracts of eyestalks and of central nervous system contain both hormones.

Attempts to induce dark-adaptation of the distal pigment by injection of various extracts (extract of tritocerebral commissure should be most suited for the purpose, according to the observation reported above) into light-adapted animals maintained in light are ineffective. The evidence for a dark-adapting retinal pigment hormone is thus indirect.[28] More direct evidence for such a hormone comes from the following experiments.[51b] The distal retinal pigment of one-eyed *Palaemonetes* migrates into a position about midway between the fully light-adapted and fully dark-adapted states when the animals are kept on black backgrounds illuminated at 270 lux. Injection of eyestalk extract into these test animals results in maximum light-adaptation of the distal pigment, followed in 2 hr by dark-adaptation that lasts about 5 hr. Injection of a mixture of tritocerebral commissure and eyestalk extracts produces less light-adaptation, presumably because of the additional dark-adapting hormone believed present in the commissure.

b. *For proximal pigment.* The regulatory mechanism for the proximal retinal pigment is still not clear. The difficulties of accepting the notion of nervous control have been described above (page 153). Injection of eyestalk extract, which causes light-adaptation of the distal and reflecting pigments in *Palaemonetes*[65] and in *Paratya*[91] is ineffective on the proximal pigments of these animals. On the other hand, in *Cambarus*, while injection of extract equivalent to material from one eyestalk does not affect the proximal pigment, injection of the equivalent of two eyestalks causes migration of that pigment to the light-adapted position.[121] Later studies involving surgical removal of the sinus gland reveal that regulation of the proximal retinal pigment is probably a much more complex process than had been supposed.

Sinus gland removal from one eyestalk in crayfish,[68,69] followed by ablation of the second eyestalk, does not interfere with the ability of the proximal pigment to adapt to light and to darkness. The proximal pigments of *Pacifastacus*[70] and of *Paratya*[95] continue to show appropriate changes in position when isolated eyestalks are placed in moist-chambers and kept in light or in darkness. Migration of the proximal pigment in two species of *Palaemon* is unaffected by sinus gland removal,[77,78] being qualitatively and quantitatively similar to that in control animals. These last three series of studies suggest that the proximal pigment cells are independent effectors, but in no case was the independent-effector hypothesis critically demonstrated to the exclusion of other possibilities. One such possibility[68] is a hormone originating outside of the eyestalk. Conclusive evidence for such might be difficult to obtain.

The possibility of nervous regulation of these pigments should also be kept open until electrophysiological studies have clarified the role of the proximal fibers from these retinular cells as they continue into the optic nerve. Histological and electrophysiological study of the compound eye of *Limulus*[118] indicates that an eccentric cell located within each ommatidium is the source and conductor of the classic visual impulse through the optic nerve of these animals; the fibers from the retinular cells in the optic nerve apparently do not give rise to conducted spikes. The eye of the isopod *Ligia*[107] also shows an eccentric intraommatidial cell which is probably the one referred to in early histological description of crustacean ommatidia as the rudimentary cell (Chapter 1). The possibility that the eccentric cell of the ommatidium may mediate the visual functions and that the fibers from the other retinular cells may be pigmentomotor is worth investigation.

c. *For reflecting pigment.* Injection of eyestalk extract into dark-adapted *Palaemonetes*[65] and into dark-adapted *Paratya*[91] brings about marked migration of the reflecting pigment to the light-adapted position. Effects of sinus gland removal on the photomechanical movements of the reflecting pigment are not reported. In the crayfish where this type of surgery has been performed, the reflecting pigment is fixed in position. Knowles (1956, personal communication) states that in *Palaemon* the reflecting pigment continues to move in response to illumination after removal of the sinus gland, but that quantitative comparison between normal and experimental retinas is difficult. At this time, therefore, results from injection experiments are the only indication that this pigment might be under endocrine control.

d. *Problems in analysis: diurnal rhythms.* In addition to movements of the various retinal pigments in response to light and to

TABLE 2

DIURNAL RHYTHMS OF RETINAL PIGMENTS PERSISTING UNDER
CONDITIONS OF CONSTANT ILLUMINATION[68,77,93]

Crustacean	Distal[a]	Reflecting[a]	Proximal[a]
Macrobrachium olfersii	NL	O	O
Macrobrachium acanthurus	NL	O	O
Sicyonia sp.	NL	Ab or F[b]	O
Trachypeneopsis mobilispinis	NL	Ab or F[b]	O
Palaemon northropi	DD and NL	DD and NL	O
Anchistioides antiguensis	DD and NL	DD and NL	O
Palaemon paucidens	DD and NL	NL	O
Paratya compressa	DD and NL	NL	O
Portunus anceps	DD	Ab[b]	DD
Parthenope serrata	DD	Ab[b]	DD
Portunus depressifrons	DD	Ab[b]	DD
Calappa flammea	DD	Ab[b]	DD
Palaemon serratus	O	DD	DD
Leander tenuicornis	O	NL	O
Latreutes fucorum	O	NL	NL
Orconectes virilis	—	—	DD
Cambarus bartonii	DD	F	DD
Hippolyte pleuracantha	DD	O	O
Penaeopsis goodei	F	F	DD

[a] Abbreviations: Ab, pigment absent; —, not reported; O, pigment shows normal photomechanical changes, but no persistence of diurnal movements under constant conditions of illumination; F, pigment is fixed in position, undergoing no changes in response to light or darkness; NL, pigment moves into a typical dark-adapted position at night, despite constant illumination, i.e. rhythm persists in continuous light; DD, pigment moves into a typical light-adapted position during the day, despite the animal's being maintained in constant darkness, i.e. rhythm persists in continuous darkness.

[b] The indicated absence of reflecting pigment may be due to its being dissolved during the histological preparation.

darkness considered above, persistent diurnal rhythms in their migrations have been reported for a number of forms when they are maintained under constant illumination or darkness (see Chapter 11, Section II,B). Many of these are summarized in Table 2. Note that the existence of such persistent rhythms may contribute conflicting evidence for mechanisms of retinal pigment control discussed above. Thus, the notion of independent effectors, particularly as it refers to the proximal pigment, becomes questionable as an exclusive mechanism in those species where the pigment moves into the light- or dark-adapted position regardless of the conditions of illumination. Similarly, any attempt to explain in all species the movements of the three retinal pigments on the basis of differential sensitivity to a single hormone is not supported by the data for persistent diurnal rhythms.

IV. COMPARISONS WITH OTHER ANIMALS

A. INSECT COLOR CHANGES

Color change in insects as in crustaceans also consists of relatively slow, morphological color change and more rapid physiological color change. The former arises from quantitative alterations in the epidermal or cuticular pigment; the latter is caused by migrations of pigment granules or of entire chromatophores. Much of the early literature has been reviewed by Hanström[58] and has been recently summarized by Bodenstein.[13]

The best-known cases of physiological color change are those reported in larval culicids (Diptera) and in phasmids (Orthoptera). In larval *Corethra*,[89] melanophores on the air sacs are dispersed when the larva is kept on a black background and concentrated when it is on a white background. Decapitation causes all the melanophores to become permanently contracted. Ligating the body of a larva with dispersed melanophores causes the melanophores on the posterior air sacs to become concentrated.[55] These results suggest the possibility that the head is the source of a hormonal factor regulating these effectors; this is supported by the melanophore dispersion resulting from implantation of one hemisphere of a larval brain or of subesophageal ganglion into the ligated posterior portion. The possible participation of nervous impulse in regulating these melanophores is uncertain. Further study[44] shows the presence of melanophore-dispersing principle in the corpora cardiaca, in the crustacean sinus gland, and in the brains of some insects (blattids, culicids, phasmids) but not in others (*Calliphora, Dytiscus, Galleria,* and *Notonecta*).

Color changes of the phasmid stick insect, *Carausius morosus,* have been investigated more than those of any other insect. Discrete cellular chromatophores do not occur in this form; instead, red and brown pigment granules, located in the cytoplasm of the epidermal cells, migrate in response to external stimuli (Fig. 8) to bring about the dark and the pale phases of physiological color change. High humidity induces the dark state, and dryness the pale state. The animals are usually dark at night and pale during the day; they become pale on illuminated white backgrounds and dark on illuminated black backgrounds. These responses to light cease when the optic tracts are sectioned or the eyes opaqued.[7,106]

The participation of nervous and endocrine factors in regulating such color changes was demonstrated by utilizing the animal's color response to high humidity.[54] When the abdomen of a pale *Carausius* is inserted into a moist-chamber leaving the head and thorax outside, darkening begins at the head and spreads posteriorly over the body.

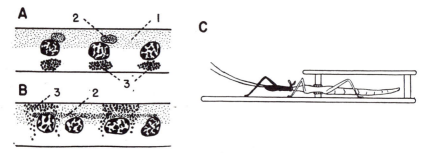

Fɪɢ. 8. Color change in *Carausius morosus*. A, integument of a pale animal; B, integument of a dark animal; C, animal ligatured at the thorax, with the abdomen placed in a moist-chamber. *1*, fixed pigment in the integument; *2, 3*, integumentary pigments that migrate in response to appropriate stimuli. (Modified after Giersberg.[54])

If this experiment is repeated with an animal whose thorax is ligated (Fig. 8), darkening begins as before at the head, and progresses posteriorly as far as the constriction; posterior to the ligature the animal remains pale; but when the constriction is loosened, darkening spreads over the rest of the animal. This indicates the liberation of a humoral substance in the anterior portion of the body as in the larvae discussed above. If the nervous system is severed between the supraesophageal and subesophageal ganglia, or between the subesophageal and thoracic ganglia, and the animal placed in the moist-chamber as before, it remains pale; but if its head is inserted into the moist-chamber, with the rest of the body outside, darkening begins at the head and spreads over the entire body. Regulation of color change therefore appears to depend on transmission of nervous impulses from receptors located over the body to the supraesophageal ganglion, followed by the release of a hormone from an endocrine center in the head.

Extracts of supposed endocrine structures of insects have been found effective on the chromatophores of crustaceans,[29,59,115] and various studies have been made of the reciprocal effects of crustacean endocrine extracts on color changes in insects; these were correlated with attempts to localize the origin of the chromatophorotropic substance in insects and to determine the chromatophorotropic properties of substances separated from insect tissues by paper electrophoresis.[44–48,80] It is still too early to speak with any certainty of the identity or nonidentity of the variously active substances so isolated. The presence of more than one such compound seems quite likely. Thus, extracts of corpora cardiaca from insects are highly active on crustacean erythropores but only moderately active on the color change of the phasmid, while the phasmid brain is strongly active on the donor's chromatophore system and completely inactive on the erythrophores of *Palaemon*, although it evokes some response by the melanophores of *Ligia* and *Crangon*.[44–46,48] Not only are there differences in the physiological effects of crustacean and insect chromatophorotropins but there are also differences in their electrophoretic behavior.[80] Undoubtedly such ambiguities will be resolved only when more quantitative comparative work is done on other crustaceans and insects.

B. Insect Retinal Pigments

In the ocelli and compound eyes of different insects there is considerable variation in which particular retinal pigments migrate and in the rate of migration.[99] In the moth *Anagasta*[41] the "accessory" pigment cells seem topographically and functionally similar to the distal pigment cells in crustaceans, and like them contain a dark screening pigment. Carbon dioxide, other anesthetics, and low temperature cause these pigment cells to move into the light-adapted position. When a small area of an otherwise opaqued eye is illuminated the corresponding accessory cells migrate into the light position while the covered areas remain dark-adapted. Severing the optic tract on one side causes permanent unilateral light adaptation, but the normal eye is still able to become dark-adapted. These results seem to exclude endocrine regulation of insect retinal pigments as well as to rule out the possibility of their being independent effectors. In contrast to the crustacean situation they suggest that pigment migration here is under nervous regulation.

C. Vertebrate Color Changes

The extensive general literature of vertebrate color changes has been reviewed in detail by Parker.[100] Other recent reviews deal with the chemistry and physiology of intermedin, the hormone believed to be largely responsible for melanophore dispersion in the poikilothermous vertebrates.[86-88,117]

Color change among the vertebrates is limited to cyclostomes, elasmobranchs, teleosts, amphibians, and reptiles. In most cases the melanophore is the dominant pigment cell and has been the chromatophore most closely investigated. Many of these vertebrates are able to adapt their color to black and to white backgrounds. The hormone, intermedin, from the intermediate lobe of the pituitary gland, seems to be the chief, and perhaps exclusive, mediator of melanophore response in cyclostomes, elasmobranchs, and amphibians; an important, but less exclusive, role of intermedin in color change is found in some teleosts and reptiles. In teleosts the melanophores generally are directly controlled by the nervous system.

According to Parker's neurohumoral hypothesis they are doubly innervated: fibers that concentrate melanophore pigment liberate an adrenaline-like mediator at their terminals in the vicinity of the melanophore, while dispersing nerve fibers similarly liberate acetylcholine as their mediator. In some teleosts intermedin also participates in regulating melanophore activity. For the commonly studied reptiles, three types of melanophore-regulating mechanisms have been reported: in *Anolis* the mechanism is entirely endocrine, with no evidence for functionally innervated melanophores; in *Phrynosoma* both endocrines and concentrating nerve fibers are thought to regulate the melanophores; in the African chameleon no evidence exists for humoral control of the melanophores which seem to be regulated entirely by nerves.

An additional hormonal mechanism, believed to originate in the pars tuberalis of the pituitary gland and causing melanophore concentration in amphibians and elasmobranchs, has been proposed by Hogben and his students. The evidence for such a blanching hormone in melanophore control comes from studies of the kinetics of melanophore response to darkness and to illuminated backgrounds, and is largely indirect; the more direct experimental results offered in support of this hypothesis can be explained on other grounds.

Any attempt to fit the various mechanisms of color change into an evolutionary scheme will face obvious difficulties. While predominantly hormonal mechanisms are involved in many invertebrates and vertebrates, responses of melanophores as independent effectors or as innervated structures can be illustrated with forms of widely scattered position in the animal kingdom.

V. GENERAL SUMMARY AND CONCLUSIONS

Regulation of the pigmentary effectors, the chromatophores, and some retinal pigments of Crustacea is largely mediated by hormones, although accessory physiological processes may participate to some extent. The controlling agent for the proximal retinal pigment is less well known; some evidence exists for endocrine control, but the possible role of the nervous system in regulating this system has not been studied with modern electrophysiological techniques, which leaves a gap in our present knowledge deserving some attention.

The demonstration and electrophoretic separation of a number of substances with chromatophorotropic activity provide the possibility that such materials are the hormones which normally act on the integumentary pigments, but as yet little direct evidence is available for this. Most of the evidence comes from injection experiments; yet here caution is necessary to distinguish a substance which acts directly on the effector from one which releases chromatophorotropins from the central nervous system and thereby influences metachrosis indirectly. In this respect too it should be noted that nothing is known of the mechanism of interaction between hormone and effector.

Most endocrinologists look forward to the time when the hormones of their particular interest can be separated in pure form and chemically identified. It then will become possible to resolve some of the anomalies, contradictions, and puzzling observations that have been presented by experimental studies. The abundance of chromatophorotropins found in Crustacea leads one to hope that such chemical separation may result in resolution of many physiological difficulties.

REFERENCES

1. Abramowitz, A. A. 1935. Color changes in cancroid crabs of Bermuda. *Proc. Natl. Acad. Sci. U. S.* 21:677–681.
2. Abramowitz, A. A. 1937a. The chromatophorotropic hormone of the Crustacea: standardization, properties and physiology of the eye-stalk glands. *Biol. Bull.* 72:344–365.
3. Abramowitz, A. A. 1937b. The comparative physiology of pigmentary responses in the Crustacea. *J. Exptl. Zool.* 76:407–422.
4. Abramowitz, A. A. 1938. The similarity between the hypophyseal chromatophorotropic hormone and the chromatophorotropic hormone of the crustacean eyestalk. *Physiol. Zoöl.* 11:299–310.
5. Abramowitz, A. A. 1940. Purification of the chromatophorotropic hormone of the crustacean eyestalk. *J. Biol. Chem.* 132:501–506.
6. Abramowitz, A. A., and Abramowitz, R. K. 1938. On the specificity and related properties of the crustacean chromatophorotropic hormone. *Biol. Bull.* 74:278–296.

7. Atzler, M. 1930. Untersuchungen über den morphologischen und physiologischen Farbwechsel von *Dixippus morosus*. *Z. vergleich. Physiol.* **13**:505–533.
8. Bennitt, R. 1924. The migration of the retinal pigment in crustaceans. *J. Exptl. Zool.* **40**:381–435.
9. Bennitt, R. 1932. Physiological interrelationship in the eyes of decapod Crustacea. *Physiol. Zoöl.* **5**:49–64.
10. Bennitt, R., and Merrick, A. D. 1932. Migration of the proximal retinal pigment in the crayfish in relation to oxygen deficiency. *Biol. Bull.* **62**:168–177.
11. Bliss, D. E., Durand, J. B., and Welsh, J. H. 1954. Neurosecretory systems in decapod Crustacea. *Z. Zellforsch. u. mikroskop. Anat.* **39**:520–536.
12. Bliss, D. E., and Welsh, J. H. 1952. The neurosecretory system of brachyuran Crustacea. *Biol. Bull.* **103**:157–169.
13. Bodenstein, D. 1953. The role of hormones in molting and metamorphosis. *In:* "Insect Physiology" (K. D. Roeder, ed.), pp. 879–931. Wiley, New York.
14. Böttger, G. 1935. Über einen neuen Intermedintest und die Intermedinreaktion der Elritze. *Z. vergleich. Physiol.* **21**:415–428.
15. Bowman, T. E. 1949. Chromatophorotropins in the central nervous organs of the crab, *Hemigrapsus oregonensis*. *Biol. Bull.* **96**:238–245.
16. Brown, F. A., Jr. 1933. The controlling mechanism of chromatophores in *Palaemonetes*. *Proc. Natl. Acad. Sci. U. S.* **19**:327–329.
17. Brown, F. A., Jr. 1934. The chemical nature of the pigments and the transformations responsible for color changes in *Palaemonetes*. *Biol. Bull.* **67**:365–380.
18. Brown, F. A., Jr. 1935a. Color changes in *Palaemonetes*. *J. Morphol.* **57**:313–333.
19. Brown, F. A., Jr. 1935b. Control of pigment migration within the chromatophores of *Palaemonetes vulgaris*. *J. Exptl. Zool.* **71**:1–15.
20. Brown, F. A., Jr. 1940. The crustacean sinus gland and chromatophore activation. *Physiol. Zoöl.* **13**:343–355.
21. Brown, F. A., Jr. 1950. Studies on the physiology of *Uca* red chromatophores. *Biol. Bull.* **98**:218–226.
22. Brown, F. A., Jr. 1952. Hormones in crustaceans. *In:* "The Action of Hormones in Plants and Invertebrates" (K. V. Thimann, ed.), pp. 171–214. Academic Press, New York.
23. Brown, F. A., Jr., and Ederstrom, H. E. 1940. Dual control of certain black chromatophores of *Crago*. *J. Exptl. Zool.* **85**:53–69.
24. Brown, F. A., Jr., Ederstrom, H. E., and Scudamore, H. H. 1939. Sinusglandectomy in crustaceans without blinding. *Anat. Record* **75** Suppl.:129–130.
25. Brown, F. A., Jr., Fingerman, M., and Hines, M. N. 1952. Alterations in the capacity for light and dark adaptation of the distal retinal pigment of *Palaemonetes*. *Physiol. Zoöl.* **25**:230–239.
26. Brown, F. A., Jr., Guyselman, J. B., and Sandeen, M. 1949. Black chromatophores of *Uca* as independent effectors. *Anat. Record* **105**:615.
27. Brown, F. A., Jr., and Hines, M. N. 1952. Modifications in the diurnal pigmentary rhythm of *Uca* effected by continuous illumination. *Physiol. Zoöl.* **25**:56–70.
28. Brown, F. A., Jr., Hines, M. N., and Fingerman, M. 1952. Hormonal regulation of the distal retinal pigment of *Palaemonetes*. *Biol. Bull.* **102**:212–225.
29. Brown, F. A., Jr., and Meglitsch, A. 1940. Comparison of the chromatophorotropic activity of insect corpora cardiaca with that of crustacean sinus glands. *Biol. Bull.* **79**:409–418.

30. Brown, F. A., Jr., and Sandeen, M. 1948. Responses of the chromatophores of the fiddler crab, *Uca*, to light and temperature. *Physiol. Zoöl.* 21:362–371.
31. Brown, F. A., Jr., and Scudamore, H. H. 1940. Differentiation of two principles from the crustacean sinus gland. *J. Cellular Comp. Physiol.* 15:103–119.
32. Brown, F. A., Jr., Webb, H. M., and Sandeen, M. 1953. Differential production of two retinal pigment hormones in *Palaemonetes* by light flashes. *J. Cellular Comp. Physiol.* 41:123–144.
33. Brown, F. A., Jr., and Wulff, V. J. 1941. Chromatophore types in *Crago* and their endocrine control. *J. Cellular Comp. Physiol.* 18:339–353.
34. Carlisle, D. B. 1955. Local variations in the color pattern of the prawn *Leander serratus* Pennant. *J. Marine Biol. Assoc. United Kingdom* 34:559–563.
35. Carlisle, D. B., and Passano, L. M. 1953. The X-organ of Crustacea. *Nature* 171:1070.
36. Carlson, S. P. 1935. The color change in *Uca pugilator*. *Proc. Natl. Acad. Sci. U. S.* 21:549–551.
37. Carlson, S. P. 1936. Color changes in brachyuran crustaceans, especially in *Uca pugilator*. *Kgl. Fysiograf. Sällskap. Lund Förh.* 6:1–18.
38. Carstam, S. P. 1942. Weitere Beiträge zur Farbwechselphysiologie der Crustaceen. *Z. vergleich. Physiol.* 29:433–472.
38a. Carstam, S. P. 1951. Enzymatic inactivation of the pigment hormone of the crustacean sinus gland. *Nature* 167:321–322.
39. Castle, E. S. 1927. The interrelation of the eyes of *Palaemonetes* as concerns retinal pigment migration. *Proc. Natl. Acad. Sci. U. S.* 13:637–639.
40. Congdon, E. D. 1907. The effect of temperature on the migration of the retinal pigment in decapod crustaceans. *J. Exptl. Zool.* 4:539–548.
41. Day, M. F. 1941. Pigment migration in the eyes of the moth, *Ephestia kuehniella* Zeller. *Biol. Bull.* 80:275–291.
42. Debaisieux, P. 1944. Les yeux des Crustacés—structure, développement, réactions à l'éclairement. *La Cellule* 50:9–122.
43. de Bruin, G. H. P., and Crisp, D. J. 1957. The influence of pigment migration on vision of higher Crustacea. *J. Exptl. Biol.* 34:447–463.
44. Dupont-Raabe, M. 1949. Réactions humorales des chromatophores de la larve de Coréthre. *Compt. rend.* 228:130–132.
45. Dupont-Raabe, M. 1951. Étude expérimentale de l'adaptation chromatique chez le phasme, *Carausius morosus* Br. *Compt. rend.* 232:886–888.
46. Dupont-Raabe, M. 1952. Substances chromactives de Crustacés et d'Insectes. Activité réciproque, répartition, différences qualitatives. *Arch. zool. exptl. et gén.* 89:102–112.
47. Dupont-Raabe, M. 1954. Répartition des activités chromatiques dans le ganglion susoesophagien des phasmides: mise en évidence d'une région sécrétoire dans la partie deuto et tritocérébrale. *Compt. rend.* 238:950–951.
48. Dupont-Raabe, M. 1957. Les mécanismes del'adaptation chromatique chez les Insectes. *Arch. zool. exptl. et gén.* 94:61–294.
49. Edwards, G. A. 1952. The influence of eyestalk removal on the metabolism of the fiddler crab. *Physiol. Comparata et Oecol.* 2:34–50.
50. Enami, M. 1951. The sources and activities of two chromatophorotropic hormones in crabs of the genus *Sesarma*. II. Histology of incretory elements. *Biol. Bull.* 101:241–258.

51. Fingerman, M. 1956. The physiology of the melanophores of the isopod, *Ligia exotica*. *Tulane Studies Zool.* 3:139–148.

51a. Fingerman, M., and Lowe, M. E. 1957. Hormones controlling the chromatophores of the dwarf crawfish, *Cambarellus shufeldtii:* their secretion, stability, and separation by filter paper electrophoresis. *Tulane Studies Zool.* 5:151–171.

51b. Fingerman, M., Lowe, M. E., and Sundararaj, B. I. 1958. Direct evidence for a distal retinal pigment dark-adapting hormone in *Palaemonetes vulgaris*. (Abstract.) *Biol. Bull.* 115:351.

51c. Fingerman, M., Sundararaj, B. I., and Sandeen, M. I. 1958. Further studies on the chromatophorotropins of *Palaemonetes vulgaris*. (Abstract.) *Biol. Bull.* 115: 352.

52. Fingerman, M., and Whitsell, J. S. 1956. Background responses of the red and white chromatophores of the dwarf crawfish, *Cambarellus shufeldtii*. *Anat. Record* 125:637.

53. Florey, E. 1952. Untersuchungen über die Natur der Farbwechselhormone der Crustaceen. *Biol. Zentr.* 71:499–511.

54. Giersberg, H. 1928. Über den morphologischen und physiologischen Farbwechsel der Stabheuschrecke *Dixippus morosus*. *Z. vergleich. Physiol.* 7:657–695.

55. Hadorn, E., and Frizzi, G. 1949. Experimentelle Untersuchungen zur Melanophoren—Reaktion von *Corethra*. *Rev. suisse zool.* 56:306–316.

56. Hanström, B. 1937a. Die Sinusdrüse und der hormonal bedingte Farbwechsel der Crustaceen. *Kgl. Svenska Vetenskapsakad. Handl.* 16(3):1–99.

57. Hanström, B. 1937b. Vermischte Beobachtungen über die chromatophoraktivierenden Substanzen der Augenstiele der Crustaceen und des Kopfes der Insekten. *Kgl. Fysiograf. Sällskap. Lund Handl.* 47:1–11.

58. Hanström, B. 1939. "Hormones in Invertebrates," 198 pp. Oxford Univ. Press, London and New York.

59. Hanström, B. 1940. Die chromatophoraktivierende Substanz des Insektenkopfes. *Lunds Univ. Årsskr.* [N.F.] Avd. 2 36:1–20.

60. Hitchcock, H. B. 1941. The coloration and color changes of the gulf-weed crab, *Planes minutus*. *Biol. Bull.* 80:26–30.

60a. Hodge, M. H., and Chapman, G. B. 1958. Some observations on the fine structure of the sinus gland of a land crab, *Gecarcinus lateralis*. *J. Biophys. Biochem. Cytol.* 4:571–574.

61. Hogben, L., and Slome, D. 1931. The pigmentary effector system. VI. The dual character of endocrine co-ordination in amphibian color change. *Proc. Roy. Soc.* B108:10–53.

62. Hosoi, T. 1934. Chromatophore-activating substance in the shrimps. *J. Fac. Sci. Imp. Univ. Tokyo Sect. IV* 3:265–270.

63. Kalmus, H. 1938. Über einen latenten physiologischen Farbwechsel beim Flusskrebs *Potamobius astacus*, sowie seine hormonale Beeinflussung. *Z. vergleich. Physiol.* 25:784–797.

64. Kleinholz, L. H. 1934. Eye-stalk hormone and the movement of the distal retinal pigment in *Palaemonetes*. *Proc. Natl. Acad. Sci. U. S.* 20:659–661.

65. Kleinholz, L. H. 1936. Crustacean eye-stalk hormone and retinal pigment migration. *Biol. Bull.* 70:159–184.

66. Kleinholz, L. H. 1937. Studies in the pigmentary system of Crustacea. I. Color changes and diurnal rhythm in *Ligia baudiniana*. *Biol. Bull.* 72:24–36.

67. Kleinholz, L. H. 1938. Studies in the pigmentary system of Crustacea. IV. The unitary versus the multiple hormone hypothesis of control. *Biol. Bull.* **75**:510–532.

68. Kleinholz, L. H. 1948a. Migrations of the retinal pigments and their regulation by the sinus gland. *Bull. biol. France et Belg.* **33** Suppl.: 127–138.

69. Kleinholz, L. H. 1948b. Factors controlling the migration of the proximal pigment of the crustacean retina. *Anat. Record* **101**:15.

70. Kleinholz, L. H. 1949. Responses of the proximal retinal pigment of the isolated crustacean eyestalk to light and to darkness. *Proc. Natl. Acad. Sci. U. S.* **35**:215–218.

71. Kleinholz, L. H. 1955. The nature of the reflecting pigment in the arthropod eye. *Biol. Bull.* **109**:362.

71a. Kleinholz, L. H. 1958. Neurosecretion and retinal pigment movement in crustaceans. *In:* "Zweites Internationales Symposium über Neurosekretion" (W. Bargmann, B. Hanström, and E. Scharrer, eds.), pp. 110–112. Springer, Berlin.

71b. Kleinholz, L. H. 1959. Purines and pteridines from the reflecting pigment of the arthropod retina. *Biol. Bull.* **116**:125–135.

72. Kleinholz, L. H., and Henwood, W. 1953. The nature of the retinal reflecting pigment in macruran crustaceans. *Anat. Record* **117**:637.

73. Kleinholz, L. H., and Knowles, F. G. W. 1938. Studies in the pigmentary system of Crustacea. III. Light-intensity and the position of the distal retinal pigment in *Leander adspersus*. *Biol. Bull.* **75**:266–273.

74. Kleinholz, L. H., and Welsh, J. H. 1937. Colour changes in *Hippolyte varians*. *Nature* **140**:851.

75. Knowles, F. G. W. 1939. The control of the white reflecting chromatophores in Crustacea. *Pubbl. staz. zool. Napoli* **17**:174–182.

76. Knowles, F. G. W. 1940. Response of isolated white chromatophores of Crustacea to change of illumination. *Nature* **146**:131.

77. Knowles, F. G. W. 1950. The control of retinal pigment migration in *Leander serratus*. *Biol. Bull.* **98**:66–80.

78. Knowles, F. G. W. 1952. Pigment movements after sinus-gland removal in *Leander adspersus*. *Physiol. Comparata et Oecol.* **2**:289–296.

79. Knowles, F. G. W., and Carlisle, D. B. 1956. Endocrine control in the Crustacea. *Biol. Revs. Cambridge Phil. Soc.* **31**:396–473.

80. Knowles, F. G. W., Carlisle, D. B., and Dupont-Raabe, M. 1955. Studies on pigment-activating substances in animals. I. The separation by paper electrophoresis of chromactivating substances in arthropods. *J. Marine Biol. Assoc. United Kingdom* **34**:611–635.

81. Knowles, F. G. W., Carlisle, D. B., and Dupont-Raabe, M. 1956. Inactivation enzymatique d'une substance chromactive des Insectes et des Crustacés. *Compt. rend.* **242**:825.

82. Koller, G. 1925. Über den Farbwechsel bei *Crangon vulgaris*. *Verhandl. deut. zool. Ges.* **30**:128–132.

83. Koller, G. 1927. Über Chromatophorensystem, Farbensinn und Farbwechsel bei *Crangon vulgaris*. *Z. vergleich. Physiol.* **5**:191–246.

84. Koller, G. 1928. Versuche über die inkretorischen Vorgänge beim Garneelenfarbwechsel. *Z. vergleich. Physiol.* **8**:601–612.

85. Kropp, B., and Perkins, E. B. 1933. The occurrence of the humoral chromatophore activator among marine crustaceans. *Biol. Bull.* **64**:28–32.

86. Landgrebe, F. W., Ketterer, B., and Waring, H. 1955. Hormones of the posterior pituitary. *In:* "The Hormones" (G. Pincus and K. V. Thimann, eds.), Vol. III, pp. 389–431. Academic Press, New York.

87. Lee, T. H., and Lerner, A. B. 1956. Isolation of melanocyte-stimulating hormone from hog pituitary gland. *J. Biol. Chem.* **221**:943–959.

88. Lerner, A. B., and Lee, T. H. 1955. Isolation of homogeneous melanocyte stimulating hormone from hog pituitary gland. *J. Am. Chem. Soc.* **77**:1066–1067.

89. Martini, E., and Achundow, J. 1929. Versuche über Farbanpassung bei Culiciden. *Zool. Anz.* **81**:25–44.

90. Megušar, F. 1912. Experimente über den Farbwechsel der Crustaceen. *Arch. Entwicklungsmech. Organ.* **33**:462–665.

91. Nagano, T. 1947. Physiological studies on the pigmentary system of Crustacea. II. The pigment migration in the eyes of the shrimps. *Science Repts. Tôhoku Univ. Fourth Series* **18**:1–16.

92. Nagano, T. 1949. Physiological studies on the pigmentary system of Crustacea. III. The color change of an isopod *Ligia exotica* (Roux). *Science Repts. Tôhoku Univ. Fourth Series* **18**:167–175.

93. Nagano, T. 1950a. Physiological studies on the pigmentary system of Crustacea. IV. Studies on the diurnal rhythm of the eye pigments of the shrimps. *Science Repts. Tôhoku Univ. Fourth Series* **18**:286–297.

94. Nagano, T. 1950b. Physiological studies on the pigmentary system of Crustacea. V. Drug action upon the pigmentary system of a shrimp. *Science Repts. Tôhoku Univ. Fourth Series* **18**:298–303.

95. Nagano, T. 1952. Physiological studies on the pigmentary system of Crustacea. IX. An analysis of the behavior of the proximal retinal pigment in the shrimp. *Science Repts. Tôhoku Univ. Fourth Series* **19**:219–220.

96. Östlund, E., and Fänge, R. 1956. On the nature of the eye-stalk hormone which causes concentration of the red pigment in shrimps (Natantia). *Ann. sci. nat. Zool. et biol. animale* **18**:325–334.

97. Panouse, J. B. 1946. Recherches sur les phénomènes humoraux chez les Crustacés. *Ann. inst. océanog. Paris* **23**:65–147.

98. Parker, G. H. 1897. Photomechanical changes in the retinal pigment cells of *Palaemonetes,* and their relation to the central nervous system. *Bull. Museum Comp. Zool. Harvard* **30**:273–300.

99. Parker, G. H. 1932. The movements of the retinal pigment. *Ergeb. Biol.* **9**:239–291.

100. Parker, G. H. 1948. "Animal Color Changes and Their Neurohumors," 377 pp. Cambridge Univ. Press, London and New York.

101. Passano, L. M. 1951. The X-organ-sinus gland neurosecretory system in crabs. *Anat. Record* **111**:502.

102. Passano, L. M. 1953. Neurosecretory control of molting in crabs by the X-organ sinus gland complex. *Physiol. Comparata et Oecol.* **3**:155–189.

103. Peabody, E. B. 1939. Pigmentary responses in the isopod, *Idothea. J. Exptl. Zool.* **82**:47–83.

103a. Pérez-González, M. D. 1957. Evidence for hormone-containing granules in sinus glands of the fiddler crab *Uca pugilator. Biol. Bull.* **113**:426–441.

104. Perkins, E. B. 1928. Color changes in crustaceans, especially in *Palaemonetes*. *J. Exptl. Zool.* 50:71–105.
105. Perkins, E. B., and Snook, T. 1931. Control of pigment migration in the chromatophores of crustaceans. *Proc. Natl. Acad. Sci. U. S.* 17:282–285.
106. Priebatsch, I. 1933. Der Einfluss des Lichtes auf Farbwechsel und Phototaxis von *Dixippus morosus*. *Z. vergleich. Physiol.* 19:453–488.
107. Ruck, P., and Jahn, T. L. 1954. Electrical studies on the compound eye of *Ligia occidentalis* Dana (Crustacea: Isopoda). *J. Gen. Physiol.* 37:825–849.
108. Sandeen, M. I. 1950. Chromatophorotropins in the central nervous system of *Uca pugilator*, with special reference to their origins and actions. *Physiol. Zoöl.* 23:337–352.
109. Sandeen, M. I., and Brown, F. A., Jr. 1952. Responses of the distal retinal pigment of *Palaemonetes* to illumination. *Physiol. Zoöl.* 25:222–230.
110. Sawaya, P. 1939. Sobre a mudança da côr nos Crustaceos. *Univ. São Paulo Fac. filosof. ciênc. e letras, Zool. No. 3, Bol.* 13:1–109.
111. Sjögren, S. 1934. Die Blutdrüse and ihre Ausbildung bei den Dekapoden. *Zool. Jahrbch. Abt. Anat. u. Ontog. Tiere* 58:145–170.
112. Smith, R. I. 1948. The role of the sinus glands in retinal pigment migration in grapsoid crabs. *Biol. Bull.* 95:169–185.
113. Stephens, G. C., Friedl, F., and Guttman, B. 1956. Electrophoretic separation of chromatophorotropic principles of the fiddler crab, *Uca. Biol. Bull.* 111:312–313.
113a. Stephens, G. C., and Green, J. P. 1958. Enzymatic inactivation of chromatophorotropic principles from the fiddler crab, *Uca. Biol. Bull.* 115:367.
114. Suneson, S. 1947. Color change and chromatophore activators in *Idothea. Kgl. Fysiograf. Sällskap. Lund Handl.* [N. F.] 58:1–34.
115. Thomsen, M. 1943. Effect of corpus cardiacum and other insect organs on the color-change of the shrimp, *Leander adspersus. Kgl. Danske Videnskab. Selskab. Biol. Medd.* 19:1–38.
116. von Frisch, K. 1908. Studien über die Pigmentverschiebung im Facettenauge. *Biol. Zentr.* 28:662–671; 698–704.
117. Waring, H., and Landgrebe, F. W. 1950. Hormones of the posterior pituitary. *In:* "The Hormones" (G. Pincus and K. V. Thimann, eds.), Vol. II, pp. 427–514. Academic Press, New York.
118. Waterman, T. H., and Wiersma, C. A. G. 1954. The functional relation between retinal cells and optic nerve in *Limulus. J. Exptl. Zool.* 126:59–85.
119. Welsh, J. H. 1930a. The mechanics of migration of the distal pigment cells in the eyes of *Palaemonetes. J. Exptl. Zool.* 56:459–494.
120. Welsh, J. H. 1930b. Diurnal rhythm of the distal pigment cells in the eyes of certain crustaceans. *Proc. Natl. Acad. Sci. U. S.* 16:386–395.
121. Welsh, J. H. 1939. The action of eye-stalk extracts on retinal pigment migration in the crayfish, *Cambarus bartoni. Biol. Bull.* 77:119–125.
122. Welsh, J. H. 1941. The sinus glands and 24-hour cycles of retinal pigment migration in the crayfish. *J. Exptl. Zool.* 86:35–49.

CHAPTER 5

E. NEWTON HARVEY

LIGHT PRODUCTION

I. OCCURRENCE AND DISTRIBUTION OF LUMINESCENCE

Among the eight subclasses of Crustacea* three contain species which are self-luminous, namely the Ostracoda, Copepoda, and Malacostraca (Orders: Mysidacea, Euphausiacea, and Decapoda). In the last of these subclasses two other orders, the Isopoda and Amphipoda, contain species which frequently become infected with luminous bacteria and become luminous until they finally succumb to the infection. For example, beach fleas sometimes appear to be luminous Crustacea, although it has been known since the luminous bacteria were isolated[19,20] that the light is of parasitic bacterial origin. A luminous isopod, a wood louse on the Palau Islands, has been described, and parasitic luminous bacteria have been isolated from the specimen.[25] A luminous *Megaligia* whose light was bacterial in origin is also known.[25]

In addition to these spurious luminescent Crustacea, apparent luminous organs have been described in the deep-sea amphipods, *Scypholanceola*[65] and in *Streetsia*,[18] although luminescence of these organisms has not been seen. Finally, Dr. T. E. Bowman has informed me by letter (1954) that *Parapronoe crustulum*, a marine amphipod of the family Pronoidae, caught off the coast of Georgia in the western North Atlantic, is luminous, although the origin of the light is unknown.

The Ostracoda were among the first small Crustacea recognized as responsible for "phosphorescence" of the sea in 1754, a discovery of

---

* The genera of Crustacea reported to contain luminous species will be found in "Bioluminescence,"[36] pages 297–354.

Godeheu de Riville, who published a very good figure of the organism in the Memoirs of the French Academy for 1760. Among the families of Ostracoda, the Cypridinidae and Halocypridae contain luminous forms. The best-known luminous genera are *Cypridina*, *Pyrocypris* and *Conchoecia*. A species of *Cypridina* is reproduced in Fig. 1. All luminous ostracods secrete a photogenic material into the sea water from glands near the mouth.

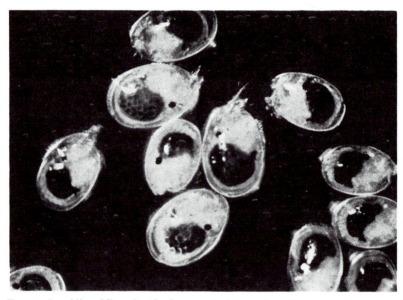

Fig. 1. *Cypridina hilgendorfii*, photographed from life. The mass of eggs can be seen in the posterior half of the animal, as well as a small black eyespot. In some specimens swimming legs protrude from the shell at the anterior end where the luminous materials are extruded to the exterior. Photo by courtesy of Dr. Yata Haneda.

The Copepoda were early recognized as a source of marine luminescence, probably first by O. Fabricius (1780), who named the organism concerned *Cyclops brevicornis* in his "Fauna Groenlandica." Among 71 families of copepods, 9 contain luminous species. The light comes from secretion of single gland cells or groups of gland cells scattered in different regions of the body. The best-known luminous genera are *Metridia*, *Pleuromamma*, *Lucicutia*, *Heterorhabdus*, *Pontella*, *Corycaeus*, and *Oncaea* (Fig. 2).

Among the Mysidacea, the Suborder Lophogastrida, containing *Gnathophausia*, and the Suborder Mysida, containing *Mysis*, are luminous, but little is known of the structure, physiology, or biochemistry of light production in these forms.

The Order Euphausiacea consists of a single family, the Euphausiidae, with 11 genera. Ten of these (*Thysanopoda, Meganyctiphanes, Nyctiphanes, Euphausia, Pseudeuphausia, Thysanoessa, Tessarabrachion, Nematoscelis, Nematobrachion, Stylocheiron*) contain luminescent species while the nonluminous genus, *Bentheuphausia*, is said to be blind. They are usually called shrimp or prawns and have not always been clearly defined from another great order, also containing shrimp or prawns, the Decapoda. Early workers gave them such names as

Fig. 2. The luminous copepod, *Oncaea conifera*, male and female *in copulo*. (From Giesbrecht.[21])

Cancer, Gammarus, or Oniscus. Their luminescence was probably recognized as early as 1746 by J. Anderson in his "Nachricht von Island, Groenland und der Strasse Davis." Euphausiids possess complicated luminous organs of lanternlike structure.

Of the 73 families of Decapoda, 7 contain luminous species and one additional family, the Atyidae, includes the genus *Paratya*, a freshwater shrimp of Lake Suwa, Japan, 1000 meters above sea level and 100 miles from the sea. This organism is not self-luminous, but regularly becomes infected while living with luminous bacteria whose characteristics have been studied by Yasaki.[66] Among the decapods with true luminescence at least 17 genera contain luminous species. The best-known forms are *Hymenopenaeus, Aristeus, Sergestes, Leptochela, Oplophorus, Systellaspis, Heterocarpus*, and *Polycheles*. The light may come from complicated lanternlike luminous organs or a luminous secretion expelled into the sea water from a multicellular gland.

Distribution of luminescence among the Crustacea is thus like that in other phyla of the animal kingdom. Some large orders contain no luminous species, others (Euphausiacea) are made up almost entirely of luminous forms. The distribution is spotty and no clear evolutionary lines of development can be discerned. One species in a genus may possess many luminous organs and a closely allied species, none. Only marine crustaceans are self-luminous, in this respect agreeing with the general fact that fresh-water organisms are not luminous.

II. *TYPES OF LUMINOUS ORGANS*

A. OSTRACODA

Among these forms, the luminous gland is situated in the upper lip and is made up of elongate cells whose contents empty by single

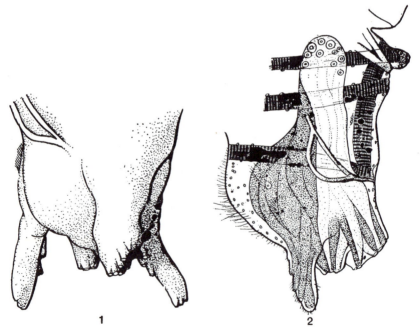

1   2

FIG. 3. The upper lip (1) and a section (2) of the luminous gland of *Cypridina hilgendorfii*, showing two types of gland cells. (After Yatsu.[67])

pores into the sea water, as indicated in Fig. 3. In *Cypridina hilgendorfii* two kinds of gland cells,[61,67] or four,[50,55] have been described. The author[29] has observed with the microscope in the living *Cypridina* two types of granules secreted from separate gland cells, one type of granule rather large (diameter 10 μ) and yellow in color (probably luciferin), the other smaller (diameter 2–3 μ) and colorless (probably luciferase). Both types dissolve in sea water and together give the typical bluish luminescence. Muscle contraction forces the granules from the gland cells, and there is no nerve supply to the gland itself. Early stages of development of the organs have been described.[51]

B. COPEPODA

Almost our entire knowledge of luminescence among copepods is due to Giesbrecht,[21,22] who described unicellular pear-shaped skin glands of a yellow color in various body regions. They do not differ from other nonluminous skin glands except in their yellow color, and they are often paired with nonluminous yellow skin glands or occur as twins (in *Heterorhabdus*) with a common opening. This arrangement suggests the condition in *Cypridina*, but Giesbrecht held that there was no mutual reaction of colorless skin glands and yellow luminous glands to produce the light. The author[23] was unable to demonstrate the luciferin and luciferase reaction among copepods. Giesbrecht could detect no nerves going to the gland cells; muscle movements of the copepod may force out the secretion.

C. MALACOSTRACA

1. *Mysidacea.* Little is known of the histology of mysid luminous organs. A luminous gland in the second maxilla at the base of the exognath in *Gnathophausia* has been described.[42] Two ducts lead the secretion to a large reservoir from which it is forced into the sea water by muscle contraction, apparently as in *Cypridina*.

2. *Euphausiacea.* Among these shrimp, the luminescence is intracellular from complicated light organs known as photospheres or photophores. They consist of a reflector, photogenic cells, a "rod mass" of doubtful function, and a lens, as shown in Fig. 4. Thin nerves to the organ have been described and one account of the luminescence[60] suggests either nervous or hormonal control. The authors in question were chiefly concerned with proving that the photospheres were not accessory eyes, which would imply a large optic nerve. Nerves have also been described in *Nematoscelis*.[13] Other histological studies have been made by Giesbrecht,[23] Trojan,[57] Dahlgren,[15] and Pierantoni.[53]

3. *Decapoda.* The decapod shrimp may emit light from photophores with a lens, like the photospheres of euphausiids, or eject a large mass of luminous secretion into the sea water from a gland on the mandible. There are many types of luminous organs among the decapod

shrimp.[3] The outstanding paper on the histology of decapod light organs is that of Dennell,[16] who has distinguished, in addition to the above-mentioned types, the following structures with no lens system:

1) Superficial photophores of *Sergestes regalis,* consisting of horizontal sheets of interwoven fibers among which are scattered photogenic units. No nerve supply was discovered.

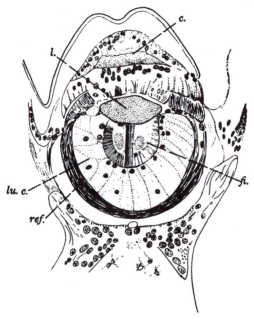

FIG. 4. Section of the photophore of the euphausiid shrimp *Meganyctiphanes norvegica. lu. c.,* luminous cells; *ref.,* reflector; *fi.,* rod mass; *l.,* lens; *c.,* blood sinus. (From Vallentin and Cunningham.[60])

2) Organs of Pesta (luminous digestive gland tubules) suspected of producing light by their discoverer, Pesta, and by Burkenroad[4] in a later study. They are internal cephalothoracic lateroventral organs present in many species of *Sergestes.* Dennell has recently observed their light in Bermuda species. They form part of the digestive gland which empties into the alimentary canal. Photophores made up of groups of modified gland tubules are also present in *Parapandalus richardi,* but their structure is different from those in *Sergestes.*

3) Linear photophores on the roof of the branchial chamber in many species of *Sergestes,* with no lens or accessory structures.

4) Photophores on the limbs of *Oplophorus novaezeelandiae*, made up of clusters of radially segmented granular masses, apparently devoid of nuclei.

A cross section of one of the lanternlike luminous organs is reproduced in Fig. 5.

The positions of the various types of light organs are most varied. They occur on every part of the body and may be 150 in number on *Sergestes challengeri*.[28] Kemp[43] has observed "a nerve-strand communicating with the photophore . . . but the exact mode of its entrance

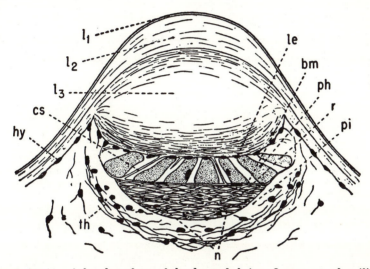

Fig. 5. Section of the photophore of the decapod shrimp *Sergestes prehensilis*. *bm*, basement membrane; *cs*, connective tissue strand; *hy*, epidermis; l_1, l_2, l_3, lens layers; *le*, lens epithelium; *n*, nerve fibers; *ph*, photogenic cells; *pi*, pigment; *r*, reflector; *th*, capsule. × 460. (From Terao.[56])

could not be discovered." Thus the anatomical features of these light organs, like those of euphausiids, are such as to imply excitation of luminescence by nerve, quite comparable to the excitation to contraction of vertebrate striped muscle tissue.

III. *PHYSICAL NATURE OF THE LIGHT*

As in other luminous organisms, the light emission of crustaceans is a chemiluminescence which consists of a short band of wavelengths in the green or blue region of the visible spectrum. Only one spectral distribution curve has been worked out, that of *Cypridina hilgendorfii*.[14,17,38a] The curve of Coblentz and Hughes is reproduced in Fig. 6 together with that of the firefly, to indicate the general form of wavelength distribution.

Despite the many measurements in arbitrary units of light intensity of luminescence of the photogenic substances (luciferin and luciferase) of *Cypridina* in aqueous solution,[36] no absolute measurements have been made during the luminous discharge in nature. The nearest approach

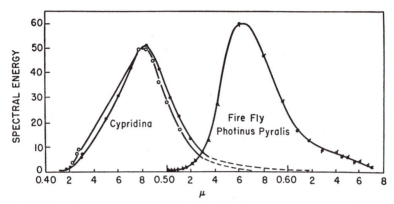

FIG. 6. Spectral energy curve of *Cypridina* luminous extracts compared with that of the firefly. Spectral energy in arbitrary units; wavelength in microns. (From Coblentz and Hughes.[14])

is that of Nichols,[47] who found a brightness of 16 millilamberts for the dried organism after moistening with water.

IV. *BIOCHEMISTRY OF LIGHT PRODUCTION*

A. Miscellaneous Observations

One of the first problems connected with the chemistry of any bioluminescence is to determine whether the luciferin-luciferase reaction can be demonstrated—i.e. whether a cold-water extract of a luminous organ, presumably containing the enzyme luciferase, will give light when mixed with a hot-water extract of the luminous organ (after cooling), which presumably contains luciferin. This reaction is particularly well shown by *Cypridina hilgendorfii* and related ostracods.

It has been tested on a number of other luminous crustaceans: on copepods,[32] and on two decapods with a luminous secretion, *Systellaspis debilis*[35] and *Heterocarpus sibogae*, as well as on one decapod with photophores, *Sergestes prehensilis*,[27] and on a euphausiid, *Meganyctiphanes norvegica*.[32] Only in the case of *Systellaspis* and *Heterocarpus* were luciferin and luciferase demonstrated. The other species have all given negative results.

It is particularly interesting to note that the luciferin of *Cypridina hilgendorfii* will react with luciferase from *Cypridina norvegica* and, conversely, *C. hilgendorfii* luciferase gives light with *C. norvegica* luciferin.[31] However, no light appears if *Cypridina* luciferin is mixed with *Systellaspis* luciferase or vice versa. The specificity of various luciferases is marked, and in fact it now seems certain that the luciferins from various groups of animals may also be quite different chemically.[37,37a]

Oxygen is necessary for luminescence in the two groups of Crustacea tested, the copepods and ostracods.[34] The relation of light intensity to O_2 pressure has been worked out for *Cypridina*.[40] Experiments should be carried out with the remaining groups to determine whether O_2 is essential for luminescence of various types of shrimp or whether they behave like the ctenophores, which do not require dissolved O_2.

In the case of *Cypridina*, only O_2, luciferin, and luciferase, dissolved in pure water, must be present for light to appear. Addition of NaCl and other salts may increase the light intensity,[2] but they are not necessary. In this respect *Cypridina* differs from certain other luminescent systems, for example that of the firefly, where adenosine triphosphate (ATP) and Mg^{++}, in addition to O_2, luciferin, and luciferase must all be present for light production.[46] In another group (the luminous bacteria), luciferase, a long-chain aldehyde, oxygen, and bacterial luciferin are all necessary.[46,54] It has been found that ATP or a long-chain aldehyde play no part in the *Cypridina* luminescence system, and tests have also indicated that ATP is not necessary for luminescence of the decapods *Sergestes* or *Heterocarpus*.[57] There seems no doubt but that bacterial luciferin is reduced flavin mononucleotide. Firefly luciferin has been called a pterin. It would be of great interest to determine the chemical structure of the luciferins of various Crustacea.

Little is known concerning the chemistry of luminescence among crustaceans, with the exception of the ostracods. In the case of *Meganyctiphanes norvegica*,[55] a pigment, rose-purple by transmitted, and yellowish green by reflected, light, is present in the light organs. This is apparently a fluorescent pigment, but its relation to the bioluminescence is unknown. John Murray in the "Narrative of the Cruise of the Challenger" (Volume I, p. 743, 1885) in speaking of *Meganyctiphanes norvegica* reported that "The phosphorescent light comes from the red pigment surrounding the lenticular space," but this statement requires confirmation.

In the case of copepods at Naples, the author[33] observed that many but not all of the previously bioluminescent spots on the organisms are brightly greenish blue fluorescent in near ultraviolet light (without the visible), the fluorescence color then being similar to that of the bioluminescence. Fluorescence of a compound is an indication that it may prove to be chemiluminescent under proper conditions, and studies on the purest *Cypridina* luciferin which has thus far been obtained indicate that it is yellow fluorescent in ultraviolet light.[59] However, only in the case of *Cypridina* have general properties of the luminous substances been adequately determined, a subject which will now be presented in some detail.

B. *Cypridina* LUCIFERIN AND LUCIFERASE

An immense amount of chemical work has been carried out on ostracods, since these animals can be dried and preserved indefinitely in the dry state without any deterioration of the luminescent substance. Addition of water to dry, powdered *Cypridina* results in a bright blue luminescence lasting some time. The dry material can be extracted with various solvents and the ordinary procedures for separating biochemical materials applied. Some of the chemical facts which have been discovered by these methods are as follows:

Cypridina luciferin is a readily diffusible compound, which rapidly oxidizes without light emission in water solutions, especially if alkaline, from dissolved O_2, or on addition of mild oxidizing agents such as ferricyanide. With strong oxidizing agents, such as permanganate or various peroxides, light will appear with luciferin in aqueous solution provided the pH is around 2.[39] However, the intensity of the luminescence with strong oxidizing agents is far less than that obtained when *Cypridina* luciferase is added at pH values between 5.5 and 8.5.[8]

In 1918, the author[30] showed that the oxidation product of luciferin in crude solutions to which luciferase had been added could be reduced by methods which involve the addition of H_2. The oxidation product was called oxyluciferin, and the oxidation proved to be similar to that of a leuco dye to the dye itself, rather than the change, hemoglobin $\rightleftarrows$ oxyhemoglobin. Also if the oxyluciferin solution stood for any length of time, it could not be reduced by reducing agents, but no distinction was made between oxyluciferin formed by spontaneous oxidation of luciferin and that formed in presence of luciferase.

Later, Anderson[1] determined that the oxidation product of purified luciferin formed by spontaneous oxidation could be 30–67% reduced if the reduction was carried out immediately after oxidation, but the oxidation product in presence of luciferase was practically nonreducible (<8%). He called the oxidation product by either method oxidized luciferin but believed the two products to be different.

It has been generally assumed that two types of oxidation occur— a dark oxidation without luciferase and one accompanied with luminescence in presence of luciferase—each type involving a different group on the luciferin molecule. That this conception may not be correct was first indicated by Chase,[7] who could find no difference in the visible absorption spectrum changes on spontaneous oxidation and on oxidation with luciferase. The latter oxidation may be 100 times more rapid, but appears to lead to an end product with the same absorption in the visible spectrum. Recently a careful absorption-spectrum study of chromatographically purified luciferin in both the visible and ultraviolet regions by Tsuji[58] has also indicated that the same chemical changes occur whether luciferin is oxidized by oxygen, by ferricyanide or by luciferase. Therefore the concept of luciferin oxidation must change. Instead of two types of oxidation, one spontaneous and one with luciferase, there appear rather to be two steps of oxidation no matter how luciferin is oxidized, the first step reversible, with a redox potential somewhat below that of the hydroquinone-quinone system, and immediately following this a second irreversible step, which is rather quickly attained in the presence of luciferase. Tsuji's absorption curves are reproduced in Fig. 7 and will serve to characterize luciferin insofar as this can be done by such data.

Lack of space prohibits a discussion of all the research on luciferin carried out during the past forty years. The reader is referred to the author's book "Bioluminescence"[36] and to the paper by Tsuji, Chase, and Harvey[59] for further details regarding the properties of luciferin. Briefly, the substance appears to be of relatively low molecular weight; soluble in the lower aliphatic monohydric alcohols, but not in true fat solvents like benzene and ether; to have acid-base properties; to move electrophoretically toward the negative pole at pH values < 5.8; to have a redox potential slightly below the hydroquinone-quinone system; to be yellow in color, changing to orange yellow to colorless on oxidation.

Luciferin is weakly yellow fluorescent in ultraviolet light in both acid and alkaline solution (with much less fluorescence after oxidation). In ultraviolet light and in visible light with sensitizers, luciferin undergoes photochemical oxidation and on hydrolysis with acid is found to be made up of amino acids and a color group. Mason[44] has designated *Cypridina* luciferin a chromopolypeptide of a cyclic nature. It is not destroyed on heating in absence of oxygen, but oxygen causes rapid

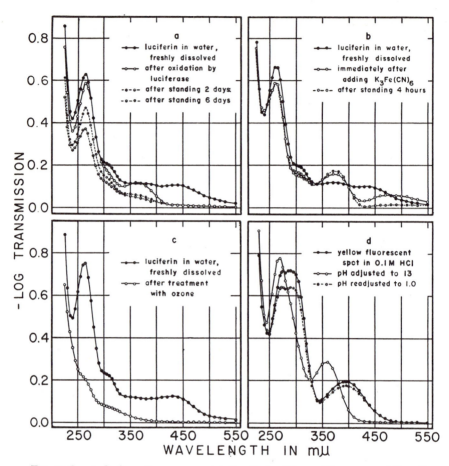

FIG. 7. Spectral absorption curves. (a) Luciferin (R_f on filter paper, 0.5; yellow in color) in distilled water, reacted with luciferase, then allowed to stand in air. (b) Luciferin in distilled water oxidized by potassium ferricyanide: final $K_3Fe(CN)_6$ concentration approximately $2 \times 10^{-5}M$. (c) Luciferin in distilled water, oxidized by ozone. (d) A blue-fluorescent impurity (R_f 0.25, nonluminescent and yellow in color) in acid and alkali. (From Tsuji.[58])

oxidation at higher temperatures. Various procedures for chromatographic purification[59] and countercurrent separation with subsequent acid hydrolysis (Marfey, Craig, and Harvey, 1958, unpublished) indicate that the amino acid content may vary, and suggest that a number of *Cypridina* luciferins may exist, made up of the color nucleus combined with different amino acid groupings.

In the most recent work,[53a] crystallization and a molecular weight of 470 are reported for *Cypridina* luciferin. An indole nucleus, glycine, and isoleucine have been identified as being present. The empirical formula is $C_{21}H_{26-28}O_2N_6 \cdot 2HCl$.

Under standard conditions, the amount of luciferin present in solution can be determined by the total light emitted, while the quantitative determination of luciferase is made from a record of the velocity constant when luciferin is oxidized under standard conditions, as indicated in Fig. 8.[9]

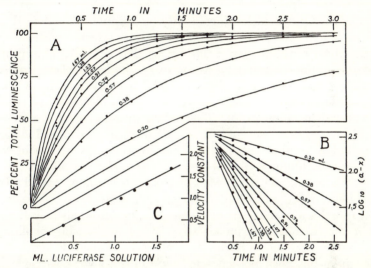

FIG. 8. Light emission as a function of luciferase concentration. A, total light emitted (in arbitrary units) for equal luciferin concentrations vs. time in minutes for different luciferase concentrations, indicated in figures on the curves. The total light is the same for a given luciferin concentration. B, $\log(a - x)$ plotted vs. time for the different luciferase concentrations. C, slopes of the log plot in B vs. luciferase concentrations, showing that the velocity constant is proportional to luciferase concentration. (From Chase.[9])

Cypridina luciferase is a nondialyzable thermolabile protein. It has been partially purified by ammonium sulfate precipitation, acetone fractional precipitation, adsorption on and elution from calcium phosphate gel by McElroy and Chase.[45] Salts are not necessary for its activity. The purified enzyme is more resistant to heat inactivation than the crude preparations, but it denatures precipitously at temperatures above about 45°C.[9] The purified material has an ultraviolet absorption maximum at 280 mμ. Luciferase is inactivated reversibly by urea,[52] as well as by the series of lower monohydric alcohols.[10,12] It presumably belongs among the dehydrogenases. Little is known concerning its chemistry, and the presence of a heavy metal or of a prosthetic group has not been established. The isoelectric point is at pH 3.3.[62] Sedimentation-constant studies of Chase[11] indicate a minimum molecular weight of 35,000. Diffusion constant studies (Fedden and Chase, 1958, unpublished) suggest a value of 45,000 for molecular weight.

V. *CONTROL OF LUMINESCENCE*

Luminous Crustacea luminesce only on stimulation, external or internal, except those forms which have become infected with luminous bacteria whose luminescence is continuous. The expelling of a luminous secretion into the sea water by ostracods results from reflex stimulation of muscle contraction, and, by copepods, possibly also from general body muscle movement, since nerves to the gland cells have not been demonstrated in either group. That reflex stimulation of luminescence occurs in *Cypridina noctiluca*, a pelagic ostracod of tropical Asia, can be inferred from the fact that this species responds by luminescence whenever a flashlight is played over the sea surface at night.[26]

Practically nothing is known of light control among mysids. In the shrimp with large mandibular secretory glands, it is probable that special muscles are active in squeezing out the luminous secretion.

It is the shrimp with photophores, either euphausiids or decapods, which presents the most interesting problems to the physiologist. Nevertheless there has been no concerted physiological work carried out on these forms, and no records of light emission have been obtained comparable to those on annelids[48,49] or on ctenophores.[6] A few scattered observations on shrimp are of interest to indicate the need for future research.

Vallentin and Cunningham[60] reported that *Meganyctiphanes norvegica* in total darkness when "swimming about in a glass jar of sea water gave out short flashes of light from time to time. Each flash was of short duration, but sometimes lasted longer than at others; when several animals gave out light simultaneously or in rapid succession, the effect was very brilliant and beautiful, but nothing like continuous luminosity was ever observed.

"When an animal was caught and removed from the water between the finger and thumb, all the organs emitted a brilliant light for 5 to 10 seconds, while the creature was flapping its abdomen vigorously and trying to escape. Then followed an interrupted series of flashes lasting 10 seconds more, and then the animal would become quiet and no light could be seen. But when slight pressure was administered, all the organs flashed again, the duration of the flash being longer when the pinch was stronger. When the animal was crushed between the fingers and the tissues rubbed between the hands, certain particles were luminous and remained continuously so until they were dry. When an organ was dissected out from the abdomen the light ceased, and by the time it was mounted and placed under the microscope all luminosity had vanished. But when the organ under the microscope was crushed the field was lit up and continued so for some time. When an eyestalk was cut off by scissors the ocular organ became luminous for an instant when the division took place. After the animals had been in captivity 24 hours, they were by no means so easily excited to give out light. Only about one in 4 became luminous on being removed from the water." On dropping the animal into fixing fluid, all the photophores glowed brilliantly.

In Japan many luminous shrimp are caught in large numbers and sold in the market for food. Terao[56] has described the luminescence of *Sergestes prehensilis* from observations in Suruga Bay at night as follows:

"Observation then made on the spot showed that, in all the freshly obtained specimens, the photophores emitted dim greenish yellow light in an intermittent way, each time starting suddenly and vanishing with as much promptitude after a longer or shorter period of illumination. Frequently, after dark intervals of varying length, the lighting up of different photophores in the same body occurred one after another in serial succession, beginning with those at the head end and thence progressing posteriorly, to finish up at the tail end. Each single photophore lighted up for nearly a moment only, and as soon as a light disappeared, another appeared a short distance behind in rapid succession, so that there were scarcely ever observed more than one light alive at a time. It took 1–2 seconds from start to finish of a single series of illumination of the above sort. At other times, only a limited number of photophores in a certain body region were observed to light up simultaneously, this time the lights remaining steadily alive for several seconds. Most frequently it was the photophores in the neighborhood of the eyes that showed this sort of activity; less frequently those of the third or of the sixth abdominal somite."

Although the author[35] has observed the secretion of luminous material from the shrimp *Systellaspis debilis*, obtained just south of Bermuda at 600–800 meters and kept in iced sea water, it was never possible to elicit luminescence from the photophores of this species, even after such strong stimulation as breaking the shrimp in half. A similar experience has been reported by Chace.[5] Concerning this matter the author ("Bioluminescence,"[36] page 352) has written: "Some species respond readily to a disturbance of any kind, but even strong stimulation will not produce light in photophores of certain species. It has been already suggested that luminescence may be connected with sexual maturity and only appear at certain seasons of the year. Another possibility is hormone control of the light organ as has been observed by Greene and Greene[24] and Harvey[38] in fish, where injection of adrenaline sets all photophores into activity. However, the author in 1931 tried injecting adrenaline into deep sea shrimp with unlighted photophores, but no light appeared and Dr. Dennell has assured me in conversation that he also could not excite Systellaspis to luminesce by adrenaline. Nevertheless other endocrines should be tested. Hormones play an important part in control of the chromatophores of Crustacea in general, and the chances are good that photophores may prove to be similarly controlled if the proper hormone is found." It is obvious that a great untouched field for investigation awaits the physiologist.

VI. *USE OF THE LIGHT*

The value of luminescence to Crustacea is largely a matter of speculation. In general light production in the animal kingdom appears to have been developed for such purposes as: 1) illumination of the ocean depths; 2) sex attraction and sex recognition; 3) species recognition; 4) to attract prey; 5) to give warning; 6) to confuse an attacking animal, which might move toward a mass of luminous secretion in the water or a suddenly displayed pattern of lights, while the dark animal by a swift maneuver, makes off in another direction.

By analogy with fish, it seems most likely that the light pattern of shrimp with photophores is a species or a sex recognition mark useful in the dark depths of the ocean where light does not penetrate to make visible a color pattern. In favor of this explanation is the correlation found between eye size and presence of photophores in deep-sea shrimp.[63,64] Thus far the distribution of light organs among shrimp has not been used by systematists to designate species, as is the practice among ichthyologists for certain deep-sea fish, nor have sexual differences in pattern been emphasized as in the case of fish, but exploration of this field seems advisable.[38]

Dennell's[16a] observations on 8 species of luminous decapod crustaceans obtained in the living condition at Bermuda led him to the conclusion that photophores do "constitute recognition signals, but it seems likely that response involves both young and adult members of the population, so causing swarming with the subsequent facilitation of mating." He observed luminescence of photophores not previously seen to produce light (e.g. in *Systellaspis debilis*) and also noted light emission from *Hymenodora gracilis*, not previously known to be luminous.

Among copepods, Giesbrecht has described 18 pear-shaped glands on various body regions and on the furca in the same positions in male and female. *Pleuromamma gracilis* had 17 light organs, *Lucicutia flavicornis* had 10, and there were at least 36 on *Heterorhabdus papilliger*. It is an interesting fact, whose significance is unknown, that sometimes the arrangement is not bilaterally symmetrical. More than 70 luminous glands are present in the female of *Oncaea conifera*, while a small number are present in the male. It is very possible that an extended study may clearly prove that the luminescence in these forms is for sex attraction. The fact previously mentioned that pelagic *Cypridina* respond to a beam of light by luminescence[26] is a clear indication that some nocturnal ostracods may signal to each other in this manner.

REFERENCES

1. Anderson, R. S. 1936. Chemical studies on bioluminescence. III. The reversible reaction of *Cypridina* luciferin with oxidizing agents and its relations to the luminescent reaction. *J. Cellular Comp. Physiol.* 8:261–276.

2. Anderson, R. S. 1937. Chemical studies on bioluminescence. IV. Salt effects on the total light emitted by a chemiluminescent reaction. *J. Am. Chem. Soc.* 59: 2115–2117.

3. Balss, H. 1944. Decapoda Leuchtorgane. *In:* "Bronn's Tierreich," Bd. 5, Abt. 1, Bch. 7, pp. 661–667. Akademische Verlagsges., Leipzig.

4. Burkenroad, M. D. 1937. Sergestidae (Crustacea Decapoda) from the lower California region, with descriptions of two new species and some remarks on the organs of Pesta in *Sergestes*. *Zoologica* 22:315–329.

5. Chace, F. A., Jr. 1940. Plankton of the Bermuda Oceanographic Expeditions. IX. The bathypelagic caridean Crustacea. *Zoologica* 25:117–209.

6. Chang, J. J. 1954. Analysis of the luminescent response of the ctenophore, *Mnemiopsis leidyi*, to stimulation. *J. Cellular Comp. Physiol.* 44:365–394.

7. Chase, A. M. 1940. Changes in the absorption spectrum of *Cypridina* luciferin solutions during oxidation. *J. Cellular Comp. Physiol.* 15:159–171.

8. Chase, A. M. 1948. Effects of hydrogen ion concentration and of buffer systems on the luminescence of the *Cypridina* luciferin-luciferase reaction. *J. Cellular Comp. Physiol.* 31:175–192.

9. Chase, A. M. 1950. Studies on cell enzyme systems. The kinetics of heat inactivation of *Cypridina* luciferase. *J. Gen. Physiol.* 33:535–546.

10. Chase, A. M. 1952. Studies on cell enzyme systems. VII. Luciferase inactivation by alcohols. *J. Pharmacol. Exptl. Therap.* 105:371–379.

11. Chase, A. M. 1955. The molecular weight of *Cypridina* luciferase. *J. Cellular Comp. Physiol.* **45**:13–20.

12. Chase, A. M., and Brigham, E. H. 1952. Studies on cell enzyme systems. VI. Competitive inhibition of *Cypridina* luciferase by butyl alcohol. *J. Cellular Comp. Physiol.* **38**:269–280.

13. Chun, C. 1896. Atlantis. Biologische Studien über pelagische Organismen. Chap. VI. Die Leuchtorgane der Euphausiden. *Zoologica, Stuttgart* **7**:196–212.

14. Coblentz, W. W., and Hughes, C. W. 1926. Spectral energy distribution of the light emitted by plants and animals. *Sci. Papers U. S. Bur. Standards* **21**:521–534.

15. Dahlgren, U. 1916. The luminous crustaceans. *J. Franklin Inst.* **181**:805–843.

16. Dennell, R. 1940. On the structure of the photophores of some decapod Crustacea. *Discovery Repts.* **20**:307-382.

16a. Dennell, R. 1955. Observations on the luminescence of bathypelagic Crustacea Decapoda of the Bermuda area. *J. Linnean Soc. London Zool.* **42**:393–406.

17. Eymers, G., and Van Schouwenburg, K. L. 1937. On the luminescence of bacteria. III. Further quantitative data regarding spectra connected with bioluminescence. *Enzymologia* **3**:235–241.

18. Fage, L. 1934. Sur la présence d'organes lumineux chez les amphipodes pélagiques. *Compt. rend.* **198**:1631–1633.

19. Giard, A. 1889. On the phosphorescent infection of the Talitri and other crustaceans. *Ann. Mag. Nat. Hist.* 4(6):476–478.

20. Giard, A., and Billet, A. 1889. Observations sur la maladie phosphorescente des Talitres et autres Crustacés. *Compt. rend. soc. biol.* **41**:593–597 and *Compt. rend.* **109**:503.

21. Giesbrecht, W. 1892. Die pelagischen Copepoden des Golfes von Neapel. *Fauna u. Flora Golfes Neapel Monogr.* **19**:1–831.

22. Giesbrecht, W. 1895. Ueber das Leuchten der pelagischen Copepoden und das tierische Leuchten im allgemeinen. *Mitt. Zool. Sta. Neapel* **11**:631–694.

23. Giesbrecht, W. 1896. Ueber den Sitz der Lichtentwicklung in den Photosphärien der Euphausiiden. *Zool. Anz.* **19**:486–490.

24. Greene, C. W., and Greene, H. H. 1924. Phosphorescence of *Portichthys notatus,* the California singing fish. *Am. J. Physiol.* **70**:500–507.

25. Haneda, Y. 1939. The terrestrial luminescent animals and plants in Palau and Yap Islands. (In Japanese.) *Kagaku Nanyo* **2**:88–93.

26. Haneda, Y. 1940. Phenomena of bioluminescence. (In Japanese.) *Seirigaku Shidoshu* **5**:18–31.

27. Haneda, Y., and Harvey, E. N. 1954. Additional data on the adenosine triphosphate and the luciferin-luciferase reactions of various luminous organisms. *Arch. Biochem. Biophys.* **48**:237–238.

28. Hanson, H. J. 1903. On the crustaceans of the Genera *Petalidium* and *Sergestes* from the "Challenger" with an account of luminous organs in *Sergestes challengeri* n. sp. *Proc. Zool. Soc. London* **1**:52–79.

29. Harvey, E. N. 1917. Studies on bioluminescence. IV. The chemistry of light production in a Japanese ostracod crustacean, *Cypridina hilgendorfii* Müller. *Am. J. Physiol.* **42**:318–341.

30. Harvey, E. N. 1918. Studies on bioluminescence. VII. Reversibility of the photogenic reaction in *Cypridina*. *J. Gen. Physiol.* **1**:133–145.

31. Harvey, E. N. 1922. Studies on bioluminescence. XIV. The specificity of luciferin and luciferase. *J. Gen. Physiol.* **4**:285–295.
32. Harvey, E. N. 1926a. Additional data on the specificity of luciferin and luciferase, together with a general survey of this reaction. *Am. J. Physiol.* **77**:548–554.
33. Harvey, E. N. 1926b. Bioluminescence and fluorescence in the living world. *Am. J. Physiol.* **77**:555–561.
34. Harvey, E. N. 1926c. Oxygen and luminescence, with a description of methods for removing oxygen from cells and fluids. *Biol. Bull.* **51**:89–97.
35. Harvey, E. N. 1931. Chemical aspects of the luminescence of deep-sea shrimp. *Zoologica* **12**:71–74.
36. Harvey, E. N. 1952. "Bioluminescence," 649 pp. Academic Press, New York.
37. Harvey, E. N. 1953. Bioluminescence: evolution and comparative biochemistry. *Federation Proc.* **12**:597–606.
37a. Harvey, E. N. 1956. Evolution and bioluminescence. *Quart. Rev. Biol.* **31**:169–199.
38. Harvey, E. N. 1957. The luminous organs of fish. *In:* "The Physiology of Fishes" (M. E. Brown, ed.), Vol. 2, pp. 345–364. Academic Press, New York.
38a. Harvey, E. N., Chase, A. M., and McElroy, W. D. 1957. The spectral energy curve of luminescence of the ostracod crustacean, *Cypridina* and other luminous organisms. *J. Cellular Comp. Physiol.* **50**:499–505.
39. Harvey, E. N., and Tsuji, F. I. 1955. *Cypridina* luciferin luminescence with strong oxidants. *J. Cellular Comp. Physiol.* **46**:341–345.
40. Hastings, J. W. 1952. Oxygen concentration and bioluminescence intensity. II. *Cypridina hilgendorfii. J. Cellular Comp. Physiol.* **40**:1–9.
41. Hastings, J. W., and McElroy, W. D. 1955. Purification and properties of bacterial luciferase. *In:* "The Luminescence of Biological Systems" (F. H. Johnson, ed.), pp. 257–264. American Association for the Advancement of Science, Washington.
42. Illig, G. 1905. Das Leuchten der Gnathophausien. *Zool. Anz.* **28**:662.
43. Kemp, S. 1910. Notes on the photophores of decapod Crustacea. *Proc. Zool. Soc. London* **1910**, Part II:639–651.
44. Mason, H. S. 1952. The beta-luciferin of *Cypridina. J. Am. Chem. Soc.* **74**:4727.
45. McElroy, W. D., and Chase, A. M. 1951. Purification of *Cypridina* luciferase. *J. Cellular Comp. Physiol.* **38**:401–408.
46. McElroy, W. D., and Hastings, J. W. 1955. Biochemistry of firefly luminescence. *In:* "The Luminescence of Biological Systems" (F. H. Johnson, ed.), pp. 161–198. American Association for the Advancement of Science, Washington.
47. Nichols, E. L. 1924. The brightness of marine luminescence. *Science* **60**:592–593.
48. Nicol, J. A. C. 1953a. Luminescence in polynoid worms. *J. Marine Biol. Assoc. United Kingdom* **32**:65–84.
49. Nicol, J. A. C. 1953b. Luminescence in polynoid worms. *J. Marine Biol. Assoc. United Kingdom* **33**:225–255.
50. Okada, Y. K. 1927. Luminescence et organe photogène des Ostracodes. *Bull. soc. zool. France* **51**:478–486.
51. Okada, Y., and Kato, K. 1949. Studies on luminous animals in Japan. III. Preliminary report on the life history of *Cypridina hilgendorfii. Bull. Biogeograph. Soc. Japan* **14**(3):21–25, a translation from *Kagaku* **16**:64–66 (1946).
52. Osborne, A. W., and Chase, A. M. 1954. Inactivation of *Cypridina* luciferase by urea. *J. Cellular Comp. Physiol.* **44**:49–62.

53. Pierantoni, U. 1921. Note di morfologia e svillupo sui fotofori degli Eufausiacei. *Pubbl. staz. zool. Napoli* 3:165–186.

53a.Shimomura, O., Goto, T., and Hirata, Y. 1957. Crystalline *Cypridina* luciferin. *Bull. Chem. Soc. Japan* 30:929–933.

54. Strehler, B. L. 1955. Factors and biochemistry of bacterial luminescence. *In:* "The Luminescence of Biological Systems" (F. H. Johnson, ed.), pp. 209–256. American Association for the Advancement of Science, Washington.

55. Takagi, S. 1936. Über Sekretbildung in dem Leuchtorgan von *Cypridina hilgendorfii* Müller, mit besondere Berücksichtigung der Mitochondrien. *Annotationes Zool. Japon.* 15:344–349.

56. Terao, A. 1917. Notes on photophores of *Sergestes prehensilis,* Bate. *Annotationes Zool. Japon.* 9:299–316.

57. Trojan, E. 1907. Zur Lichtentwicklung in den Photosphärien der Euphausien. *Arch. mikroskop. Anat. u. Entwicklungsmech.* 70:177–188.

58. Tsuji, F. I. 1955. The absorption spectrum of reduced and oxidized *Cypridina* luciferin isolated by a new method. *Arch. Biochem. Biophys.* 59:452–464.

59. Tsuji, F. I., Chase, A. M., and Harvey, E. N. 1955. Recent studies on the chemistry of *Cypridina* luciferin. *In:* "The Luminescence of Biological Systems" (F. H. Johnson, ed.), pp. 127–159. American Association for the Advancement of Science, Washington.

60. Vallentin, R., and Cunningham, J. T. 1888. The photospheria of *Nyctiphanes norvegica. Quart. J. Microscop. Sci.* [N.S.] 28:318–341.

61. Watanabe, H. 1897. The phosphorescence of *Cypridina hilgendorfi. Annotationes Zool. Japon.* 1:69–70.

62. Weir, J. H., Tsuji, F. I., and Chase, A. M. 1955. The isoelectric point of *Cypridina* luciferase. *Arch. Biochem. Biophys.* 56:235–239.

63. Welsh, J. H., and Chace, F. A., Jr. 1937. Eyes of deep sea crustaceans. I. Acanthephyridae. *Biol. Bull.* 72:57–74.

64. Welsh, J. H., and Chace, F. A., Jr. 1938. Eyes of deep sea crustaceans. II. Sergestidae. *Biol. Bull.* 74:364–375.

65. Woltereck, R. 1905. *Scypholanceola,* eine neue Hyperidengattung mit Reflektororgan. *Zool. Anz.* 29:413–416.

66. Yasaki, Y. 1927. On the cause of luminescence in the fresh-water shrimp, *Xiphocaridina compressa* (De Haan). *J. Infectious Diseases* 40:404–407.

67. Yatsu, N. 1917. Note on the structure of the maxillary gland of *Cypridina hilgendorfii. J. Morphol.* 29:435–440.

CHAPTER 6

C. A. G. WIERSMA

THE NEUROMUSCULAR SYSTEM

I. *INTRODUCTION*

The neuromuscular system of decapod Crustacea has been more intensively studied than that of any other group except the higher vertebrates. It has been conclusively shown that there are a number of major differences between the two systems. The question of whether other phyla conform to one or the other of these two types cannot be answered at this time. In other arthropods the crustacean type seems to be present. Insects are clearly similar to the decapods in many ways, but significant differences have been found. For present purposes, the lack of data for lower crustaceans is especially to be regretted. As these are small forms in general, it has not been possible to investigate them with the methods which have been successful in the decapods.

The most characteristic difference between the vertebrate and the decapod neuromuscular systems is that in the former a number of motor nerve fibers, all with similar properties, innervate each muscle, whereas in the latter only a very few efferent axons, each with a different effect, form the supply for the muscles. As in the vertebrates, these efferent axons originate in the central nervous system, where their cell bodies are located. No peripheral ganglion cells are present in the somatic neuromuscular system. However, these do occur in the visceral nervous system and have been especially studied in the neurogenic heart (see Chapter 7; Chapter 5, Vol. I). In several other phyla the presence of entirely peripheral motor neurons is either proven or quite likely, as in the Echinodermata and the Mollusca, thus differentiating them from both Vertebrata and Arthropoda.

The small number of motor axons in Crustacea demands a control mechanism for muscular contraction differing from the familiar one by motor units in the higher vertebrates. As will be shown, such control is obtained by the use of several types of neuromuscular mechanisms in a single muscle and even for single muscle fibers. In many muscles the excitatory innervation consists of only two motor neurons. In these cases they can be distinguished as "fast" and "slow" axons. The terms do not refer to their conduction speeds, but to the rapidity of the contractions resulting from their stimulation.

Another distinctive feature of the decapod crustacean neuromuscular system is the presence of peripheral inhibitory axons. Excitation of these neurons suppresses contractions caused by the firing of the motor neurons. It is as yet uncertain if other animals, including the lower Crustacea, also possess this type of axon. Only in insects has the occurrence of similar fibers been reported, but even for this class it has not been possible to demonstrate peripheral inhibitory action in the more extensively investigated muscles of grasshoppers and cockroaches.

Historically the study of crustacean nerve muscle preparations dates back to the investigations of Richet and of Biedermann in the 1880's. The former[50] paid special attention to the phenomena of facilitation. Working with the claw of crayfish, he observed that stimuli might often be ineffective when given singly, but that a contraction would appear when they were repeated. He called this phenomenon "latent addition." It is an important part of the mechanism regulating the strength of contraction. Biedermann[6] concluded from histological data and experiments in which one antagonistic muscle was prevented from contracting by a cut, that peripheral inhibition was present in these preparations. The evidence obtained by both of these workers was of such a nature that their conclusions would be regarded today with the greatest reservation. Nevertheless, later results have proved that they were essentially correct.

Lucas[44] was the first to observe the existence of two types of contraction in a single crustacean muscle. His observations, also made on the crayfish, eventually led to the discovery of polyneuronal motor innervation of single muscle fibers. At the time, however, he postulated two independent neuromuscular systems combined in one muscle, much as has been recently shown[39] to occur in some frog muscles.

The experiments of Hoffmann[29] provided a much firmer basis for belief in peripheral inhibition. Investigating the crayfish and the lobster, he found two distinct nerve bundles in the meropodite and observed that for the opener and closer muscles of the claw, stimulation of the thinner one resulted in opener excitation and closer inhibition, whereas stimulation of the thicker one gave closer contraction and opener inhibition. Histological investigation confirmed the presence of single nerve fibers with the pathways necessary for the inhibitory actions.

In subsequent developments two improvements have made more precise studies possible. The use of adequate physiological solutions permitted the isolation of single functional axons. With this method all efferent axons of a given leg muscle can be stimulated separately.[65] The internal leading off of muscle membrane potentials with microelectrodes[24] made it possible to demonstrate directly many phenomena which had previously been postulated. In addition this procedure has shown that the neuromuscular transmission mechanisms are more complicated and variable than was previously realized.[32-34]

II. *EFFERENT NERVE FIBERS AND THEIR PROPERTIES*

On the whole, the efferent axons are thick. In Stomatopoda, motor axons of 40–70 μ are found; in Natantia, up to 50 μ; whereas in certain Reptantia (Palinuridae) some axons exceed 200 μ. In contrast sensory fibers are mainly much thinner, but some reach sizes of the same order as the smaller of the efferent fibers: Hence size by itself is not a reliable indication of function. Large axons are enveloped in a sheath formed by "Schwann's cells." This covering is often thick and adheres strongly to the axon. On the other hand, the connective tissue between the fibers is usually poorly developed, and these two factors together make it possible to isolate single fibers capable of functioning. The nerve as a whole is surrounded by a connective tissue sheath, which, especially near the ganglia and sometimes elsewhere, is elastic and strong, though usually rather thin. This sheath may be comparable to the epineurium of the vertebrates.

Concerning the myelination of axons the picture is not clear. In the Natantia Decapoda, shrimps and prawns, a rather heavy myelin sheath is present. In fibers larger than 13 μ it shows interruptions reminiscent of nodes of Ranvier, but spaced at quite irregular intervals.[30] Other interesting differences compared with vertebrate nodes are that branching rarely occurs at the level of the nodes, but usually somewhere between them, and that the myelin sheath is not completely interrupted in the nodal region, though it becomes very thin.[49]

In the Reptantia Decapoda and in the Stomatopoda, material like myelin is present in the sheath surrounding the axon, but in relatively small quantities.[85] Nodal gaps, if present at all, are not prominent.

The nuclei of the cells comparable to Schwann's cells are located in all Crustacea on the inside of the myelin sheath and not on the outside, as in vertebrates. These relations have not yet been interpreted physiologically, but it may be noted that the conduction velocity of the heavily myelinated fibers of shrimps, like the central giant fibers, is of the same order as that of the lightly myelinated but much larger similar fibers of the crayfish (see Table 1).

TABLE 1
VELOCITIES OF IMPULSE CONDUCTION IN DECAPOD AXONS

Species	Type of fiber	Diameter[a]	Velocity (m/sec)	Temp. 0°C
Palaemon serratus[30]	Medial giant	26(int), 35(ext)	18–23	17
Callianassa californiensis[55]	Giant	35–40	6–7.5	20–22
Homarus americanus[54]	Medial giant	102–163	11.7(8–18)	16–30
Procambarus clarkii[66]	Medial giant	100–250	15–20	20
	Lateral	75–200	10–15	20
Homarus americanus[47]	Motor	—	9.2	—
Munida[30]	Motor	55	6.8	—
Carcinus maenas[26]	Motor	30	4–5.5	21
Macrocheira kaempferi[36]	Motor	135[48]	Approx. 4.5	21

[a] Diameters are all external except for *Palaemon*, where first figure (int) represents the internal diameter.

The action potential of crustacean nerve has been studied in a number of cases. Large, isolated axons have properties similar to the unmyelinated giant fibers of the squid.[26,28] The height of the action potential is directly related to the external Na^+ concentration of the surrounding fluid, and the conduction velocity to the diameter of the fiber. Conduction is ascribed to an initial change in sodium permeability followed by an increase in potassium permeability. In agreement with this, and in contrast to the findings for crustacean muscles, the external sodium is essential for conduction and cannot be replaced by other substances.[9] External sodium is also necessary for obtaining a local response to subthreshold stimulation.[81] A fall in the membrane resistance, similar to that in the squid, has been found to occur on passage of the conducted potential in the giant fibers of the lobster.[54] The length of fiber depolarized during the passage of the spike is short, only 4 mm as against 40 mm in vertebrate motor fibers.

Although the action potentials of different axons are similar, fibers differ considerably in other properties. Direct-current stimulation discriminates at least three types of neuron.[27] One fiber group reacts to this type of stimulation with a high-frequency burst of spike potentials of short duration. A second group gives a prolonged series of impulses at lower frequency; in a third group repetitive discharges are difficult to obtain at all.*

Detailed study of various motor fibers of the crayfish and lobster[82,84] shows that these axons differ from each other in several respects. The opener axon, which is most prone to give repetitive discharges, has the lowest average threshold; the fast closer fiber which seldom gives repetitive discharges, the highest. Accommodation is slow in the opener and much more rapid in the fast closer. By changing the ion content of the external solution these properties can be altered. Thus, with more potassium present, the opener axon acquires the properties normal for the fast closer axon. The local potentials on electrical stimulation are of longer duration in the repetitively firing type of fibers than in the nonrepetitive type.[83] The same ionic changes which promote or hinder repetitive firing lengthen or shorten the duration of the local potentials.

Such differences between the motor axons may be of considerable functional importance as they may be related to the thresholds and the duration of discharges on central stimulation. Whether any of the observed peripheral differences, such as facilitatory and contractile effects, can be attributed to them is uncertain. However, there is one type of observation which is readily explained on this basis. On cutting the nerve to a chela of the crayfish, the claw first closes, then opens for a considerable period, and finally relaxes slowly. This phenomenon results from stimulation of the motor axons by the demarcation current for periods related to their properties.

The heat production of crustacean nerve has been measured and found to be large compared to that of vertebrate nerve.[4,25] When this work was done, the possibility of repetitive discharges was not realized and so the real difference may be smaller than measured. The "negative retention" of the nerve action potential[23,42] is of doubtful validity for this same and an additional reason. The phenomenon consists of a maintained depolarization which is larger the more impulses have

---

* Note that this tendency to repetitive discharge combined with the muscle fiber's need for facilitation makes it impossible to determine the chronaxie of these preparations by using muscle contraction as the indicator.

passed. Recent unpublished experiments in this laboratory have shown that with modern techniques this effect appears readily near the cut end of a nerve, because in this area recovery is more and more delayed, and is accompanied by a concomitant reduction in spike amplitude. But in a stretch of nerve away from the cut end there is no noticeable reduction nor a negative retention unless the frequency of impulses is high. Although crustacean nerve may fatigue more easily than vertebrate nerve, a crustacean axon was found to respond for more than 3 hr when stimulated fifty times per second.[45]

III. *NEUROMUSCULAR CONNECTIONS*

A. HISTOLOGY

Typically the efferent axons in crustacean nerves branch only when they reach the muscle they supply. The branching occurs at the same place in all such axons innervating a given muscle. This gives rise to the remarkable diplo-, triplo-, and quintuplotomic branchings which show clearly with methylene blue staining (Fig. 1). In diplo- and triplotomic branching the divisions can be followed even to single muscle fibers.* When more than one axon ends on a muscle fiber, its innervation is called polyneuronal. In quintuply innervated muscles it has not been shown histologically that all five fibers innervate the same muscle fiber; but physiological evidence implies that some, but not all, muscle fibers do receive branches of all five axons (see page 215).

Each axon divides profusely and reaches each muscle fiber at many places along the latter's length. Each axon branch penetrates the sheath surrounding the individual muscle fiber together with the branches of the other axons, and a subsequent division is regularly found. This has been described as sublemnal branching, but it is doubtful whether the axons penetrate through the plasma membrane of the muscle fibers, although they may indent it. Underneath the sheath of the muscle fiber the branchings become thinner and thinner, usually appearing to

---

* Throughout this paper the term "muscle fiber" will be used for those structures present in the leg muscles, which on the evidence from various sources appear to be single, anatomical, and functional units. It should, however, be realized that their identity is not as firmly established as that of vertebrate muscle fibers. Indeed, especially in the muscles of the body wall, similar appearing structures have histological features which throw considerable doubt on their unit nature. For these reasons, Alexandrowicz[2] prefers the use of the noncommittal term "bundle of myofibrils."

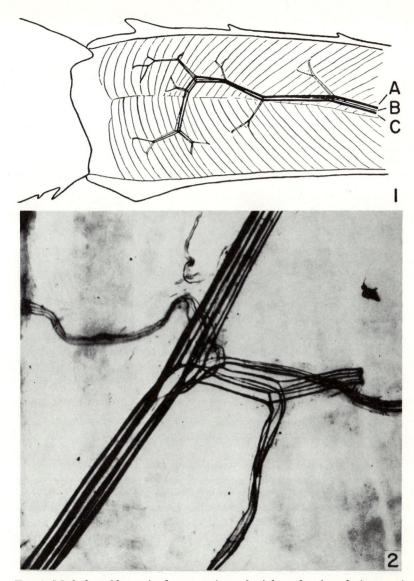

Fig. 1. Methylene blue-stained preparations of triple and quintuple innervations. 1. Drawing of triplotomic branching of nerve fibers on the surface of the extensor of the carpopodite in *Procambarus clarkii*. *A*, fast; *B*, inhibitory; *C*, slow axon. (From van Harreveld and Wiersma.[60]) 2. Quintuplotomic branching of nerve fibers on the surface of the main flexor muscle of the carpopodite in *Panulirus interruptus*. (From van Harreveld.[57])

end without specialized accessory structures.[56] An axon has thus many endings on each muscle fiber it innervates; this is called multiterminal innervation (Fig. 2). Possible differences between various species are indicated by older investigations. In the crayfish the branches remain on the "inner" surface of the muscle fibers, whereas in *Homarus* and

F'IG. 2. Multiterminal endings of the motor and inhibitory axons on a single muscle fiber, 3.5 mm in length, of the opener of *Procambarus clarkii*. Silver stain. Dots, endings; crosses, broken branches to neighboring fibers. (From van Harreveld.[56])

Palinurus they penetrate between the bundles of myofibrils so that the endings run parallel to the Z-bands.[12]

B. TYPICAL RESPONSES TO EFFERENT STIMULATION

Many decapod crustacean muscles are innervated by three axons, the slow and fast motor axons and an inhibitory axon. But the electrical and mechanical responses to stimulation of one type of axon show considerable differences even between the muscles of one species. In order to facilitate discussion, it is profitable to consider each axon and the reactions its impulses cause in the muscle it innervates as a "system." In the following sections a general description of slow, fast, and inhibitory systems will be presented first, then the main variants known to exist will be treated in Section VII below.

1. *Slow motor system.* Characteristic of the slow motor system is the absence of sudden contractions. This is related to the ineffectiveness of single nerve impulses. Weak contractions can be obtained by suitable low-frequency stimulation, but beginning with the lowest effective frequency, which may be only two per second, they are completely smooth tetani. Even when extra shocks are administered to the axon during such stimulation, the result is either completely imperceptible or at most a small and sustained increase in the contraction. When a given series of impulses is ended, a relatively long-lasting facilitation remains. Thus renewed stimulation, applied not too long after the first, results in a quicker contraction which rises faster, the shorter the preceding rest period.

At medium rates of stimulation (e.g. 50 per second), the development of peak muscular contraction still takes many seconds (Fig. 3). Only at the highest possible frequencies (e.g. 200 per second) does the tension develop really speedily and at the same time strongly. Under these last conditions the muscle may develop almost as much tension on stimulation of the slow axon alone as on simultaneous stimulation of fast and slow.

The electrical events recorded from the muscle mirror the mechanical ones to a certain extent. Single slow axon impulses do not cause noticeable deflections when external leads are used, nor, in most muscle fibers, do they with intracellular electrodes. On repetitive stimulation a gradual facilitation is observed, but at low frequencies the

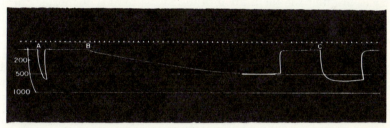

Fig. 3. Fast and slow isometric contractions at same stimulation frequency (approximately 50 per second) of closer of *Pacifastacus trowbridgii*. A and C on fast fiber, B on slow fiber stimulation. Tension in grams; time in seconds. (From van Harreveld and Wiersma.[59])

electrical changes may not yet be evident at a time when a definite mechanical effect is registered. At higher frequencies each nerve impulse, after the first few, results in a readily observable deflection, and a partial fusion of the potentials becomes evident. If the frequency is high, an obvious summation of the electrical potentials is also obtained. On repeating a stimulation shortly after a preceding one, the facilitation of the action potentials is greater than after rest.

Fatigue of the action potential mechanism occurs before that of contraction, and the electrical deflections may even be declining while the contraction is still increasing. Hence two distinct facilitatory processes have been distinguished: one for the action potentials, and the other for the contractile process. Further evidence for these two processes will be presented when inhibition is discussed (page 218).

2. *Fast motor system.* There are much greater differences between fast systems from different muscles than between slow systems. In many, but not all cases, contraction speed is clearly greater when

the fast axon is stimulated compared to similar stimulation of the slow (Fig. 3). Several fast systems respond to a single fast axon impulse with a smaller or larger twitch contraction. In a system which needs more than a single impulse, the contraction resulting from the lowest effective frequency, which may be higher than for the slow system in the same muscle, is usually quite distinct from a slow contraction. The maximum tension is reached much more quickly, or irregular increases and even decreases in contraction are obtained during such stimulation, instead of the smooth, gradually increasing contraction of the slow. Another way to distinguish the two contractions is by the use of a few impulses which follow each other quickly. The fast causes a twitch-like shortening with fewer impulses than the slow. Other general differences are that the facilitation of the fast system is of shorter duration than that of the slow, and that fatigue is much more quickly evident in the former. However, there is no pronounced difference in the speed of contraction relaxation, although some must be present in order to explain the fact that incomplete tetani are obtainable with most fast systems but not with slow ones. The differences in the electrical potentials, which are often pronounced, are described below.

3. *Inhibitory system.* Stimulation of an inhibitory axon alone does not lead to any readily observable change, unless the muscle happens to be in a state of tonus, which then disappears during and often after the stimulation. When a motor fiber is stimulated simultaneously with the inhibitor, the contraction normally resulting will be either completely suppressed or reduced as long as the inhibitor fires (Fig. 4). The amount of reduction depends on the relation between the frequencies of stimulation of the two axons. Against a slow contraction, it is usually sufficient to stimulate the inhibitor at only half the frequency of the excitatory stimulation to obtain a complete suppression of the contraction. Against a fast contraction the inhibitory frequency must invariably be more than half, and usually more than the full excitatory frequency, to obtain the same effect even when the fast contraction is smaller than the slow at the same excitatory frequency.

In most instances the ratio of inhibitory to excitatory impulses at which contraction is just suppressed (the Rc value) is constant for different frequencies. Thus if 10 inhibitory impulses per second are necessary to suppress a contraction obtained at 20 per second, 100 per second will be needed to suppress the contraction from 200 motor impulses per second. A partial explanation of this constant relation is that the inhibitory process, like the excitatory one, is not maximal at the start of stimulation, but shows considerable facilitation. This can be proved by testing the effectiveness of continued inhibitory stimulation against short test contractions. If the relation of the frequencies is adjusted so that the test contractions shortly after the start of inhibitory stimulation are suppressed only partially, they later become more completely inhibited through the facilitation of inhibition. The same experiment

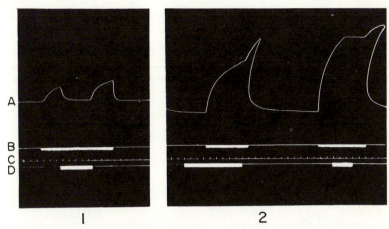

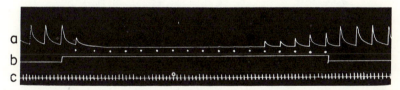

Fig. 4. Inhibition of slow and fast contractions of the bender muscle of *Procambarus clarkii* showing that equal inhibitory stimulation is more effective on the slow contraction. *A*, isotonic mechanogram; *B*, excitatory stimulation signal; *C*, time in seconds; *D*, inhibitory stimulation signal; 1, slow contraction; 2, fast contraction. (From van Harreveld and Wiersma.[60])

Fig. 5. Facilitation and fatigue of inhibition in opener of *Pagurus* during continued stimulation of the inhibitory axon at 40 per second, demonstrated with test contractions obtained by stimulating motor axon with square shocks of 36 msec duration. *a*, mechanogram, isotonic; *b*, inhibitory stimulation signal; *c*, time in seconds. Dots, moments of test stimulations during inhibition. (From Wiersma and van Harreveld.[74])

shows that when the inhibitory mechanism fatigues, the test contractions eventually grow again in size (Fig. 5). That this is true fatigue of the peripheral inhibitory mechanism and not of the inhibitory axon follows from the restoration of inhibition by an increase in the frequency of inhibitory stimulation.

These and other observations are evidence that the inhibitory mechanism has many essential features in common with the excitatory one,

C. Innervation Patterns in Different Crustacea

Because of the small number of efferent axons, it has been possible by isolation to determine their number, function, and course for leg muscles in different species. Staining the axons with methylene blue is a great aid in checking the physiological findings.[72] Investigations of this type were started by Biedermann[5] in 1887, and the later work of Hoffmann,[29] although performed without axon isolation, already showed some of the more intriguing complexities present.

The known motor patterns for the thoracic leg muscles of the Reptantia are all identical. Seven muscles are present which move the

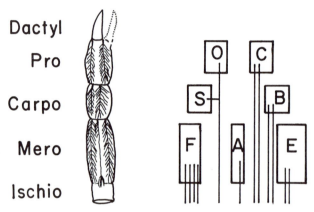

Dactyl

Pro

Carpo

Mero

Ischio

Fig. 6. Distribution of the motor fibers in the Decapoda Reptantia. Left, schematic drawing of a thoracic appendage showing the location of the different muscles in the leg segments. Right, diagram of these muscles, represented by rectangles, and their motor axons. O, opener (abductor of dactylopodite); C, closer (adductor of dactylopodite); S, stretcher (extensor of propodite); B, bender (flexor of propodite); F, main flexor (of carpopodite); A, accessory flexor (of carpopodite); E, extensor (of carpopodite). (From Hoyle and Wiersma.[32])

three distal joints of the appendage. These receive twelve motor fibers in total (Fig. 6). Two separate muscles are innervated by a single shared motor fiber in all species. None of the other eleven axons innervates more than one muscle. Note that three muscles have a single motor innervation, three others a double one, and one a quadruple.*

---

* For the brachyuran decapod, *Macrocheira kaempferi*, the main flexor muscle is said to have a double motor innervation instead of a quadruple, and the accessory flexor a double, instead of a single, motor innervation.[48]

In muscles with double motor innervation, one axon invariably gives contractions of the slow type, whereas the other elicits a faster contraction. The four kinds of contractions obtained from the muscles with quadruple motor innervation differ in several respects from each other.[61] Here one may distinguish a slow contraction, a fast contraction, and two of an intermediate nature, but such a division seems rather arbitrary since these systems have thus far been analyzed in only a few forms.

In the rest of the body musculature the evidence for the same type of innervation rests mainly on the fact that methylene blue staining

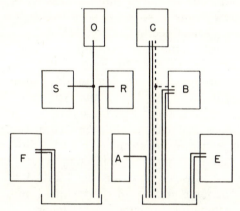

Fig. 7. Innervation pattern of a pereiopod in the shrimp *Stenopus hispidus* (incomplete). Solid lines, motor fibers; broken line, inhibitory fiber. Muscles marked as in Fig. 6. *R* is rotator of propodite not present in Reptantia. (From Wiersma and Ripley.[72])

demonstrates axon patterns like those in the leg muscles. Furthermore, many of these muscles are known to have at least two types of contraction. There can be no reasonable doubt that in these muscles mechanisms similar to those of the leg muscles exist.

In Natantia the innervation scheme of the leg muscles has been partly worked out. It is much like that of the Reptantia; here again the opener and the stretcher share one motor axon (Fig. 7). The most noticeable difference is the presence of an eighth muscle, a rotator of the propodite, which has one special motor axon. Double motor innervation is present in all the muscles which show it in Reptantia, but the main flexor may have only double, instead of quadruple, motor innervation.

In Stomatopoda, in which the large second maxilliped has been studied, double motor innervation is present in the closer, and probably in the bender, muscles. Here the muscles homologous with the opener and stretcher each appear to have a separate motor fiber instead of sharing the same one. As in the Natantia a rotator with a separate single motor axon is present.

The pattern of inhibitory innervation has been studied mainly in Reptantia. Unlike that of the motor axons it differs considerably in the different groups. According to these findings, Reptantia should be considered to contain four groups, the Palinura (Scyllaridea), Astacura (Nephropsidea), Anomura, and Brachyura, each with a pattern constant in the group, but mutually quite different. In other ways, too, the nervous system points to an important division between the superfamilies of Macrura as defined in Chapter 1, Vol. I.

The four patterns found are presented in Fig. 8. For the seven peripheral leg muscles in the Brachyura (8a) and Anomura (8b) there are three inhibitory axons; but in the Palinura (Scyllaridea) (8c) only two occur. The number in the Astacura (Nephropsidea) is uncertain at present. Although Fig. 8d shows four, it is likely that at least two of these are branches of the same axon. In the Anomura and Brachyura the opener and the stretcher muscles show a triple innervation with one excitatory and two inhibitory axons. One of the latter also provides other muscles, and has been called the "common" inhibitor. Possibly in some anomuran species this common inhibitor does not send branches to both the opener and stretcher.

When inhibition was originally described, it was postulated that antagonistic muscles would be reciprocally inhibited during the contraction of the agonists. Yet from the innervation patterns it is obvious that this cannot be the case. However, note that the two muscles with a common motor axon always have at least one inhibitor which does not inhibit the other muscle. Hence there is the possibility of selective contraction of these muscles by inhibition of the other, though in Palinura (Scyllaridea) all other leg muscles also have to receive inhibitory impulses in order to have the stretcher contract without the opener.

The function of the common inhibitor is not clear. In Astacura (Nephropsidea) and Palinura (Scyllaridea) the inhibitor, which innervates, among others, the bender muscle, may be homologous with it. Since in all groups it makes connection with many muscles, and in some cases with all of them, it forms a pathway by which the central nervous system inhibits the periphery unselectively. During molting such an occurrence might be of functional significance in preventing contractions caused by reflex or even peripheral excitation arising from mechanical stimulation of motor neurons. By these means the soft new skeleton might be protected against mechanical deformations resulting from muscular contractions.

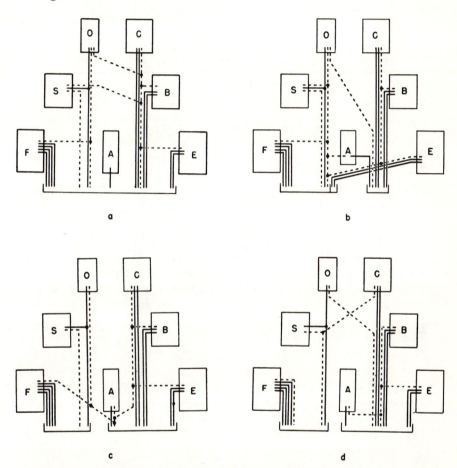

Fig. 8. Thoracic limb innervation in different Decapoda Reptantia. a, Brachyura; b, Anomura; c, Palinura (Scyllaridea); d, Astacura (Nephropsidea). Solid lines, motor axons; broken lines, inhibitory axons. Lettering as in Fig. 6. (From Wiersma and Ripley.[72])

The true inhibitors may be considered as private pathways using the same basic mechanism as the common inhibitor but specialized to counteract specifically the contractions of one muscle. This makes it possible to grade the otherwise quite similar and simultaneous contractions of the opener and stretcher independently. Obviously the peripheral inhibitory mechanism of the decapod crustaceans cannot provide for reciprocal innervation. It is strongly indicated that, as in vertebrates, central mechanisms govern the walking patterns in Crustacea. If this is so, central inhibitory phenomena, which do occur (Chapter 7), must regulate them.

IV. ELECTROPHYSIOLOGY OF NERVE-MUSCLE PREPARATIONS

A. MEMBRANE POTENTIAL OF MUSCLE FIBERS

Like vertebrate striated muscle fibers, those of the Crustacea are formed from many embryonic cells. It is therefore an important question whether, like the former, they act physiologically as single units. The same question arises in other cases such as the squid giant axons which are composed of the axons of many nerve cells. The main physiological difference between these syncytial structures and bundles of unicellular elements is that the former have a single, electrically polarized, enveloping membrane instead of a separate membrane enclosing each part. Although the physiological unity of the squid giant axon is beyond doubt, in other similar cases where small bridges of tissue form the only connection between fibers, it is difficult to decide on anatomical or physiological grounds whether one or more units are present.

The large muscle fibers of crustacean leg muscles are almost certainly single functional units (see, however, footnote on page 196). Localized responses cannot be ascribed to the action of subunits. Fatt and Katz[15] found that usually on entering a fiber with a microelectrode, the membrane potential is immediately fully developed and does not show changes on further penetration. In certain cases, when penetration is still very superficial, the potential difference disappears with a small further penetration, to reappear soon after. This might well be due to a slight fold in the membrane, or perhaps even more likely to penetration of the microelectrode into a space surrounding a nerve ending lined by an invagination of the muscle membrane.

Inside the muscle fiber there are no indications of internal membranes; nor are they found when penetration is made with two microelectrodes and measurements of the resistance between the pair are made. This latter method is the more convincing of the two because it proves the absence of high-resistance membranes within the muscle fiber, whereas the sudden potential changes expected when a single electrode enters a space between adjoining compartments might easily be missed.

The resting potential of crustacean muscle is about equal to that of other muscles, in the neighborhood of 70 millivolts. However, the crustacean muscle membrane does differ from other excitable membranes in several important respects. Its capacity has a value of the order of 40 $\mu F/cm^2$, whereas the membrane resistance is about 100 Ω cm.[2]* These values are about ten times larger and smaller, respectively, than the means for other excitable tissues, like crustacean and cephalopod nerve fibers, as well as vertebrate muscle fibers. However, the figures quoted are based on the assumption that the membrane consists of a smooth cylinder with uniform properties surrounding the muscle fiber. Because the many nerve endings may be surrounded by invaginations of the muscle membrane and hence increase its surface, the area of the membrane may be larger than calculated on this assumption. This would tend to diminish the differences cited. There are also indications that the membrane properties on the innervated and noninnervated side of the muscle fiber may be different, as discussed below.

Experiments in which the muscle membrane is activated with an internal electrode give results unlike those of other excitable tissues so far studied.[15] In a number of fibers the only effect of a cathodal current consists of a small, nonconducted potential. Abortive or propagated spikes accompanied by a twitch contraction occur in other muscle fibers. The numbers of such "spiking" fibers vary considerably with the species of crab used for the experiment. Spikes obtained in this manner often do not equal the value of the membrane potential, their mean being only 60 mv instead of 70 mv. From the high value of the membrane capacity and the low one of the membrane resistance, it can be predicted that conduction spread will be slow and the safety factor for propagation small, as has been found. The speed of conduction of a propagated spike was only about 30 cm/sec though the diameter of the fibers ranged from 100 to 250 μ.

B. ELECTRICAL CHANGES CAUSED BY MOTOR AXON STIMULATION

Motor stimulation may give rise to a variety of responses in the muscle fiber: junctional potentials, abortive spikes, nonconducted

---

* These data were obtained in marine crustaceans. For muscle fibers of *Astacus astacus* the membrane capacity is about 20 $\mu F/cm^2$, whereas the resistance varies considerably, but is higher than in crabs (1000 up to 5000 Ωcm^2).[14a]

spikes, and conducted spikes. Junctional potentials are considered to be completely local phenomena at the nerve endings. They always precede spikes, which are evoked by them. Abortive spikes occur when a secondary process takes place in the membrane. If the secondary process develops quickly, it becomes regenerative, and a full spike develops. However, only when the safety factor for conduction is high enough does the spike travel any distance away from the nerve ending and really become conducted.

The magnitude of junctional potentials depends greatly on a number of circumstances, such as the degree of facilitation present, the motor axon stimulated, and the properties of both the muscle and the muscle fiber concerned. Thus a single impulse from a slow axon does not cause a noticeable membrane potential change. Junctional potentials show both facilitation and summation, but again, to different degrees in different preparations. They are present throughout the fiber, and although their amplitude may vary from place to place along the fiber length and at different depths within it, this variability is at most 40%.[16]

Spikes are obtained much more readily in certain systems than in others. Several fast systems regularly show spikes in part of the muscle fibers on single impulses, at least in fresh preparations. In general the spikes arise when the junctional potential surpasses a certain value, and this can be brought about through facilitation of the junctional potentials by either repetitive fast or slow axon stimulation. In a few instances these spikes are all-or-none in nature at such times, but much more often abortive spikes occur as long as the impulses do not follow each other closely[22] (Fig. 9).

Even spikes which overshoot the zero membrane potential level can still be rather local events as shown by investigations in which two internal microelectrodes are applied to the same muscle fiber. In the contractile part of the stretch receptors in the abdomen of crayfish and lobster, when spikes arise all along the muscle fiber, they are initiated at each locus by the junctional potential at that locus, since the delay between the two potentials is the same at all points.[21] Moreover, often only part of the fiber will spike on a single nerve impulse, whereas another part shows merely a junctional potential. If a second impulse follows soon after the first, both parts may show a spike potential. With the nerve spreading the excitation all along the muscle fibers, conducted spikes might be regarded as unlikely, were it not for those evoked by stimulation with internal electrodes.

The difference in these two types of large spikes may account for records obtained with external leads. In most cases when the distal lead is located on the apodeme and the proximal lead on the muscle, the former becomes negative, whereas the latter acts like an indifferent electrode, as was first reported in 1888 by Biedermann.[6] A more recent study[78] of this phenomenon has shown that in the crayfish these "positive" potential changes can largely be explained if only the innervated side of each muscle fiber changes potential, and hence

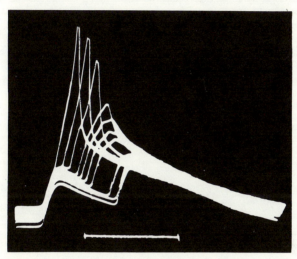

FIG. 9. Summation of fast junctional potentials and genesis of spikes in a muscle fiber of the main flexor in *Panulirus interruptus*. The "fastest" motor axon was stimulated with successive pairs of shocks separated by continually decreasing intervals. Note summation of junctional potentials, gradual increase of abortive spikes, and absence of all-or-none relation even when true spiking occurs. Time unit, 20 msec. (From Furshpan.[21])

shows a localized response. But in the lobster, *Homarus gammarus*, the same leads record pronounced diphasic potentials. Here it seems likely that in contrast to the crayfish, the spikes are truly conducted, accounting for the difference.[68]

An additional electrical change in the membrane which occurs on repetitive stimulation of either motor axon is the maintained depolarization.[32,34] In many, but again not all, muscle fibers, continued stimulation leads to a gradually established reduction of the membrane potential, roughly proportional to the frequency of the stimulation. This change may be wholly due to the summation of residual junctional potentials, but its amplitude appears more directly related to the contraction size than to that of the junctional potentials. Maintained depolarization does not develop when regenerative spikes are present.

C. MEMBRANE POTENTIAL AND INHIBITION

Early reports stated that, in crustacean muscle, stimulation of an inhibitory axon produces a deflection of the electrical potential in the

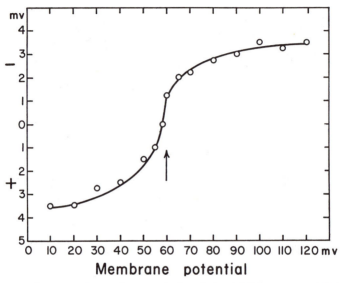

FIG. 10. Relation between the magnitude of the inhibitory potential (ordinate) and the membrane potential in a muscle fiber of the opener of *Procambarus clarkii.* Arrow indicates resting level of membrane potential which was changed with the aid of a second microelectrode. Inhibitory axon stimulated 30 times per second. Note that when the membrane potential is lowered, inhibitory potentials increase the polarization, but decrease it when the membrane potential is increased. Compare with Fig. 11. (From Hoyle and Wiersma.[33])

reverse direction from that during excitation. Such increased polarization of the muscle membrane during inhibition would be quite consistent with the effect of inhibition in other structures such as the spinal motor neuron of vertebrates[13] and the sensory cell body of the crustacean stretch receptor.[40] However, in later research on crustacean muscle with external leads, no positive deflections were observed.[41,45]

Investigations with muscle fibers impaled on capillary electrodes have shown that, depending on circumstances, a variety of membrane changes may occur. At the arrival of a single inhibitory impulse, many muscle fibers show no noticeable effect when the membrane potential is at its normal resting value.[17] If this potential is experimentally lowered with a second electrode, impulses will often, but not always, give rise to increased membrane polarization. In some fibers such inhibitory potential increases may reach 2–3 mv when the membrane is depolarized by 30 mv. On the contrary, raising the membrane

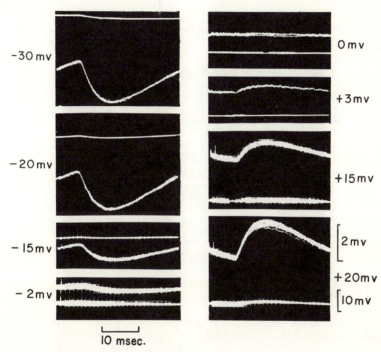

FIG. 11. Electrical responses of the type used to obtain Fig. 10. Changes in the membrane potential produced with the second microelectrode are labeled in the margin, and the resulting inhibitory potentials (negative upward) to a barrage of 30 impulses per second in the inhibitory axon shown in the lower record line (left column) or in the upper line (right column). (From Hoyle and Wiersma.[33])

potential similarly leads to depolarizing inhibitory potentials of comparable magnitudes (Figs. 10 and 11). All three of these response types have also been encountered in untreated fibers of diverse muscles. In the opener of the crayfish, *Procambarus clarkii*, the type of response depends on the season; in fall, polarizing potentials occur in most fibers; in spring, depolarizing ones, although the membrane potentials do not show a corresponding shift.

Like excitatory junctional potentials, inhibitory ones show facilitation, summation, and a maintained potential change. In *Panulirus interruptus*, where large effects follow single inhibitory impulses, little facilitation occurs. In other species noticeable potential changes often are seen only after repetitive stimulation.

The time course of inhibitory potentials is independent of the sign of the inhibitory potential, and is much like that of excitatory ones,

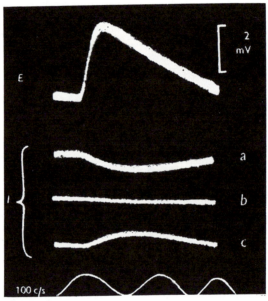

Fig. 12. Excitatory and inhibitory junctional potentials of one muscle fiber of the opener of *Pagurus*. *E*, excitatory potential; *I*, inhibitory potentials; *a*, when fiber was depolarized through a second internal electrode to 48 mv membrane potential; *c*, when membrane potential was raised to 95 mv; *b*, when membrane was at resting potential, as in *E*, of 73 mv. Note the reversal in sign of inhibitory junctional potential from *a* to *c* and the slower development of the inhibitory potentials compared to the excitatory one. (From Fatt and Katz.[17])

though invariably slower, both in development and decay. In selected fibers, in which large changes can be brought about in size and sign, these take place without differences in the time relations (Fig. 12).

The influence of inhibitory stimulation on the electrical effects of excitatory stimulation appears in many systems to be limited to the algebraic summation of their separate effects. Because of the smallness of the individual inhibitory potentials, little change results in the junctional potentials. However, the maintained depolarization due to excitatory stimulation often is noticeably reduced by the sustained porlarization brought about by inhibition. This type of inhibition which occurs with little or no change in individual junctional potentials is called simple or β-inhibition.

In contrast a number of the inhibitors specific for openers or stretchers affect the height of the excitatory junctional potentials profoundly if the inhibitory impulses are so timed that they arrive at the

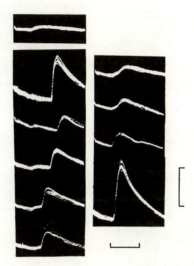

Fig. 13. Supplemented inhibition in the opener of *Procambarus clarkii* in a fiber where the inhibitory potential was naturally depolarizing. Top, inhibitory potential. Second picture in first column, and last in second column, normal excitatory junctional potentials. Note growth due to continued facilitation as well as different degrees of junction potential reduction with changes in the relation of the arrival times of the excitatory and inhibitory impulses. Time, 10 msec; voltage, 10 mv. (From Hoyle and Wiersma.[33])

nerve endings just before the motor ones. The consequent potential reduction may be as much as 90% in impaled muscle fibers, but has never been found to be complete.[17] This type of inhibition is called supplemented or α-inhibition. It is also present when the inhibitory potentials are depolarizing, as occurs in normal fibers in the opener of the crayfish[33] (Fig. 13).

D. MEMBRANE POTENTIAL AND DOUBLE MOTOR INNERVATION

Experiments with internal electrodes have confirmed the fact that single muscle fibers receive branches from both motor axons. This was deduced originally from the histology (described above) and the direct observation that certain muscle fibers contracted on stimulation of either axon.[58] In the majority of such muscles each fiber was found to have two types of junctional potentials, fast and slow, but these vary considerably in their relations. Four types of muscle have been described to represent the major possibilities.[32] In the first type neighboring muscle fibers show great variation in the sizes of their junctional

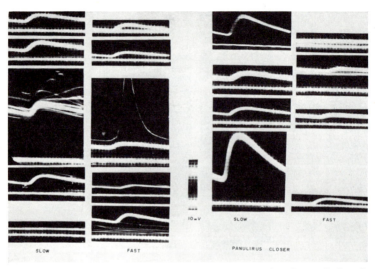

FIG. 14. Electrical responses occurring in nine muscle fibers of the closer of *Panulirus interruptus* with a stimulation frequency of 45 per sec (several traces superimposed). The responses are paired: left, slow; right, fast. Maintained depolarization is shown in each case by the space between the upper and lower trace, which represents the resting membrane potential level. Note that at random the slow or the fast deflections are larger, and that either may give a greater maintained depolarization. Also note that in the third fiber from above on the left, slow stimulation causes abortive spikes, whereas a large spike is caused by the fast axon, in this pair from a lower maintained potential level. (From Hoyle and Wiersma.[32])

potentials after full facilitation. In some cases the slow response is larger than the fast, in others they are equal in size, while in the remainder the fast responses are larger. Muscles belonging to this group are the closers of *Panulirus* and of *Cancer* (Fig. 14).

In the second type, part of the muscle comprises specialized fibers, some innervated only by the fast axon, others by the slow. The latter are further distinguished by responding with a large junctional potential to a single impulse. The fast muscle fibers often spike on a single impulse. In the closer muscle of *Pachygrapsus* these specialized fibers are limited to a bundle of proximal fibers, whereas the more peripheral fibers respond to both axons, like muscles of the third group. In this type, represented by the closer of *Procambarus clarkii*, the response to slow axon stimulation is rather uniform and small in all muscle fibers; in contrast, the electrical response to the fast varies greatly from small junctional potentials to full spikes. In the fourth muscle type all fibers react nearly alike, with the slow potentials being invariably smaller than the fast. Hence the records for a single fiber in this case resemble those obtained from the whole muscle with external leads.

Independent of these four types, the time relations of slow and fast junctional potentials may in some muscles be almost identical; less commonly, in others the slow may be of much longer duration than the fast. In no case are slow potentials known with shorter durations than the fast.

As yet the condition in certain insect muscles, where the majority of fibers is innervated solely by the fast motor fiber and only some by both fast and slow axons,[31] has not been found in crustacean muscles with double motor innervation. But such may well occur since in certain specialized muscles described in the next section a similar situation is present.

E. QUADRUPLE MOTOR INNERVATION

The number of axons innervating individual muscle fibers of the main flexor muscle of the carpopodite in the legs of *Panulirus interruptus* have been studied by penetrating a number of muscle fibers with a capillary electrode and stimulating the four axons separately.[21] Deflections are obtained in a number of fibers on stimulation of any of the four axons. Thus there can be no doubt that polyneuronal motor innervation by four axons is a physiological fact. However, the number found is a relatively small percentage (7%) of the total number of muscle fibers tested. In the other fibers, triple, double, and single motor innervations are observed with roughly equal incidence. No fibers are found without apparent innervation. Of the fibers innervated by one axon, the great majority (90%) are supplied by the fiber causing the largest potential with external electrodes and the fastest contraction. Spikes can be obtained by repetitive stimulation of one axon and also sometimes by combining the junctional potentials of different axons through their simultaneous stimulation. The junctional potentials of different axons always show summation.

These results clearly show that the main flexor muscle has a heterogeneous structure with regard to the innervation of its fibers. But a certain regularity in the pattern seems to exist. Thus, superficial fibers are often innervated by the fastest axon alone, and in a distal area of the muscle this axon does not innervate the interior fibers.

V. *PROCESSES BETWEEN NERVE IMPULSE AND CONTRACTION*

Although any scheme for the number and kind of steps involved in crustacean neuromuscular transmission must still be highly speculative, discussion in these terms is useful in indicating the present state of the problem. In the diagram (Fig. 15), the processes resulting from stimulation of the three main types of efferent axons are assumed to be as alike as possible. Obviously certain relations diagrammed are not universally present. For instance the fast axon impulse is shown giving rise to a large junctional potential, the slow to a small, but this does not happen in all muscle fibers of certain muscles (page 214).

The first effects of the nerve impulse's arrival at the nerve terminal is considered to be the liberation of a transmitter substance, which is subject to facilitation. The latter is demonstrated by the increase in junctional potential amplitude with repetitive stimulation. Facilitation may be considered as a gradual increase in the quantity of transmitter liberated by successive nerve impulses. The evidence for neuromuscular transmitters is still indirect for Crustacea, in contrast to the liberation of acetylcholine at the vertebrate end plate, but appears to be by far the most likely possibility (Chapter 8).

Each axon is represented as liberating a specific transmitter substance. For excitatory and inhibitory axons this specificity would seem likely, but for the two excitatory axons liberation of the same transmitter at a different place and in different quantities might appear to be a simpler hypothesis. Thus the variation in the size of the junctional potentials in different muscle fibers of each system might be explained by such means. However, quantitative differences cannot account for certain of the differences between slow and fast systems, such as the longer duration of the slow system potentials and the greater ease with which slow contractions can be inhibited. The further assumption that transmitter splitting enzymes occur in different amounts at the two endings might explain some but not all of these. It is therefore simpler to hypothesize two excitatory transmitters, a slow one (S) and a fast one (F), with similar but slightly different properties in addi-

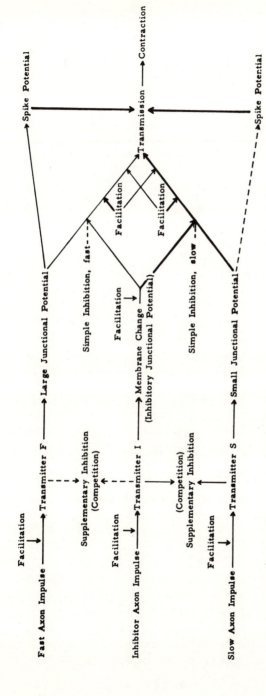

FIG. 15. Diagram to illustrate the transmission processes between nerve impulses and contraction for a triply innervated muscle. Explanation in the text.

tion to an inhibitory one (I) with a quite different structure. This would also imply that where one muscle receives a double inhibitory innervation, the specific and common inhibitors each have a slightly different inhibitory transmitter.

In Fig. 15, the membrane changes caused by the transmitters are represented as links in the chain of events. They may also be considered as unimportant by-products of transmitter action on the next step, which may be called activation (for inhibition, deactivation) of the contractile mechanism. Spike potentials, on the other hand, seem to have a strong causal link to contraction. In the case of junctional potentials only future analysis can show which is the more appropriate description.

In the scheme, inhibitory reduction of the excitatory junctional potentials is shown as a competition of the transmitter I with S and F for the membrane site responsible for the junctional potentials. Its localization at this level rather than at an earlier stage follows from the fact that facilitation of junctional potentials is influenced little or not at all by supplemented inhibition. Note that reduction, as here presented, is of rare occurrence. It has been observed only in a few muscle fibers with double motor innervation. However, the situation for supplemented inhibition in an opener would be similar.

While neuromuscular transmission as far as the level of junctional potentials seems likely to depend on transmitter substances and ion movements, the subsequent processes are entirely deduced from the mechanical events, and their nature is quite hypothetical. The intensity of the coupling between steps here is shown by the type of line, heavy ones being strong, broken ones weak. The transmission from the slow junctional potentials to the contraction is given as strong, since the mechanical effect is out of proportion with the smallness of the potentials. On the other hand, this link is much more liable to block by inhibition than the similar process in the fast system, as indicated by the difference in the inhibitory processes. The facilitations shown at this level are inferred from such facts as the continued increase in contraction after the potentials have reached full size, or even started to diminish, and the mutual facilitation of contraction by fast and slow axon stimulation.[77] The similarity of these steps to the corresponding ones shown in the inhibitory chain offers a way of visualizing simple inhibition and its facilitation.

The paradox of fast and slow contractions found in certain double motor innervated muscles has, more than any other single phenomenon, forced the splitting of the transmission mechanism into a number of steps. It was discovered in the closer muscles of the brachyuran *Randallia ornata* and the anomuran *Blepharipoda occidentalis*,[75] in which stimulation of the slow closer axon at a low frequency results in a smooth tetanic, though weak contraction, while similar stimulation of the fast has no mechanical effect. Yet the accompanying potentials were very small on slow, and quite large on fast, stimulation (Fig. 16). Recently it has been found in *Randallia* that all individual muscle fibers tested show a similar relation between the two types of junctional potentials. These muscles happen to belong to type four described above, in which all muscle fibers give similar reactions; hence

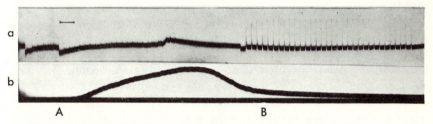

Fig. 16. Paradox relating action potentials and contraction in the slow and fast motor systems of the closer in the crab, *Randallia ornata*. *a*, electrogram; *b*, isotonic mechanogram; *A*, stimulation of slow axon; *B*, of fast (both at 14 per second). Slow contraction occurs without noticeable action potentials, whereas fast action potentials facilitate without evoking contraction while relaxation of previous slow contraction continues. (From Wiersma and van Harreveld.[75])

the contractions of the slow system cannot be due to specialized muscle fibers.[34] This observation is one of the more important reasons for postulating the presence of two excitatory transmitters as well as for several other features of the scheme in Fig. 15. An additional interesting property of these muscles is that twitches can be evoked by two or more fast impulses, without any development of spikes; this shows that even fast developing tensions can·result merely from junctional potentials in some muscles.

VI. *PROPERTIES OF MUSCLE FIBERS*

A. ANATOMY

The cross-sectional areas of crustacean muscle fibers show a wide range, but in general they are thick in relation to their length. In many muscles the fibers originate on the inside of the exoskeleton surrounding the body, or on elements which are invaginations of this shell (Chapter 14, Vol. I). Sometimes the origin is on a membrane-like part of the endoskeleton. The muscle insertions are usually on apophyses or apodemes which in turn attach to the shell of and generally move the segment posterior or distal to the one in which the muscle is located. Many joints allow movement in only one plane; two muscles are sufficient to obtain all possible positions of the joint, yet in some cases such joints nevertheless have more than two muscles. Other joints allow movement in more than one direction, in which case extra muscles (like the rotator in the legs of shrimps), or special properties of one of the two usual muscles, may be present to use this extra freedom.

Many muscles have a pinnate fiber arrangement which in larger ones becomes more and more complicated as the apodeme receives fibers from more directions. Thus in the closer muscles of decapod chelae, the apodeme, which is usually a rather flat band in small muscles, shows a cross-like structure, allowing muscle fibers to attach to it from almost all directions. More often the cross section is T-shaped with the flat surface turned toward that of the antagonist. It is of interest that in many muscles of the abdomen the muscle fibers do not run straight, but twist, both individually and in bundles. The functional significance of this arrangement has not been worked out, but it evidently provides for considerable force to be developed and transmitted through the bundles to the skeletal parts. In this connection the possibility that the innervated side of the muscle fibers may contract more readily than the noninnervated one is a matter of interest.

All fibers show a marked cross striation. A relation between the speed of contraction and the closeness of the striation appears present since in the same animals quicker-contracting muscles show a finer striation. Thus the cross striation of the closer of *Eriocheir* shows a finer striation than the opener.[7] The mean value of the closer $A + I$ bands was about 7.5 μ; for the opener, 8 μ. The ratio of A to I was also found to be somewhat smaller in the closer than in the opener. Similar differences have been found in a few other instances, e.g. in the opener (coarse striation) and closer (fine) of *Carcinus maenas*.[35] Another case occurs in the muscular part of the abdominal stretch receptors, of which the faster contracting (RM2) shows finer striation than the slower (RM1).[1,38] However, a wider study of preparations in which the motor nerve supply is known will be necessary to permit generalization of these findings.

B. METABOLISM AND BIOCHEMISTRY

In many respects the composition of crustacean muscle fibers is similar to that of vertebrate ones, but some interesting differences are present (Chapters 4 and 9, Vol. I). It is not yet known if these are connected with the physiological differences.

The ionic content of the muscle fibers is given in Table 2 for a whole muscle and also for isolated single fibers of the crab *Carcinus maenas*.[52] The mean weight of single fibers of this muscle was 0.5 mg. As is usually the case in excitable tissue, the sodium content within the muscle is low by comparison with the high content of the blood,

TABLE 2

ELECTROLYTE CONTENT IN MILLIOSMOLES OF MUSCLE AND BLOOD IN
Carcinus maenas[a]

	Na	K	Ca	Mg	Total cations	Cl⁻
Whole muscle	54	120	13.8	35.8	222.6	54
Single muscle fibers	—	112	10.4	33.8	—	53
Blood	468	12.1	35	47.2	562.3	524

[a] Adapted from Shaw.[52]

while the potassium ratios are the reverse of the sodium ones. There is a marked deficiency of inorganic anions in muscle. Organic anions must therefore be present in quantity, and it has been reported repeatedly that the amount of nonprotein nitrogen and the content of free amino acids is very high in crustacean muscle and also in nerve.[53]

In this connection the differences in amino acids present in the nerves and in the muscles of *Carcinus maenas*[43] are interesting. The muscles of various species seem to contain different amino acids, some of which may be species specific. In marine forms generally the amino acid content is higher than in related fresh-water species.[11] Of the amino acids, a number may serve as anions, but others can be considered important mainly in osmotic equilibrium, since they are most weakly ionized. Whether they may also be connected with the activation and contractile mechanisms is not known. In muscle fibers of *Carcinus* the pH was found[10] to be about 6.9 and not to change markedly with injury. In many ways the contractile process in Crustacea seems analogous to that in other muscles; myosin, actin, and adenosine triphosphate (ATP) are present. It was established long ago that the phosphagen involved is arginine phosphate.[46]

The heat production of crustacean muscle has been investigated a few times. In crab closer muscles the development of tension on repetition becomes much "cheaper" in terms of heat produced.[8] However, stimulation of the whole nerve was used in these experiments, so that the amount to which the fast and slow systems were involved is uncertain. In the crayfish, study of the two contractions separately shows that in lactic acid production and in splitting of arginine phosphate there is no important difference between fast and slow contractions which perform the same amount of work.[3] However, similar studies of the heat production under these circumstances showed the fast to be about twice as expensive as the slow.[37] Both systems functioned more economically when the contractions were repeated, but the differences found were much less than those reported for the crab.

At present these relations are in need of renewed study. For instance, the question of glycogen function in muscle metabolism is uncertain. The glycogen content of the muscles seems highly variable with circumstances (see von Buddenbrock[62] for literature). According to Scheer,[51] who injected radioactive glucose into the circulation, this is not used as a substrate in muscular contraction; instead most of it finds its way into deposits of chitin; none of it appears as radioactive CO_2; but this analysis does not seem to be generally acceptable without more evidence (Chapters 2 and 8, Vol. I).

VII. COMPARISON OF DIFFERENT INNERVATION SYSTEMS

As pointed out above, even when the innervation of different muscles seems identical with regard to the number and kind of efferent axons, the reactions to these axons varies greatly. In fact a complete description is impossible, because at least some differences exist between almost every muscle studied. This fact illustrates how versatile the control mechanisms in crustacean neuromuscular systems are. A number of special features shown by particular systems will be discussed below. On the one hand, these will review the most important of such observations, and, on the other hand, will indicate the fundamental nature of some differences between them.

A. COMPARISON OF SLOW SYSTEMS AND OPENER SYSTEMS

Slow systems of muscles with double motor innervation do not show any striking differences among themselves with regard to their contractions or their electrical responses obtained with external leads.

But with intracellular recording this apparent similarity disappears with respect to the activity of single muscle fibers. Thus the slow closer system of *Procambarus clarkii* and the slow extensor of *Panulirus interruptus* have junctional potentials which are much alike in all fibers. But in the closers of *Panulirus* and *Cancer antennarius* great differences in the size of the junctional potentials occur after facilitation; some fibers show hardly any membrane change, others very considerable ones. In the closer of *Pachygrapsus*, some of these fibers are innervated by the slow axon only. Their junctional potentials are remarkable since they are large after a single impulse, but contrary to other slow junctional potentials, show little facilitation.[32]

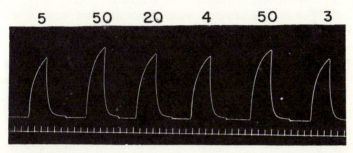

FIG. 17. Influence of impulse spacing on a slow contraction in the closer of *Procambarus clarkii*. Numbers above the contractions give the interval in milliseconds between numbers of a pair. Repetition rate of paired shocks, 10 per second. Abscissa, time in seconds. Note that a slight negative spacing effect is present since contractions are largest when the impulses in each pair are farthest apart. (From Wiersma and Adams.[69])

Notwithstanding the presence of these fibers, the slow contraction of the *Pachygrapsus* closer has no distinctive mechanical features. For instance, no "spacing" effect is noticed in this muscle.[69] Where present this effect results, especially in certain fast systems, when stimuli are paired instead of regularly spaced, and then usually involves an increased contraction, although occasionally negative effects may be obtained (Fig. 17). A few slow systems show a slight spacing effect, but in the closer of *Pachygrapsus* it is absent.

Between the monaxonically innervated opener and stretcher muscles more obvious variations occur. In all cases, low-frequency stimulation leads to smooth tetani, in which the individual impulses are not at all, or only barely, discernible. The minimum frequency at which contraction takes place is generally somewhat higher than for typical slow systems, and for the crayfish is about 10 per second. When intercalated shocks or stimulus spacing are used, some of them, like the opener system of *Pachygrapsus crassipes*, still react like a typical slow system. However, in the rock lobster, *Panulirus interruptus*, and even more in the crayfish, *Procambarus clarkii*, marked spacing effects and small twitches in response to single intercalated shocks occur. Such responses closely resemble those in certain fast systems. The junctional potentials of these muscles are usually similar in all muscle fibers and do not differ much between muscles. With high frequencies of stimulation, small spikes are more readily obtained than in ordinary slow systems.

The tendency of opener and stretcher systems to acquire fast properties is strongly pronounced in the opener muscle of *Pagurus bernhardus*.[67] With low frequencies of stimulation (e.g. 3 per second) a gradually developing smooth tetanus results, but regular twitches follow three or four closely spaced impulses. A similar mixture of fast and slow features is shown by the electrical responses recorded with external leads. Closely spaced impulses produce large summating monophasic deflections, much like those of the fast closer system of *Blepharipoda* (Fig. 19), yet at low stimulating frequencies small and facilitating potentials, indistinguishable from those of a typical slow system, are obtained. These observations suggest that two types of nerve endings from the single motor axon are present in this muscle, some like fast ones with short-lasting but strong facilitation, others like slow ones with long-lasting but only gradually developing facilitation. Whether or not these two types of endings occur on a single muscle fiber will remain uncertain until internal leads are used.

B. COMPARISON OF FAST SYSTEMS

The versatility of the crustacean neuromuscular mechanism is most apparent in the wide range of mechanical responses of fast systems. From a functional standpoint, the highest specialization has been attained in such muscles as the closer of the chelae in crayfish and in the shrimp *Stenopus hispidus*, in which a single impulse suffices to cause a twitch which closes the claw. But in the homologous muscles of the other thoracic legs, such twitches are much weaker and may even be absent.

There can be no doubt that in many muscles a twitch is always accompanied by a spike potential in the contracting muscle fibers. Stronger twitches can be brought about in these cases by recruitment of fibers through the spiking mechanism. This relation has been shown to exist in *Procambarus* and *Pachygrapsus* closer muscles by the use of internal leads.[32] The reactions of the different closer muscles of

Homarus gammarus, which so far have been studied only with external leads, can be ascribed to the same phenomenon, which in this case shows an interesting additional feature.[68] The closer of the cutter claw hardly responds to single impulses, but reacts powerfully to two in quick succession. The strength of this contraction and the size of the correlated electrical deflection indicate that the great

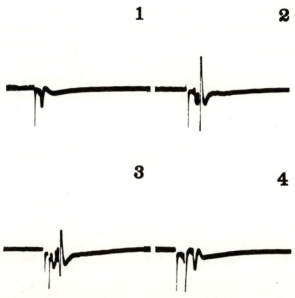

FIG. 18. Action potentials recorded with external leads from the closer of the cutter claw of *Homarus gammarus* comparing single and paired stimuli of different spacing. 1, single shock. Local potential produced but no visible contraction. 2, pair with interval of 2 msec. Large diphasic deflection on second stimulus and strong twitch contraction. 3, pair with interval of 10 msec. Smaller diphasic potentials, weak twitch contraction. 4, interval of 20 msec. Deflection on second shock much as on first, no visible contraction. (From Wiersma.[68])

majority of the muscle fibers are activated, presumably by conducted spikes (Fig. 18). On the other hand, the closer muscles of the crusher claw and the fourth and fifth pair of walking legs respond to two impulses with summated monophasic, instead of diphasic, electrical deflections and minute or no contractions. Finally in the chelae of the second and third legs, diphasic deflections of rather small size, accompanied by weak twitches, are obtained on a single impulse. In contrast to the events in the cutter claw, two impulses bring about only a moderate amount of recruitment, the electrical response on the second being somewhat larger than on the first, and the summated contraction not yet strong enough to cause complete closing. In the second and third legs, muscle fibers with greatly different facilitatory properties must therefore be present, whereas in the muscle of the cutter claw, the fibers are much more uniform.

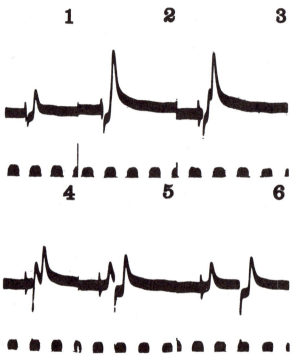

FIG. 19. Action potentials of the closer of *Blepharipoda occidentalis* on stimulation of fast axon with double shocks. Intervals in 1, 1.4 msec; 2, 1.6 msec; 3, 3.6 msec; 4, 7.2 msec; 5, 14.4 msec; 6, 34 msec. Note summation of monophasic deflections without any indication of diphasic deflections when twitching occurs. No contractions resulted for 1, 5, and 6; for 2 and 3 a strong twitch was obtained; for 4, a small one. Time marks, 1/60 sec. (Modified from Wiersma and van Harreveld.[76])

Although in *Homarus* conducted spikes, and in *Procambarus* and *Pachygrapsus* abortive spikes, seem to be a prerequisite for twitching, in *Randallia* and *Blepharipoda* completely localized junctional potentials appear to be just as efficient. No sign of spiking has been encountered in these last two either with external or internal leads. Nevertheless twitches of considerable magnitude readily occur after two nerve impulses, and are accompanied by summated junctional potentials (Fig. 19). In this case fast junctional potentials are unusually effective in causing contraction, though, as shown by the paradox, they still are not as efficient as the slow junctional potentials. Certainly in other muscles like the extensor of the carpopodite of *Panulirus* fast junctional potentials are able to bring about contractions, but whether this also occurs in muscles which often show abortive spikes, such as the

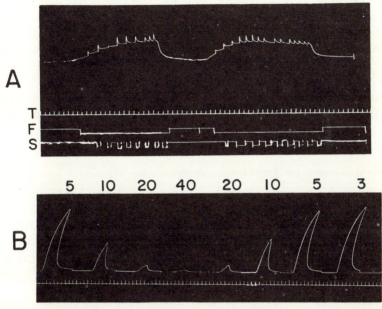

Fig. 20. Effect of intercalated shocks (A) and stimulus spacing (B) in the fast contraction of the main flexor of *Panulirus*. A, two faradic stimuli during which single extra induction shocks were given to the motor axon through another pair of electrodes. Note twitches in response to most, but not all, make-and-break stimuli. *T*, time in seconds; *F*, faradic stimulation signal; *S*, single-shock signal. B, marked positive spacing effect at 10 double shocks per second when the interval between the stimuli in each pair is decreased from 40 to 3 msec (numbers over record). Duration of stimulation in each case 3 sec. Abscissa, time in seconds. (From Wiersma and Adams.[69])

closer of *Procambarus*, has not yet been decided. In such heterogeneously reacting muscles this problem could only be solved by registering the contractions of differently reacting muscle fibers separately, which may be technically impossible.

Stimulus spacing seems to be especially effective in those fast systems which need considerable facilitation to produce contraction. In some instances, as in several muscles of *Panulirus*, stimulation of the fast axon may result in no contraction, or a very small one, when the stimuli are equally spaced, whereas the same number of impulses may be highly effective when they are administered in closely spaced pairs, each pair being separated by a compensatory interval (Fig. 20). In such systems intercalated shocks invariably lead to twitches. In other fast systems the effect of these procedures is often smaller and sometimes even negative.

One other special feature of some muscles may be mentioned. In the hermit crabs and in dromiids, the joint between carpopodite and propodite can be moved in more than one plane, permitting rotation of the propodite. But unlike the situation in shrimps (page 203), no special muscle is present here for this purpose. Instead, the fast axon rotates the propodite inward, the slow outward. Differences in the distribution of the axons on the muscle fibers may be the reason for this phenomenon, but other explanations are not excluded.[73] At any rate, bundles of fibers in one muscle again must differ in their properties.

C. Comparison of Inhibitory Systems

There can be no doubt that crustacean peripheral inhibitory mechanisms, like the motor ones, show profound differences between each other. But since inhibition can be tested only against excitation, differences observed may depend on excitatory factors in addition to the inhibitory ones. In the case of muscles with a double inhibitory nerve supply, this possible confusion can be excluded. For example, in the openers of crabs both inhibitors can suppress contractions totally, but one is more efficient than the other.[70] Invariably the inhibitor specific for the muscle in question is the more effective, although in some species this difference is more pronounced than in others (Table 3). Simultaneous stimulation of both inhibitors has an additive effect in reducing contractions.[65]

Most data in Table 3 are more useful for the comparison of the excitatory systems than for the inhibitory ones. For instance, it can be seen that in all cases inhibition has a stronger influence on the slow than on the fast system of a muscle. In some instances the fast system cannot be inhibited at all. The reason for this may be the presence of spikes in these systems (fast closer of *Procambarus*, fast closer and bender of *Pachygrapsus*). However, it is not clear why inhibition is ineffective in preventing their occurrence in the latter two cases since the slow system of these muscles is easily suppressed. The effect of the same inhibitor often varies considerably in the muscles it innervates, and in many instances this can be ascribed to the relative effectiveness of the excitatory systems. But sometimes, as in the case of the stretcher inhibitor of the crayfish, this explanation fails. This inhibitor is quite effective against stretcher contractions, but hardly influences the slow closer system, whereas there is no obvious difference between these two contractile mechanisms. Nor is there evidence that this difference is due to fewer inhibitory endings on the closer muscle fibers than on those of the stretcher, although this factor may be responsible.

In general, inhibition does not speed up relaxation after contraction. The only known instance is that of one of the four systems in the

TABLE 3

Rc Values[a] for the Inhibitory Systems of the Four Most Distal Muscles of Decapod Crustacean Thoracic Legs[70]

Species	Opener		Stretcher		Fast closer	Slow closer	Fast bender	Slow bender
	Specific	Common	Specific	Common				
Panulirus interruptus	0.50	—	0.5[b]	—	1.25[b]	0.80	1.25	0.75
Procambarus clarkii	0.41	—	0.41	—	∞	5.0[b]	1.25[b]	0.70
Cancer anthonyi	{0.60[c] 0.75	1.0[b]	{0.5 0.6	1.0[b]	1.0[b]	0.75[b]	1.00	0.75
Cancer antennarius	{0.55 0.75	0.93	{0.53 0.75	1.0[b]	1.3[b]	{0.65[b] 0.95[b]	1.1[b]	0.50
Loxorhynchus grandis	{0.45 0.56	1.5[b]	{0.45[b] 0.75	1.5[b]	1.5[b]	1.0[b]	1.4[b]	0.58
Pachygrapsus crassipes	0.40	1.40[b]	0.45[b]	1.25	∞	0.45[b]	∞	0.33

[a] Ratio of inhibitory to excitatory impulse frequencies at which contraction is just suppressed.
[b] These values show a rather wide variation.
[c] Where two figures appear in brackets, two different Rc values were found at different times.

main flexor muscle of *Panulirus interruptus* which shows an unusually slow relaxation. A considerable acceleration of this process results from stimulating the inhibitory axon during the relaxation period.[61]

The presence or absence of supplemented inhibition is not correlated with the mechanical effectiveness of inhibition. Thus in *Pachygrapsus* the specific inhibitors which can cause supplemented inhibition are more effective in the opener and stretcher muscles than the common one, which cannot do so. Yet the latter is highly efficient in mechanical inhibition of the slow bender system even though here, too, it produces no noticeable reduction of the excitatory potentials. Supplemented inhibition is almost completely limited to opener and stretcher systems of the Astacura (Nephropsidea), Brachyura, and Anomura, stimulated by the specific inhibitors. Even with internal leads no evidence can be obtained that the common inhibitors reduce the action potentials noticeably in any fiber of these muscles. However, the common inhibitor does so in occasional fibers of closer and bender muscles in various species of these groups; this effect has also been reported in slow and fast closer systems of crabs and crayfish studied with external leads.[41] In Palinura (Scyllaridea) supplemented inhibition has not been encountered at all, even though the inhibitory potentials are often unusually large.[33]

A difference in the mechanism of supplemented inhibition has been noted between crayfish and crabs.[71] In the former, maximal

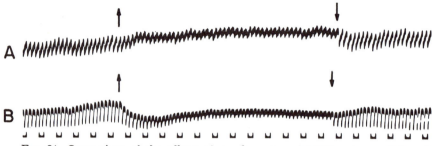

Fig. 21. Comparison of the effects of supplementary inhibition in crayfish and crab. A, inhibition of the action potentials of the stretcher in *Procambarus clarkii*. Note gradual reduction at beginning, but immediate rebound after end of inhibitory stimulation. B, stretcher of *Cancer anthonyi*. Observe that initial reduction is more gradual and after end of inhibitory stimulation there is only partial rebound followed by gradual increase. Arrows indicate start and stop of inhibitory stimulation. Time marks, $\frac{1}{50}$ sec. (From Wiersma and Ellis.[70])

reduction of the excitatory potentials occurs more quickly after the onset of inhibition than in crabs, and on its release, the full magnitude of the potentials is resumed instantly in crayfish, whereas in crabs some facilitation occurs (Fig. 21). Nevertheless, no differences between the inhibition of the mechanical events can be observed in general when simple and supplemented inhibition are compared. However, at very low frequencies of stimulation supplemented inhibition is clearly the more effective in preventing contraction in an Australian crayfish opener system.[41] When long-lasting (e.g. 1 min) supplemented inhibition of the opener of the crayfish *Procambarus clarkii* is compared to similar simple inhibition, another difference between the effects of the two types becomes apparent.[45] Following simple inhibition the electrical responses remain unchanged in size after inhibition is released and are equal to those which occur on excitatory stimulation alone for the same period. But after supplemented inhibition the magnitude of the deflections becomes much larger, and consequently so does the ensuing contraction. Thus a type of rebound occurs; this has been attributed to the prevention of fatigue of the action potential mechanism by a reduction in potential size. Such fatigue, which occurs normally in all excitatory stimulation is the factor which limits the growth of muscle action potentials during any low-frequency stimulation.

VIII. *EFFECTS OF DRUGS AND IONS*

A. DRUGS

The pharmacological effects of a considerable number of substances on crustacean neuromuscular systems have been investigated with results which are rather disappointing with respect to a clarification of the issues at hand. This may well be due to failure of many of these substances to influence the neuromuscular transmission processes as such.[14] When a nerve-muscle preparation is treated with a substance having an effect, further investigation has usually shown that either the nerve impulse or, in a few cases, the contractile mechanism is the element influenced. In some instances there is also an effect on the transmission, but in no case is it certain that the main influence is on transmission.* However, the absence of such effects cannot rightly be used as a basis to conclude that no transmitter substances are involved. For it is conceivable and perhaps likely that the location of the nerve endings underneath the sheath surrounding each muscle fiber protects them against the influences of many substances.

No action of acetylcholine on the peripheral nerve muscle preparation has been found in a number of investigations, in contrast to a clear effect on the heart rate (Chapter 5, Vol. I), and on the movements of the intestine which are speeded up. Only once has quick injection of acetylcholine been reported to cause fast contractions,[18] but evidence is lacking that the fast nerve fiber itself was not stimulated by this procedure. The effect of drugs which would influence a cholinergic transmission is somewhat less clear cut. Curare was found by most investigators to be without effect, even in high concentrations. Wright

---

* But glutamic acid in concentrations of $35 \times 10^{-6}M$ recently was found to cause muscular contractions in various Cructacea. These are preceded by muscle action potentials. Until the amino acid is washed out again, no contractions can be obtained by motor axon stimulation. Inhibitory stimulation depresses the contractions induced by glutamic acid.[58a,58b]

found, however, that curare and, even more, α-erythroidin, have a paralytic effect, the fast twitch being more sensitive than the slow contraction.[80] If the latter was also blocked, direct stimulation was still effective. These results are not sufficient to prove the presence of a fast and a slow transmitter, nor can they be taken as valid proof of a cholinergic transmitter mechanism since the necessary concentrations are very high. Muscarine, nicotine, and pilocarpine are ineffective, even in high concentrations. Atropine has a depressing effect, but only in high concentrations which have a similar effect when the nerve alone is exposed to it. Injection of physostigmine gives rise to contractions, but this effect again may be largely on the motor axons because a single impulse sets up multiple responses in a part of a nerve fiber exposed to the drug.

Adrenaline (epinephrine) has little or no effect. Slow contractions caused by 5-hydroxytryptamine are not due to a direct effect of the drug on the transmission mechanism, but to initial stimulation of sensory fibers, which in turn activate motor axons by ephaptic transmission.[20] Veratrine and hydrastinine have an influence presumably located at the neuromuscular junction in addition to an effect on the nerve fiber. The effect of veratrine appears to be about equally distributed throughout the system as this drug affects the nerve impulse, the transmission chain, and the contractile process. Hydrastinine increases the action potential of the fast closer and at the same time reduces the height of the twitch contraction. This may represent an opposite influence of the drug on the two postulated transmission processes (Fig. 15) between the impulse in the fast fiber and the twitch contraction.

No drug influences on inhibition could be demonstrated in earlier work.* However, an extract of mammalian brain tissue when injected into the opener muscle of the crayfish prevents contraction when the stimulation frequency of the motor axon is low, but allows contraction at higher frequencies.[19] This finding may be taken as an encouraging lead, because it shows that specific substances can mimic the effect of inhibition on crustacean neuromuscular transmission.

Two of the drugs which affect the nerve impulse especially may be briefly discussed. Yohimbine has the remarkable effect of delaying the recovery without affecting conduction, thus causing a long refractory

---

* But recently picrotoxin at a concentration of $10^{-6}M$ was shown to block peripheral inhibition selectively in the opener muscle of a crayfish. Its action most likely involves combination with a receptor for the inhibitory transmitter.[50a]

period. Consequently the axons are able to respond regularly only to stimuli with a frequency of one every second or lower. Slow contractions cannot then be elicited, whereas higher-frequency stimulation of the fast axon results in occasional twitch contractions of different magnitude.[14] Conversely low concentrations of DDT (dichlorodiphenyltrichloroethane) result in hyperexcitability of the nerve fiber, which starts either to fire spontaneously or to respond to a single stimulus with repetitive discharges. As a result, single stimuli to the slow fiber can cause slow contractions. The effects of DDT have been attributed to a mechanism whereby the free calcium is bound, and the hyperexcitability is due to the consequent lack of free calcium ions.[64]

B. Ions

Changing the ionic concentrations in the perfusion fluid has profound effects on neuromuscular preparations. But here too, the effects will not usually be limited to any single step in the chain of events. Hence the results are, with a few exceptions, not yet analyzed with enough precision to allow conclusions. The most interesting and significant results have been obtained by direct stimulation of the muscle fibers with an internal electrode after bathing them in different solutions. Thus when external sodium is replaced with certain quaternary ammonium ions, the electrical response of the muscle fiber is not only maintained but improved.[15] The amplitude of the action potential increases from 70 mv normal, to 80 mv in choline, and 100 mv in tetraethyl ammonium. The increase is accompanied by a longer duration of the electrical response and often of a similar increase in the duration of the contraction (Fig. 22). But the effect of tetrabutyl ammonium consists of prolongation of the electrical event, while the contraction becomes smaller and disappears irreversibly. In crustacean nerve fibers, on the other hand, the same quaternary amines cause a decrease in excitability and block the conducted impulses. These observations indicate that in crustacean muscle the inward movement of sodium, which, in squid and crustacean nerve among others, is considered the mechanism responsible for the rising phase of the conducted action potential,[28] may not function. The same conclusion is indicated by the fact that strontium and barium can replace sodium in the perfusion fluid of crayfish muscle.[14a] However, the particular factors involved in the rising phase of the crustacean muscle spike are uncertain at present although calcium ion movements are implicated.

From these observations it is at once clear that the effect of ions on the nerve muscle preparation as a whole must be very complicated, for it is likely that ions influence the different processes in opposite directions. Magnesium excess causes smaller contractions than normal and when great enough can result in complete block. At these concentrations the nerve is not affected. Probably the action is mainly on the second transmission process, since magnesium appears to have

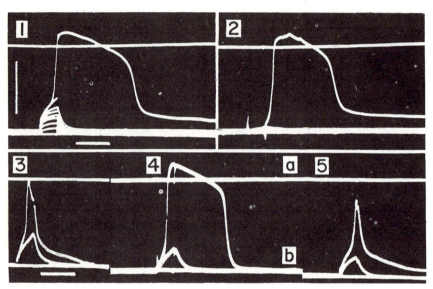

Fig. 22. Effect of replacing sodium with choline in the perfusion fluid on the intracellular potentials of a muscle fiber of *Portunus*. Stimulation with a second internal electrode. The small deflections are responses to subthreshold stimulation of increasing strength shown by multiple exposures. *1* and *2*, potentials of one fiber in choline. Electrode distance in *1*, 0.13 mm; in *2*, 2 mm. Notice overshoot of zero membrane potential. *3*, *4*, and *5*, potentials from another fiber; *3* and *5*, in sodium-containing medium, spike does not overshoot and is of short duration; *4*, in choline, overshoot and prolonged deflection. Electrode distance in *3*, *4*, and *5*, 0.5 mm. Resting potential shown by distance between lines *a* and *b*. Time, 20 msec; voltage, 50 mv. (From Fatt and Katz.[15])

a greater effect on contraction height than on the action potentials. An increase in potassium has different effects on the slow and the fast systems.[63] The slow contractions are reduced and the fast ones enhanced by moderate increases in the K^+ concentration. The effect of calcium is quite erratic. Here too, there are indications that slow and fast systems show a difference in their reactions to this ion.

The effect of ions on inhibition has been studied by determining whether the ratio of excitatory to inhibitory impulses needed to suppress contraction underwent a change. It was found that changes in potassium, calcium, and magnesium which strongly influenced the contraction did not alter this ratio.[79] Evidence for an increased chloride permeability during stimulation of the inhibitory axon has been obtained by bathing the muscle in different concentrations of potassium and chloride.[6a]

IX. *SUMMARY AND CONCLUSIONS*

Since so few motor axons form the innervation of whole muscles in the Crustacea, and the nerve impulses are all-or-none, the neuromuscular transmission system obviously must have special provisions for regulating the speed and strength of contraction. Clearly these must be independent of any classic type of motor unit organization like that which the vertebrate skeletal muscle uses for this purpose. Two such control mechanisms are present, facilitation and inhibition, which are usually regarded as properties of the central nervous system. Of these, the first is by far the more important. Muscles as well as individual muscle fibers differ in their response to facilitation, and it is in this way that the great individuality in reaction shown by crustacean muscles is obtained.

It is certain that the same muscle fiber can react to impulses in different motor axons (polyneuronal motor innervation), but the way this multiple reaction is brought about is not yet fully understood. Particularly striking is the absence of a strict correlation between the electrical and mechanical responses effected by the different motor axons. The study of these relations is made more difficult by the heterogeneity in properties of the different fibers of a given muscle, a condition which is much more pronounced in some muscles than in others.

At least in all long muscle fibers, the motor axon(s) terminates on each fiber at many places, and the spread of excitation is largely and often completely provided by this branching of the nerve fibers (multiterminal innervation), and not by a conducted muscle action potential.

Although the contractile mechanism of crustacean muscle appears to be much like that of vertebrate striated muscle, the electrical events may differ fundamentally from those of other excitable tissues studied, including crustacean nerve. The fact that external sodium is not required for their occurrence, and uncertainties with regard to their exact location, make it difficult to evaluate their significance. It may be hoped that eventually these findings will materially contribute to a better understanding of the relation between membrane potentials and contraction, which is still obscure for all contractile tissues.

The presence of peripheral inhibition is of considerable interest for the study of transmission mechanisms, since it provides a convenient way of demonstrating different steps in the coupling processes which link nerve impulse and contraction. From a functional standpoint its importance is not too certain. It does not provide for reciprocal inhibition of antagonistic muscles. However, peripheral inhibition does offer a means for separate control of the two leg muscles in the decapod Crustacea which are innervated by a single motor axon, but this must be regarded as a late and secondary development.

Compared to the effort spent on the neuromuscular system of the vertebrates, the amount of research done on Crustacea is almost insignificant. Yet the results obtained so far seem sufficiently rewarding and stimulating to justify the hope that the future will see a continuing and vigorous attack on these problems. For an understanding of the development of this type of neuromuscular system and its comparative physiology, investigations on lower Crustacea are most urgently needed.

REFERENCES

1. Alexandrowicz, J. S. 1951. Muscle receptor organs in the abdomen of *Homarus vulgaris* and *Palinurus vulgaris*. *Quart. J. Microscop. Sci.* 92:163–199.
2. Alexandrowicz, J. S. 1952. Muscle receptor organs in the Paguridae. *J. Marine Biol. Assoc. United Kingdom* 31:277–286.
3. Bergren, W. R., and Wiersma, C. A. G. 1938. Chemical changes in the adductor muscle of the cheliped of the crayfish in relation to the double motor innervation. *J. Gen. Physiol.* 22:193–206.
4. Berisina, M., and Feng, T. P. 1933. The heat production of crustacean nerve. *J. Physiol. (London)* 77:111–138.
5. Biedermann, W. 1887. Zur Kenntniss der Nerven und Nervenendigungen in der quergestreiften Muskeln der Wirbellosen. *Sitzber. Akad. Wiss. Wien Math.-naturw. Kl.* 96:8–39.
6. Biedermann, W. 1888. Beitrage zur allgemeine Nerven- und Muskelphysiologie 21. Über die Innervation der Krebsschere. *Sitzber. Akad. Wiss. Wien Math.-naturw. Kl. Abt. III* 97:49–82.
6a. Boistel, J., and Fatt, P. 1958. Membrane permeability change during inhibitory transmitter action in crustacean muscle. *J. Physiol. (London)* 144:176–191.
7. Brenner, H. 1939. Die Beziehung zwischen Muskelreaktion und Querstreifung. *Z. Zellforsch. u. mikroskop. Anat.* 29:251–276.
8. Bronk, D. W. 1932. The heat production and economy of maintained contractions in crustacean muscle. *J. Cellular Comp. Physiol.* 2:285–294.
9. Burke, W., Katz, B., and Machne, X. 1953. The effect of quaternary ammonium ions on crustacean nerve fibres. *J. Physiol. (London)* 122:588–598.

10. Caldwell, P. S. 1954. An investigation of the intracellular pH of crab muscle fibres by means of micro-glass and micro-tungsten electrodes. *J. Physiol.* (*London*) 126:169–180.

11. Camien, M. N., Sarlet, H., Duchâteau, G., and Florkin, M. 1951. Non-protein amino acids in muscle and blood of marine and freshwater Crustacea. *J. Biol. Chem.* 193:881–885.

12. D'Ancona, U. 1925. Per la miglior conoscenza delle terminazione nervose nei muscoli somatici dei crostacei decapodi. *Trabajos Lab. invest. biol. Univ. Madrid* 23:393–423.

13. Eccles, J. C. 1957. "The Physiology of Nerve Cells," 270 pp. Johns Hopkins Press, Baltimore.

14. Ellis, C. H., Thienes, C. H., and Wiersma, C. A. G. 1942. The influence of certain drugs on the crustacean nerve-muscle system. *Biol. Bull.* 83:334–352.

14a. Fatt, P., and Ginsborg, B. L. 1958. The ionic requirements for the production of action potentials in crustacean muscle fibres. *J. Physiol.* (*London*) 142:516–543.

15. Fatt, P., and Katz, B. 1953a. The electrical properties of crustacean muscle fibres. *J. Physiol.* (*London*) 120:171–204.

16. Fatt, P., and Katz, B. 1953b. Distributed "end-plate potentials" of crustacean muscle fibres. *J. Exptl. Biol.* 29:433–439.

17. Fatt, P., and Katz, B. 1953c. The effect of inhibitory nerve impulses on a crustacean muscle fibre. *J. Physiol.* (*London*) 121:374–389.

18. Florey, E. 1954a. Über die Wirkung von 5-Oxytryptamin (Enteramin) in der Krebsschere. *Z. Naturforsch.* 9b:540–547.

19. Florey, E. 1954b. An inhibitory and an excitatory factor of mammalian central nervous system, and their action on a single sensory neuron. *Arch. intern. physiol.* 62:33–53.

20. Florey, E., and Florey, E. 1954. Über die mögliche Bedeutung von Enteramin (5-Oxy-Tryptamin) als nervöser Aktionssubstanz bei Cephalopoden und dekapoden Crustaceen. *Z. Naturforsch.* 9b:58–68.

21. Furshpan, E. J. 1955. Studies on certain sensory and motor systems of decapod crustaceans. 144 pp. Thesis, California Institute of Technology, Pasadena.

22. Furshpan, E. J., and Wiersma, C. A. G. 1954. Local and spike potentials of impaled crustacean muscle fibers on stimulation of single axons. *Federation Proc.* 13:51.

23. Furusawa, K. 1929. The depolarization of crustacean nerve by stimulation or oxygen want. *J. Physiol.* (*London*) 67:325–342.

24. Graham, J., and Gerard, R. W. 1946. Membrane potentials and excitation of impaled muscle fibers. *J. Cellular Comp. Physiol.* 28:99–117.

25. Hill, A. V. 1929. The heat-production and recovery of crustacean nerve. *Proc. Roy. Soc.* B105:153–176.

26. Hodgkin, A. L. 1939. The relation between conduction velocity and the electrical resistance outside a nerve fibre. *J. Physiol.* (*London*) 94:560–570.

27. Hodgkin, A. L. 1948. The local electric changes associated with repetitive action in a non-medullated axon. *J. Physiol.* (*London*) 107:165–181.

28. Hodgkin, A. L. 1951. The ionic basis of electrical activity in nerve and muscle. *Biol. Revs. Cambridge Phil. Soc.* 26:339–409.

29. Hoffmann, P. 1914. Über die doppelte Innervation der Krebsmuskeln. Zugleich ein Beitrag zur Kenntnis nervöser Hemmungen. *Z. Biol.* 63:411–442.

30. Holmes, W., Pumphrey, R. J., and Young, J. Z. 1942. The structure and conduction velocity of the medullated nerve fibers of prawns. *J. Exptl. Biol.* 18:50–54.

31. Hoyle, G. 1955. Neuromuscular mechanisms of a locust skeletal muscle. *Proc. Roy. Soc.* B143:343–367.

32. Hoyle, G., and Wiersma, C. A. G. 1958a. Excitation at neuromuscular junctions in Crustacea. *J. Physiol.* (*London*) 143:403–425.

33. Hoyle, G., and Wiersma, C. A. G. 1958b. Inhibition at neuromuscular junctions in Crustacea. *J. Physiol.* (*London*) 143:426–440.

34. Hoyle, G., and Wiersma, C. A. G. 1958c. Coupling of membrane potential to contraction in crustacean muscles. *J. Physiol.* (*London*) 143:441–453.

35. Jasper, H. H., and Pezard, A. 1934. Relation entre la rapidité d'un muscle strié et sa structure histologique. *Compt. rend.* 198:499–501.

36. Kamada, T., and Kinosita, H. 1937. Graded response of the muscle of Japanese giant crab for indirect stimulation. *Proc. Imp. Acad.* (*Tokyo*) 13:374–377.

37. Keighley, G., and Wiersma, C. A. G. 1941. Heat production of slow and fast contractions of a crustacean muscle with double motor innervation. *J. Cellular Comp. Physiol.* 17:305–314.

38. Kuffler, S. W. 1954. Mechanisms of activation and motor control of stretch receptors in lobster and crayfish. *J. Neurophysiol.* 17:558–574.

39. Kuffler, S. W. 1955. Contracture at the nerve-muscle junction: the slow muscle fiber system. *Am. J. Phys. Med.* 34:161–171.

40. Kuffler, S. W., and Eyzaguirre, C. 1955. Synaptic inhibition in an isolated nerve cell. *J. Gen. Physiol.* 39:155–184.

41. Kuffler, S. W., and Katz, B. 1947. Inhibition at the nerve muscle junction in Crustacea. *J. Neurophysiol.* 10:395–408.

42. Levin, A. 1927. Fatigue, retention of action current and recovery in crustacean nerve. *J. Physiol.* (*London*) 63:113–129.

43. Lewis, P. R. 1952. The free amino-acids of invertebrate nerve. *Biochem. J.* 52:330–338.

44. Lucas, K. 1917. On summation of propagated disturbances in the claw of *Astacus* and on the double neuro-muscular system of the adductor. *J. Physiol.* (*London*) 51:1–35.

45. Marmont, G., and Wiersma, C. A. G. 1938. On the mechanism of inhibition and excitation of crayfish muscle. *J. Physiol.* (*London*) 93:173–193.

46. Meyerhof, O., and Lohmann, K. 1928. Über die natürlichen Guanidinophosphorsäuren (Phosphagene) in der quergestreiften Muskulatur. *Biochem. Z.* 196:22–72.

47. Monnier, A. M., and Dubuisson, M. 1931. Étude à l'oscillographe cathodique des nerfs pédieux de quelques Arthropodes. *Arch. intern. physiol.* 34:25–57.

48. Nagahama, H. 1941. "Nerve-map" of walking legs of Japanese giant crab *Macrocheira kaempferi*. *J. Fac. Sci. Imp. Univ. Tokyo Sect. IV* 5:497–506.

49. Nageotte, J. 1916. Note sur les fibres à myéline et sur les étranglements de Ranvier chez certains Crustacés. *Compt. rend. soc. biol.* 79:259–263.

50. Richet, C. 1882. "Physiologie des Muscles et des Nerfs," 924 pp. Ballière, Paris.

50a.Robbins, J., and van der Kloot, W. G. 1958. The effect of picrotoxin on peripheral inhibition in the crayfish. *J. Physiol.* (*London*) 143:541–552.

51. Scheer, B. T., and Scheer, M. A. R. 1951. Blood sugar in spiny lobsters. *Physiol. Comparata et Oecol.* 2:198–209.

52. Shaw, J. 1955. Ionic regulation in the muscle fibres of *Carcinus maenas*. *J. Exptl. Biol.* **32**:383–396.
53. Silber, R. H. 1941. The free amino acids of lobster nerve. *J. Cellular Comp. Physiol.* **18**:21–30.
54. Tobias, J. M., and Bryant, S. H. 1955. An isolated giant axon preparation from the lobster nerve cord. *J. Cellular Comp. Physiol.* **46**:163–182.
55. Turner, R. S. 1950. Functional anatomy of the giant fiber system of *Callianassa californiensis*. *Physiol. Zoöl.* **23**:35–41.
56. van Harreveld, A. 1939a. The nerve supply of doubly and triply innervated crayfish muscles related to their function. *J. Comp. Neurol.* **70**:267–284.
57. van Harreveld, A. 1939b. Doubly-, triply-, quadruply-, and quintuply-innervated crustacean muscles. *J. Comp. Neurol.* **70**:285–296.
58. van Harreveld, A. 1939c. The motor innervation of a triply innervated crustacean muscle. *J. Exptl. Biol.* **16**:398–402.
58a. van Harreveld, A. 1959. Compounds in brain extracts causing spreading depression of cerebral cortical activity and contraction of crustacean muscle. *J. Neurochem.* **3**:300–315.
58b. van Harreveld, A., and Mendelson, M. 1959. Glutamate-induced contractions in crustacean muscle. *J. Cellular Comp. Physiol.* **54**:85–94.
59. van Harreveld, A., and Wiersma, C. A. G. 1936. The double motor innervation of the adductor muscle in the claw of the crayfish. *J. Physiol.* (*London*) **88**:78–99.
60. van Harreveld, A., and Wiersma, C. A. G. 1937. The triple innervation of crayfish muscle and its function in contraction and inhibition. *J. Exptl. Biol.* **14**:448–461.
61. van Harreveld, A., and Wiersma, C. A. G. 1939. The function of the quintuple innervation of a crustacean muscle. *J. Exptl. Biol.* **16**:121–133.
62. von Buddenbrock, W. 1940. Die Muskelphysiologie. *In:* "Bronn's Tierreich," Bd. 5, Abt. I, Bch. 7, pp. 988–1004. Akademische Verlagsges., Leipzig.
63. Waterman, T. H. 1941. A comparative study of the effects of ions on whole nerve and single isolated nerve fiber preparations of crustacean neuro-muscular systems. *J. Cellular Comp. Physiol.* **18**:109–126.
64. Welsh, J. H., and Gordon, H. T. 1947. The mode of action of certain insecticides on the arthropod nerve axon. *J. Cellular Comp. Physiol.* **30**:147–172.
65. Wiersma, C. A. G. 1941. The inhibitory nerve supply of the leg muscles of different decapod crustaceans. *J. Comp. Neurol.* **74**:63–79.
66. Wiersma, C. A. G. 1947. Giant nerve fiber system of the crayfish. A contribution to comparative physiology of synapse. *J. Neurophysiol.* **10**:23–38.
67. Wiersma, C. A. G. 1951. A bifunctional single motor axon system of a crustacean muscle. *J. Exptl. Biol.* **28**:13–21.
68. Wiersma, C. A. G. 1955. An analysis of the functional differences between the contraction of the adductor muscles in thoracic legs of the lobster, *Homarus vulgaris* L. *Arch. néerl. zool.* **11**:1–13.
69. Wiersma, C. A. G., and Adams, R. T. 1950. The influence of nerve-impulse sequence in the contractions of different crustacean muscles. *Physiol. Comparata et Oecol.* **2**:20–33.
70. Wiersma, C. A. G., and Ellis, C. H. 1942. A comparative study of peripheral inhibition in decapod crustaceans. *J. Exptl. Biol.* **18**:223–236.

71. Wiersma, C. A. G., and Helfer, R. G. 1941. The effect of peripheral inhibition on the muscle action potentials of the crab. *Physiol. Zoöl.* 14:296–304.
72. Wiersma, C. A. G., and Ripley, S. H. 1952. Innervation patterns of crustacean limbs. *Physiol. Comparata et Oecol.* 2:391–405.
73. Wiersma, C. A. G., and Ripley, S. H. 1954. Further functional differences between fast and slow contractions in certain crustacean muscles. *Physiol. Comparata et Oecol.* 3:327–336.
74. Wiersma, C. A. G., and van Harreveld, A. 1934. On the nerve-muscle system of the hermit crab (*Eupagurus bernhardus*). Inhibition of the contraction of the abductor of the claw. *Arch. néerl. physiol.* 19:458–468.
75. Wiersma, C. A. G., and van Harreveld, A. 1938a. The influence of the frequency of stimulation on the slow and the fast contraction in crustacean muscle. *Physiol. Zoöl.* 11:75–81.
76. Wiersma, C. A. G., and van Harreveld, A. 1938b. A comparative study of the double motor innervation in marine crustaceans. *J. Exptl. Biol.* 15:18–31.
77. Wiersma, C. A. G., and van Harreveld, A. 1939. The interactions of the slow and the fast contraction of crustacean muscle. *Physiol. Zoöl.* 12:43–49.
78. Wiersma, C. A. G., and Wright, E. B. 1947. The nature of the action potentials of crustacean muscles. *J. Exptl. Biol.* 23:205–212.
79. Wiersma, C. A. G., and Zawadzki, B. 1948. On the relation between different ions and peripheral inhibition in crustacean muscle. *J. Cellular Comp. Physiol.* 32:101–103.
80. Wright, E. B. 1949. The action of erythroidin, curare, and chlorobutanol in the crayfish. *J. Cellular Comp. Physiol.* 33:301–332.
81. Wright, E. B. 1956. Effect of sodium lack on local response of the single crustacean motor axon. *Proc. Soc. Exptl. Biol. Med.* 93:318–320.
82. Wright, E. B., and Adelman, W. J. 1954. Accommodation in three single motor axons of the crayfish claw. *J. Cellular Comp. Physiol.* 43:119–132.
83. Wright, E. B., and Adelman, W. J. 1956. "Local or initial" potential of the crustacean single motor axon. *Federation Proc.* 15:203–204.
84. Wright, E. B., and Coleman, P. D. 1954. Excitation and conduction in crustacean single motor axons. *J. Cellular Comp. Physiol.* 43:133–164.
85. Young, J. Z. 1936. The structure of nerve fibres in cephalopods and Crustacea. *Proc. Roy. Soc.* B121:319–337.

CHAPTER 7

C. A. G. WIERSMA

REFLEXES AND THE CENTRAL NERVOUS SYSTEM

I. *INTRODUCTION*

Knowledge about the functioning of central nervous systems in invertebrates is still sharply limited; the crustacean central nervous system (CNS) is no exception. The reasons for this limitation are varied. The histology, though studied to a certain extent, is different from that of vertebrates; most of the available forms are small; and such little experimental work as has been performed has mainly used methods fruitful in vertebrates, but possibly inadequate for crustaceans. Both the histology and recent physiological evidence show that in a number of respects the properties of the crustacean nervous system may not closely resemble the vertebrate one.

An outstanding feature of the crustacean CNS is the small number of neuronal elements which constitutes it. This makes possible a type of analysis which will be difficult to achieve in vertebrates. As an example of how this situation provides insight into the functional significance of individual neurons, the intrinsic ganglion system of the crustacean neurogenic heart may well be cited (see Chapter 5, Vol. I). This can be considered as a small yet complex "CNS" with an intrinsic automatism, an output in the form of spikes in the motor axons to the heart muscle cells, and an input in the form of impulses reaching it from the real CNS via the accelerating and inhibitory nerve fibers. Though the relations in the CNS are many times more complicated, it is the opinion of this writer that they are similar. This point of view has been basic in writing the present chapter; a more conventional approach is used in von Buddenbrock's review.[38] Most of the material presented below is restricted to the decapod Cructacea, with but few references to other forms. For many of the latter, anatomical descriptions of the nervous system are available, but not the corresponding physiological data.

The basic plan of organization of all crustacean nervous systems is a ladder-like pattern, in which each half body segment possesses a ganglion. These ganglia are cross-connected by commissures and longitudinally linked by connectives. In all forms, among both lower and higher groups, the number of somites is larger than that of the ganglia, since some of the latter have fused to form a "brain." In most species a similar condensation has taken place in the ganglia serving the mouth parts, and this sometimes extends also to more posterior somites, as in crabs. Furthermore, abdominal segments which become vestigial may lose their ganglia and receive their innervation from more anterior ganglia. In this respect a great variety of conditions exists in different forms, and interesting correlations between the size of the ganglia and their function can be noted.

As an example of a crustacean nervous system in which relatively little specialization has taken place, that of the crayfish (Fig. 1) may be selected. In this animal, as in most crustaceans, the two ganglia in each segment fuse strongly, forming one unit. The resulting structure will be considered below as one ganglion. Typically each ganglion has three pairs of nerves leaving it, two ventral and one dorsal. The first root carries the axons which innervate the appendage, the second one, those which innervate most of the somite. These two roots are large and mixed, containing both sensory and motor axons. The third root, which is much smaller, may be completely motor and provides for the innervation of the flexor musculature of the body in swimming forms.

In most Crustacea which can swim by flapping their abdomen, giant fibers occur in the central nervous system. These structures range among the largest nerve fibers known, although they are somewhat smaller than those found in squids. Their properties have been physiologically investigated to a considerable extent with results that are important because they provide insight into the functioning of crustacean interneurons in general.

II. HISTOLOGY

The detailed cytology of crustacean nerve cell bodies has been repeatedly investigated; this work is reviewed by Balss.[4] Most of the ganglion cells in the CNS are monopolar. Neurofibrils and Nissl sub-

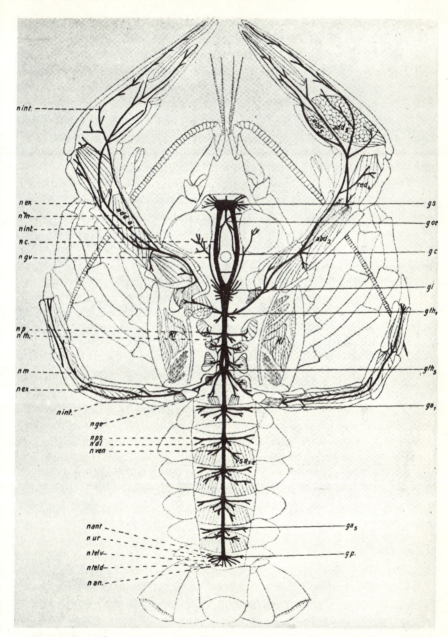

FIG. 1. Central nervous system of *Astacus astacus* and some of the peripheral nerves. The different ganglia are indicated as follows: *g s*, brain; *g oe*, ganglion of stomatogastric system; *g c*, commissural ganglion; *g i*, subesophageal ganglion; *g th*, thoracic ganglia; *g a*, abdominal ganglia; *g p*, telson ganglion. (After Keim.[19])

stance are present, together with Golgi apparatus, mitochondria, and often vacuoles. The nucleus is usually large and has one or two nucleoli. In general the axon branches within a short distance of the cell body; one branch divides repeatedly, forming dendritic structures. These enter the neuropiles formed by the endings of the sensory axons and branchings of central and efferent neurons. The other division of the axon continues further and, in the case of the efferent fibers, enters a peripheral nerve trunk. On this branch synapses with other fibers can occur; they consist of a slight invagination of the axoplasm of one fiber by that of the other and are called lateral synapses.

The most fruitful method for studying the course taken by different axons has been staining with methylene blue, which Retzius,[29] Allen,[3] and Bethe[7] have applied to a number of species. Allen used different stages in development of the lobster, which has the advantage that different fibers are more easily stained at one stage than at another, hence a more complete picture was obtained. Luck plays an important part in methylene blue staining, and one can never be certain that all branches of a given axon are visible, or that certain types of fibers are not overlooked completely because they do not stain. From the results obtained, the following generalizations can be abstracted.

A. Sensory Fibers

The great majority of these fibers have their cell body in the periphery. In general the sensory axons which enter a given ganglion break up in one of its neuropiles, of which there is at least one pair, but often more, in each ganglion. So far it has been impossible to resolve the connections made in this way with other fibers. From physiological evidence it seems certain that specific sensory axons also send a direct branch to other ganglia and there is also histological evidence for such fibers (Fig. 3, s). Sensory units with cell bodies in the CNS are represented by the photoreceptors in the telson ganglion[23] and by muscular receptors in the coxal region of the thoracic legs.[2]

B. Efferent Fibers

The cell bodies of most motor fibers, but certainly not all, are located in the ganglion through whose roots they run to the periphery. The cell bodies are found typically in a layer on the ventral side of the ganglion. The axons may often cross to the other side. Branches into the neuropiles seem to be invariably present. The best-studied motor fibers are the so-called giant root fibers in shrimps and crayfish; they show considerable differences. In the crayfish *Orconectes limosus* there are two independent fibers which cross each other quite dorsally near the medial giant fibers[16] (Fig. 2A). In the prawn *Palaemon serratus* the two fibers fuse into a single structure near the middle of the ganglion and then redivide[15] (Fig. 2B). Thus it is not certain that they do cross, but this is of no consequence, since functionally they

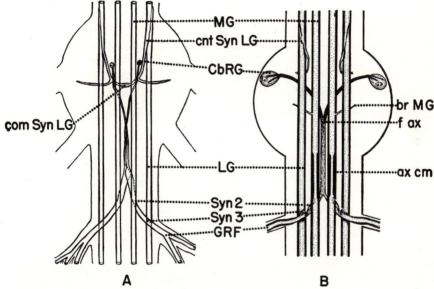

A   **B**

FIG. 2. The course of the giant motor root fibers in an abdominal ganglion and their relation to the central giant fibers. A. *Orconectes limosus* (after Johnson[16]). B. *Palaemon serratus* (after Holmes[15]). *MG*, medial giant fiber; *LG*, lateral giant fiber; *GRF*, giant motor fiber of the third root; *cnt Syn LG*, macrosynapse between segments of lateral giant fibers in connective; *CbRG*, cell body of the giant root fiber; *Syn 2*, synapse of *GRF* with *MG* on side of the root; *Syn 3*, synapse of *GRF* with *LG* (*Syn 1* of *GRF* with *MG* on side of cell body is not marked for crayfish and may be absent in prawn); *com Syn LG*, synapse between *LG* of same ganglion (has not been described in prawn); *br MG*, branch of medial giant into ganglion; *f ax*, fusion of the two *GRF*; *ax cm*, constriction, heavily myelinated, of *MG*. The last three features are absent in crayfish.

can be considered as a single neuron, in contrast to those of the crayfish which are independent also in their physiological action.[41] In their course through the ganglion the giant motor fibers show successive synapses with the central giant fibers (Fig. 2). The details of this system are given on page 250 for the crayfish.

At least one instance is known in which a single neuron sends axons into roots of several different ganglia. In the anterior part of the nerve ring of *Carcinus* a nerve cell occurs whose axon branches at least four times, each branch entering the nerve trunk of a different leg[7] (Fig. 3, *d*). Conceivably this is the common inhibitor of the leg muscles (Chapter 6).

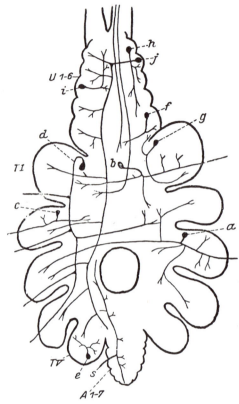

Fɪɢ. 3. Types of nerve cells revealed by staining with methylene blue in the thoracic nerve ring of *Carcinus maenas*. *a–d*, motor neurons; *e–j*, interneurons; *s*, sensory axon; *U 1–6*, the six segments of the subesophageal ganglion; *T I–V*, thoracic ganglia; *A 1–7* vestiges of the abdominal ganglia. (After Bethe.[7])

Neurosecretory neurons in the central nervous system are discussed in Chapter 8.

C. Interneurons

A number of neurons are wholly restricted to the central nervous system. Different types have been described, but their relative abundance is unknown. In the lobster several classes may be distinguished.[3] 1) The cell body is located in the brain or in a ganglion of the cord and has an axon running posteriorly. These axons, in most cases, give off collaterals to the neuropiles of each ganglion through which they pass. 2) The cell body is located in a cord ganglion and the axon runs toward the brain. 3) The cell body is in a cord ganglion and the axon runs anteriorly, ending in the second ganglion after having given off a collateral in the ganglion in between. Most likely a number of other types of connection are present. For instance, in crabs some inter-neurons may remain wholly within the limits of a single ganglion (Fig. 3, *e*). At least in the simpler ganglia of the abdominal chain of the crayfish and lobster, this type is evidently absent. The sensory fibers would then connect directly with the motor fibers for the purely segmental reflexes.

Among the interneurons, the course of the giant fibers in *Homarus* and *Procambarus* is known best. The medial giant fibers of the lobster each have a single large cell body located anteriorly in the brain.[3] The axon soon gives off a collateral to the neuropile, and in the posterior part of the brain crosses to the other side. The fibers are situated dor-somedially for the whole length of the cord from the subesophageal ganglion back, and lie in close proximity to each other. On leaving the brain their diameter first increases greatly, then tapers distally. In the commissures the diameter may be 200 μ in the crayfish; just before the telson ganglion it may be only 150 μ or less. Great in-dividual differences, both in diameter and in amount of taper, are present. The axons are surrounded by a thick sheath in which there are nuclei located near the axon membrane. Their synapses with motor fibers are described below.

The lateral giant fibers, like the medial ones which they often adjoin, are located near the dorsal surface of the cord. They are more complex in structure since they consist of a series of neurons, each of which probably originates from a single large cell body in the ventral side of a cord ganglion. The axon decussates and runs first dorsally, then anteriorly along with the medial giant fibers to the next ganglion where it terminates in a junction with the axon arising in that ganglion (Fig. 4). After the decussation each axon gives off a conspicuous side branch into the ipsilateral neuropile, but before that there may also be a collateral to the neuropile of the other side. A synapse with the contralateral partner is indicated in the middle of the decussation. The longitudinal junctions are such that superficially a continuous axon seems to be present. In contrast to the medial giant fibers, the diameters of crayfish lateral giants are far larger in the abdominal cord (200 μ) than in the esophageal commissures (80 μ).

The extent to which the various ganglia of the crustacean CNS are connected by interneurons is indicated by the number of fibers between them. Sections show that in the crayfish the interconnection of the two halves of each ganglion consists of many fibers forming two major tracts,[20] but the number has not been determined. Like the

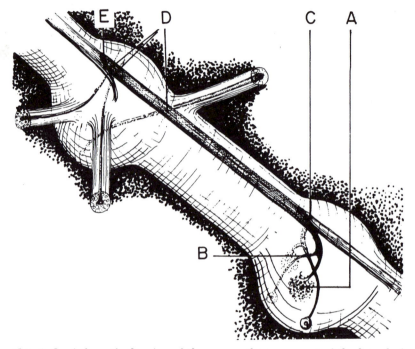

Fig. 4. Semischematic drawing of the course of one segment of the lateral giant fiber system with its synapses. Ganglion at right contains the cell bodies, the dotted one being that of the fiber fully drawn. A, neuropile in opposite part of ganglion which may be main source of sensory stimulation; B, commissural synapse between left and right lateral giant fibers; C, synapse with posterior segment; D, synapses with motor fibers of the three roots in the anterior ganglion; E, end of segment in synapse with anterior segment. (From Wiersma.[43])

connectives, these commissures contain sensory and motor fibers as well as interneurons, and the first two comprise a strongly predominant fraction in them. In cross sections of *Procambarus* connectives, the number of longitudinal fibers in the CNS is obviously small compared to vertebrates (Fig. 5). Actual counts show only 2000 fibers on each side between the brain and the subesophageal ganglion, including very thin ones. Between the thoracic ganglia the number is larger, being about 3000 in each half, whereas in the abdominal chain the corresponding figure is only about 1000.[43]

In *Procambarus clarkii* the cell bodies in all the ganglia have been counted to determine the number of neurons present. The accuracy of such an estimate is decreased by the presence of cells of all sizes and shapes throughout the cell layers.[46] Particularly the smaller nerve cells are difficult to distinguish from glial elements. About 500 cells occur in each abdominal ganglion and about 2000 in each of the

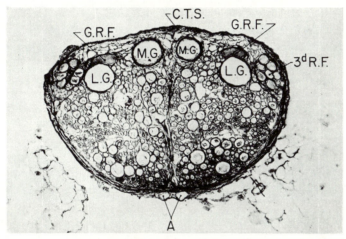

FIG. 5. Cross section through abdominal cord of *Procambarus clarkii* just behind a ganglion. *M.G.*, medial giant fiber; *L.G.*, lateral giant fiber; *G.R.F.*, giant motor root fibers near place where they synapse with lateral giant fibers; 3^d *R.F.*, bundle of other motor fibers which will enter the third root; *C.T.S.*, connective tissue sheath surrounding the cord; *A*, artery on ventral side of cord. Notice the other large and small fibers, numbering about 2000. (Picture courtesy of Dr. J. D. Robertson.)

thoracic ganglia. In the brain and the subesophageal ganglion cell layers with a mixed population like those in the other ganglia are present, but in addition there are layers of a uniform small cell type. Excluding these, the brain contains about 10,000 cells; the subesophageal ganglion, 6000. In the brain the layers of small cells, which in contrast to the other cell layers are much thicker and very compact, were estimated to contain 65,000 cells; in the subesophageal ganglion the similar layers contain only about 1000 cells. For the whole CNS, including the commissural ganglia but not the ganglion cells in the optic ganglia, the total number counted was 28,722 plus

66,000 small cells. Possibly the latter are neurosecretory in function, or they may be the site of "higher nervous functions."

D. Synaptic Connections

Besides the type of connection made in the neuropiles, of which no details are available, more direct connections between axons are known to exist, at least for the giant fiber system. In shrimps the giant axons

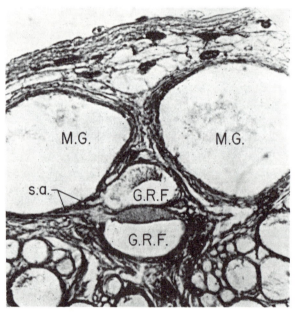

Fig. 6. Cross section through an abdominal ganglion of *Procambarus clarkii* at the level where the third root motor giant fibers cross each other. *M.G.*, medial giant fiber; *G.R.F.*, third root giant fiber; *s.a.*, synaptic area to which the third root giant fibers send branches. (Picture courtesy of Dr. J. D. Robertson.)

of the CNS give off near each third root a small tuft which envelops and presumably stimulates the giant third root motor axon (Fig. 2B). In the crayfish, however, it is the postsynaptic motor fiber which comes in contact with the presynaptic giant fiber by means of axoplasmatic material penetrating the sheath of the latter (Fig. 6). The electron microscope shows that in this type of lateral synapse the axoplasm of the two neurons is closely approximated, in places perhaps being separated only by the thickness of two axolemmal membranes, each about 300 A thick[30] (Fig. 7). From physiological evidence there cannot be any doubt that transmission occurs here. These structures are obvious only because of the large size of both fibers. Smaller fibers probably make similar connections with the central giant ones; this type of connection may quite possibly be widespread. Even the synaptic connections between the fibers in the neuropiles may be of this kind. Because of the difficulty in locating lateral synapses, erroneous interpretation of central nervous function is difficult to avoid. Thus

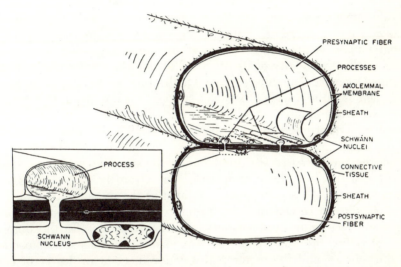

FIG. 7. Schematic drawing of the type of synaptic connection made by the central and peripheral giant fibers in *Procambarus clarkii*. A flap of the presynaptic axolemmal membrane is reflected to show two synaptic processes in presynaptic Schwann cell cytoplasm. The inset is an enlargement (reconstructed from electron micrographs of the area designated by the dotted lines). A process of postsynaptic axoplasm surrounded by the postsynaptic axolemmal membrane is shown in presynaptic Schwann cytoplasm. The close apposition of pre- and postsynaptic axolemmal membranes is indicated. (From Robertson.[30])

Allen,[3] by overlooking the lateral synapses in the lobster, concluded tentatively that the medial giant fibers are motor interneurons exclusively for muscles of the uropods and thus would function in steering the animals during swimming, rather than eliciting the whole swimming movement.

III. *REFLEXES*

Most Crustacea, like other advanced forms, have a large variety of reflexes, in contrast to the majority of invertebrates, which have monotonous reflex patterns. In Crustacea the considerable variety of the appendages which the animal possesses may be one of the main reasons for such reflex differentiation. By isolation of ganglia it can be shown that many of the reflex pathways are restricted to the same ganglion into which the sensory fibers enter. There are more homolateral reflexes than heterolateral or bilateral ones. No extensive survey has yet been made, but undoubtedly the number of reflexes governed by each single ganglion will be directly correlated with the number of possible movements that the musculature of its body segment can make. Another correlate of the number of reflexes governed by single ganglia may be the size of the ganglion, since this seems directly related to the complexity of its function. Striking examples can be found in the Decapoda Anomura, in which the relative development of the abdomen is quite variable between species and the abdominal ganglia vary correspondingly. Another example of a relation between functional importance and size of a part of the CNS is the relative diameter of the esophageal commissures in crabs. In agile forms, like the Grapsidae, the commissures are thick, but in the slow-moving spider crabs, like *Loxorhynchus*, the commissures are extremely thin strands, and the main bulk of nervous tissue is located in the thoracic ring.

Reflexes can be classified according to the number of neurons forming the direct chain between sense organ and effector. In the simplest type of reflex, the axon reflex, the same axon functions simultaneously as the sensory and the motor pathway for it. Next in degree of complexity are monosynaptic reflexes, in which the motor fiber is directly activated by primary sensory fibers. But since present knowledge of the crustacean nervous system in most cases does not yet allow us to decide whether a given reflex is monosynaptic or not, the true reflexes will be divided merely into "simple" and "complex" ones. Among the former will be monosynaptic reflexes and all others in which there is no evidence that the reflex itself influences the subsequent movements. In the complex reflexes, the movements may be quite complicated and depend on feedback, or on a chain of simple reflexes resulting successively from the stimuli provided by each preceding movement. Such complex reflexes merge without a sharp boundary into behavioral patterns. It is shown below that at least some reflexes which appear quite complicated are brought about mainly by the action of a single interneuron.

A. AXON REFLEXES

This type of reflex has been invoked to explain the remarkable reactions of isolated appendages. Autotomized limbs, particularly from certain species, not only can go through a number of spontaneous movements, but also may show more or less stereotyped reactions to certain stimuli. Tonner[35] explained this by assuming the presence of a peripheral nerve net in which axon reflexes would take place. By staining he claimed to have found nerve fibers connecting a net with the muscles, although the nerve endings on the muscle fibers were never found. However the presence of a peripheral nerve net itself is unlikely, and the elements stained were probably connective tissue cells.[1]

Consequently the reactions of isolated limbs must be due to another pathway of impulses, namely through ephaptic transmission between sensory and motor fibers. Near their cut central ends, the motor fibers are hyperexcitable and hence they "reflect" sensory impulses.[5] In many cases the sensory axons mainly involved are those coming from the sense organs in the joints, which often run close to the motor fibers. Actual movement patterns of the isolated limbs, such as alternate extension and flexion, probably depend on anatomical relations of the axon's course in the ischiopodite, but this aspect of the problem has not been worked out. Perhaps the movements of fluid within the limb act as a variable shunt for the external currents arising from the sensory action potentials within the narrow channel formed by the ischiopodite, where the transmission usually occurs. The latter fact can be demonstrated by cutting the nerve in the middle of the meropodite, which usually stops all such reactions.

These phenomena are not axon reflexes and occur only in isolated legs. Although they do not take part in the normal reflex patterns they may nevertheless be of considerable value to the animal in some species. For instance, in the ghost shrimp *Callianassa* the autotomized claw twitches rhythmically for a minute or more after being thrown off and may therefore distract the attention of a predator.

Whether true axon reflexes are present in the peripheral "nerve nets" of the heart and the intestinal tract is unknown. The possibility of their presence is indicated by the complex course of certain axons in these structures and by the suggestion that stretch may stimulate some of the dendrites (Chapter 5, Vol. I).

B. SIMPLE REFLEXES

A slight touch on any appendage of an intact animal leads to localized reactions, which are specific for the part stimulated. For example, touching the inner surface is followed by an inward movement of the appendage. In general, little study has been made of this type of reflex response and only a few have been worked out in any detail.

1. *Eyestalk withdrawal.* In Crustacea with movable eyestalks, the eye is generally withdrawn when its cornea is touched. The same movement occurs on touching the hairs around the eye, the rostrum, and the anterior carapace. Stronger stimuli are required when they occur further from the eye. But in crabs the strongest possible stimulation of more remote body parts, such as the posterior carapace, never elicits this reflex. On the other hand, stronger stimulation of the parts mentioned nearer the eye results in withdrawal movements of other head appendages. According to Bethe[6] the reaction can spread to the homolateral antennule and antenna as well as to the heterolateral eye, but never involves the heterolateral antenna.

2. *Claw closing.* Another simple reflex, which does not spread to the opposite side, is the closing reflex of the chela. Touching the inside of the dactylopodite or the pollux of the propodite causes the claw to close. Isolation of the cheliped ganglion shows that this reflex is mediated by it.[39] Touching any other parts of the chela fails to evoke this reflex; on the contrary, stimulation of hairs on the outside of the two parts mentioned causes opening. The closing reflex, although simple in nature, is not as "obligatory" as the eye reflex. For although it seldom fails to appear promptly when the animal is held out of water, touch alone is often insufficient under water unless the animal is in an excited state. Such a state can be brought about, for example, by chemical stimulation. But out of water the closing reflex is obtainable even in a crayfish in which a state of immobility is induced by standing it on its head with claws folded under the body (Wiersma, unpublished).

3. *Claw opening.* This reflex is also one for which only a single thoracic ganglion is necessary. But in contrast to the closing reflex there appears to be some bilateral connection since opening on one side may be obtained by summation of electrical stimulation of the nerve trunk on the other side.[8]

4. *Autotomy.* When a leg is strongly stimulated it may be cast off at the level of the joint between the basi- and ischiopodite by a clean break induced by the contraction of a special muscle.[53] This phenomenon and the subsequent regeneration are discussed in detail in Chapter 17, Vol. I. Different animals and appendages show great differences in the threshold for this reflex. In some species it appears on

the slightest provocation, in others it is absent. Autotomy in the great majority of instances is a segmental reflex and always unilateral. When the segmental response does not suffice to rid the animal of the injured leg, other legs on the same side often assist in its removal. At least in the hermit crab, the brain is not necessary for this obviously complex reflex.[21]

5. *Escape.* In forms which can swim backwards by flapping the tail such movements seem to serve solely for flight. In each flap a large number of muscles is involved. Nevertheless, it is a rather simple reflex in which only a few interneurons take part. In lobsters and crayfish these are the medial giant fibers for stimuli in the head region and the lateral or segmental giant fibers for stimuli in the tail region. A single impulse in any of these axons is sufficient to cause the necessary complex muscular contractions. To set up an impulse in the giant fibers, the sensory stimulation must be intense, and in operated animals it is difficult to obtain them by this means. But, in the intact animal, visual stimulation alone is often sufficient to elicit escape swimming. However, other sensory modalities certainly can also cause the medial giant fiber to discharge, as shown by pinching the flagella of the antennae. Posteriorly, noxious stimulation causes the lateral giant fibers to discharge. Once started, a longer or shorter series of tail flaps occurs in the intact animal. The later impulses in the giant fibers probably originate largely from the strong sensory influx evoked by the movements themselves. The stretch receptors of the abdomen will respond strongly, and their sensory impulses may cause reinforcement.

Steering is possible during prolonged swimming in the crayfish but its mechanism has not been investigated. Single impulses in the giant fibers lead only to symmetrical movements and thus to straight backward swimming. In *Callianassa*, which lacks lateral giant fibers, an impulse in one medial giant fiber causes an asymmetrical movement of the uropods.[36] In hermit crabs, where also only the medial pair of giant fibers may be present, the withdrawal reflex into the shell is presumably mediated by impulses in them.

6. *Defense.* When a crab, crayfish, lobster, or prawn is faced with a mildly threatening situation, the claws are raised and the front part of the body is lifted.[6] This apparently complex action may be considered a simple reflex because its main components arise in the crayfish from the stimulation of a single fiber in the circumesophageal commissure. Accessory regulation, such as turning with the threatening object, is provided by different interneurons. Because both flight and

defense depend for their full development on more than one inter-neuron, they can also be classified as complex reflexes. Defense differs from flight in that repetitive firing of the interneuron is necessary to initiate and maintain the necessary muscle contractions.

C. COMPLEX REFLEXES

In crabs which flee by running away instead of executing swim-ming movements, the escape response must be a chain of reflexes. Similarly the set of reactions executed by a crab when two or three neighboring legs are held, is due to such a chain. The crab first tries to escape; if unsuccessful, it turns and attempts to grasp the object holding the legs first with the homolateral claw, and if necessary, after further turning, with the heterolateral claw.[6]

1. *Feeding.* Even after a decapod's brain is removed, an object brought into contact with a claw will be grasped and brought forward. It is then first transferred to the maxillipeds, afterward to the mouth parts, and finally swallowed if the taste is acceptable. Obviously this action consists of a whole chain of more simple reflexes in which chemoreception plays a part (Chapter 3). A brainless animal will continue feeding even when the stomach is completely filled, and as a result it may eventually burst, which implies the presence of a center controlling the reflex in the brain.[6]

2. *Copulation.* The combination of reflexes involved in copulation may likewise be considered as a reflex pattern present in the cord since it, too, can be executed without the presence of the brain. Here again, brain removal results in failure to stop the action. The brain must have, in this case more certainly than in the previous one, a truly superimposed inhibiting effect on the response.

3. *Righting.* Removal of the brain interferes strongly with right-ing movements. However, to ascribe a major function to the brain in this reflex may be unwarranted since removal of the brain or cutting of the commissures will interrupt the pathway of sensory impulses from the statocysts traveling down the cord. The great importance of the statocysts in righting is evident from the fact that their removal alone changes the righting reflex to almost the same degree as cutting both commissures.[6] In crabs, righting is still possible after either the statocysts or the brain are removed, but the movement is then of a different type. With the statocysts intact the animal somersaults around its transverse axis, whereas after their removal it turns around its anteroposterior axis. Various lines of evidence imply that

the impulses involved in normal righting cross to the other side of the brain. Thus cutting the brain longitudinally in the mid-line does not influence most actions, but does change righting to the type shown by a brainless animal.

D. EFFECTS OF SURGICAL INTERFERENCE*

Mention has been made above of changes in reflexes resulting from certain surgical operations. It has also been pointed out that conclusions drawn from such data are of doubtful validity; this will become more evident when the facts disclosed by unit analyses are presented. The structure of the CNS in decapods makes it quite impossible to cut certain pathways selectively and not interfere with

FIG. 8. *Eriocheir* (♀), nine days after cutting right circumesophageal commissure. Usually the effect is less pronounced than shown here. (From Herter.[14])

any others. For example, after the removal of the globuli in a crab brain, a greater excitability appears. But the concomitant change in the righting reflex to the one shown by animals without statocysts may well result, as in the case cited above, from cutting the pathway for the sensory impulses and not from the removal of synaptic connections.

The results of cutting one commissure have been frequently studied. After this operation the animal moves in a circle, the so-called manège movement. At rest the side of the body on which the cut is located is carried higher than the uncut one (Fig. 8), but again removal of the heterolateral statocyst leads to about the same effect. Electrical stimulation with implanted electrodes on the posterior part of the cut commissure can counteract the manège movement.[17] Wider and wider circles appear with increased strength of stimulation, until straight sideward running results. Still further increase in stimulus

---

* This is discussed from a behavioral point of view in Chapter 13.

strength causes circling to the other side. The legs on both sides are influenced when only one commissure is cut; the homolateral legs having an increased flexor tone, those of the heterolateral side an increased extensor tone.[33] In the swimming crab, *Portunus*, the three pairs of walking legs show a similar change in tone, but exactly the opposite reaction appears in the two swimming legs. The swimming leg on the side of the cut is kept extended, which causes the swimming animal to circle in the same direction as it would in walking.[14]

When both commissures are cut, the legs are kept underneath the body much more than is normal. From this it has been concluded that the brain has an inhibiting influence on flexor tone. Walking is still possible after brain removal or cutting of both commissures, but disappears after removal of the subesophageal ganglion in decapods. In the Stomatopoda, as in insects, the thoracic ganglia suffice for walking movements. Another effect reported after removal of the anterior ganglia is that the strength of reflex contractions weakens considerably.[34] This may be due to a lack of reinforcement. The isolated subesophageal ganglion can control the feeding movements of the maxillipeds and mouth parts, described above. With different degrees of condensation of the ganglia, the subesophageal ganglion may vary in function. In species in which it is well separated from the thoracic ganglia, it may have little or no influence on the inherent motor patterns for leg movements, whereas in forms like crabs with a thoracic nerve ring, it may play a prominent part as their controlling center.

An important discovery made with surgical interference is that the cell bodies of monaxonic neurons are not necessary for the execution of reflexes. First Bethe[6] for a crab, and later Hardy[13] for a crayfish, reported that for a considerable time after cutting axons near their cell bodies, the reflex pattern governed by these axons remains unchanged. This agrees well with the view that the location of all synaptic connections is away from the cell bodies. In this relation the very slow degeneration of cut fibers in crustaceans should be mentioned. Because of it, the degeneration technique is not suited for tracing the course of nerve fibers in this class.

IV. *SPONTANEOUS ACTIVITY*

By electrical recordings from the commissures and other parts of the CNS, Prosser[22] observed that a good deal of activity remains when all peripheral connections are severed. Even completely isolated single ganglia show this spontaneous activity, which consists of repetitive firing in a number of single units and is present in both the central ends of peripheral nerves and the connectives to other ganglia. It is highly unlikely that all of this activity arises in sense organs within the ganglia, although certain cells in the CNS must be regarded as sensory. For instance the caudal photoreceptor consists of light-sensitive cells in the telson ganglion (Chapter 1), and cells sensitive to chemical changes are indicated in the subesophageal ganglion for the regulation of ventilatory impulses (Chapter 2, Vol. I).

The activity of most units must be considered as truly "spontaneous" if they fire without any external stimulation when their environment is of normal composition. Changes in environment undoubtedly can influence this firing rate, and thus changes in temperature, in ion content, and in oxygen level will definitely influence frequency.[25-28] During the initial stages of asphyxia many units start to fire which were silent before. For most interneurons this may be considered an abnormal reaction without functional significance. But a firm decision on what is normal and what is abnormal activity cannot be made in our present state of knowledge.

Comparison of the impulse patterns in different interneurons reveals that each fires in its own particular way and that there are marked differences in the types of discharge present.[49] Some interneurons fire with strictly regular rhythm, each at its own frequency. For instance, of two such fibers coming from the brain, one fires at about 60 per second and the other at 20. Their discharge frequency is often so regular that the impulses can be easily synchronized for considerable periods with the oscillograph sweep. Other units vary their rhythm constantly, and still others fire in bursts with considerable pauses between each series of impulses. In this case, the frequency in each burst is higher at the start than at the end.

The occurrence of slow waves of potential change, a type of spontaneous activity which is widespread in the vertebrate CNS, has not been found in the Crustacea or in many other invertebrates.[9] However, slow potential changes undoubtedly occur in each spontaneously firing neuron. The presence of such a slow change, which must be regarded as the precursor of the action potential in the axon, has been well demonstrated in the stretch receptor ganglion cells (Chapter 2) where the frequency of firing is directly related to the amount of depolarization present. The independent firing rates of the spontaneously discharging neurons indicate that their depolarizations have different time courses. Under these circumstances it is scarcely surprising that no regular pattern of slow waves can be recorded with external electrodes.

V. PHYSIOLOGY OF CENTRAL UNITS

A. Giant Fiber System

Giant fibers occur in Decapoda Natantia, in Astacura (Nephropsidea), and in Anomura. They are absent in the Brachyura. In the Palinura (Scyllaridea) they are not at all conspicuous histologically, even though they would be expected to be prominent from the functioning of the system. The anatomical relations have been described above (page 247). Its physiological properties have been studied especially in the crayfish *Procambarus clarkii*, but appear to be similar in other species. The medial giant fibers, as well as the lateral ones, can be prepared as single functional units in the esophageal commissures, but because of their large size, their impulses are easily registered even from only partially exposed parts of the cord. Stimulation of one medial giant fiber may result in a response in the other. This transfer takes place within the brain, and none occurs at any level in the cord.[52]

Such transmission may be "ephaptic" and not truly synaptic because it cannot be facilitated when fatigued. In this respect it resembles the interneuronal transmission between giant fibers in several worms.[10] In the crayfish and in *Callianassa*[36] the most likely place in the brain for this crossover is at the point of decussation. Impulses in the two medial giant fibers are remarkably independent of each other in the rest of their course through the cord. Spikes, which are started quite close together, do not influence each other's conduction speeds, notwithstanding the large external electrical fields. It is not known whether an impulse arising from the brain in one medial giant fiber invariably leads to an impulse in the other under natural conditions. Functionally this would make little difference, because each fiber causes identical motor effects as a result of its synaptic connections with the motor neurons.

The interneuronal relations of the lateral or segmental giant fiber system are more complex. As stated, these fibers consist of a series of units, each of which runs only from one ganglion to the next more anterior one. The junctions between them have hardly any influence on spike transmission. Under normal circumstances they do not cause a noticeable delay, but anoxia stops conduction much sooner in the lateral than in the medial giant fibers.[41] This may indicate a lower safety factor at their junctions. No synaptic properties are found when a pair of microelectrodes are juxtaposed across the boundary between units.[18] On the other hand, this thick membrane separating two units interrupts the axoplasm to the extent that it is impossible to displace the contents from one part to the other.[41] However, free ion interchange may still be possible, and further study will be necessary to elucidate the manner of transfer.

Transmission across these junctions occurs with equal ease in both directions, as it does also between the paired units in the right and left halves of each ganglion. In contrast with the longitudinal connective junction, the transverse commissural type has definite synaptic properties. Not only is there a delay, which seems too long to be explained by conduction time alone, but fatigue of transmission and subsequent facilitation by a second impulse occur. In the thoracic ganglia, this transmission is easily fatigued and therefore may usually be absent in the most anterior ones, whereas in the telson ganglion it remains even when all other abdominal ganglia have ceased to give one-to-one transmission.[41] These commissural synapses between the lateral giant fibers are important in the flight reflex since they provide for symmetrical excitation of the third-root motor fibers. This is necessary because the lateral giant fibers synapse only with one of the two third-root giant motor fibers, unlike the medial giant fibers which connect with those on both sides. As mentioned above, the synapse between the two lateral elements is believed to occur at the place where they cross each other; this is thought to be a two-way conducting structure.

In contrast with the medial giant fibers, in which impulses normally originate only within the brain, each segment of the lateral giant fibers can generate impulses. Thus strong stimulation of any body segment, at least from the second thoracic backward, brings the lateral giant system into action. Collision of impulse will occur in certain places, and the whole lateral system may be considered as a nerve net of rather simple structure. If one of the two connectives between abdominal ganglia is cut, this does not prevent the conduction of the impulse in both lateral giant fibers behind the cut. However, the impulse in the cut fiber will be delayed because it originates through a cross transfer from the other side behind the cut.

B. Transmission from Giant Fibers to Motor Fibers

The transmission of a single impulse in the giant fibers to the largest giant motor fiber of the third root of the abdominal ganglia is unidirectional and normally one-to-one (Fig. 9). The transmission occurs across the synapse which Robertson[30] has studied in the cray-fish (Section II above). With one microelectrode in the prefiber, another in the postfiber, it can be shown that transmission is dependent on the voltage differences of the axoplasms, and even more important, that the synaptic area possesses a strong rectifying effect.[12]

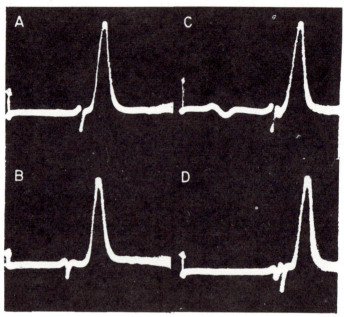

Fig. 9. Action potentials in a third root of an abdominal ganglion of *Procambarus clarkii* caused by the stimulation of the central giant fibers, prepared in the circumesophageal commissures. A, response to medial giant fiber impulse on same side as root; B, to other medial giant fiber; C, to lateral giant fiber on side of root; D, to other lateral giant fiber. Note the difference in conduction speed of the giant fibers (heterolateral medial giant fiber conducting fastest) and the difference in latency between giant fiber and root responses. In C, the early diphasic deflection is due to a spontaneous impulse in a small root fiber. (From Wiersma.[41])

Current passes readily through the membranes when either the prefiber is made more negative than the postfiber, or the postfiber more positive than the prefiber. But under the opposite conditions the amounts of current passed are negligible. This factor alone suffices to explain why transmission is unidirectional.

These results are strongly in favor of a purely electrical transmission mechanism. The blocking or facilitating actions of different agents and the appearance of shorter and longer synaptic delays can be correlated to a large extent with the actual current flow through the synaptic membrane. Whether transmission is wholly electrical or whether an additional chemical transmission process is also involved may be established soon. In this connection the prolonged duration of the synaptic delay (5 msec or more) after the administration of certain drugs and the double action of nicotine (Section VI, below) will have to be considered.

When a single giant fiber impulse no longer causes transmission in a particular preparation, two impulses closely following each other will generally do so. Rather surprisingly this type of summation is obtained both with two impulses in the same giant fiber or in two different ones. The former are more effective as a postfiber impulse can be obtained for longer intervals. The summation by two impulses in different giant fibers shows an unexpected feature. When the two impulses arrive at their synapses simultaneously, or nearly so, no summation takes place. This inert period is followed by a period during which summation is possible. The time relations depend on the distance between the stimulated synapses. When they are neighbors, the inert period is short (1 msec) and the summation period long (e.g. 15 msec), but when they are separated by an inactive synapse, the inert period is longer (2 msec) and the summation period shorter (e.g. 5 msec). Impulses always appear to arise at a synapse, in this case at the one of the prefiber stimulated last. Unless some specific process has reached its synaptic area no summation occurs. The speed with which this process spreads is estimated at 0.3 m per second, which is much slower than that of the postfiber spike which travels at 7 m per second.[42] Possibly an electrotonic spread takes place which lowers the threshold effectively only when it reaches the second synapse before the prefiber impulse arrives.

Occasionally simultaneous, or nearly simultaneous, bilateral arrival of impulses in the two medial giant fibers leads to a discharge. The postfiber impulse then arises at the synapse stimulated earliest. This effect can be explained by enhanced current flow through the synaptic area due to the strong electrical field surrounding the giant fibers when an impulse passes. In fatigued preparations the third root impulse often shows two peaks, the second of which drops out before the first. They have been ascribed to two different root fibers, but may possibly represent the synaptic potential and the subsequent spike which gradually lags behind and becomes abortive. Preparations from old crayfish usually do not respond with a root potential on a single giant fiber impulse. This may be a normal effect of age, not limited to these synapses. It is readily observed that young crayfish have a lower threshold for flight-inducing and other stimuli than old specimens.

Fatiguing a third-root motor fiber synapse by repetitive stimulation of one giant fiber blocks the transmission in others if the synapses are more centrally located, but has no influence when they are on the peripheral side of the fatigued one. The effect is thus polar, in contrast to the summating effect of two prefiber impulses for which it makes little difference, whether the peripheral or central synapse is stimulated first.[52]

In the first and second roots of each abdominal ganglion one or two motor fibers show a response quite similar to that of the large third-root motor fiber. The transmission is also one-to-one and the synaptic delay is short, strongly indicating the same type of lateral synaptic connections. But histological investigations have so far failed to discover these.

Efferent fibers with a repetitive response are present in all three roots of the abdominal ganglia.[44] The units concerned are smaller fibers, and the response is seen best in the second roots. A single impulse in any of the four giant fibers starts a train of impulses, the first of which appears after a delay of as much as 8 msec. Each burst may consist of up to 10 identical impulses at a frequency of 250–300 per second. The discharges in the right and left roots of one ganglion are much the same when any one giant fiber is stimulated. The train of impulses shortens more and more on repeated stimulation of the giant fiber unless at least several seconds of rest separate the single stimuli (Fig. 10). But the frequency in the shortened train does not alter. It is not definitely known how these repetitive impulses are generated. Peripheral feedback is completely excluded because the trains occur readily in preparations without any peripheral connections. Central feedback seems unlikely since the frequency of impulses in the train is as high as a peripheral nerve fiber can carry, and higher than is normally possible in one-to-one synaptic transmission. The long duration of the burst makes purely electrical transmission unlikely and suggests that a transmitter substance is released by the giant fibers causing a depolarization of the synapse for the period of the impulse train.

Functionally such multiplying synapses would be especially important when the efferent fiber involved innervates a muscle which responds only to repetitive stimulation (Chapter 6). A contraction would ensue on a single prefiber impulse, but after a considerable delay. In the case of the second root, which innervates the extensor musculature of the tail, extension could automatically follow the flexion caused by the single impulse in the third-root motor fiber. By this mechanism the tail would resume the position necessary for a subsequent flip in continued swimming as a direct result of the preceding single impulse in the giant fiber.

C. OTHER CENTRAL FIBERS, MOTOR ASPECT

In the vertebrate cord, most interneurons can be considered as either motor or sensory. But for short reflex pathways in which a

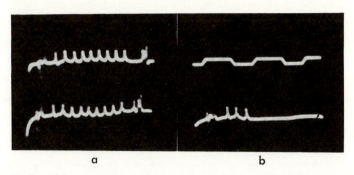

a   b

FIG. 10. Repetitive responses in the two second roots of an abdominal ganglion of *Procambarus clarkii* after a single impulse in a medial giant fiber. *a*. Upper tracing, response of heterolateral root; lower, of homolateral root simultaneously recorded. Note the almost but not completely identical responses. *b*. Same preparation after stimulation of medial giant fiber for 30 seconds at 1 per second. Upper tracing, time—60 per second, lower, homolateral root. Notice identical frequency of the impulses as in *a*, but much shorter duration of discharge. (From Wiersma.[44])

single interneuron is intercalated between the sensory and motor fibers, such classification is inappropriate. In Crustacea the latter type of interneuron appears to be widespread. The segmental unit of the lateral giant fiber is an example of this type. In most instances first- and second-order interneurons cannot be distinguished with certainty, and a single nerve cell may have features of both at once. For instance, the medial giant fibers receive optic impulses through one or more intercalated neurons, but mechanical afferent spikes from the antennae seem to reach them by direct connection with primary sensory axons. For these reasons the description of the interneurons will be based on the methods used to investigate them. Hence at least one fiber appears in both this section and the next.

Stimulation of the giant fibers leads to motor reactions throughout the animal. The question thus arises whether other interneurons have similar widespread connections or whether they connect only with one specific group of motor neurons in a single ganglion. The necessary restriction of stimulation to single units is possible only for a few of the larger fibers. Except the giant fibers, no interneurons have been found to evoke a motor reaction with a single impulse, but reproduceable and recognizable reactions can be obtained on repetitive stimulation. The most outstanding instance is one fiber which on such stimulation brings about the main features of the defense reflex. This axon, which runs central to the medial giant fiber, causes symmetrical movements. Both claws are raised, the thorax is lifted by the fourth and fifth legs, and in experiments the tail is always extended. In life the latter part of the reflex can be inhibited if the tail is already flexed when the reflex starts; a normal crayfish often keeps its tail bent under in the defense position. The same fiber in each commissure causes identical movements which clearly involve all body segments. Similar results are obtained on stimulation of several other interneurons which cause less readily described complex movements involving from a few to many body segments. In no case can the contraction of a single muscle be achieved by stimulation of an interneuron.[43]

These results support the view that in Crustacea regulation of body movements by the brain depends on a small number of interneurons governing extensive preformed patterns. Necessary adjustments are probably made in each ganglion when the local reflex pattern conflicts with the response induced by the interneuron. Thus in the defense reflex it will usually be necessary for the position of the legs with respect to the available ground support to be adjusted in this way.

In each commissure simple synapses apparently connect the two central interneurons (one inhibitor and one accelerator) which regulate the heartbeat by exciting the corresponding interneurens of the extrinsic heart nerves running between the subesophageal and the heart ganglion. As far as is known, the central interneurons connect bilaterally only with these more peripheral ones and with no others. Stimulation of the central inhibitory neurons is more effective than that of the extrinsic cardiac inhibitor since the latter requires stimulation at 20 per second to cause noticeable inhibition, whereas the former does so at a frequency of 1 per second. This indicates that the synapses between these inhibitory interneurons are of the multiplying type. In contrast, the synapses between the central and extrinsic cardiac accelerators must depend on facilitation since central stimulation is less effective than peripheral. The results of severing the extrinsic nerves show that in both cases each central fiber makes bilateral connections. Either left or right cardiac inhibitor can be cut without preventing the effect of central stimulation, and the same is true for cutting the cardiac accelerators.[48]

D. Other Central Fibers, Sensory Aspects

Another method of studying the connections made by interneurons is to record their responses to sensory stimulation. Generally both

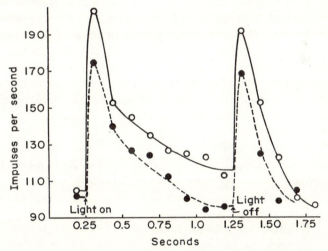

Fig. 11. Responses recorded from the circumesophageal commissures to illumination of one eye in the crayfish *Orconectes virilis*. Average number of impulses in 0.125-second intervals. Solid line, average in twenty-one experiments of responses in the commissure of the same side as the illuminated eye. Broken line, average in ten experiments of the other commissure. Notice quick adaptation and strong off-effect. (From Prosser.[23])

spatial and temporal summation are necessary to make an interneuron fire. Thus in stimulating caudal hairs, about four adjoining hairs have to be touched to obtain a postsynaptic impulse.[26]

Responses to illumination of either eye are readily recorded from the intact circumesophageal commissures, with the homolateral eye giving the stronger reaction. These responses appear both on illumination and on darkening of the eye, the former being slightly stronger. Little evidence was found for the existence of fibers which continued to discharge during the period of light (Fig. 11). Similar, though somewhat smaller, responses to eye illumination occur in the thoracic ganglia, but none were found in the abdominal ganglia. Responses from the "caudal" eye can be registered throughout the cord and in both commissures.[23] These matters are discussed with relation to vision and light sensitivity in Chapter 1.

Responses can be obtained in whole leg nerves on stimulation of practically any other body appendage; with some exceptions, thresholds are lowest for nearby homolateral appendages and highest for remote heterolateral ones. Contralateral responses are much more frequent in certain ganglia than in others. They are numerous in the brain and in the telson ganglia. In the abdominal ganglia they are much less evident, although certainly present.[24] Such studies made with large bundles of nerve fibers give a general idea of the course of the impulses and types of neural connections but do not provide the detailed information obtained by recording from single active units.[49] The latter technique, however, has been successfully applied so far only to fibers in the esophageal commissure and provides no information about short connections between the ganglia of the cord and within the brain.

Not all the axons which are in the esophageal commissures and respond to sensory stimulation are interneurons. A number of them must be considered as primary sensory fibers. Most numerous are fibers each of which represents one hair pit on the carapace. Though the nerve from these hairs enters the subesophageal ganglion and possibly sends collaterals into the neuropiles of this ganglion, the axons continue their course to the brain, which must be their main integrating center. Other primary sensory axons ascending to the brain arise from the tonic stretch receptor nerve cells of the tail,[45,47] whereas some descending ones come from a few hairs on the second segment of the antenna.

1. *Stimuli causing responses in interneurons.* In most of the interneurons studied, impulses arise only after one type of stimulus. But some have been found in which different qualities of sensory stimulation elicit discharges. Since only a few types of stimulation have been used so far, their number may be larger than it now seems. Undoubtedly the medial giant fibers belong to this group, because swimming follows optical stimulation as well as touching various parts such as the antenna. However, the giant fibers have a high threshold, and more convincing evidence for this type of integration has been obtained in an axon believed to be identical with the one which causes the defense reflex on electrical stimulation.

A large fiber located in the area where the defense reflex fiber can be prepared discharges on stimulation of the eyes with light, of hairs on the head by touching, and most likely also on manipulation of joints in the head appendages.

2. *Type of response.* Some interneurons respond only to change in stimulus intensity, others discharge more or less continuously as long as the stimulus lasts. This is especially clear in response to joint manipulations, but is also true for touch and for light. It is thus possible to speak of tonic and phasic interneurons, although this division cannot be sharply drawn. In many cases these differences depend on the type of response shown by the primary sensory fibers, but in others the properties of the interneurons themselves are involved.

3. *Location and distribution of the sensory fields.* Many interneurons respond solely on stimulation of one or more sensory areas on the homolateral side. In addition, a fair number of such nerve cells react to stimulation of both sides, while some are restricted to the heterolateral side. A few fibers respond to stimulation of different areas on the two sides; these are called asymmetric.[47]

Some interneurons respond solely to a sensory area located in one segment, but unlike primary sensory fibers, they integrate the impulses of a large number of sense organs in such a field. Other interneurons, in contrast, have sensory fields in all segments of the body and thus integrate similar sensory stimuli from all. Still others are restricted to different numbers of consecutive segments. As a consequence, stimulation of any sensory field will cause stimulation of several interneurons, and each sensory field will have a specific pattern of interneurons activated by its stimulation. This property is common to all of the types of interneurons previously mentioned. Representation of one specific sensory field by several axons can theoretically be considered to provide for coordinated movements in the following manner.

The axon specific for the stimulated region elicits the particular reflex connected with that part; the axon for all similar sense cells of the body influences the threshold of all reflexes of this type in relation to other types. Axons common for similar sensory fields in neighboring segments govern reflexes allied to the specific one, but more general in nature. However, our knowledge is much too limited to make this more than speculation; this becomes clear when the fourteen interneurons which are stimulated by a single sensory field, the hairs on the lower part of the crayfish cheliped, are enumerated. These neurons and their sensory fields are as follows:

Homolateral axons

1) Responds to touch of hairs on the three distal segments (carpo-, proto-, and dactylopodites) (Figs. 12 and 13).

2) Stimulated by touch on the four distal segments of all five thoracic legs (Fig. 12).

3) Responds to touch of hairs all along third maxilliped and legs 1–5, but not of hairs at base.

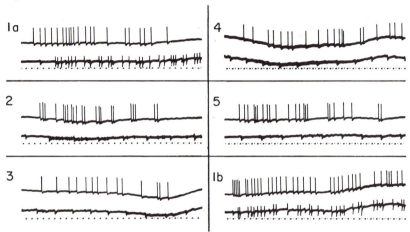

Fig. 12. Simultaneous records from two interneurons responding to stimulation of hairs on the lower part of the legs of *Procambarus clarkii*. Upper record in each frame is from the interneuron responding to stimulation of any of the five homolateral legs; lower record from axon specific for the cheliped. Frame 1a, response on stimulation of cheliped; 2, second leg; 3, third leg; 4, fourth leg; 5, fifth leg; 1b, cheliped again. Note that a fiber which is spontaneously active at about 20 per second is included in small bundle with cheliped fiber. Time signal 60 and 120 cycles per second. (From Wiersma, Ripley, and Christensen.[49])

4) Responds to touch of hairs on legs 1–5 and of thoracic region and carapace.

5) Stimulated by hairs on all thoracic and abdominal appendages and on dorsal abdomen, but not on carapace.

6) Responds to hair stimulation anywhere on whole homolateral body half, including carapace and abdomen.

Bilateral axons

(These are paired fibers, one in the homolateral, the other in the heterolateral commissure.)

7 and 8) Stimulated by touching hairs on inside of first three thoracic legs and third maxillipeds.

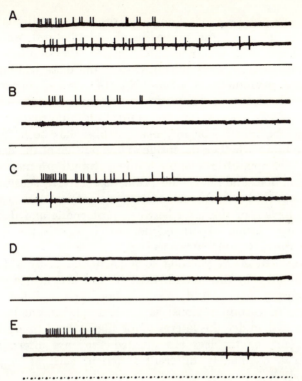

Fig. 13. Simultaneous records of two interneurons. The upper records of the neuron which responds to stimulation of hairs on legs 1, 2, 3 homolateral and 2 heterolateral. The lower records of the neuron responding exclusively to stimulation of the homolateral cheliped. Response in A, hairs on lower segment of homolateral cheliped; B, second homolateral leg; C, third homolateral leg; D, heterolateral cheliped (a control); E, second heterolateral leg. Note tendency of cheliped fiber to discharge without actual stimulation. The reason may be deterioration of the preparation causing spontaneous impulses. (From Wiersma, Ripley, and Christensen.[49])

9 and 10) Respond to stimulation of hairs on all body appendages from third maxilliped to uropods, but not on carapace or abdomen.

11 and 12) Stimulated by hairs anywhere on body.

Heterolateral axons

13) Responds to stimulation of hairs anywhere on whole heterolateral body half.

Asymmetrical axons

14) Responds to touch of hairs on five peripheral segments of claw, legs 2 and 3 homolateral, and leg 2 heterolateral (Fig. 13).

Thus there are 14 axons known to respond on stimulation of the hairs on the inside of the propodite of one cheliped, and no doubt some additional ones are present. As stated, the significance of this type of representation is unknown. One of the more baffling problems concerns the asymmetrical fiber (No. 14), whose occurrence and function are difficult to understand.

The crayfish's lack of precise centralized information of certain kinds should be noted. For instance, no fiber has been found which informs the brain whether the inside or the outside of the dactylopodite is touched. Yet opposite responses to these stimuli are mediated by the cheliped ganglion. Indirectly the brain does receive sensory impulses dependent on claw movement because one interneuron responds specifically to flexion of the joint between protopodite and dactylopodite, thus signaling closing. Another interneuron signals the extension of all joints of the claw and hence opening.

The interneurons responding to a particular sensory field do not collect in bundles in the commissures. True tracts are found only for primary sensory fibers. And although one type of interneuron may predominate in certain regions, as for example in the lateral region of the cord just under the lateral giant fiber where many fibers with motor influence on the legs are situated, they are intermingled with fibers with a completely different function, such as responding to touch of body hairs.

4. *Central inhibition.* In a few interneurons it is possible to inhibit the normal discharge by stimulation of specific sensory fields. For example an interneuron which responds rather tonically to stimulation of hairs on the basal joints of the homolateral antenna is inhibited when hairs of surrounding parts, such as the antennal flagellum, are stimulated. This inhibition is not peripheral because another axon is known which discharges on the stimulation of either area. This phenomenon reminds one of the "contrast" present in our own sense organs and in the lateral eye of *Limulus.* If widespread, it might have considerable significance in determining the pattern of neurons firing when a given area is excited. But so far only one or two other fibers have shown this type of reaction.[47]

In addition to evidence mentioned above that the brain may have a tonic inhibitory action on certain reflexes, stimulation of the brain inhibits rhythmic opening and closing of the anus as well as the tail flexion brought about by stimulation of the abdominal chain.[11] One of the interneurons with a complicated response to joint manipulations, named Sherrington's fiber,[45,47] shows central inhibition clearly. This fiber is tonically discharged by proprioceptive impulses from the joints of the walking legs. Those of the fourth and fifth legs, which normally carry most of the body weight, stimulate it more effectively than those of the more anterior legs. The joint especially involved is the one between the basi- and ischiopodites. Extension of these joints on the homolateral side or flexing on the heterolateral side increases the discharge frequency. Thus a maximum rate of firing occurs in the fiber of one commissure when the animal leans to one side and a minimal one when it leans to the other; the fiber in the other commissure responds in exactly the opposite manner. In the symmetrical position both will be firing at an intermediate frequency. Inhibition is evident when the legs on the homolateral side are first stretched, giving a strong discharge, and then the fourth or fifth leg is bent maximally and kept in that position. This causes a temporary stopping of the discharge, followed by its reappearance with gradual increase in frequency until a rate somewhat lower than the original one is reached. The type of information carried by these fibers is obviously of great importance for signaling the relative position of the legs with regard to the body. In conjunction with the statocysts they may provide the mechanism by which the crayfish's orientation in space is obtained (Chapter 2).

VI. *PHARMACOLOGY*

Our knowledge of the pharmacology of the CNS is slight. Information about the site of drug or ion action is particularly lacking. The CNS as a whole is much more easily influenced by drugs than the peripheral neuromuscular system, but less so than the heart ganglion cells. Apparently, sensitivity to drugs and ions depends markedly on the central phenomenon concerned. Studies of the synaptic transmission between giant fibers and third-root fibers have shown that these lateral synapses are insensitive to many drugs, a noticeable exception being nicotine.[31] This drug has a complex action, for although it is a blocking agent, initially it has a facilitating effect on fatigued transmission. As a result fresh synapses are blocked by it much sooner than fatigued ones are. Another remarkable feature of blocking with nicotine is that a spontaneous recovery takes place, after which the synapse is insensitive to the drug.[50]

Although acetylcholine (Ach) has a marked influence on the spontaneous discharges of the heart ganglion cells and also provokes a discharge in the nerve cells of the abdominal stretch receptors, it does not influence the lateral synapses, nor does it markedly affect the spontaneous activity of most interneurons. To explain such pronounced differences in effect by assumed variations in speed of penetration seems unwarranted. Probably true differences in sensitivity to various drugs are present between particular nerve cells.

Eserine, while it does not bring to light any effect of Ach, itself enhances spontaneous activity and blocks synaptic transmission in the crayfish.[26] It resembles nicotine in its actions, and can also protect transmission from block by nicotine.[51] But in *Callianassa*, although it increases spontaneous activity as in the crayfish, it fails to block transmission.[37] Table 1 summarizes the central actions of various drugs.

The effects of ions on the spontaneous discharge rate in the CNS have been tested especially by Prosser.[27,28] Increase in potassium or decrease in calcium enhance the activity initially, but later cause a

TABLE 1

EFFECT OF DIFFERENT DRUGS ON SYNAPTIC TRANSMISSION AND SPONTANEOUS DISCHARGE

Drug	Effect on synaptic transmission	Effect on spontaneous discharge
Nicotine	Block after enhancement[26,31,37]	Marked increase[26,37,44]
Acetylcholine	No effect[26,31,37]	No effect[26,37]
Eserine	Block[26,51]; none[37]	Increase[26,37]
Prostigmine	No effect[26,31]	—
Atropine	No effect[26,31,37]	Increase[37]
Adrenaline	Block after enhancement (10^{-4})[26] No effect (10^{-3})[31]	Increase[26] —
Ergotoxin	No effect[26]	—
Triethylamine	Block[37]	—
DFP[a]	Block[31,37]	Slight increase[37]
Amyltrimethylammonium	Enhancement[51]	—
Hexyldimethylamine	Block[51]	—

[a] Diisopropyl fluorophosphate.

depression. The state of the preparation affects the results considerably, and they are so variable that the only conclusion that can safely be drawn is "that the intrinsic activity of neurons depends upon the sum total of ionic conditions around the cells."[27]

Spontaneous discharge and synaptic transmission may be differentially influenced; both oxygen lack and nicotine enhance the spontaneous discharge of cells at the same time that synaptic transmission is diminished by them. Potassium, on the other hand, in subnormal concentrations enhances, and in higher concentrations depresses them both simultaneously.

In Cirripedia the effect of ions and drugs on the nervous system has been tested by bathing the whole animal in them, and measuring their effects on the rhythmic movements of the cirri.[40] In some cases the influence may really be on central nervous tissue, but many other factors undoubtedly play a more or less important role. Therefore the results have to be analyzed carefully. A rhythmic center with properties similar to the heart ganglion apparently is responsible for the regular rhythm, whereas a reflex center mediates the reflex withdrawal on stimuli such as a shadow or a vibration. It is not known whether the latter reflexes result from an inhibition of the rhythmic center, or from direct action on the periphery.

VII. *GENERAL CONCLUSIONS*

The central nervous system of decapod Crustacea is strikingly different from that of vertebrates. There are no tracts present although a certain bundling of axons with similar function may occur in some instances. Single crustacean interneurons fulfill the function of whole tracts in vertebrates. This is possible because the synaptic connections of the interneurons are not limited to their ends and because there are special connections with highly efficient transmission between segmental interneurons so that in effect these interneurons function as one fiber. Such connections can be claimed with certainty only for the lateral giant fibers, but they may also be present in some of the many interneurons which run similarly for long distances through the cord.

Problems of facilitation and inhibition in the crustacean CNS are peculiar because the synapses of an interneuron are not limited to one region of the cell. A more precise knowledge of the histology together with a further study of the interactions of cell parts may lead to a reevaluation of many aspects of central nervous mechanisms. In this connection it is significant that the histological description of neurons in the reticular formation of mammals resembles the one given here for crustacean interneurons in many respects. There, too, many synapses are present and they are of several types: dendritic, somatic, and axonal. Such axons are known in several instances to run for long distances and to give off many side branches at different levels.[32]

The fact that all interneurons investigated transmit messages by series of all-or-none nerve impulses supports the widely accepted view that this is the way different parts of the nervous system communicate with each other. The influence which different synapses of one postsynaptic fiber have on each other, as demonstrated by the junctions of the giant motor fibers in the third roots, is unlikely to extend beyond the range of a ganglion. Nevertheless, some such influence is present, and future research on this problem may contribute to our understanding of the nature of the central excitatory state. In this respect, further investigation of the spontaneous activity shown by many cells may be of importance.

Experiments concerning the localization of higher nervous functions in Crustacea are unsatisfactory. The size and structure of the brain is unfavorable for experimentation. Possibly certain interneurons spread throughout the CNS are involved in such functions. Such a diffuse system would be difficult to analyze because removal of any specific major part of the CNS would not aid in its localization. In view of the claim that the vertebrate cord shows signs of learning, it would not be strange to find that among the complex integrating axons of the crayfish some should show similar phenomena.*

There can be no doubt that in all arthropods the number of central nerve cells is small. Each interneuron has a specific and often complicated task to perform which involves receiving and making many synaptic connections. In certain instances differences between the pair of neurons in each half of the central nervous system are slight, so that one can replace the other to a considerable extent. But in many other cases the loss of one fiber must involve considerable loss of function, which may be mitigated to a certain extent by the overlapping fields of different neurons. This overlap may also be the basis for the so-called plasticity of the nervous system which is responsible for immediate changes such as the new walking patterns which appear when legs are lost (Chapter 9).

Continued analysis of the crustacean central nervous system at the level of single units seems a promising approach to obtain better understanding of this and many other problems.

REFERENCES

1. Alexandrowicz, J. S. 1957. Notes on the nervous system in the Stomatopoda. V. The various types of sensory nerve cells. *Pubbl. staz. zool. Napoli* **39**:213–225.
2. Alexandrowicz, J. S., and Whitear, M. 1957. Receptor elements in the coxal region of Decapoda Crustacea. *J. Marine Biol. Assoc. United Kingdom* **36**:603–628.
3. Allen, E. D. 1894. Studies on the nervous system of Crustacea. I. Some nerve elements of the embryonic lobster. *Quart. J. Microscop. Sci.* **144**:461–482.

---

* Behavioral aspects of crustacean learning are discussed in Chapter 13.

4. Balss, H. 1938. Crustacea Decapoda, Histologie des Nervensystems. *In:* "Bronn's Tierreich," Bd. 5, Abt. 1, Bch. 7, pp. 343–350. Akademische Verlagsges., Leipzig.

5. Barnes, T. C. 1932. Responses in the isolated limbs of Crustacea and associated nervous discharges. *Am. J. Physiol.* **99**:321–331.

6. Bethe, A. 1897a. Vergleichende Untersuchungen über die Funktionen des Centralnervensystems der Arthropoden. *Arch. ges. Physiol. Pflüger's* **68**:449–545.

7. Bethe, A. 1897b. Das Nervensystem von *Carcinus maenas. Arch. mikroskop. Anat. u. Entwicklungsmech.* I, **50**:462–546; II, **50**:589–639; III, **51**:382–452.

8. Bonnet, V. 1938. Contribution à l'étude du système nerveux ganglionnaire des Crustacés. *Arch. intern. physiol.* **47**:397–433.

9. Bullock, T. H. 1945. Problems in the comparative study of brain waves. *Yale J. Biol. and Med.* **17**:657–679.

10. Bullock, T. H. 1953. Properties of some natural and quasi-artificial synapses in polychaetes. *J. Comp. Neurol.* **98**:37–68.

11. Caselli, A. 1899. Untersuchungen über die reflexhemmende Funktion des oberen Schlundganglions der Languste. *Arch. ges. Physiol. Pflüger's* **74**:158–163.

12. Furshpan, E. J., and Potter, D. D. 1957. Mechanism of transmission at a crayfish synapse. *Nature* **180**:342–343.

13. Hardy, W. B. 1929. Note on the central nervous system of the crayfish. *J. Physiol.* (*London*) **67**:166–168.

14. Herter, K. 1932. Beiträge zur Zentrenfunktion zehnfüssiger Krebse. *Z. vergleich. Physiol.* **17**:209–266.

15. Holmes, W. 1946. The giant myelinated nerve fibres of the prawn. *Phil. Trans. Roy. Soc. London* **B231**:293–311.

16. Johnson, G. E. 1924. Giant nerve fibers in Crustaceans with special reference to *Cambarus* and *Palaemonetes. J. Comp. Neurol.* **36**:323–386.

17. Jordan, H. 1920. Die Leistungen des Gehirns bei den krebsartigen Tieren, besonders bei *Cancer pagurus.* (Abstract.) *Biol. Zentr.* **30**:310–316.

18. Kao, C. Y., and Grundfest, H. 1956. Conductile and integrative functions of crayfish giant axons. *Federation Proc.* **15**:104.

19. Keim, W. 1915. Das Nervensystem von *Astacus fluviatilis* (*Potamobius astacus* L.). *Z. wiss. Zoöl.* **113**:485–545.

20. Krieger, K. R. 1880. Ueber das Centralnervensystem des Flusskrebses. *Z. wiss. Zoöl.* **33**:527–594.

21. Morgan, T. H. 1902. The reflex connected with autotomy in the hermit crab. *Am. J. Physiol.* **6**:278–282.

22. Prosser, C. L. 1934a. Action potentials in the nervous system of the crayfish. I. Spontaneous impulses. *J. Cellular Comp. Physiol.* **4**:185–209.

23. Prosser, C. L. 1934b. Action potentials in the nervous system of the crayfish. II. Responses to illumination of the eye and caudal ganglion. *J. Cellular Comp. Physiol.* **4**:363–377.

24. Prosser, C. L. 1935a. Action potentials in the nervous system of the crayfish. III. Central responses to proprioceptive and tactile stimulation. *J. Comp. Neurol.* **62**:495–505.

25. Prosser, C. L. 1935b. Action potentials in the nervous system of the crayfish. IV. The influence of temperature on nerve impulses arising "spontaneously" in abdominal ganglia. *J. Gen. Physiol.* **19**:65–73.

26. Prosser, C. L. 1940. Action potentials in the nervous system of the crayfish. Effects of drugs and salts upon synaptic transmission. *J. Cellular Comp. Physiol.* **16**:25–38.

27. Prosser, C. L. 1943. An analysis of the action of salts upon abdominal ganglia of crayfish. *J. Cellular Comp. Physiol.* **22**:131–145.

28. Prosser, C. L., and Buehl, C. C. 1939. Oxidative control of "spontaneous" activity in the nervous system of the crayfish. *J. Cellular Comp. Physiol.* **14**:287–297.

29. Retzius, G. 1890. Zur Kenntniss des Nervensystems der Crustaceen. *In:* "Biologische Untersuchungen von Prof. Gustaf Retzius," N.F., Vol. 1. pp. 1–50. Central Druck, Stockholm.

30. Robertson, J. D. 1953. Ultrastructure of two invertebrate synapses. *Proc. Soc. Exptl. Biol. Med.* **82**:219–223.

31. Schallek, W., and Wiersma, C. A. G. 1948. The influence of various drugs on a crustacean synapse. *J. Cellular Comp. Physiol.* **31**:35–48.

32. Scheibel, M. E., and Scheibel, A. B. 1958. Structural substrates for integrative patterns in the brain stem reticular core. *In:* "Reticular Formation of the Brain" (H. H. Jasper, ed.), 766 pp. Little, Brown, Boston, Massachusetts.

33. Segaar, J. 1929. Über die Funktion der nervösen Zentren bei Krustazeen. Zugleich ein Beitrag zur Theorie zentraler Hemmung. *Z. vergleich. Physiol.* **10**:120–226.

34. ten Cate, J. 1930. Beiträge zur Physiologie des Zentralnervensystems der Einsiedlerkrebse. *Arch. néerl. physiol.* **15**:242–252.

35. Tonner, F. 1933. Das Problem der Krebsschere. *Z. vergleich. Physiol.* **19**:762–784.

36. Turner, R. S. 1950. Functional anatomy of the giant fiber system of *Callianassa californiensis*. *Physiol. Zoöl.* **23**:35–41.

37. Turner, R. S., Hagins, W. A., and Moore, A. R. 1950. Influence of certain neurotropic substances on central and synaptic transmission in *Callianassa*. *Proc. Soc. Exptl. Biol. Med.* **73**:156–158.

38. von Buddenbrock, W. 1945–1954. Crustacea Decapoda, die Physiologie des Zentralnervensystems und die Muskelphysiologie. *In:* "Bronn's Tierreich," Bd. 5, Abt. 1, Bch. 7, pp. 921–1004. Akademische Verlagsges., Leipzig.

39. von Uxkühl, J., and Gross, F. 1913. Studien über Tonus. VII. Die Schere des Flusskrebses. *Z. Biol.* **60**:334–357.

40. Waldes, V. 1939. Ueber die chemische Beeinflussung des Rhythmus und der Retraktionsdauer der Cirren von *Balanus perforatus*. *Z. vergleich. Physiol.* **26**:347–361.

41. Wiersma, C. A. G. 1947. Giant nerve fiber system of the crayfish. A contribution to comparative physiology of synapse. *J. Neurophysiol.* **10**:23–38.

42. Wiersma, C. A. G. 1949. Synaptic facilitation in the crayfish. *J. Neurophysiol.* **12**:267–275.

43. Wiersma, C. A. G. 1952a. The neurons of arthropods. *Cold Spring Harbor Symposia Quant. Biol.* **17**:155–163.

44. Wiersma, C. A. G. 1952b. Repetitive discharges of motor fibers caused by a single impulse in giant fibers of the crayfish. *J. Cellular Comp. Physiol.* **40**:399–419.

45. Wiersma, C. A. G. 1956. The neuronal connections in the central nervous system of crayfish. *Commun. XXth Intern. Physiol. Congr., Brussels*, pp. 967–968.

46. Wiersma, C. A. G. 1957. On the number of nerve cells in a crustacean central nervous system. *Acta Physiol. et Pharmacol. Neerl.* 6:135–142.
47. Wiersma, C. A. G. 1958. On the functional connections of single units in the central nervous system of the crayfish, *Procambarus clarkii* Girard. *J. Comp. Neurol.* 110:421–471.
48. Wiersma, C. A. G., and Novitski, E. 1942. The mechanism of the nervous regulation of the crayfish heart. *J. Exptl. Biol.* 19:255–265.
49. Wiersma, C. A. G., Ripley, S. H., and Christensen, E. 1955. The central representation of sensory stimulation in the crayfish. *J. Cellular Comp. Physiol.* 46:307–326.
50. Wiersma, C. A. G., and Schallek, W. 1947. Protection of synaptic transmission against block by nicotine. *Science* 106:421.
51. Wiersma, C. A. G., and Schallek, W. 1948. Influence of drugs on response of a crustacean synapse to preganglionic stimulation. *J. Neurophysiol.* 11:491–496.
52. Wiersma, C. A. G., and Turner, R. S. 1950. The interaction between the synapses of a single motor fiber. *J. Gen. Physiol.* 34:137–145.
53. Wood, F. D., and Wood, H. E. 1932. Autotomy in decapod Crustacea. *J. Exptl. Zool.* 62:1–55.

CHAPTER 8

J. H. WELSH

NEUROHUMORS AND NEUROSECRETION

I. *INTRODUCTION*

No longer can a clear-cut distinction be made between nervous and endocrine coordinating systems, nor can the actions of neurons be explained solely in electrical terms. Instead the most characteristic feature of a neuron would seem to be its ability to synthesize and release specific chemical agents which act in a hormone-like manner. In this sense the nervous system may be looked upon as a complex endocrine organ in which electrical phenomena are of no greater significance than they are in muscle.

Some chemical products of neurons act at close range as transmitter agents at synapses and neuromuscular junctions. At least one of these, acetylcholine, is normally quickly destroyed after it leaves the neuron and has acted. It is a short-range transmitter agent. Others such as noradrenaline (norepinephrine) and 5-hydroxytryptamine sometimes act at short range, although noradrenaline at least may enter the circulation and act at some distance from the point of release. Acetylcholine, noradrenaline, and 5-hydroxytryptamine are often referred to as neurohumors.

Other chemical products of neurons act at a distance quite like the classic vertebrate hormones. They are released into the circulation, are quite stable, and may affect structures at many different points throughout the body. In the vertebrates, oxytocin and vasopressin represent such long-range messengers. Since the neurons that produce oxytocin, vasopressin, and other such products are specialized for secretion they have been referred to as neurosecretory cells and their products as neurosecretory substances.[93,94] Neurohumors and neuro-secretory substances are so obviously related in their functions as co-ordinating agents, that a common word for them is desirable. The term neurohormone has been suggested for this.[114]

Much is already known about the ways in which crustaceans pro-duce and use neurohormones, yet many questions remain to be an-swered. A good deal is known particularly about the acetylcholine system in these animals, but its function is not fully understood. Many crustacean nerve cells are arranged in systems for producing, storing, and releasing a variety of extremely active physiological agents no one of which has yet been isolated in pure form and chemically identified. Neurosecretion is a new field with many challenging problems to be solved. There is work for the histologist and histochemist, for the physiologist and biochemist, and much that the electron microscopist can contribute. It will be seen in the following pages that crustaceans provide excellent material in which to study these phenomena.

II. *ACETYLCHOLINE*

Acetylcholine (Ach) is a neurohumor. At one time there was un-certainty regarding its occurrence in the Crustacea, but now the evidence for the presence of the Ach system in this group is reasonably adequate. The over-all transmitter mechanism consists of 1) choline acetylase and coenzyme A, which together are responsible for the acetylation of choline to form Ach, 2) the receptor-response component of the system activated by released Ach, and 3) the hydrolyzing en-zyme, cholinesterase, which breaks down Ach that has already per-formed its normal function or that may be present in excess of normal needs.

A. EVIDENCE FOR THE ACH SYSTEM IN CRUSTACEANS

Some of the evidence for the presence of the Ach system in crus-taceans is summarized in the following three sections. Other, quite different, lines of evidence such as the physiological actions of applied Ach and the pharmacological actions of drugs known to act on known Ach systems, are presented in Section II,B below and elsewhere in Chapters 6 and 7; Chapter 5, Vol. I.

1. *Quantitative distribution of Ach.* Thus far, Ach has not been isolated from crustaceans and chemically or chromatographically identified as it has in the insects.[8,27,65] Instead, its tentative identifica-tion in the former rests on the evidence of extracts and bioassays where

potentiation by anticholinesterases and destruction by added cholinesterase follow a pattern identical with that of systems known to involve Ach. Such criteria leave little doubt that Ach exists in the crustacean nervous system, although the presence of other closely related choline esters is not excluded. Data on the quantitative distribution of Ach in decapods are summarized in Table 1. Largely because

TABLE 1

ACETYLCHOLINE CONTENT OF VARIOUS TISSUES IN MICROGRAMS ACH PER GRAM

Species	Ganglia	Nerve fibers	Muscle	Blood	Heart
MACRURA					
Astacus astacus[29]	30–75	—	—	—	—
Astacus astacus[44]	18–43	—	0.1–0.2	—˙	—
Astacus astacus[57]	Up to 20	—	—	—	0.4–1.2
Orconectes limosus[98]	—	—	—	0.7–1.1[b]	—
Orconectes limosus (fall)[98]	30–66	8–20	—	—	—
Orconectes limosus (spring)[98]	10–20	2–5	—	—	—
Orconectes virilis[36]	22 ± 4	—	—	—	—
Orconectes virilis[89]	9.8[a]	—	—	—	—
Procambarus clarkii[98]	—	—	—	0.18–0.7[b]	—
Homarus americanus[89]	15.9[a]	—	—	—	—
BRACHYURA					
Callinectes sapidus[89]	6.6	—	—	—	—
Cancer irroratus[89]	3.1	—	—	—	—
Cancer pagurus[29]	15–20	—	—	—	—
Carcinus maenas[110]	10	2	—	—	—
Carcinus maenas[106]	2–6	—	—	—	—
Carcinus maenas[57]	2–4	—	—	—	0.2
Libinia emarginata[89]	4.6	—	—	—	—
Maja squinado[29]	4–12	—	—	—	—

[a] Ganglia and connectives = nerve cord.
[b] Micrograms per milliliter.

of small size there is no comparable information for other crustacean groups.

The Ach estimates in Table 1 were obtained through a variety of extraction procedures and methods of bioassay. This could account for some of the different values obtained by various workers using the same species. However, seasonal variation in Ach content such as that observed in *Orconectes limosus*[98] may also be involved. In spite of such variability there is nevertheless rather good agreement in the values obtained by different workers for a particular group of decapods. Thus the nervous systems of the Macrura clearly have a higher Ach content than do those of the Brachyura. Also, muscle and blood have a low titer of Ach. The high levels found in some crustacean nervous systems are comparable to those found in vertebrate autonomic ganglia. Also, as might be expected, they are within the range found for insect nervous systems.[65]

2. *Cholinesterase.* Early investigators who tested for cholinesterase activity in crustacean blood and muscle reported that it was absent, or present only in trace amounts. However, the crustacean nervous system was found to have unusually high levels of cholinesterase activity. The ventral nerve cord of *Homarus gammarus* hydrolyzes 150–200 mg Ach per gram of tissue per hour.[66] This rate is about twenty times that obtained similarly with the sciatic nerve of a frog. In contrast, a muscle homogenate of the lobster hydrolyzes only 2–5 mg Ach per gram per hour.[66]

The most complete study of cholinesterase in a crustacean is that of Walop and Boot[108] on *Carcinus maenas.* Using a manometric method for estimating cholinesterase activity and expressing results in terms of microliters of CO_2 evolved from bicarbonate in 30 min by activity in 100 mg of tissue, the following values were obtained: hemolymph = 0; liver = 10; heart = 50; leg muscle = 90; cerebral ganglia = 250; abdominal ganglia = 1400. A comparative measurement made on the brain of *Rana esculenta* yielded a value of 290.

Preparations of leg muscle and ganglia of *Carcinus* hydrolyze Ach and acetyl-β-methylcholine (Mecholyl), but not benzoylcholine or methyl butyrate.[108] In these respects *Carcinus* cholinesterase resembles vertebrate "specific," "true" cholinesterase (acetylcholinesterase). Some splitting of benzoylcholine by certain crustacean tissue preparations has been reported,[7] but no splitting of benzoylcholine is effected by a preparation of *Homarus* abdominal ganglia.

The effects of substrate concentration on rate of splitting of Ach by a preparation of *Carcinus* nerve tissue, as well as the quantitative inhibition of this reaction by physostigmine, further indicate the close resemblance of *Carcinus* nerve cholinesterase to vertebrate acetylcholinesterase.[108] Such studies, and others reviewed by Prosser,[85] indicate that the nervous systems of the higher crustaceans are unusually rich in a type of cholinesterase for which Ach is the normal substrate. This is also true for cholinesterase in the heads of flies (*Musca*).[123]

3. *Ach synthesis.* The ability of crustacean nerve tissue to synthesize Ach has been demonstrated in vitro.[36,106,107] After standing for 2

hours in van Harreveld's solution at 16°C, isolated ventral nerve cords of *Orconectes virilis* show a doubling of Ach-like activity.[36] This indicates an apparent Ach synthesis, which can also be demonstrated with an acetone powder preparation of ventral ganglia of *Cancer irroratus*.[36] In addition to the acetone powder prepared from the tissue, the following must also be present: sodium fluoride to inhibit ATPase, physostigmine to inhibit cholinesterase, choline and sodium acetate to be substrates, a liver extract containing coenzyme A, and a preparation containing ATP as a source of energy. Such a mixture (with various modifications) synthesizes Ach, under anaerobic conditions, at a rate of 45–200 μg per gram of acetone powder per hour.[36]

Similar synthetic activity occurs in a homogenate of abdominal ganglia of *Carcinus maenas*. The supernatant, with appropriate additives, synthesizes Ach at rates between 96 and 244 μg per hour per gram tissue.[106,107] Activation by cysteine takes place as it does with acetone powder preparations of vertebrate brain, but there is no inhibition by α-keto acids.

These studies demonstrate that crustacean nerve tissue contains a choline acetylase whose properties resemble those of the comparable enzyme in vertebrates.[43,70] In the heads of blowflies, which yield an acetone powder containing a large amount of choline acetylase, the synthesis of Ach is a two-step process consisting first of the formation of acetyl coenzyme A and then the acetylation of choline. The rate of formation of acetyl coenzyme A is the limiting factor.[97]

4. *"Free" and "bound" Ach.* An interesting problem, and one not yet fully resolved, concerns the storage of Ach within nerve cells. Observations on crustacean nerve tissue indicate that a fraction of the total Ach exists in the so-called bound form. This bound fraction decreases, and free, or physiologically active, Ach increases in proportion to the amounts of potassium in the perfusing medium. Thus the nerve cord of *Homarus americanus*, ground in a medium containing no potassium, has 32% of its total Ach in the free form. Ground in a medium containing 7.5 mM K$^+$, there is 53% free Ach; while with 15mM K$^+$, 65% of the Ach is free.[89] Further increase in K$^+$ has relatively little effect in releasing more Ach. The exact mode of action of K$^+$ in releasing Ach is not yet clear. Early studies on rat brain indicated that an appreciable portion of the total Ach therein exists in a physiologically inactive or bound form. It can be freed by a variety of procedures such as those which denature proteins or disorganize lipid membranes and by increasing the potassium in the medium in which tissue slices are bathed. Thus the crustacean data

show certain interesting parallels to those for vertebrates. Suggestive evidence is accumulating that the reserve Ach is contained in a cell particulate where it is bound to protein or lipoprotein and enclosed in a membrane with permeability properties resembling those of mitochondria.

B. FUNCTION OF ACH

Although relatively large amounts of Ach appear to be present in the nervous systems of decapod crustaceans, an important and clear-cut physiological role for Ach has been difficult to demonstrate in these animals. A brief summary of the current state of this problem follows; for further discussion see Chapters 6 and 7; Chapter 5, Vol. I.

1. *Transmission at neuromuscular junctions.* Several attempts to demonstrate a transmitter action of Ach from nerve to skeletal muscle in crustaceans have all produced uniformly negative or inconclusive results.[9,10,41,58] Perfusion of isolated crustacean legs with a variety of drugs known to modify neuromuscular transmission in many other types of animals is without significant effect on the muscle response to indirect stimulation. Certain chemicals such as DDT may profoundly affect crustacean nerve-muscle preparations but their action is directly on nerve fibers (especially the fine terminals) rather than on neuromuscular junctions or through the transmission process.[116]

While evidence for a transmitter action of Ach in crustacean skeletal muscle is lacking, one must remember that here the junctions themselves seem peculiarly resistant to drugs and to ion imbalance in perfusion media. Even where clear effects have been demonstrated,[109] it is difficult to be sure that the nerve and muscle also are not affected by the substances tested. The histology of the motor nerve endings suggests that they are embedded in the muscle fiber, or otherwise protected by relatively impermeable membranes so that the junctional area may be quite inaccessible to externally applied chemicals. However, the fine structure of neuromuscular junctions in Crustacea is not known, but that of a wasp has been described.[39] Conceivably the evolution of an open circulation in arthropods, and the close proximity of two or more types of nerve endings on the same muscle fiber, have been accompanied by a high degree of isolation of specific postjunctional areas from one another and from the general circulation.

2. *Action of Ach on the heart.* Acetylcholine has repeatedly been shown to have an excitor action on crustacean hearts[31,64,88,110–112,121] (Chapter 5, Vol. I). The *Daphnia* heart appears to be an exception to

this rule.[11,13,84] The pattern of drug action, in general, supports the view that Ach normally acts in crustacean cardiac regulatory processes. Thus physostigmine potentiates the action of Ach, atropine blocks its action, and the effect of Ach is mimicked by certain other choline esters and by nicotine.

The locus (or loci) of Ach action on the crustacean heart is not readily determined. It may act as a transmitter between extrinsic excitor nerves and the cardiac ganglion.[99] It may act directly on cells of the cardiac ganglion[69] or on cardiac muscle.[32] However, the fact that relatively high concentrations of Ach are required to stimulate some hearts, especially when freshly set up, suggests that Ach may not be a normal excitor agent for the crustacean heart.[50] Other possible cardio-excitor agents are discussed in Section III below.

3. *Ach and electrical activity of isolated ganglia.* Since it was first studied by Prosser,[82] the isolated abominal nerve cord of the crayfish has been a favorite object for observing so-called spontaneous activity in an invertebrate ganglion. A short length of cord, with at least one intact ganglion, placed on electrodes may continue to discharge for many hours. Kept cool and bathed occasionally, such a preparation remains active for 1–2 days. The electrical discharges of isolated crayfish cord are quickly abolished by large doses of nicotine, but nicotine concentrations from 10^{-6} to 10^{-5} gm/ml have an immediate stimulating action.[82] A simple and spectacular demonstration consists of blowing a few puffs of tobacco smoke on a length of crayfish nerve cord while recording spikes electrically. Within seconds, the frequency of discharge increases greatly, presumably due to the nicotine content of the smoke.

In many instances where the action of Ach is nicotine-like, as in vertebrate autonomic ganglia and junctions between nerve and skeletal muscle, nicotine in low concentrations mimics the action of the transmitters, while in high concentrations it has a blocking action. One might deduce, therefore, that nicotine's action on the crayfish nerve cord is of this sort. If so, Ach applied in low concentrations might be expected to increase the discharge frequency of crayfish ganglion cells. There has been one report[16] that this was true, but in our laboratory and elsewhere[83] massive doses (10^{-4} to 10^{-2} M) were required to increase the discharge rate. However, Ach is a quaternary ammonium base and may penetrate poorly the cellular sheath surrounding the crayfish cord. Quaternary ammonium bases such as prostigmine penetrate cells with difficulty, while tertiary amines such as physostigmine enter.[20]

This has often been presented as an explanation for lack of action of externally applied Ach and prostigmine. The cockroach abdominal nerve cord is surrounded by a sheath of squamous epithelial cells and connective tissue that restricts the diffusion of K^+ and Na^+ and completely prevents the action of externally applied Ach on synaptic transmission. After removal of the sheath Ach does act, albeit in high concentrations.[102,103] Physostigmine and prostigmine are both effective anticholinesterases and their actions closely mimic that of Ach, mainly due to the accumulating Ach that follows their application. The former, in small doses, increases electrical discharge in isolated crayfish ganglia,[83] while large doses of prostigmine act similarly (J. K. Hichar, 1958, personal communication). Similar effects of Ach, physostigmine, and nicotine have been observed on the electrical activity of the isolated nerve cord of the cockroach *Periplaneta americana*.[87] Thus Ach quite likely plays some role in the activity of abdominal ganglia in both the crayfish and cockroach, but the nature of this role is not clear.

Ach has an excitor action on the isolated stretch receptors of the crayfish (Chapter 2). Physostigmine potentiates the action of Ach, while atropine blocks its action. These data suggest that Ach is involved in the normal functioning of these mechanoreceptors.[48,120]

4. *Ach and synaptic transmission.* The most intensively studied synaptic transmission in crustaceans is the one between longitudinal giant fibers and motor neurons to abdominal flexor muscles in the crayfish *Procambarus clarkii* (Chapter 7). Under appropriate experimental conditions these junctions show facilitation and fatigue, and in other ways give evidence for chemical transmission.[118,119] The general pattern of drug action here suggests that Ach is involved in the transmission process, but Ach itself is strikingly ineffective when applied externally to the cord. Therefore it was concluded[90] that this substance could not have a transmitter action at these synapses. Yet the following considerations indicate that this conclusion is possibly unjustified.

The synapses in question are highly sensitive to nicotine in the perfusion fluid surrounding the cord.[90] A concentration of 10^{-6} gm/ml causes immediate facilitation followed later by depression. With increasing doses of nicotine, facilitation is followed by block, until at 10^{-5} gm/ml, there is no facilitation, and block occurs in 1 min. The general pattern follows here the action of nicotine found at certain vertebrate synapses, such as those in autonomic ganglia, where Ach is rather generally accepted to have a transmitter action. Certain quaternary ammonium bases and amines influence these crayfish synapses[92] as if they might be acting through an Ach system. Eserine and diisopropyl fluorophosphate (DFP) block them but prostigmine is without action even in strong doses.[91]

Results of other studies of Ach and drug action on crustacean synapses[83,101] suggest a normal transmitter action of Ach, although Ach alone or after eserine is peculiarly lacking in action. When any applied hormone, drug, or other chemical fails to act on a cell it can always be argued that it did not reach the proper site. This generally is an unsatisfactory type of reasoning, but in the present case may have some justification.

In the anomuran *Petrolisthes*, injected Ach induces, facilitates, or inhibits autotomy depending on the amount injected. Small doses of eserine facilitate, and high doses inhibit, the response. This and other evidence implicate Ach in the normal autotomy reflex of this form, but do not specify where the Ach is acting[117] (Chapter 17, Vol. I).

5. *Ach and ion flux.* In some way, not yet clear, cholinesterase, and a choline ester by implication, appear to be involved in the active transport of sodium chloride through gills of the crab, *Eriocheir sinensis.*[63] These gills hydrolyze Ach at a relatively high rate. Basic dyes known to inhibit cholinesterase, as well as classical inhibitors of this enzyme, reduce the rate of active uptake of sodium chloride by *Eriocheir's* isolated gills. This may be comparable, for example, to vertebrate neuromuscular junctions, where the depolarizing action of released or applied Ach is considered by some to result from increased ionic conductance of the end-plate membrane.[33]

III. *AMINES*

Adrenaline and noradrenaline excite crustacean hearts (Chapter 5, Vol. I), and depress the autotomy reflex in *Petrolisthes.*[117] This suggests that these, or related compounds, may normally act in crustacean nervous transmission as they are known to do in vertebrates. However, neither of these compounds has been certainly found to occur in crustaceans.[71]

5-Hydroxytryptamine (5-HT, serotonin, enteramine) is an indole alkylamine which also may be a neurohumor. It has been shown to have a marked excitor action on crustacean hearts.[50,115] Furthermore, the application of relatively low concentrations of 5-HT causes proprioceptors in crustacean legs and abdomens to discharge.[46] An unidentified substance with properties resembling those of 5-HT was found in nerve tissue of a variety of decapod crustaceans.[50] 5-HT, itself, occurs in various tissues, including the nervous systems, of vertebrates[28] and mollusks.[115] Some indication of the possible transmitter action of 5-HT was obtained from studies of cardiac excitation in mollusks.[113]

A substance resembling adrenaline in some respects but differing in others occurs in the pericardial organs of decapod crustaceans.[6] It has been tentatively identified as 5-HT[115] or a dihydroxyindole.[22] While one or more such active amines apparently occur in crustaceans, their chemical identity is yet uncertain.

IV. *FACTOR I*

Although Ach in some animals can have either an excitor or inhibitor action depending on the nature of the junction and the concentration, a more specific inhibitor substance may be present in certain normally inhibitory neurons. A fraction (Factor I) with marked inhibiting effects on a variety of crustacean organs has been extracted from mammalian brain by Florey.[47–49] It antagonizes the excitor action of Ach both on the isolated intestine and on stretch receptors of crayfish. It also inhibits the normal discharge of the stretch receptors, slows or stops the crayfish heart, and blocks peripheral neuromuscular transmission.[49] A substance with similar properties to Factor I can be obtained from crustacean nerve tissue.[48]

Further evidence for a specific inhibitory factor in the crustacean nervous system is found in the actions of picrotoxin which is a powerful convulsant for crustaceans.[45] It excites the isolated nerve cord of the crayfish in low concentrations, an effect which is reversed but slowly with washing (J. K. Hichar, 1958, personal communication). The inhibitory action of Factor I on the crayfish stretch receptor is prevented by previous application of picrotoxin.[12,40] Also, picrotoxin blocks the action of the inhibitor axon to the opener muscle of the dactyl in *Orconectes virilis*.[105]

Factor I now appears to be a complex of substances, one of which is γ-aminobutyric acid.[12] The latter inhibits discharge of crayfish stretch receptors at concentrations of 10 $\mu g/ml$ and less.[38,46] Injection of 0.2 mg into the hemocoele of a 45-gm crayfish produces flaccid paralysis. Although the evidence that γ-aminobutyric acid or some related compound acts as a neurohumor is incomplete, it would appear probable that such will shortly be forthcoming.

V. NEUROSECRETORY SYSTEMS

A neurosecretory system may be defined as a group of related neurons specialized for synthesis, storage, and release of chemical agents that act as hormones. Since ordinary neurons may release neurohumors that function in the transmission process at synapses and neuroeffector junctions, a neurosecretory system is distinguished by the grouping and specialization of axon terminals for storage and release of its products, usually into the circulation.* Groups of nerve endings, so modified, have been called neurohemal organs,[23] and the crustacean sinus gland is a good example. More than one type of neurosecretory system is found in crustaceans. In addition to the sinus gland complex there are the sinus plates or postcommissural organs and the pericardial organs of Alexandrowicz.[3-5]

A. SINUS GLAND SYSTEM

The most fully studied neurosecretory system in crustaceans is the complex associated with the sinus gland. It is comparable in many respects with the hypothalamic-neurohypophyseal system of vertebrates and the brain-corpus cardiacum-corpus allatum system of insects.[55,93] The crustacean sinus gland complex is organized as follows.

1. *General plan.* The sinus gland complex as found in the Brachyura is shown schematically in Fig. 1. Neurosecretory cells in various regions of the nervous system send their axons to a common release center in each eyestalk, the so-called sinus gland. These centers, made up of groups of bulbous nerve endings, usually are located in the dorsolateral portion of the stalk, often between the medulla externa and medulla interna. The nerve endings are so arranged that materials released traverse a thin membrane before entering the hemolymph.

Of the various neurons contributing to the sinus gland, the group of secretory nerve cell bodies situated in the median ventral portion of the medulla terminalis of brachyurans is of particular interest since they have been shown to be the major source of molt-inhibiting hormone.[75] Following Hanström's terminology, this region has been referred to by some as an X-organ.

Currently, opinions differ regarding the precise application of the

---

* Additional features that identify neurosecretory cells are briefly mentioned below (page 294).

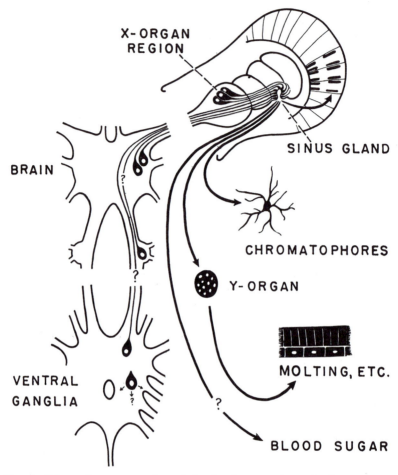

Fig. 1. Schematic representation of the brachyuran sinus gland neurosecretory system. Axons from neurosecretory cells of the ventral ganglia and commissural (paraesophageal) ganglia probably end together with those from brain and eyestalk. Neurosecretory cells in regions of the eyestalk other than the X-organ region have not been shown. Target organs for neurohormones from sinus gland include distal retinal pigment, chromatophores, and Y-organs.

term X-organ.* In decapod Natantia the X-organ region described by Hanström is near the epidermis and usually somewhat distal to the medulla terminalis. However, in the Reptantia Anomura and Brachyura, the structure is closely associated with the medulla terminalis and commonly far from the epidermis.[54,55] The position of the X-organ, or

---

* This problem is also discussed in Chapter 15, Vol. I.

at least of its concentric-layered structures, may change during development.[86] Thus in *Homarus americanus* larvae the region containing lamellar bodies lies next to the eye papilla and epidermis, while in adults it is found near the medulla terminalis and far from the epidermis.

In certain recent studies on the Brachyura, the term X-organ has been applied to a region of the medulla terminalis having unusually large neurosecretory cells, with nearby concentric-layered bodies.[14,15,75] In the Natantia, however, the separation of the neurosecretory cells in the medulla terminalis from the region where the concentric bodies are found has led to the suggestions that the latter be referred to as the distal part of the X-organ,[24] or the sensory pore or papilla X-organ,[60] while the proximal part be called the pars ganglionaris. In *Crangon allmanni*, both parts of the X-organ are derived from neuroblasts in the anterior wall of the medulla terminalis ganglion layer.[30]

It is not yet clear whether the concentric-layered structures or "onion bodies" are neurosecretory products. Until this question is settled and more is learned of the functions of the neurosecretory cell groups contributing endings to the sinus glands, the homologies of the structures concerned are uncertain and hence a definitive terminology is difficult to devise. The matter of designating other groups of neurosecretory cells in eyestalks and brain also remains unsettled. Meanwhile a system of letters and numbers such as that already employed[14,15,35] is useful in labeling the various regions in eyestalks and brain where neurosecretory cells have been found.

2. Histology and cytology

a. *Sinus glands.* The general appearance and location of the sinus glands in the eyestalks and head are known in representative species of most orders of the Malacostraca.[54,55] Early workers believed these structures were endocrine glands which released hormones. But it is now clear that the supposed glands are, instead, aggregates of nerve endings arranged for storage and release of substances into the circulation.[15,74] Although the sinus glands of few crustacean orders have been re-examined in the light of the newer knowledge, the original descriptions[54,55] are still useful in surveying the locations and relation of these nerve endings to blood sinuses in all major malacostracan groups.

Potter has made a detailed study of the sinus glands in portunid crabs, especially *Callinectes.*[81] Their inner blood sinus is rather intermediate in complexity between the simple cup form in certain Natantia and the much-branched or subdivided inner sinus of the crayfishes and *Homarus*. Axons approach the inner sinus mostly by way of a large tract, the sinus gland nerve or tract. In *Callinectes* each axon branches to form five to ten endings. In sections, these endings appear to radiate from the cavity of the sinus or its branches. In the crayfish, *Orconectes virilis*, the arrangement of nerve endings in a sinus gland is less orderly than in *Callinectes*, as the result of the many small blood channels of the inner sinus and the varied orientation of the neurosecretory axons approaching these channels.[35]

A membrane 1.00–1.25 μ in thickness forms a boundary between nerve endings of the sinus gland and the circulating hemolymph. In *Carcinus* and *Callinectes* the individual fiber endings are filled with granules ranging in diameter from 0.15 to 0.30 μ. Within a single terminal the particles appear uniform in diameter. In addition, mitochondria are present and stain characteristically with Janus green B. Fresh preparations of *Callinectes* sinus glands, under phase contrast, are found to contain droplets between 0.75 and 3.0 μ in diameter in the nerve endings. These stain with neutral red.[81]

Although many earlier workers reported merely that the region of the sinus gland contains acidophilic and basophilic materials, azan and aldehyde fuchsin staining techniques demonstrate five[80] or six[81] tinctorial types of nerve endings in *Callinectes*. These types do not intergrade in respect to color and, therefore, could represent six materials with characteristic staining properties rather than stages in the formation of some smaller number of substances.

b. *Neurosecretory cells.* In some neurosecretory systems the best way to identify a neurosecretory cell body is to trace its axon to a release site adjacent to the circulatory system and to show that the axon terminals are modified for storage and release of material into the circulation. Since ordinary neurons synthesize, transport, and release neurohumors, cytological signs of secretory activity by themselves may not be sufficient to identify neurosecretory cells.

Fortunately there are several characters which help in locating the cell bodies of secretory neurons in the sinus gland system. They are: 1) presence of bluish-white refractile granules in living axons and often in cell bodies, 2) cell shape and size, 3) nuclear shape and size, 4) relative abundance of stainable material and its appearance after special fixing and staining techniques.[14,15,21,35,42,60,67,68,73,80,81] In a few species of crabs and a crayfish, these criteria have been used to locate the various cell bodies in the sinus gland system. In the crab *Gecarcinus*, these lie in several parts of the eyestalk ganglia and in the brain.[14,15] Even some cells in the thoracic and paraesophageal ganglia may send their axons through the brain and optic lobe peduncles to the sinus glands.[15,42,68]

Three or more cell types contribute to the sinus gland system of decapod crustaceans. In *Sesarma* three types of neurosecretory cells are present in eyestalk and brain,[42] while four can be distinguished in *Orconectes* brain and eyestalk.[35] In decapod crustaceans the pars ganglionaris of the X-organ makes an especially important contribution to the sinus gland system. This group of cells is the chief source of the molt-inhibiting hormone (see Chapter 15, Vol. I). In *Callinectes,* five or six types of neurosecretory cells can be distinguished in the X-organ.[81] Among their distinctive cytological features these cells show granules with staining properties corresponding with the various endings seen in the sinus gland. This suggests that the X-organ alone may produce several different hormones.

Since the X-organ and sinus gland apparently produce and release several hormones, the question of the control of this release is of much interest. Ordinary neurons might synapse with neurosecretory neurons so that a given hormone would be released by appropriate excitation of a particular group of neurosecretory cells. Fine processes branching from the large axons of X-organ cells of *Callinectes* have been seen to enter the surrounding neuropile.[81] These branches may well be the dendrites of the neurosecretory cells.

B. Postcommissural and Pericardial Organs

Since the circumesophageal connectives and postesophageal commissures of *Crangon* contain hormones[17,19] they have been examined in a variety of crustaceans.[59,60] Associated with them are structures called postcommissural organs which consist of groups of nerve fibers ending in a neuropile-like mass of fine terminations in close spatial relationship to the blood system. In *Penaeus,* thin areas containing the nerve endings are fused to the wall of a blood sinus in which blood travels from the gills. The postcommissural organs seem anatomically complex because they are traversed by through motor fibers to muscles that may be involved in molting.[60]

In *Squilla mantis* there are groups of fine nerve endings in the dorsal blood sinus.[3,4] These belong to the system of median connectives and the system of dorsal trunks (Chapter 5, Vol. I). They have no obvious motor or sensory function, and staining with azan demonstrates an abundance of droplets, both inside and outside the fibers. Consequently these neuropiles may constitute a neurosecretory system. Similar systems of fine nerve endings occur in the pericardial cavities of a variety of decapod crustaceans where they have been called pericardial organs.[5] Although the arrangement of nerve trunks and associated fine nerve endings varies in different groups of decapods, they are all located in the pericardial cavity, so that they are bathed by blood entering the cavity from the gills. Thus they are well situated for releasing substances into the blood before it enters the heart, which, indeed, they appear to do[6,69a] (Chapter 5, Vol. I).

VI. *NEUROSECRETORY SUBSTANCES*

A. Diversity and Chemical Nature

The number of neurosecretory substances in crustaceans is not known. There may be two or more chromatophorotropins, one or two retinal pigment-regulating hormones, a molt-inhibiting hormone that may also help to regulate calcium and water metabolism, an ovarian growth-regulating factor, and possibly one that regulates blood sugar. Until further work is done to separate and purify these neurohormones, their chemical nature and their number will remain in question. However, the ground work has already been done. Histochemical studies of the sinus gland have been started, methods for separating and concentrating the chromatophorotropins have been developed and suitable assays are available. These preliminary studies may be briefly summarized as follows.

1. *Histochemical studies.* Conventional histological stains provide some data on the general nature of the contents of sinus gland nerve endings. For example, in the sinus glands of *Gecarcinus* stained with the chrome-hematoxylin-phloxin method of Gomori,[53] many endings are filled with an acidophilic homogeneous substance staining with phloxin. Scattered through the endings are basophilic granules with an affinity for the chrome-hematoxylin.[15] The Gomori method is known to stain selectively the contents of neurosecretory cells in various animals including insects and vertebrates. However, it was originally used to stain the islets of Langerhans and therefore is not specific for neurosecretory material.

Changes associated with molting have been observed several times in the relative amounts of acidophilic and basophilic materials in the sinus gland.[34,35,51,52,86] For example, in *Orconectes virilis*, there is a marked increase in basophilia in the early postmolt period.[86] This is related to the secretory activity of the Type 2 cells of the X-organ.[35]

In a variety of decapod crustaceans, the granules which stain with chrome-hematoxylin consist of a nonbasic protein containing little if any histidine, tryptophan, arginine, and primary amino groups. They contain tyrosine and relatively large amounts of cystine (M. Rehm, 1957, personal communication).* Neurosecretory materials of the vertebrate posterior pituitary[95] and of insect corpora cardiaca[96] are also rich in cystine and likewise have a high affinity for chrome-hematoxylin. In *Carcinus*, the chrome-hematoxylin staining granules are most abundant shortly before and after molting and they largely disappear during the intermolt. Three other types of proteins are present in the sinus gland of *Carcinus:* one has the properties of a histone, a second is rich in tryptophan, while the third is strongly acidophilic and selectively demonstrated by reactions for primary amino groups (Rehm). These four proteins could represent actual neurohormones, hormone precursors, or carrier proteins.

The cystine-containing protein and the histone may occur together in the same neuron ending so that variations in their relative proportions during the molt cycle could give the impression of three or four tinctorial types of endings. The other two proteins occur, each in a separate type of ending.

2. *Chemical separation.*   Some progress has been made in the isolation and characterization of crustacean chromatophore activating substances (Chapter 4). This is partly because of the ease with which they may be assayed. Early studies on the *Palaemonetes* lightening hormone showed it to be water soluble and heat stable.[78,79] The molecule concerned is relatively small, dialyzable, soluble in "pure alcohol" but not in ether, and stable when boiled briefly in dilute HCl or NaOH.[25] The substance is not species specific.

The darkening substance tested in eyestalkless *Uca* has properties similar to those of the *Palaemonetes* lightening substance.[1,2] In addition it shows incomplete solubility in ethanol and methanol, only slight solubility in acetone (dry?) and insolubility in benzine, chloroform, and ether. One attempt at fractionating the active material from *Uca* eyestalks yielded a product that not only lightened both *Palaemonetes* and *Crangon* but also darkened eyestalkless *Uca*.[2] However, other work suggests that a separation of *Palaemonetes* lightening hormone from *Uca* darkening hormone can be made on the basis of alcohol solubilities since the former is more soluble in absolute ethanol.[18]

Except for the observation that *Palaemon* (*"Leander"*)[†] lightening hormone could be inactivated by incubation with extracts of certain

---

* Now published.[86a]

† Ed. note: European forms properly referred to the Genus *Palaemon* have been widely misnamed *Leander*, which occurs only as the gulf weed shrimp (*L. tenuicornis*) and two Indo-Malayan species. For example, *Leander adspersus* is a synonym for the correct name *Palaemon squilla*. Other synonyms will be found in the Index.

tissues,[26] little more was done on the chemistry of the chromatophoro-tropins for the period from 1940 to 1955. Recently two new and independent approaches to the problem have been tried, one using electrophoretic separation,[61,100] the other chromatographic and countercurrent distribution methods as well.[37,72] Electrophoresis of untreated sinus glands and postcommissure organs of *Palaemon* yields a fraction active in concentrating both the large and the small red pigment cells of this animal.[61] This was called Substance A; it does not dialyze and has a low mobility at pH 7.5. If sinus glands ground in distilled water are applied to the paper strip, instead of freshly dissected glands, subsequent electrophoresis yields more than one active area. Their eluates concentrate only the small red chromatophores. The active materials (called alpha substances) are dialyzable and have a high mobility at pH 7.5.

Electrophoresis of sinus glands from *Uca pugilator* placed directly on filter paper strips produces several active peaks in eluates tested on black, red, and yellow chromatophores of *Uca*.[100] These results as well as those on the substances active on *Palaemon* erythrophores are difficult to interpret, but at least one of the chromatophorotropins of *Uca* sinus glands is contained in granules which release their contents only after treatments affecting their surrounding membranes.[77] This may partly account for the differences between electrophoresis of fresh glands and treated glands.

Considerable progress has been made in the purification of the red pigment-concentrating hormone,[37,72] using eyestalks of *Pandalus borealis* as a source of material and eyestalkless *Palaemon squilla* as test animals. Chromatophorotropic activity has been assayed in terms of "Leander units,"* which are defined as the smallest amount of hormone that will cause distinct blanching of eyestalkless *Palaemon squilla* in 20 min.[72]

A *Pandalus* eyestalk contains 50–100 Leander units per milligram of dry weight. Consequently one 30 mg eyestalk would have 2000–3000 units. This may be concentrated enormously by the following procedure. After extraction of eyestalks with acetone, evaporating, and washing with ether, an ethanol soluble fraction is dried, taken up in 80% acetone and placed on a column of aluminum oxide. After elution, the active fraction is concentrated to a syrupy residue with an activity of 100,000 Leander units per milligram. Further partition

---

* Unfortunately the hormone assay unit chosen uses an incorrect taxonomic name for the experimental animal concerned. See footnote, page 297.

chromatography using a silica preparation and a 1:1 water-saturated mixture of n-butanol and amyl alcohol yields fractions which, when pooled and concentrated, have an activity of 900,000 units per milligram. Final purification by Craig countercurrent distribution gave 20–30 mg of a product (from about 5 kg of eyestalks) with an activity of 10,000,000 units per milligram.[37]

When the final product is chromatographed on paper using a water-saturated mixture of n-butanol and amyl alcohol (1:1) an R_f value of 0.43 is obtained. No chemical reaction is known that will identify the active area, so localization must be made by bioassay. After paper electrophoresis at pH's ranging from 2.5 to 9.0 the hormone moves a little toward the anode, with the distance traveled increasing somewhat with an increase in pH. In 1 min 200,000 units of the hormone are inactivated by a 1:1000 concentration of crystalline chymotrypsin at pH 7.8 and 18°C. Tested on a variety of crustaceans and chromatophore types, the purified hormone produces no effects other than the concentration of the pigment of red chromatophores.[37]

Although Östlund and Fänge[72] originally believed that this red pigment-concentrating hormone might be an amine, they later concluded,[37] from results with trypsin, chymotrypsin, and boiling in 6 N HCl, that the hormone is more likely a polypeptide. Incubation at 37°C for 16 hr with crystallized trypsin as well as prolonged boiling in HCl[62] had been found to destroy Substance A of Palaemon. This implies that the active molecule contains peptide linkages. Working in the author's laboratory, Mendelsohn has found that the Uca darkening principle also is quickly destroyed by incubation with crystalline chymotrypsin.

The red pigment-concentrating hormone and Uca darkening hormone apparently are different but may be related polypeptides. If this should prove true, it would help to account for the difficulties of separating these two chromactive principles, because studies on vasopressin and oxytocin, as well as on intermedin and ACTH already show that the complete separation of closely related polypeptides is not easy. Determination of the exact chemical natures of the chromatophorotropins and other hormones of the sinus gland system will be of great interest.

B. STORAGE AND RELEASE

Neurosecretory substances appear to be synthesized in the cell body and then to migrate via the axoplasm to the axon terminals where they are stored. In crustaceans, these terminal processes are of two major types: 1) the bulbous endings as found in the sinus glands; 2) the much branched terminals of pericardial and postcommissural organs as well as the neurosecretory structures of the dorsal blood sinus of *Squilla* (page 295). The multibranched endings would appear to provide more surface for release of a neurohormone, and it is perhaps significant that such endings are found in association with crustacean hearts where the fast release of a heart-regulating substance could be of survival value.

There has been much speculation concerning the manner in which neurohumoral substances are stored in nerve terminals. It has long been known that stored acetylcholine is held inactive in a bound form until it is released by methods that denature proteins or destroy lipid membranes. Recent studies are casting new light on the problem of storage. Observations with the light microscope[76,81] and with the electron microscope[56] both reveal that nerve endings in the sinus gland are filled with particles ranging from 0.1 to 0.3 μ in diameter. These particles, when stained, give the characteristic colors to the nerve endings.[80] Figure 2, A and B, are electron micrographs of the sinus gland area of *Gecarcinus lateralis*, a West Indian land crab.

A tangled network of axons distinguished by their content of neurofibrillae enters the sinus gland region. Granules occur at the periphery of some of these axons, which agrees with the observation that the characteristic stainable granules in the sinus gland nerve tract of *Gecarcinus* lie at the axon periphery, as viewed in cross section.[15] Other regions of Fig. 2, A and B, are filled with electron-dense granules of rather uniform diameter in any given area. These regions are the axon terminals. The granules have well-defined boundaries suggesting that they are surrounded by membranes. The majority of granules to be seen in Fig. 2, A and B, range in diameter from 0.1 to 0.2 μ. However, in one ending they average about 0.05 μ in diameter.

This and other evidence suggests that a given neurosecretory material may be packaged in granules of a characteristic size range. Preliminary observations in other crustaceans indicate that after

---

Fig. 2. Electron micrographs of the sinus gland region of *Gecarcinus lateralis*. A. Section through tangled axons and axon terminals near the periphery of a sinus gland. Arrow points to an ending with granules of smaller size than those seen in majority of endings. B. As in A, but at a higher magnification. G = electron-dense neurosecretory granules; M = mitochondria; N = neurofibrillae. Line at lower right hand corner of each figure = 1 μ. (Micrographs supplied by Mary H. Hodge and George B. Chapman.)

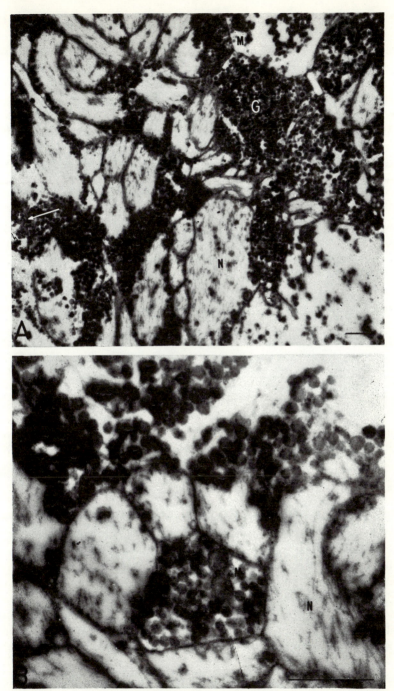

FIG. 2 (See legend on opposite page.)

301

osmium tetroxide fixation, electron-dense granules are to be found generally in sinus glands. Furthermore, the secretory nerve endings of the pericardial organs[69a] are full of similar granules (D. M. Maynard, E. Maynard, and D. D. Potter, 1957, personal communication). In *Cancer irroratus* and *Carcinus maenas*, nerve fibers in the pericardial organs may be filled with uniform particles ranging in diameter from 0.1 to 0.3 μ. Neurosecretory granules are also found in nerve endings of the corpora cardiaca of the roach, *Leucophaea maderae*.[122]

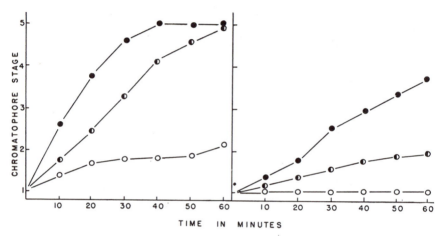

FIG. 3. Response of black chromatophores of eyestalkless *Uca pugilator* to homogenates of *Uca* sinus glands in distilled water (left) and in 1.3 M sucrose (right). ●, 0.2 sinus glands per milliliter; ◐, 0.02 sinus glands per milliliter; ○, 0.002 sinus glands per milliliter. Equal volumes (0.1 ml) of each dilution injected at zero time. Chromatophore stage 1 is fully concentrated pigment and stage 5 fully dispersed pigment. (Redrawn from Pérez-González.[77])

Recent studies by Pérez-González[77] provide further indirect evidence that one of the color change hormones of *Uca* is stored in packets with membranes having properties similar to those found in chromaffin granules and mitochondria. Sinus glands of *Uca pugilator* homogenized in approximately isosmotic sucrose are less active than homogenates made with distilled water, when tested on the black chromatophores of *Uca pugnax* (Fig. 3). Heating, freezing and thawing, detergents, and digitoxin also release hormone in sucrose homogenates. These results are similar to those obtained in studies on vertebrate chromaffin granules of the adrenal medulla.

Not only does it appear necessary for neurohormones to be released from storage compartments (granules) but they must, also, be released from the nerve endings. Some neurohormones of crustaceans such as those regulating color changes, retinal pigment movements and heart rate must be quickly set free when the need arises. Likewise, the release must be quickly stopped. It seems highly probable that sensory messages are relayed by the central nervous system to the proper storage endings by way of ordinary nerve impulses. This, however, remains to be proved. If it takes place, the depolarization of the membranes of one type of nerve ending may allow the release of the corresponding neurohormone.

In the case of the molt-inhibiting hormone from the X-organ-sinus gland system, either there are long periods of release during intermolt, followed by shorter periods when it is withheld, or there are cycles of production and nonproduction of the molt-inhibiting principle. Histochemical evidence would tend to favor the latter suggestion.

C. Functions

The functions of neurosecretory substances are discussed elsewhere in this book. An account of the heart-regulating factor of pericardial organs is given in Chapter 5, Vol. I, of pigment-controlling hormones in Chapter 4, and of the hormonal regulation of molting in Chapter 15, Vol. I, with its dependent processes such as growth (Chapter 16, Vol. I) and regeneration (Chapter 17, Vol. I).

VII. COMPARISONS AND CONCLUSIONS

Our knowledge of neurohumors is more complete for man and certain other mammals than for any other animal group, either vertebrate or invertebrate. The quantitative distribution of Ach, 5-HT, adrenaline, and noradrenaline are known for different parts of the nervous systems of a variety of common laboratory mammals. Likewise the metabolism of these neurohumors is well understood. Many of the enzymes involved in their synthesis and destruction have been isolated and extensively studied in vitro. Knowledge of the manner in which these transmitter agents are stored and released is growing rapidly. Their physiological actions have been demonstrated. Little is known, however, of their mechanisms of action at cellular and molecular levels. This remains an aspect of neurohumors about which we are largely ignorant.

Knowledge of the nature and distribution of neurohumors in the various invertebrate groups is sketchy. Identifications and quantitative estimates in nervous systems can be made readily only in the larger species. This is a severe limitation. Ach is known to be widely distributed and is found in the nervous systems of annelids, mollusks, crustaceans, and insects. The distribution of the biologically active amines is less well known. Adrenaline and noradrenaline are found in insects. 5-HT is present in molluscan nervous systems. Which active amines occur in crustacean nervous systems remains to be finally determined.

In some of the invertebrates such as annelids and mollusks, it is quite clear that the neurohumors play an important role in transmission between nerve and muscle or other effectors. Their possible role in central synaptic transmission is less clear. In insects and crustaceans, however, exact physiological functions are still doubtful and modes of action have been scarcely touched upon. Nevertheless, important and useful methods of insect control employ modern insecticides known to be powerful inhibitors of cholinesterase and to cause the accumulation of excessive amounts of Ach in the poisoned insect. These same insecticides, used unwisely, can decimate the crustacean fauna of our lakes and streams, thereby cutting off an important food supply for higher organisms in the food chain. Likewise, commercial crustaceans such as *Callinectes*, the blue crab, can be destroyed in great numbers by the injudicious spraying of shore areas. Both for practical and theoretical reasons we need to know more about neurohumoral systems of crustaceans and other invertebrates.

In contrast with the neurohumors, our understanding of neurosecretory systems and neurosecretion in arthropods approaches that for the vertebrates. Many investigators have helped to create, over a period of a few years, a working concept of the X-organ-sinus gland system in decapod crustaceans. The work of Berta Scharrer and others on the pars intercerebralis-corpus cardiacum system of insects has often served as a guide in the studies on Crustacea. These two neurosecretory systems of arthropod groups in a sense provided a pattern for the hypothalamic-neurohypophyseal system of vertebrates.

Concentrated efforts of several groups of chemists resulted in the isolation, identification, and synthesis of the vertebrate octapeptides, oxytocin and vasopressin, which are the only neurohormones from neurosecretory cells that have been chemically characterized. Comparable efforts will eventually isolate and identify the probably more numerous products of invertebrate neurosecretory systems.

In the normal functioning of nervous systems, neurosecretory cells are regulated by ordinary neurons, and their neurohumors. Although details are not fully clear, cholinergic or aminergic synapses, or both, intervene between an appropriate stimulus and the release of a posterior pituitary factor. Work now in progress suggests the same to be true for the crustacean sinus glands. In the Cecropia silkworm brain the level of cholinesterase, and consequently of a cholinergic substance, determines the degree of activity of the neurosecretory cells and hence controls diapause.[104] Such findings give a new insight to the chemical complexities of central nervous transmission, excitation, and inhibition. These processes are involved in the release of neuron products that are carried in the circulation to act at many points within the organism.

Clearly we have entered upon another era in our understanding of the complexities of the nervous system. Already, studies on crustaceans have contributed in important ways to our basic knowledge of neurohumors and neurosecretion. They may be expected to continue to supply experimental material for important future work.

REFERENCES

1. Abramowitz, A. A. 1937. The chromatophorotropic hormone of the Crustacea: standardization, properties and physiology of the eye-stalk gland. *Biol. Bull.* 72:344–365.
2. Abramowitz, A. A. 1940. Purification of the chromatophorotropic hormone of the crustacean eyestalk. *J. Biol. Chem.* 132:501–506.
3. Alexandrowicz, J. S. 1952. Notes on the nervous system in the Stomatopoda, I. The system of median connectives. *Pubbl. staz. zool. Napoli* 23:201–214.
4. Alexandrowicz, J. S. 1953a. Notes on the nervous system in the Stomatopoda, II. The system of dorsal trunks. III. Small nerve cells in motor nerves. *Pubbl. staz. zool. Napoli* 24:29–45.
5. Alexandrowicz, J. S. 1953b. Nervous organs in the pericardial cavity of the decapod Crustacea. *J. Marine Biol. Assoc. United Kingdom* 31:563–580.
6. Alexandrowicz, J. S., and Carlisle, D. B. 1953. Some experiments on the function of the pericardial organs in Crustacea. *J. Marine Biol. Assoc. United Kingdom* 32:175–192.
7. Augustinsson, K.-B. 1948. Cholinesterases. *Acta Physiol. Scand.* 15, Suppl. 52:1–182.
8. Augustinsson, K.-B., and Grahn, M. 1954. The occurrence of choline esters in the honeybee. *Acta Physiol. Scand.* 32:174–190.
9. Bacq, Z. M. 1935. La choline-estérase chez les Invertebrés. L'insensibilité des Crustacés à l'acétylcholine. *Arch. intern. physiol.* 42:47–60.
10. Bacq, Z. M. 1947. L'acétylcholine et l'adrenaline chez les Invertebrés. *Biol. Revs. Cambridge Phil. Soc.* 22:73–91.
11. Baylor, E. R. 1942. Cardiac pharmacology of the cladoceran, *Daphnia. Biol. Bull.* 83:165–172.
12. Bazemore, A., Elliott, K. A. C., and Florey, E. 1956. Factor I and γ-aminobutyric acid. *Nature* 178:1052–1053.

13. Bekker, J. M., and Krijgsman, B. J. 1951. Physiological investigations into the heart functions of *Daphnia*. *J. Physiol.* (*London*) 115:249–257.
14. Bliss, D. E., Durand, J. B., and Welsh, J. H. 1954. Neurosecretory systems in decapod Crustacea. *Z. Zellforsch. u. mikroskop. Anat.* 39:520–536.
15. Bliss, D. E., and Welsh, J. H. 1952. The neurosecretory system of brachyuran Crustacea. *Biol. Bull.* 103:157–169.
16. Bonnet, V. 1938. Contribution à l'étude du système nerveux ganglionnaire des Crustacés. *Arch. intern. physiol.* 47:397–433.
17. Brown, F. A., Jr., and Ederstrom, H. E. 1940. Dual control of certain black chromatophores of *Crago*. *J. Exptl. Zool.* 85:53–69.
18. Brown, F. A., Jr., and Scudamore, H. H. 1940. Differentiation of two principles from the crustacean sinus gland. *J. Cellular Comp. Physiol.* 15:103–119.
19. Brown, F. A., Jr., and Wulff, V. J. 1941. Chromatophore types in *Crago* and their endocrine control. *J. Cellular Comp. Physiol.* 18:339–353.
20. Bullock, T. H., Nachmansohn, D., and Rothenberg, M. A. 1946. Effects of inhibitors of choline esterase on the nerve action potential. *J. Neurophysiol.* 9: 9–22.
21. Carlisle, D. B. 1953. Studies on *Lysmata seticaudata* Risso (Crustacea Decapoda). VI. Notes on the structure of the neurosecretory system of the eyestalk. *Pubbl. staz. zool. Napoli.* 24:435–447.
22. Carlisle, D. B. 1956. An indole-alkylamine regulating heart-beat in Crustacea. (Abstract.) *Biochem. J.* (*London*) 63:32.
23. Carlisle, D. B., and Knowles, F. G. W. 1953. Neurohaemal organs in crustaceans. *Nature* 172:404.
24. Carlisle, D. B., and Passano, L. M. 1953. The X-organ of Crustacea. *Nature* 171:1070.
25. Carlson, S. P. 1936. Color changes in Brachyura crustaceans, especially in *Uca pugilator*. *Kgl. Fysiograf. Sällskap. Lund Förh.* 6:1–18.
26. Carstam, S. P. 1951. Enzymatic inactivation of the pigment hormone of the crustacean sinus gland. *Nature* 167:321–322.
27. Chefurka, W., and Smallman, B. N. 1956. The occurrence of acetylcholine in the house-fly, *Musca domestica* L. *Can. J. Biochem. and Physiol.* 34:731–742.
28. Correale, P. 1956. The occurrence and distribution of 5-hydroxytryptamine (enteramine) in the central nervous system of vertebrates. *J. Neurochem.* 1: 22–31.
29. Corteggiani, E. 1938. Contribution à l'étude de l'acétylcholine libre et dissimulée sous forme d'un complexe dans le cerveau. 144 pp. Thesis, University of Paris.
30. Dahl, E. 1957. Embryology of *X* organs in *Crangon allmanni*. *Nature* 179:482.
31. Davenport, D. 1941. The effects of acetylcholine, atropine, and nicotine on the isolated heart of the commercial crab, *Cancer magister* Dana. *Physiol. Zoöl.* 14:178–185.
32. Davenport, D. 1942. Further studies in the pharmacology of the heart of *Cancer magister* Dana. *Biol. Bull.* 82:255–260.
33. del Castillo, J., and Katz, B. 1956. Biophysical aspects of neuro-muscular transmission. *In:* "Progress in Biophysics and Biophysical Chemistry" (J. A. V. Butler, ed.), Vol. VI, pp. 121–170. Pergamon Press, London.
34. Dethier, F. 1942. Cytological evidences for function in the sinus gland of the crayfish. 19 pp. Senior thesis, Radcliffe College, Cambridge, Massachusetts.

35. Durand, J. B. 1956. Neurosecretory cell types and their secretory activity in the crayfish. *Biol. Bull.* **111**:62–76.
36. Easton, D. M. 1950. Synthesis of acetylcholine in crustacean nerve and nerve extract. *J. Biol. Chem.* **185**:813–816.
37. Edman, P., Fänge, R., and Östlund, E. 1958. Isolation of the red pigment concentrating hormone of the crustacean eyestalk. *In:* "Zweites Internationales Symposium über Neurosekretion" (W. Bargmann, B. Hanström, and E. Scharrer, eds.), pp. 119–123. Springer, Berlin.
38. Edwards, C., and Kuffler, S. W. 1957. Inhibitory actions of gamma aminobutyric acid on an isolated nerve cell. *Federation Proc.* **16**:34.
39. Edwards, G. A., Ruska, H., and de Harven, E. 1958. Electron microscopy of peripheral nerves and neuromuscular junctions in the wasp leg. *J. Biophys. Biochem. Cytol.* **4**:107–114.
40. Elliott, K. A. C., and Florey, E. 1956. Factor I—inhibitory factor from brain. *J. Neurochem.* **1**:181–191.
41. Ellis, C. H., Thienes, C. H., and Wiersma, C. A. G. 1942. The influence of certain drugs on the crustacean nerve-muscle system. *Biol. Bull.* **83**:334–352.
42. Enami, M. 1951. The sources and activities of two chromatophorotropic hormones in crabs of the genus *Sesarma*. II. Histology of incretory elements. *Biol. Bull.* **101**:241–258.
43. Feldberg, W., and Mann, T. 1945. Formation of acetylcholine in cell-free extracts from brain. *J. Physiol. (London)* **104**:8–20.
44. Florey, E. 1951a. Neurohormone und Pharmakologie der Arthropoden. *Pflanzenschutz Ber.* **7**:81–141.
45. Florey, E. 1951b. Vorkommen und Funktion sensibler Erregungssubstanzen und sie abbauender Fermente im Tierreich. *Z. vergleich. Physiol.* **33**:327–377.
46. Florey, E. 1954a. Über die Wirkung von 5-Oxytryptamin (Enteramin) in der Krebsschere. *Z. Naturforsch.* **9b**:540–547.
47. Florey, E. 1954b. Über die Wirkung von Acetylcholin, Adrenalin, Nor-Adrenalin, Factor I und anderen Substanzen auf den isolierten Enddarm des Flusskrebses *Cambarus clarkii* Girard. *Z. vergleich. Physiol.* **36**:1–8.
48. Florey, E. 1954c. An inhibitory and an excitatory factor of mammalian central nervous system, and their action on a single sensory neuron. *Arch. intern. physiol.* **62**:33–53.
49. Florey, E. 1956. The action of factor I on certain invertebrate organs. *Can. J. Biochem. and Physiol.* **34**:669–681.
50. Florey, E., and Florey, E. 1954. Über die mögliche Bedeutung von Enteramin (5-Oxy-tryptamin) als nervöser Aktionssubstanz bei Cephalopoden und dekapoden Crustaceen. *Z. Naturforsch.* **9b**:58–68.
51. Gabe, M. 1952. Sur l'existence d'un cycle sécrétoire dans la glande du sinus (organe pseudofrontale) chez *Oniscus asellus* L. *Compt. rend.* **235**:900–902.
52. Gabe, M. 1954. La neuro-sécrétion chez les Invertebrés. *Année biol.* **30**:5–62.
53. Gomori, G. 1941. Observations with different stains on human islets of Langerhans. *Am. J. Pathol.* **17**:395–406.
54. Hanström, B. 1939. "Hormones in Invertebrates," 198 pp. Oxford Univ. Press, London and New York.
55. Hanström, B. 1947. The brain, the sense organs, and the incretory organs of the head in the Crustacea Malacostraca. *Kgl. Fysiograf. Sällskap. Lund, Handl.* [N.F.] **58**:3–44.

56. Hodge, M. H., and Chapman, G. B. 1958. Some observations on the fine struc-
    ture of the sinus gland of a land crab, *Gecarcinus lateralis. J. Biophys.
    Biochem. Cystol.* 4:571–574.
57. Jullien, A., and Vincent, D. 1938. Sur les esters de la choline et la cholin-
    estérase chez les Crustacés. *Compt. rend. soc. biol.* 129:845–848.
58. Katz, B. 1936. Neuro-muscular transmission in crabs. *J. Physiol. (London)* 87:
    199–221.
59. Knowles, F. G. W. 1953. Endocrine activity in the crustacean nervous system.
    Proc. Roy. Soc. B141:248–267.
60. Knowles, F. G. W., and Carlisle, D. B. 1956. Endocrine control in the Crustacea.
    Biol. Revs. Cambridge Phil. Soc. 31:396–473.
61. Knowles, F. G. W., Carlisle, D. B., and Dupont-Raabe, M. 1955. Studies on
    pigment-activating substances in animals. 1. The separation by paper electro-
    phoresis of chromactivating substances in arthropods. *J. Marine Biol. Assoc.
    United Kingdom* 34:611–635.
62. Knowles, F. G. W., Carlisle, D. B., and Dupont-Raabe, M. 1956. Inactivation
    enzymatique d'une substance chromactive des Insectes et des Crustacés. *Compt.
    rend.* 242:825.
63. Koch, H. J. 1954. Cholinesterase and active transport of sodium chloride
    through the isolated gills of the crab *Eriocheir sinensis* (M. Edw.). *In:* "Recent
    Developments in Cell Physiology" (J. A. Kitching, ed.), pp. 15–27. Butter-
    worths, London.
64. Krijgsman, B. J. 1952. Contractile and pacemaker mechanisms of the heart of
    arthropods. *Biol. Revs. Cambridge Phil. Soc.* 27:320–346.
65. Lewis, S. E., and Smallman, B. N. 1956. The estimation of acetylcholine in
    insects. *J. Physiol. (London)* 134:241–256.
66. Marnay, A., and Nachmansohn, D. 1937. Cholinestérase dans le nerf de
    homard. *Compt. rend. soc. biol.* 125:1005.
67. Matsumoto, K. 1954. Neurosecretion in the thoracic ganglion of the crab,
    Eriocheir japonicus. Biol. Bull. 106:60–68.
68. Matsumoto, K. 1956. Migration of the neurosecretory products in the thoracic
    ganglion of the crab, *Chionoectes opilio. Biol. J. Okayama Univ.* 2:137–146.
69. Maynard, D. M. 1955. Activity in a crustacean ganglion. II. Pattern and inter-
    action in burst formation. *Biol. Bull.* 109:420–436.
69a. Maynard, D. M., and Welsh, J. H. 1959. Neurohormones of the pericardial
    organs of brachyuran Crustacea. *J. Physiol. London* 149:215–227.
70. Nachmansohn, D., and Machado, A. L. 1943. The formation of acetylcholine.
    A new enzyme: "Choline acetylase." *J. Neurophysiol.* 6:397–403.
71. Östlund, E. 1954. The distribution of catechol amines in lower animals and
    their effect on the heart. *Acta Physiol. Scand.* 31, Suppl. 112:1–67.
72. Östlund, E., and Fänge, R. 1956. On the nature of the eye-stalk hormone
    which causes concentration of red pigment in shrimps (Natantia). *Ann. sci.
    nat. Zool. et biol. animale* 13:325–334.
73. Parameswaran, R. 1956. Neurosecretory cells of the central nervous system of
    the crab, *Paratelphusa hydrodromous. Quart. J. Microscop. Sci.* 97:75–82.
74. Passano, L. M. 1951. The x organ-sinus gland neurosecretory system in crabs.
    Anat. Record 111:86–87.
75. Passano, L. M. 1953. Neurosecretory control of molting in crabs by the x-organ
    sinus gland complex. *Physiol. Comparata et Oecol.* 3:155–189.

76. Passano, L. M. 1954. Phase microscopic observations of the neurosecretory product of the crustacean X-organ. *Pubbl. staz. zool. Napoli* **24,** Suppl. :72–73.

77. Pérez-González, M. D. 1957. Evidence for hormone-containing granules in sinus glands of the fiddler crab *Uca pugilator*. *Biol. Bull.* **113:**426–441.

78. Perkins, E. B. 1928. Color changes in crustaceans, especially in *Palaemonetes*. *J. Exptl. Zool.* **50:**71–105.

79. Perkins, E. B., and Snook, T. 1931. Control of pigment migration in the chromatophores of crustaceans. *Proc. Natl. Acad. Sci. U. S.* **17:**282–285.

80. Potter, D. D. 1954. Histology of the neurosecretory system of the blue crab, *Callinectes sapidus*. *Anat. Record* **120:**716.

81. Potter, D. D. 1956. Observations on the neurosecretory system of portunid crabs. 267 pp. Ph.D. Thesis, Harvard University.

82. Prosser, C. L. 1934. Action potentials in the nervous system of the crayfish. I. Spontaneous impulses. *J. Cellular Comp. Physiol.* **4:**185–209.

83. Prosser, C. L. 1940. Action potentials in the nervous system of the crayfish. Effects of drugs and salts upon synaptic transmission. *J. Cellular Comp. Physiol.* **16:**25–38.

84. Prosser, C. L. 1942. An analysis of the action of acetylcholine on hearts, particularly in arthropods. *Biol. Bull.* **83:**145–164.

85. Prosser, C. L. 1946. The physiology of nervous systems of invertebrate animals. *Physiol. Revs.* **26:**337–382.

86. Pyle, R. W. 1943. The histogenesis and cyclic phenomena of the sinus gland and X-organ in Crustacea. *Biol. Bull.* **85:**87–102.

86a. Rehm, M. 1959. Observations on the localization and chemical constitution of neurosecretory material in nerve terminals of *Carcinus maenas*. *Acta Histochem.* **7:**88–106.

87. Roeder, K. D., and Roeder, S. 1939. Electrical activity in the isolated ventral nerve cord of the cockroach. I. The action of pilocarpine, nicotine, eserine and acetylcholine. *J. Cellular Comp. Physiol.* **14:**1–12.

88. Sawaya, P. 1943. Sôbre a ocorrência da acetilcolina no tecido cardíaco de *Callinectes danae* Smith e seu efeito sôbre o coraçâo dêste Crustáceo Decápodo. *Univ. São Paulo Fac. filosof. ciênc. e letras, Zool.* No. **7:**261–304.

89. Schallek, W. 1945. Action of potassium on bound acetylcholine in lobster nerve cord. *J. Cellular Comp. Physiol.* **26:**15–24.

90. Schallek, W., and Wiersma, C. A. G. 1948. The influence of various drugs on a crustacean synapse. *J. Cellular Comp. Physiol.* **31:**35–47.

91. Schallek, W., and Wiersma, C. A. G. 1949. Effects of anti-cholinesterases on synaptic transmission in the crayfish. *Physiol. Comparata et Oecol.* **1:**63–67.

92. Schallek, W., Wiersma, C. A. G., and Alles, G. A. 1948. Blocking and protecting actions of amines and ammonium compounds on a crustacean synapse. *Proc. Soc. Exptl. Biol. Med.* **68:**174–178.

93. Scharrer, E., and Scharrer, B. 1954a. Hormones produced by neurosecretory cells. *Recent Progr. Hormone Research* **10:**183–240.

94. Scharrer, E., and Scharrer, B. 1954b. Neurosekretion. *In:* "Handbuch der mikroskopischen Anatomie des Menschen" (W. Bargmann, ed.), Vol. VI, pp. 953–1066. Springer, Berlin.

95. Sloper, J. C. 1955. Hypothalamic neurosecretion in the dog and cat, with particular reference to the identification of neurosecretory material with posterior lobe hormone. *J. Anat.* **89:**301–316.

96. Sloper, J. C. 1957. Presence of a substance rich in protein-bound cystine or cysteine in the neurosecretory system of an insect. *Nature* **179**:148–149.

97. Smallman, B. N. 1956. Mechanisms of acetylcholine synthesis in the blowfly. *J. Physiol. (London)* **132**:343–357.

98. Smith, R. I. 1939. Acetylcholine in the nervous tissues and blood of crayfish. *J. Cellular Comp. Physiol.* **13**:335–344.

99. Smith, R. I. 1947. The action of electrical stimulation and of certain drugs on cardiac nerves of the crab, *Cancer irroratus. Biol. Bull.* **93**:72–88.

100. Stephens, G. C., Friedl, F., and Guttman, B. 1956. Electrophoretic separation of chromatophorotropic principles of the fiddler crab, *Uca. Biol. Bull.* **111**:312.

101. Turner, R. S., Hagins, W. A., and Moore, A. R. 1950. Influence of certain neurotropic substances on central and synaptic transmission in *Callianassa. Proc. Soc. Exptl. Biol. Med.* **73**:156–158.

102. Twarog, B. M., and Roeder, K. D. 1956. Properties of the connective tissue sheath of the cockroach abdominal nerve cord. *Biol. Bull.* **111**:278–286.

103. Twarog, B. M., and Roeder, K. D. 1957. Pharmacological observations on the desheathed last abdominal ganglion of the cockroach. *Ann. Entomol. Soc. Am.* **50**:231–237.

104. van der Kloot, W. G. 1955. The control of neurosecretion and diapause by physiological changes in the brain of the Cecropia silkworm. *Biol. Bull.* **109**: 276–294.

105. van der Kloot, W. G., Robbins, J., and Cooke, I. M. 1958. Blocking by picro-toxin of peripheral inhibition in crayfish. *Science* **127**:521–522.

106. Walop, J. N. 1950. Acetylcholine formation in the central nervous system of *Carcinus maenas. Acta Physiol. et Pharmacol. Neerl.* **1**:333–335.

107. Walop, J. N. 1951. Studies on acetylcholine in the crustacean central nervous system. *Arch. intern. physiol.* **59**:145–156.

108. Walop, J. N., and Boot, L. M. 1950. Studies on cholinesterase in *Carcinus maenas. Biochim. et Biophys. Acta* **4**:566–571.

109. Waterman, T. H. 1941. A comparative study of the effects of ions on whole nerve and isolated single nerve fiber preparations of crustacean neuromuscular systems. *J. Cellular Comp. Physiol.* **18**:109–126.

110. Welsh, J. H. 1939a. Chemical mediation in crustaceans. I. The occurrence of acetylcholine in nervous tissues and its action on the decapod heart. *J. Exptl. Biol.* **16**:198–219.

111. Welsh, J. H. 1939b. Chemical mediation in crustaceans. II. The action of acetylcholine and adrenalin on the isolated heart of *Panulirus argus. Physiol. Zoöl.* **12**:231–237.

112. Welsh, J. H. 1942. Chemical mediation in crustaceans. IV. The action of acetylcholine on isolated hearts of *Homarus* and *Carcinides. J. Cellular Comp. Physiol.* **19**:271–279.

113. Welsh, J. H. 1953. Excitation of the heart of *Venus mercenaria. Arch. exptl. Pathol. Pharmakol. Naunyn-Schmiedeberg's* **219**:23–29.

114. Welsh, J. H. 1955. Neurohormones. *In:* "The Hormones" (G. Pincus and K. V. Thimann, eds.), Vol. III, pp. 97–151. Academic Press, New York.

115. Welsh, J. H. 1957. Serotonin as a possible neurohumoral agent: Evidence obtained in lower animals. *Ann. N. Y. Acad. Sci.* **66**:618–630.

116. Welsh, J. H., and Gordon, H. T. 1947. The mode of action of certain insecticides on the arthropod nerve axon. *J. Cellular Comp. Physiol.* **30**:147–171.

117. Welsh, J. H., and Haskin, H. H. 1939. Chemical mediation in crustaceans. III. Acetylcholine and autotomy in *Petrolisthes armatus* (Gibbs). *Biol. Bull.* 76: 405–415.
118. Wiersma, C. A. G. 1947. Giant nerve fiber system of the crayfish. A contribution to comparative physiology of synapse. *J. Neurophysiol.* 10:23–38.
119. Wiersma, C. A. G. 1949. Synaptic facilitation in the crayfish. *J. Neurophysiol.* 12:267–275.
120. Wiersma, C. A. G., Furshpan, E., and Florey, E. 1953. Physiological and pharmacological observations on muscle receptor organs of the crayfish, *Cambarus clarkii* Girard. *J. Exptl. Biol.* 30:136–150.
121. Wiersma, C. A. G., and Novitski, E. 1942. The mechanism of the nervous regulation of the crayfish heart. *J. Exptl. Biol.* 19:255–265.
122. Willey, R. B., and Chapman, G. B. 1960. The ultra structure of certain components of the corpora cardiaca in orthopteroid insects. *J. Ultrastruct. Research.* 4:1.
123. Wolfe, L. S., and Smallman, B. N. 1956. The properties of cholinesterase from insects. *J. Cellular Comp. Physiol.* 48:215–235.

CHAPTER 9

JOHN H. LOCHHEAD

LOCOMOTION

I. *INTRODUCTION*

The efficiency and variety of crustacean locomotion are conspicuous. Perhaps every type of locomotion, except free flight, is to be found in at least some crustacean; often there are several types in a single species. For example, *Talorchestia longicornis,* an amphipod living on sandy beaches, can run, jump, climb, and burrow with great skill, and is able to swim if necessary.[141] When the development of the species includes a series of larval stages, striking changes in the methods of locomotion may occur between one instar and the next. These changes often involve not only questions of mechanics, but also patterns of central nervous regulation and responses related to body orientation. The swimming crab *Macropipus,** for instance, hatches as a zoea, which swims with its dorsal surface first by means of exopodites on the maxillipeds.[43] The megalops swims forward with the pleopods and walks sideways by means of four pairs of legs. The adult crab swims sideways by the use of paddles on its last pair of legs.[130]

Crustacean evolution has been closely tied in with adaptations for locomotion, which have to a large extent determined the form of the body and of the appendages. Obviously, such adaptations were always limited by whatever parts or functional mechanisms were available at any particular stage of evolution. Although early investigators tended to assume that the arthropod appendage developed from annelid parapodia, such lateral parapodia, stiffened by acicula, now scarcely seem a likely origin for the ventrolateral legs of simple arthropods.[103,144]

---

* See footnote, p. 341.

The latter have certain important features not found in annelids, notably an ability to shorten extrinsic limb muscles in the middle of each propulsive stroke, a jointed exoskeleton to which both extrinsic and intrinsic muscles are attached, and distinctly striated muscle fibers.[103]

The controversial and speculative question of whether the primitive crustacean limb was monopodial, biramous, or even phyllopodial is briefly discussed in Chapter 1, Vol. I. Presumably the successive pairs of legs were all alike in the earliest crustaceans, as indeed they are in many Branchiopoda. There has, however, been a tendency for the more anterior and posterior appendages to become specialized in various ways, leaving to the central ones the function of walking. Among living Malacostraca, the most primitive species generally have a shrimplike form, adapted for swimming. Their ancestors, however, are thought to have been bottom-living animals, and indeed the division of the trunk into thorax and abdomen probably arose as an adaptation for walking.[103]

Many Malacostraca have secondarily returned to a bottom-living habit.[16,31] Some of these forms have in their turn reacquired an ability to swim.[130] Similar evolutionary series are found among entomostracans, notably in the Cladocera.[37] Adaptive radiation in other directions, such as for burrowing, climbing, and jumping, has also occurred repeatedly. Although nearly all Crustacea are aquatic, terrestrial locomotion has been developed in a number of quite separate groups.[49,54,136]

II. GENERAL FEATURES

A. BIOMECHANICS

1. *Modifications of the exoskeleton.* In some crustacean appendages, such as phyllopodia, the cuticle is everywhere flexible. In most cases, however, the appendage consists of more or less rigid exoskeletal segments, flexibly connected at the joints by the cuticular arthrodial membrane. Mechanically, then, the crustacean appendage comprises a jointed system of hollow levers moved by internal muscles. The direction and freedom of movement at each joint is determined by the extent and physical properties of the arthrodial membrane and by the shapes of the opposing exoskeletal parts, which may have definite bearing surfaces, restraining grooves and ridges, or other special modifications. Simple hinge joints, often with two pairs of bearing surfaces, approximately 180° apart,[84] occur most frequently, but in some cases the joint also permits some rotation.[78] More complex

arrangements, analogous to a vertebrate ball-and-socket joint, though rather less efficient, sometimes occur, as, for example, between the coxa and basis in an isopod walking leg.[153] The same degree of freedom of movement for the limb as a whole is more often provided by a series of hinge joints, with their axes oriented at different angles.[84] Fusions between joints, both in appendages and in the body, have played an important part in the evolution of locomotor adaptations.

The functional mechanics of the exoskeleton are discussed further in Chapter 14, Vol. I.

2. *Arrangement of muscles.* The muscles of crustacean appendages (Fig. 1) have their origins usually on fairly extensive areas of

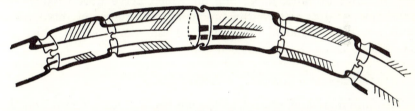

FIG. 1. Segments of a brachyuran limb showing diagrammatically the type of joints and the arrangement of muscles. Distal end toward the left. Note that insertions and origins of muscles lie on the same side of the limb; also that because of mechanical relations the positions of extensors and flexors with respect to the direction of bending are the same as in the endoskeletal joints of vertebrates. (From Schäfer.[130])

the exoskeleton or endoskeleton. Typically each inserts by a tendon, either on the distal border of an arthrodial membrane or on a condyle of the exoskeleton at the proximal end of a segment.[10,25,72,84,130,153] The muscle fibers typically have a pinnate arrangement, converging on the tendon in one or more planes. A curious spiral twisting of the muscle fibers and their bundles is a notable feature of some of the abdominal extensor and flexor muscles in the Malacostraca.[27,47] The mechanical advantages of this arrangement are not known.

3. *Influence of turgor and molting.* Flexion at crustacean joints is much influenced by internal turgor. If this is too high, the body and the appendages become stiff and almost incapable of movement[114]; if turgor is too low, parts with a flexible cuticle, such as phyllopodia, collapse.[149] Increased turgor after molting gives the appendages of some large crustaceans just enough rigidity to be used for locomotion despite the temporarily soft cuticle. But some large species, such as crayfish and lobsters, can then use their legs only like oars flat on the

substratum.[77] Small forms and larvae usually can continue normal locomotion almost immediately after a molt. In isopods the situation is peculiar because the posterior half of the body molts some days before the anterior half, which temporarily leaves a large species with only the most anterior walking legs available for locomotion.[153]

4. *Characteristics of muscle.* The skeletal muscle fibers of Crustacea are all cross-striated and have very little sarcoplasm. In general the striations are closer together, and therefore more numerous, the faster the potential contraction rate.[17,159] Maximal speeds of contraction fall somewhat below those recorded for the faster muscles in insects and vertebrates. Fibers with multiple motor innervation can contract at different rates, depending on which nerve fiber supplies the stimulation. Unfortunately, the functional importance of this kind of motor innervation and of the peripheral inhibitory system which accompanies it is not well understood (Chapter 6).

B. INTEGRATION AND CONTROL OF LOCOMOTION

The initiation and control of locomotion obviously depend on the coordinating and sensory elements concerned. The ultimate problem of whether the movement patterns established arise mainly as chains of reflexes or as a centrally determined series of responses reflexly adjusted has not been critically studied in Crustacea. However, considerable information on certain of the controlling elements in their locomotion is available.

1. *Neuromuscular factors.* The crustacean neuromuscular system, which is mainly known from studies on decapod legs, differs in many significant ways from the more familiar vertebrate case (Chapter 6); some of these peculiarities are of special importance for locomotion. To begin with, there are no motor units in the classic sense since contraction of a decapod muscle apparently always involves all of its fibers and the whole muscle never receives more than five motor axons. Consequently the rate and strength with which these structures exert tension must be controlled almost entirely by other mechanisms than the recruitment of motor units. These mechanisms essentially are the peripheral processes of facilitation and inhibition.

Although certain muscles like the claw closer of the crayfish respond rapidly and strongly to a single motor impulse, facilitation at the neuromuscular junction is usually highly developed. In general, frequency and number of motor spikes markedly affect the speed and amplitude of the resultant muscle response. Furthermore, the muscle reacts differently to impulses in various axons of its polyneuronal innervation, which thus may provide a means of response regulation. For example, in the crayfish claw closer, referred to above, a single impulse in its fast motor fiber suffices for a strong, quick twitch; the slow fiber in contrast requires a barrage of impulses to produce any mechanical response, which even then is a slow, tonic contraction. This is an extreme case; mechanical differences between responses to the several motor axons are usually less marked. In some cases the multiple innervation may be an adaptation to obviate fatigue at the neuromuscular junction by rotating activity from one set of axon terminals to another. This notion is consonant with the fact that the weight-sustaining postural muscles at the base of the legs have the largest number of motor axons (four).

Also important is the peripheral inhibition induced by impulses in special efferent axons. This inhibition may reduce or prevent contraction in a particular muscle and can accelerate the relaxation of a sustained tonus. While the potential significance of this negative control is obvious for locomotion, its actual application is less so. The distribution of inhibitory fibers cannot be related in a simple way to such functions as reciprocal inhibition, so that central inhibition may have to supplement the peripheral kind during normal movements (Chapter 6).

2. *Central nervous regulation.* The central nervous system of crustaceans, as exemplified by the crayfish, possesses several fundamental distinctions from a system like that of the vertebrates (Chapter 7). Most striking are the paucity of interneurons, the extensive multiple peripheral connections, and the functional complexity of the intercellular junctions. Undoubtedly these features all have important consequences for locomotor control, but in what ways is not at present known. However, many data are available on the locomotor results of severing or removing specific elements in the crustacean central nervous system.[3,124] Unfortunately, the interpretation of such operative effects usually cannot be rigorous, and their normal significance in locomotion often remains uncertain. Obviously, too, the wide variety of the Crustacea and of their locomotor patterns requires extensive information for adequate understanding.

In general, single intact segments can carry out quite complex appendage movements. Thus, in the amphipod *Ampithoe* the pleopods continue to beat rhythmically on a completely isolated abdominal segment.[68] The fifth pleopods of the penaeid *Sicyonia* beat reflexly on stimulation after the abdominal cord has been isolated, but more anterior swimmerets have increasingly high thresholds.[107] Thoracic legs also may show complex movements when they are connected merely to thoracic ganglia (*Artemia*,[109] *Branchipus*,[109] *Astacus*[11]). Series of segments in certain cases show coordinated movements in the absence of more anterior ("higher") centers. Thus in *Triops cancriformis*, cutting the ventral nerve cord yields, after recovery from the operation, two series of trunk limbs beating metachronally but independently.[104] Here the pacemaker for the successive leg movements is in the most posterior segment of a series, an inversion of the more usual situation where more anterior elements dominate.

Evidence is widespread for the latter condition where ganglia anterior to the region being coordinated are essential. For example, in *Astacus* the first abdominal ganglion is required to maintain the strength and frequency of more posterior pleopod beats.[11] Similarly thoracic ganglia may be needed (*Squilla*[11,106]) or accessory (*Sicyonia*,[107] *Astacus*[11]) in initiating and coordinating pleopod movements. Preabdominal ganglia must be intact also for low threshold (*Astacus*) or repeated (*Squilla*) beats of the tail fan.[11] Correspondingly the subesophageal ganglion initiates and modulates certain locomotor activities in the thorax and perhaps in the abdomen of some forms. Thus rhythmic coordination of the thoracic legs during forward locomotion is lost in *Artemia*,[109] *Branchipus*,[109] *Astacus*,[11] and *Carcinus*[12] when the subesophageal ganglion is severed from the thoracic ventral cord. Spontaneity of walking (*Squilla*) and abdominal reflex facilitation (*Astacus*) may also depend on connections to this ganglion.[11]

A variety of locomotor controls on more posterior segments has been described as well for the brain, or supraesophageal ganglion. Thus alterations in leg muscle tonus (*Astacus*,[11,66] *Carcinus*,[12] *Macropipus*,[66] *Squilla*[11]) and chronaxie (*Crangon*[159]) occur on its partial or total removal. Both facilitating and inhibiting effects are also known. In the former category, forward walking (*Astacus*), pleopod beat, and swimming with the tail fan (*Squilla*) are no longer spontaneous in the absence of impulses from the brain.[11] More drastic effects occur, too, where specific kinds of locomotion are impossible without the brain (walking sideways in *Carcinus*,*[12] *Eriocheir*,[66] and *Macropipus*[66]; swimming in *Macropipus*[66]). Inhibitory influences of the brain, perhaps originating in the optic ganglia,[132] also affect the movement of *Sicyonia*,[107] crayfish,[11,66,132] *Homarus*,[124] *Palinurus*,[124] and *Macropipus*.[66] The highly complex nature of the actual relations existing here is suggested by the apparently contradictory effects observed.

---

* Forward walking is possible in this crab without the brain.

Although this discussion is limited to longitudinal coordination, transverse effects coordinating the two sides of the animal's movement are also known (Chapter 7).[11,12,123]

Spontaneous activity apparently occurs all the time in crustacean ganglia (Chapter 7), but little is known about the relation of this to the possible pacemakers for locomotor patterns. Sometimes different sets of appendages have the same rhythm, as in the thoracic exopodites and pleopods of the bathypelagic shrimp *Acanthephyra*[34]; this suggests a common pacemaker. However, experiments suggest that separate centers control the apparently similar rhythms of the heart and swimming appendages in the anostracan *Tanymastix*[113] and that there is separate control of these rhythms and of the ventilation beats in *Daphnia*.[39,46,145]

3. *Sensory components.* Most of the known nervous regulation of crustacean locomotion probably is of sensory origin. Thus the rhythmic stepping movement of *Carcinus* pereiopods while walking, is dependent on each leg's making contact with the substrate. Erratic leg movement results when the crab is suspended in air by a thread.[76] However, in the anomuran *Birgus* the controlling mechanism would appear to be different, since the reduced fourth pereiopods of the young are said to share in the walking rhythm before they have become long enough to reach the ground.[56] Furthermore, organized swimming movements of the appendages in the swimming crab *Macropipus* are actually induced by loss of contact with the substratum.[78] The stumps of autotomized legs behave differently in this animal when walking and when swimming. In walking, each stump is held motionless, as is any leg in other crabs which does not make contact with the substratum, but in swimming, such stumps participate in the regular swimming pattern. In general, the rate of beat of the swimming legs in this crab is related to the resistance to movement which they encounter, although results differ concerning the contralateral effects of an experimental increase or decrease in this resistance on one side.[78,130] The normal, propellerlike movements of these swimming paddles (fifth pereiopods) depend on a sensory inflow from their fringe of feathery mechanoreceptor setae; shaving off the latter results in completely disoriented limb action.[130] A somewhat similar regulatory function is apparently subserved by sensory setae in Cladocera[122] and *Acanthephyra*,[34] but such setae are lacking on the swimming paddles of the crab *Matuta* which may be used more like oars.[130]

Various other sense organs are known to affect the rhythmic and tonic components of walking in decapods. Particularly significant are the statocysts, as are their analogs in the vertebrates. Statocyst damage in *Palaemon*,[34] *Carcinus*,[12] and other Decapoda leads to tonus alterations in the appendages and consequent effects on locomotion. Presumably the tonic discharge of impulses by these sense organs is involved (Chapters 2, 13). Clearly it is important in all such work where localized areas are made inoperative or removed that primary effects are distinguished from those due merely to interruption of other transmission pathways. This was done in much of Bethe's classic work[12] on *Carcinus*, but not frequently in other cases.

4. *Plasticity*. A high degree of plasticity is often inherent in the nervous regulation of normal crustacean locomotion. However, this feature is most clearly seen after various limbs have been amputated or otherwise rendered ineffective. Then, if plasticity is well developed, the remaining limbs at once adopt a different gait or other modified form of movement, usually one appropriate for the maintenance of locomotory efficiency. The varying degrees of such plasticity observed in different Crustacea might be related to the substrate roughness normally encountered,[4] but the well-developed plasticity in swimming portunid crabs[78] seems inconsistent with this notion.

In *Carcinus* each of many combinations of leg amputations tested evoked adaptive changes in the crab's mode of walking (254 possibilities were calculated for removing one or more of the eight walking legs, always leaving at least one).[13] For *Astacus*, von Holst reports that locomotor plasticity is similar to that which he studied quantitatively in insects and centipedes.[164] Here the variation in phase differences between two successive legs was analyzed under various conditions. The range of variation, and often the position of the mode, were found to change when the animal had to walk on a steep or rough surface, or when other legs were amputated, even though they were at a distance from the two being studied. It seems unlikely, particularly in view of the few interneurons in crustacean central nervous systems, that the observed versatile locomotor adaptability depends on pre-existing specific neuronal arcs.[13] Von Holst concludes that the degree of central coupling can vary, and that coordination is of a shifting type involving inherent frequencies and coupling factors responsive to the sensory input.[164,165] A similar shifting type of coordination was reported for fishes, but not for the earthworm or for medusae. In mammals comparable plasticity appears to be quite limited.[147]

Further study should be directed toward clarifying the reasons for such considerable differences. Probably the marked functional distinctions between the central nervous systems of crustaceans and vertebrates dictate locomotor regulation by different means in the two cases. A suggested neural mechanism for the decapod crustacean case is presented in Chapter 7.

5. *Factors influencing the rate of locomotion.* The rate of locomotion in crustaceans is proportional to the temperature. In aquatic species an increase in this rate results partly from a higher metabolic rate, partly from a decreased viscosity of the water. For the rate of limb beat in the anostracan *Tanymastix*, the Q_{10} for each of these two effects was found to be the same, namely, 1.23, the total Q_{10} being 1.51 ($= 1.23^2$), within the animal's optimal temperature range.[113] This identity suggested that perhaps protoplasmic viscosity is limiting metabolism by establishing the rates at which materials move through cells, but certainly the rates of metabolic reactions are affected, too. A critical point in the relation between speed of swimming and temperature appears as a break in the curve at 18.5°C for the zoea of the crab *Pinnotheres*.[171] The possible involvement of rate-limiting reactions in such phenomena is mentioned in Chapter 8.

Locomotor responses to changes of temperature may sometimes be so slow that acclimation (Chapter 12, Vol. I) would seem to be involved. Thus when *Daphnia*, kept for two months at 5–7°C, were transferred to 25°C, and vice versa, several days elapsed before their antennae had accelerated or slowed to the frequency characteristic for the other temperature.[94] However, nutritional differences between the two cultures may have influenced this result.

The rate of locomotion of many crustaceans is proportional to the light intensity and may also be influenced by the wavelength.[9] The receptor aspects of this photokinesis are discussed in Chapter 1 and the responses themselves in Chapter 10. According to some investigators the speed of locomotion and a diurnal rhythm in locomotory activity are controlled in decapods by a hormone from the eyestalks, but the results obtained thus far are contradictory.[35,158]

Variations in the load carried, or in the shape and size of the body, might be expected to influence the rate of locomotion. An interesting natural example of this effect occurs in *Daphnia magna*; its antennae beat at a higher frequency the greater the number of eggs or embryos present in the brood pouch.[42] The effective factor in this case appears to be the posterior displacement of the center of gravity, rather than any change in total specific gravity, body size, or state of nutrition.

III. *TYPES OF LOCOMOTION*

A. WALKING AND RUNNING

1. *Methods of study.* The rhythms and gaits employed in walking by various terrestrial arthropods have recently been studied in detail by Manton,[101] using photography, cinematography, and records of the tracks left on smoked paper. She refers to crustaceans only briefly.[101,103] Other investigators have published more detailed studies of crustacean walking, but have not used adequate methods. Cinematography when tried has been at speeds too slow to yield sharp pictures.[13,66] Tracks have been recorded only rarely and with insufficient detail.[12,84] Most studies have been concerned with the mechanics of individual limb action, merely inferred from the anatomy and from visual observations. Similar methods have been used in the study of limb movements after operations on the appendages and the nervous system. Unfortunately, the movements of crustacean limbs are in most cases too rapid, too complex, and too variable to be adequately recorded by such means.

2. *Mechanics.* The jointed legs of crustaceans permit a wide variety of stance and of movement. Ostracods and some others stand upright. In many Peracarida the walking endopodites slant lateroventrally, affording a wide base of support.[152] Isopods have developed a half-hanging stance,[101] highly adapted for clinging.[152] Most decapods hang from their legs in a fashion that gives maximum stability against being upset.[101] In *Astacus,* which typifies this stance, the segments of a single leg all lie in approximately one plane, and the planes of all the legs are inclined so as to intersect close to the animal's center of gravity.[4]

As it swings to and fro, a crustacean walking leg often executes rather complex movements. Usually it is flexed at several joints near the middle of its swing, while at either end of the swing the leg may be fully extended, thus utilizing the maximum possible stride. During its forward movement a leg may be raised and sufficiently flexed to avoid the necessity of swinging out to the side. If successive legs overlap, precise stepping is needed to prevent collisions.[101] When two overlapping legs are both in their propulsive stroke, they form a triangle with the body, which would become locked in position if it were not for the flexibility of the legs at their joints. Orientation of the body is maintained by complex autoregulation of the angles between the segments of all the legs. *Astacus* always keeps the sagittal plane of its body vertical, and the longitudinal axis parallel to the substratum.[4] The isopod *Ligia* keeps its entire frontal plane parallel to the substratum, regardless of the pull of gravity.[153]

The propulsive action of individual legs varies with the position of the leg on the body. Posterior legs mostly push, anterior legs chiefly pull, intermediate pairs of legs may first pull and then push. Details of the mechanical action have been studied in a number of crustaceans, often with conflicting results, as in the crayfish for example, where the three major accounts all differ from each other.[4,84,161] According to the most recent of these,[4] an adult *Astacus* may walk slowly with great plasticity, or rapidly in a more fixed rhythm. During rhythmic walking, the fourth or last legs push the animal forward by a scissor-opening type of action. The third legs first of all pull, then "row," and finally push. The second legs pull, and play an important part in steering. The first legs may either only pull or, like the third legs, pull, row, and push. During a turn, one first leg may pull while the other pushes. Pulling, by any one of the first three legs, is accomplished by a scissor-closing type of action. Both rowing and pushing, by a first or a third leg, are achieved mainly by the action of the distal three segments, which swing like a pendulum from the merocarpal joint. Evidently such complex actions almost defy description, and indeed the difficulties at times may confuse the describer, as inconsistencies in Baldi's account attest.

In many crustaceans the walking legs are assisted by the action of some additional appendages which may create a current similar to that used in swimming, but less powerful. Among Malacostraca, the pleopods are often used in this way as are the thoracic exopodites in various mysids,[180] the swimming paddles in portunid crabs when walking sideways,[78] the posterior trunk limbs in Notostraca,[86] and the antennae in certain Cladocera, such as *Leydigiopsis*.[129] In some cases other appendages may provide assistance to the walking legs by pushing or pulling. Thus in gammarids, when walking upright, the gnathopods may sometimes pull and the uropods push.[120] Many ostracods and some Cladocera, such as *Alona* and *Ophryoxus*, may push with the caudal furca.[111] Other Cladocera, such as *Streblocerus*[149] and *Drepanothrix*,[111] use special setae on the proximal segments of the antennae for the same purpose. Ostracods may balance with the antennules, as in *Candona*,[73] or use them to clear away debris from in front, as in *Darwinula*.[111]

In some tiny Crustacea, such as harpacticoid copepods,[146] and various other forms adapted to living between grains of sand,[127] walking is accompanied by lateral undulations of the body. Such undulations are generally absent in larger species, with some consequent saving in energy expenditure.[101]

3. Rhythms and gaits for walking forward

a. *General considerations.* The gaits employed by crustaceans may vary in the amplitude of swing of the legs, the forestroke:backstroke ratio, the phase difference between successive legs on one side, the phase difference between the appendages of each pair, and the number of limbs used. During the propulsive and supporting phase of its beat (the so-called backstroke), a leg swings backward relative to the body, but forward relative to the substratum. The relative durations of the fore- and backstrokes can vary, and the ratio between the two determines the average number of legs which are propulsive.

Characteristically, the legs are swung in a metachronal rhythm. The phase difference between successive legs establishes the number of legs in each wave and is generally expressed as that fraction of a whole beat by which one leg is ahead of the leg immediately in front. Accordingly, when the phase difference is said to be 0.7, the leg in front is 0.3 of a beat ahead of the leg behind. When the phase difference between successive legs is less than 0.5, the metachronal waves appear to pass forward, and successive propulsive legs diverge from each other. When the phase difference between successive legs is more than 0.5, the waves appear to pass backward, and successive propulsive legs converge.[101] No convention exists as to which leg of each pair should be considered first, so that their phase differences are always equal to or less than 0.5.

Although the total number of gaits theoretically possible for crustaceans is very great, certain practical requirements sharply limit the number actually employed.[101,103] According to Manton's useful analysis, a gait in order to be reasonably practical should do the following: 1) avoid excessive overlap between legs; 2) provide continuous, well-balanced support for the body; 3) keep the number of propulsive legs approximately constant; 4) keep the animal poised for sudden shifts in speed or direction; 5) provide power suitably geared for the job to be done; 6) avoid excessive lateral or dorsoventral twisting action on the body; 7) correlate appropriately with the number of legs that are available.

Some of these factors are discussed briefly in the following paragraphs.

b. *Overlap between legs.* Legs may overlap during the backstroke, during the forestroke, or when swinging in opposite directions.

Among terrestrial arthropods any overlap during the backstroke is notably slight or absent.[101] This finding fits in with the fact, pointed out earlier, that overlapping propulsive legs would tend to lock the body position. The amount of overlap between legs can be reduced or eliminated in several ways, such as: suitable spacing or disposition of the legs; shortening of their length; reducing their swing; choice of a suitable phase difference between successive legs; and selection of an appropriate forestroke:backstroke ratio. A study of Fig. 2 will help to clarify some of the effects of the last three of these factors.

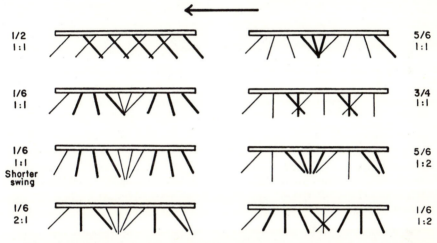

Fig. 2. Examples of gaits theoretically possible for an animal with ten pairs of legs, at various phase differences, angles of swing, and forestroke:backstroke ratios. Legs in the backstroke drawn thicker than the others. Legs at the posterior point of their swing regarded as still in the backstroke; those at the anterior point of their swing regarded as still in the forestroke. The arrow at the top represents the direction of locomotion.

c. *Body support.* During walking, the legs must provide support, either to prevent sagging of the body between jointed segments, or to maintain balance about the center of gravity if the body segments are fused. Some of the ways in which the distribution of support can vary in different gaits may be seen in Fig. 2. Note that maximum support is provided when the phase difference between successive legs is less than 0.5 and when the backstroke is of relatively long duration. An important part is also played by the phase difference between the legs of each pair.

d. *Number of propulsive legs.* If the number of propulsive legs is to be kept constant, a proper relationship is necessary between the number of legs, the phase difference between successive legs, and the forestroke:backstroke ratio. Sometimes a suitable phase difference between the legs of each pair will also be required.

For example, in a crustacean with three pairs of legs, walking with a phase difference of one third between successive pairs of legs, and a forestroke:backstroke ratio of 1:2, the number of legs in active propulsion is four ($\frac{2}{3}$ of the total) at all phases of the gait. In actual practice the phase difference between successive legs might be, say, $\frac{11}{30}$, thereby ensuring that each leg would be put down just before the lifting of the leg in front. Then the number of propulsive legs could no

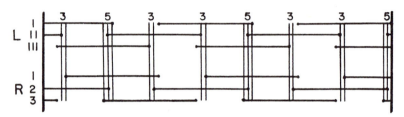

Fig. 3. Hypothetical gait for an animal with three pairs of legs. Horizontal lines indicate durations of propulsive strokes for each leg. Figures at the top indicate the number of propulsive legs whenever this number is not four. Forestroke:backstroke ratio, 1:2. Phase differences, $\frac{11}{30}$ between successive legs, $\frac{1}{3}$ between the legs of each pair.

longer be quite constant, and to keep the number as uniform as possible would require adjustment of the phase difference between the legs of each pair; in this particular case a value of one third appears to be the most favorable (Fig. 3).

e. *Speed versus pushing power.*   Most crustaceans live in water, which offers considerable resistance to their movements. The isopod *Ligia* when on land runs with exactly the same gait that it uses under water, but the pace duration is much shorter and the speed correspondingly greater.[101]

The speed at which a crustacean walks or runs depends not only on the duration of each entire pace, but also on the relative duration of the backstroke, the lengths of the legs, and the angular extent of swing. Manton has likened the various forestroke:backstroke ratios to a series of gears, using the term "middle gear" when the ratio is 1:1, and the terms "low gear" and "high gear" when the relative duration of the backstroke is longer or shorter. The concept of gears can also be applied to variations in leg length, the gear being higher when the legs are longer.

The extent to which higher gears can be utilized by an arthropod for the attainment of speed will depend on the amount of resistance to be overcome while walking. It seems probable that no crustacean walking under water will be found to employ a very high gear. Species which must push through mud or over a rough substratum, or which often climb steep slopes, presumably will be found to employ low gears.

f. *Number of legs.* Most crustaceans use two to seven pairs of legs for walking. Two pairs are used by many Ostracoda, Paguridea, and the brachyuran Dorippidae and Goneplacidae, while seven pairs are used by many Syncarida and Peracarida. Exceptions include *Anaspides*, which may use for walking seven pairs of thoracic legs plus up to five pairs of pleopods[100]; Notostraca, which may walk mainly with the anterior eleven of their many pairs of legs[86]; and the cyprid larvae of barnacles, which walk by means of their antennules alone,[79] being perhaps the only bipedal arthropods.

When the number of walking legs is reduced to five pairs or less, they can be longer, well fanned out, and sometimes of different length, so that they can execute a variety of gaits with a minimum of overlapping. Three pairs, however, are the minimum number which can provide a stable tripod of support in all phases of each pace. The retention of such stability has been said to account for the great ability of insects to make sudden stops or shifts in direction.[69] It may be significant in this connection that crustaceans having only two pairs of walking legs seem mainly to be species which can escape from their enemies by retreating within a shell or by the use of camouflage.

g. *Crustacean gaits.* Several investigators have studied the gaits of *Astacus*, with rather various results (Table 1). The most curious of these data are the different stepping sequences on the two sides of the body[11,84] and the lack of uniformity in the phase differences between successive legs.[4,66] The most careful study of stepping sequences was made by Voelkel, who concluded that List and Bethe had erred in their descriptions.

With regard to the phase differences between successive legs, no detailed studies appear to have been published. Figure 4a represents an effort to portray Voelkel's views more precisely than was done by Herter, notably in showing that the third leg steps just after the first, and the fourth leg just after the second. The gait shown, especially when slightly modified, as in Fig. 4b, is like that reported for various terrestrial arthropods.[101] List stated that the second leg of *Astacus* is put down just before the first leg is lifted, so perhaps Fig. 4b does resemble at least one of the gaits which the animal employs.

For the spiny lobster, *Palinurus*, walking on five pairs of legs, Bethe[13] reported that the successive sets of supporting legs do not follow a simple, crisscross sequence. He also claimed that the legs of each

TABLE 1
GAITS REPORTED FOR *Astacus*[a]

	List[84]	Bethe[11]	Voelkel[161]	Herter[66]	Baldi[4]
Forestroke:backstroke ratio	1:3		1:1	1:1	1:1
Stepping sequence R.	1 3 2 4	1 3 2 4	1 3 2 4	1 3 2 4	1 2 4 3
Stepping sequence L.	3 1 4 2	3 1 4 2	2 4 1 3	2 4 1 3	4 3 1 2
Phase difference between legs of each pair	$\frac{1}{2}$	$\frac{1}{2}$	$\frac{1}{2}$	$\frac{1}{2}$	$\frac{1}{2}$
Phase difference between legs 1 and 2				$\frac{1}{2}$	$\frac{24}{32}$
Phase difference between legs 2 and 3				$\frac{1}{4}$	$\frac{13}{32}$
Phase difference between legs 3 and 4				$\frac{1}{2}$	$\frac{11}{32}$

[a] Phase differences between successive legs based on measurements of diagrams.

pair always move alternately, but Manton[101] states that they move together. Typically, three pairs of legs are used in the walking of *Squilla mantis*, although quite frequently only the last two of these pairs are active.[11] It was claimed that when three pairs are used the body is always supported by a triangle of three legs, alternately L.1-R.2-L.3, and R.1-L.2-R.3. Such a gait implies a forestroke:backstroke ratio of 1:1 and phase differences of one half between successive legs and between the legs of each pair. However, other hexapod arthropods have a backstroke of slightly longer duration, and a phase difference between successive legs of slightly less than one half.

The ostracod *Cypridopsis vidua* employs a hopping gait in which the second antennae swing forward, followed by the second thoracic legs, after which both pairs of appendages simultaneously propel the animal forward.[72,74]

4. *Walking sideways.* Many crustaceans having fewer than six pairs of legs are able to walk sideways, for example *Panulirus*,[82] with five pairs of legs, and *Astacus*,[84] with four pairs. However, only among certain Anomura, and more especially in the Brachyura, has

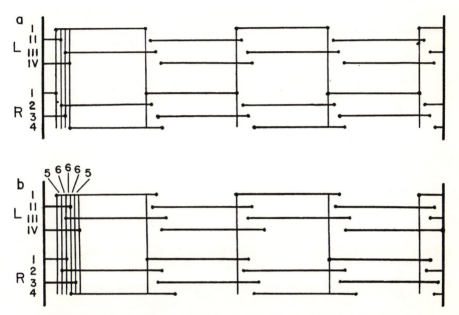

FIG. 4a. Approximate gait employed by *Astacus*, based on the description given by Voelkel.[161] Stepping sequence, 1,3,2,4. Forestroke:backstroke ratio, 1:1. Number of propulsive legs, always four. Phase differences, $^{19}\!/_{40}$ between successive legs, $\frac{1}{2}$ between the legs of each pair.

b. Same as "a" but with a forestroke:backstroke ratio of 18:22, which makes certain that each leg is put down before the leg in front is lifted. Number of propulsive legs, no longer always four.

walking sideways become a highly specialized adaptation. A closely similar functional anatomy occurs in the crab spiders (Thomisidae),[130] none of which, however, reach the proficiency seen in many of the true crabs. The habit of walking sideways involves a number of peculiar physiological features. The animal's progression is at right angles to the direction of the metachronal waves passing along the successive appendages. Problems of overlapping between the legs are largely avoided because they swing laterally.[101] Consequently the leg-bearing segments of the body can be very short, a wide range of gaits becomes practicable, and successive propulsive legs will not tend to diverge or converge as a result of changes in the phase difference between them.

The action of the legs on the two sides of the body is quite different. The leading legs pull by flexing, while the trailing legs push by extending. Maintaining a well-balanced distribution of supporting legs, or a constant number of propulsive legs, requires adjustments of phase differences, or of stroke-duration ratios, in terms of legs which are in the propulsive stroke rather than in terms of legs which are in the backstroke or which are undergoing flexion or extension.

Although crabs usually walk sideways, they also can go diagonally or directly forward. *Macropipus*[78] and *Ocypode*[75] walk forward quite often, while *Eriocheir* has its legs so positioned that it can run forward almost as fast as it does sideways.[66] However, most crabs go forward and diagonally only for changing direction or to interchange the leading and trailing sides.[13,28,130] The beach crab *Ocypode*, when fleeing across the sand, often rotates its body 180° while continuing to run in the same direction.[75] This habit would appear to allow the tired flexors in one set of legs to be relieved by the extensors, while in the other set of legs the equally tired extensors are relieved by the flexors.

Although four pairs of legs are usually used by crabs for walking, there are many exceptions. For instance, *Eriocheir* often uses its chelipeds as a fifth pair of legs,[66] portunid swimming crabs have only three pairs of walking legs,[66,78] and *Dorippe* walks on only two pairs. *Ocypode* achieves its fastest speeds running on only three,[75] or in some cases, perhaps, two[50] pairs of legs, yet it retains the advantages of having four pairs available for sudden stops or changes of direction. *O. occidentalis*, when foraging at the water line, can escape sudden waves by lightning-fast spurts, regardless of the orientation of the body at the moment.[136]

The gaits used by crabs have not been investigated with adequate methods. Among the few accounts available, the most detailed is that of Bethe[13] for *Carcinus*. In this crab two principal gaits were distinguished. Bethe's gait diagrams show that during his observations the crabs walked with a quite irregular rhythm. However, average values for the main features of each gait can be calculated from the diagrams (Table 2).

Gait I approximates the simplest one possible and was observed to be used only for short distances or, rather surprisingly, for running fast.[12] In Gait II, although the observed rhythm was especially variable, the crab evidently is using a relatively high gear, with an appropriately large phase difference between successive legs.

Bethe has reported two distinct patterns of phase difference between the legs of each pair in *Carcinus*, which has led to some confusion in the literature. In one account[13] the legs of a pair, particularly in Gait I, are supposed to alternate in their propulsive action, and hence must be extended or flexed together. Support is then provided essentially by two alternating quartets of legs, R.1-L.2-R.3-L.4 and L.1-R.2-L.3-R.4. This general type of gait has been reported not only for *Carcinus* but also for *Macropipus*,[66,78] *Polybius*,[78] and *Dromia*,[130] all of which walk on only three pairs of legs, which in *Dromia* consist of

TABLE 2
Characteristic Gaits of *Carcinus*[a]

	Gait I	Gait II
Recovery stroke:propulsive stroke ratio	12:13	17:8
Phase difference between successive legs	$\dfrac{23}{50}$	$\dfrac{31}{50}$
Phase difference between legs of each pair (in terms of legs commencing the propulsive stroke)	$\dfrac{1}{2}$	$\dfrac{11}{25}$

[a] Figures are averages calculated from diagrams in Bethe.[13]

two pairs of walking legs plus the chelipeds. In the other account[12] of Gait I the legs of each pair are supposed to alternate in their flexion and extension, which means that both legs are propulsive together. In such a gait, support would be provided by the four legs, R.1-L.1-R.3-L.3, alternating with R.2-L.2-R.4-L.4. This sequence appears somewhat improbable, but its occurrence in *Eriocheir* and some other genera seems to be implied in at least one report.[76]

5. *Other methods of walking.* Many crustaceans can walk backward, for example *Astacus*,[4,84] *Panulirus*,[82] *Birgus*,[1] *Macropipus*,[78] and *Eriocheir*.[121] The isopod *Cruregens* runs forward or backward with equal facility.[152] In isopods such as *Ligia*, the three posterior pairs of thoracic legs pull the animal backward when the anterior half of the exoskeleton has recently been molted.[152] Some crustaceans can glide, rather than walk, over the substratum by using suitable appendages to create a current slightly less powerful than that required for swimming. Forms employing this type of locomotion include *Argulus*,[97]

Homarus,[157] and the zoea larva of the pea crab, *Pinnotheres*.[2] Locomotion somewhat like that of a looper caterpillar has been described for *Squilla*[11] and for the amphipod *Corophium*.[60] The peculiar way in which Gammaridea skitter across the substratum on one side is familiar to many zoologists, but accounts vary as to just how this movement is accomplished.[80,120,142,152]

6. *Speeds achieved in running.* Among crustaceans which walk or run, the fastest speeds probably are achieved by species of the crab *Ocypode*, living on sandy beaches. *O. gaudichaudii* may reach a speed of 1.6 meters per second (almost 6 km per hour), running on three pairs of legs.[75] *O. cursor* perhaps exceeds this speed, seeming to run on only two pairs of legs, with the body raised higher off the ground.[50] In the isopod *Ligia oceanica* the duration of the backstroke when running on land has been reported to be 0.03 seconds.[102] Since the forestroke is of the same duration,[101] each leg executes over sixteen steps per second, one of the highest frequencies recorded for any arthropod. In a specimen 35 mm long, each leg would swing a distance of about 15 mm,[101] corresponding to a speed of about 50 cm per second (1.8 km per hour). Speeds of crustaceans running under water have not often been recorded, but *Carcinus* is said to run after shrimps at a speed of 1 meter per second.[12] To achieve this speed, a specimen with a carapace width of 45 mm would have to execute twenty steps per second, assuming that Gait I was used, with propulsive strokes occupying one half of each pace,[12] and that each leg would swing a distance of 25 mm.[101] Such a rate of stepping under water seems somewhat improbable, especially since rates of from one to eight steps per second have been reported by the same observer. *Panulirus*, a considerably larger animal with much longer legs, has been reported to walk at a maximum speed of 30–60 cm per second.[82]

B. CLIMBING

Many crustaceans climb expertly. In most cases the climbing mechanism seems to resemble that used in walking, and no particular adaptations are evident, other than sharp claws and sometimes an anterior pair of appendages modified for grasping. Several types of crustaceans climb nimbly up the narrow stems of plants, instances of such ability being found in various ostracods,[74,135] in many chydorid Cladocera,[37] and in some species of the amphipod *Orchestia*.[142] Certain crabs such as *Eriocheir*[121] and *Birgus*[1] can climb trees, while other rough surfaces are climbed by Notostraca,[93] Oniscoidea, *Homarus*,[5]

Macropipus,[78] and many others. *Homarus* usually has to help itself up by rapid beating of its pleopods. *Macropipus* often uses its swimming paddles in the same way, going up backward to take advantage of their action. *Orchestia*, Oniscoidea, and the tree-climbing crabs, on the other hand, are strong enough to climb on land without the support afforded by water. When climbing down, some forms, such as *Orchestia*, descend head first, while others, like *Birgus*, come down backward.[7]

More noticeably specialized for climbing are a number of crustaceans which live among hydroids, algae, and other branching organisms. The legs of these crustaceans are highly adapted for grasping, and those legs which have found a suitable branch can support the body while others reach out in search of the next branch. Many crabs, including *Hyas*,[130] are adapted in this manner, as are such amphipods as *Caprella*[173] and *Ampithoe*,[68] and isopods like *Astacilla*.[80] To enable the legs to reach in different directions, the body may be modified in various ways. In *Hyas*, for example, the thoracic sternites are arranged radially so that the legs project out like the spokes of a wheel. In *Caprella* the elongated body is unusually flexible with some of the joints permitting both lateral and dorsoventral flexures.

C. PLOWING THROUGH MUD OR SAND

A considerable number of crustaceans plow their way forward partly or wholly beneath the surface of mud or sand. This type of locomotion usually occurs under water, but the ostracod *Mesocypris terrestris* pushes itself through forest humus,[54] and the isopod *Cirolana salvadorensis* "swims" with its thoracic legs through the dry sand of tropical beaches.[136]

The mechanism used for pushing through the substratum may be essentially the same as that used in walking, but this is generally supplemented by the action of appendages which create a current. Crustaceans which seem to use this type of mechanism include Notostraca,[37,93] the cladoceran *Graptoleberis*,[37] many ostracods,[112,135] harpacticoids such as *Canthocamptus*,[111] some cumaceans,[40] and certain isopods like *Chiridotea* and *Serolis*.[155] In others the mechanism may be much the same as that used in swimming, sometimes assisted by pushing with suitable caudal appendages. This type has been reported in conchostracans such as *Leptestheriella*,[86] the cladoceran *Ilyocryptus*,[37,53] *Nebalia*,[19] *Nebaliella*,[21] and some mysids such as *Hemimysis lamornae*[23] and *Gastrosaccus spinifer*.[156]

Probably all crustaceans with the plowing habit are shaped in some way which reduces resistance to the substratum. A flattened shield-shaped form, somewhat like that of trilobites, might be one such adaptation expected. Some Crustacea (e.g. Notostraca, *Graptoleberis, Chiridotea,* and *Serolis*) do indeed possess such a form, but Notostraca and *Graptoleberis* usually stay on top of the mud[37] and many species which do plow under the surface are shaped quite differently. Thus in *Nebaliella* the anterior end is vertically flattened and formed like a plow.[21]

D. BURROWING

Crustaceans burrow by a great variety of methods. Probably every appendage is used for this purpose by at least some crustacean, if larvae and those parasites which burrow into their hosts are included. The burrowing process can be divided into a series of steps. At the start certain appendages, like the antennae, may have to be folded out of the way, as in the amphipod *Talorchestia.*[126] Usually the substratum is attacked by suitably shaped walking legs. However, this job may be wholly or partly done by other appendages such, for example, as the antennae of the amphipods *Urothoe*[168] and *Corophium,*[60,133] the uropods in the anomuran *Emerita*[118] and in the amphipod *Bathyporeia,*[167] the rapidly beating pleopods in sand shrimps,[160] the similarly active thoracic exopodites in the mysid *Gastrosaccus spinifer,*[156] and parts of the body rocked to and fro by certain appendages in the crab *Calappa*[130] and in the chalimus postlarva of the copepod *Caligus.*[61]

During this digging the body may be braced by certain appendages, or may be pushed down into the excavation. In *Talorchestia,* for example, the first and second gnathopods dig, while the second and third pereiopods brace the body, and the fourth and fifth pairs push the animal downward.[126] Loosened substratum may be transported away by a variety of methods. Sometimes the digging appendages also push the material aside, as in many crabs[118,130] and Cumacea,[33,44] or fan it away by their rapid movements, as in *Gastrosaccus* and the sand shrimp. In other cases, special appendages rake the loosened material into position for its final removal. Thus in *Talorchestia* the first[126] (or the first three[141]) pairs of pereiopods sweep the sand back to within reach of the telson and uropods, while in *Callianassa* the third maxillipeds and fourth pereiopods are used to push mud up where it can be grasped by some of the maxillipeds' more basal segments.[96]

The final removal of excavated material may be achieved by one of several methods. A number of amphipods such as *Talorchestia*[126] and *Niphargus*[48] throw it clear by a sudden extension of the abdomen.

Some Cumacea create a current with the thoracic exopodites,[181] and in several amphipods, particularly *Haustorius*,[30,134] a pleopod-driven current is crucial. *Callianassa* uses its third maxillipeds to carry mud up to the top of its burrow,[96] and the related *Upogebia* does the same with a basket formed by the chelipeds and the second pereiopods.[95] The fiddler crab *Uca pugilator* carries a pellet of sand with pereiopods two to four on the side having the small chela. Once out of its burrow, *Uca* may use the corresponding pereiopods on the other side to push the pellet as far as one meter across the beach.[28]

Species which construct a burrow may employ particular appendages for walking within it. Thus in *Callianassa* and *Upogebia* the third and fifth pereiopods are used for this purpose, while the fourth pereiopods are held up against the sides for balance.[95,96] Morphological adaptations used by crustaceans for burrowing have been noted most often on the appendages. However, several over-all adaptations of the body for burrowing have been described in the highly modified burrower *Emerita*[143] and in a number of brachyuran crabs.[130]

E. JUMPING

The chydorid cladoceran, *Camptocercus rectirostris*, uses its abreptor[37] as a springing lever, which with one vigorous movement may project the animal several times its own body length through the water.[51] Much greater distances can be achieved by crustaceans jumping in air. Most remarkable are the talitrid amphipods, found on sandy beaches. One of these, *Talorchestia*, only 1–2 cm long, can apparently jump 20–40 cm vertically,[141] or over a meter horizontally.[80] No data on the necessary mechanical energy are available for these performances, but figures for grasshoppers[62] suggest that talitrids must be among the most efficient of all jumping animals. The mechanism used is a sudden extension of the abdomen, probably assisted by a strong backward movement of the uropods.[141] All other Gammaridea seem to have a similar anatomical structure, but jumping has been observed only in talitrids.[81]

F. SWIMMING

1. *Methods of study.* Most of the many reports on crustacean swimming habits are based on simple visual observations, although a few are derived from experiments. In some cases the animal has been fixed, either in still[138] or flowing[90] water. In other cases currents created by the appendages have been visualized with added fine particles and

dyes[23,86,90,91] or by flow birefringence.[86,89] With regular limb beats, details of the movement can be observed through a stroboscope.[20,91]

Both still photography[37,41,91] and cinematography[78,90,109,151] have been tried, although both have severe limitations,[37] which have sometimes led to strange conclusions.[109] Some kinds of movement can be demonstrated with a modified type of cinematography, in which several pictures are taken on each frame of film.[90,91] A number of investigators have observed the swimming abilities of crustaceans after the amputation of certain parts or appendages.[43,78,91,108,113,116,172,176] Simple wind tunnel experiments have been conducted with portunid crabs,[130] but hydrodynamic studies of Crustacea appear not to have been made.

2. *Propulsive mechanisms.* The propulsive mechanisms used by swimming Crustacea are not easy to classify. However, five main types may perhaps be distinguished. In three of these (Fig. 5) the appendages provide the motive force by 1) acting like oars, 2) creating vortexes by rapid rotary beats, or 3) acting like propellers which move at right angles to the path of locomotion. In the two remaining types, propulsion is provided by 4) single or repeated blows of the abdomen which drive the animal forward, or 5) sudden flexure of the abdomen, with the tail fan expanded, so that the animal shoots rapidly backward. This last type of propulsion is in most cases employed as an escape mechanism, and it will be dealt with under that heading.

The antennae are used as oars in nauplii,[115,119,150] Conchostraca,[86] Cladocera,[176] Ostracoda,[72,135] the copepods *Anomalocera* and *Candacia*,[91] the calyptopis larvae of euphausiids,[128] and the protozoea larvae of penaeid shrimps.[119] In these protozoeae and in many nauplii and Ostracoda the antennules also act as oars, as do the mandibles in the two copepods and in most nauplii. Trunk or thoracic legs appear to be used as oars in Notostraca,[86] Conchostraca,[86] Copepoda,[151] Branchiura,[65] cypris larvae, some isopods,[80] perhaps some Gammaridea,[80] the shrimp *Argis*,[80] and several genera of crabs.[78,98,121,130] Exopodites of the thoracic appendages beat straight back and forth, like oars, in some Syncarida.[100] In many Malacostraca abdominal pleopods act as oars, while in *Emerita* the uropods alone act in this way.[118,143]

Fig. 5. Diagrams to show three main types of swimming. Top: *Daphnia;* appendages acting like oars. Center: *Calanus;* rotary beats of appendages producing vortexes and a slow forward glide. Bottom: *Portunus;* rapid sideways swimming produced by the paddles, appropriately slanted to act like propellers during both forward and backward strokes. Heavy arrows indicate direction of locomotion; thin-line arrows, direction of propulsive limb beat; broken-line arrows, water currents.

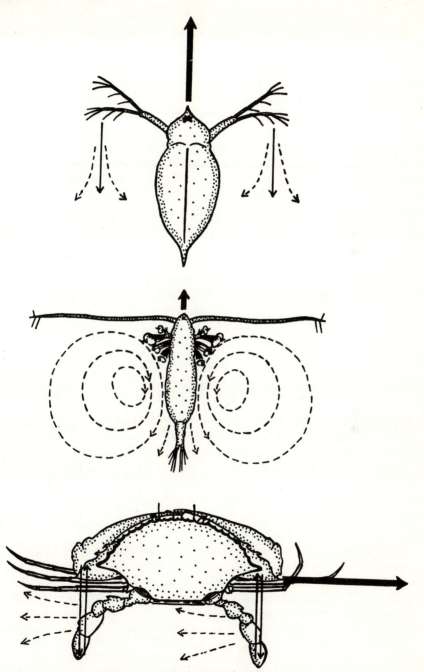

FIG. 5 (See legend on opposite page.)

337

In a few cases the appendages really are used like the oars of a boat, with long, slow sweeps, as in the cladoceran *Leptodora*.[176] More usually, the appendages beat at smaller amplitudes and considerably higher frequencies. Sometimes, as in *Daphnia*, the strokes may occur singly with relatively long pauses between.[176]

Especially interesting is a propulsive mechanism described for calanoid and cyclopoid copepods,[32,151] which are well known to make extremely fast leaps through the water. On the basis of cinematography, Storch[151] described a succession of events as follows. During the rest pauses between jumps, the antennules project laterally, stiffened presumably by considerable internal turgor. A few milliseconds before each jump the antennules become limp, thought to be because of the opening of proximal valves. The five pairs of biramous thoracic legs then beat strongly backward in rapid succession, the most posterior pair first. During the leap which ensues, the antennules lie back passively, while the abdomen carries out complex stabilizing and steering movements. After the first pair of legs has completed its backstroke, all five pairs swing forward together to resume their resting position pointing anteriorly close under the body. Lastly, the antennules are once more extended, the expansion progressing from their bases toward their tips.

Although Storch's technique failed to provide adequate proof of the mechanism described, his account is the most convincing available. Claims that the antennules play an active part in the leaping type of propulsion[91] have not been followed up with the promised evidence. Hardy and Bainbridge,[55] without reference to the literature and on the basis of purely visual observations, claim that "both violent movement of the antennae* and flexing of the abdomen appear to be employed." They attribute to the thoracic legs the entirely different, gliding type of locomotion which these copepods also display. An earlier worker[116] found that *Labidocera* can leap normally, though not quite so far as usual, after amputation of the antennules or of the caudal furca. After removal of both structures the leaps no longer occurred, although the animals could still glide. The conclusions drawn from these facts were the same as those of Hardy and Bainbridge, but the ability of some of the operated animals to leap almost normally would seem rather to support the views of Storch.

Other interesting propulsive mechanisms which resemble rowing occur among the crabs. Forms like *Eriocheir*[121] and *Cancer magister*[98]

---

* Probably antennules are meant.

can swim sideways by "dog-paddling" with their walking legs. *Matuta* does the same with its legs, which have their dactyls expanded into flattened blades.[130] Portunid swimming crabs may paddle similarly with their three pairs of walking legs (flattened distally in *Polybius*), while their specialized last legs act like propellers.[78] The last legs of *Orithyia* and *Nautilocorystes* are shaped like paddles also,[80] but how they function appears not to be known.

Portunid swimming crabs can swim not only sideways but also backward and even, sometimes, forward. They go backward for the most part only when swimming slowly at one level, doing so apparently by an oarlike action of the two fifth pereiopods, which beat back and forth alternately.[78] Each describes a figure eight, with its paddle pressing against the water only when moving forward near the top of the stroke, well above the back of the animal. To prevent wobbling, the fourth pereiopods keep up a counterbeat, or if they have been amputated, the third pair perform the same task.

The second type of swimming mechanism, in which vortexes are produced by a rotary beat of the appendages, is often difficult to distinguish from examples of the first type, in which the appendages act like oars. The distinction depends on whether the appendages mainly beat back approximately parallel to the direction of locomotion, or on each side create vortexes which induce relatively weak swimming currents.

Limb action intermediate between the two types occurs in the Anostraca. Their trunk limbs beat backward and forward quite directly, and so might be said to act as oars. Cannon[22] stated that as the limbs beat back, a propulsive stream of water is thrown out posteriorly from the interlimb spaces. However, rotary action of the exopodites[90] produces vortexes which the use of suitable dyes indicates are much more powerful than is the stream of water expelled from between the limbs.[86] *Chirocephalus* can swim forward, hover, drift slowly backward, rise, or fall, an ability attributed by Lowndes[90] to alterations of the planes in which the exopodites beat, brought about by changes in limb or body position. It seems, however, that it is the exopodites themselves which can change the direction of their beat.[86]

Gliding slowly and even hovering in one spot seem to be characteristic abilities when the appendages have a rotary type of action. Nevertheless, hovering sometimes also occurs when they have a more direct type of beat, as in *Argulus*[65] and in the amphipod *Haustorius*.[30] Appendages having a rotary action often beat at a high frequency, which may be possible because not much water is moved posteriorly, and relatively little energy is required to overcome viscous drag in the vortexes which are created.[20] Among calanoid copepods, rates of from 600 to 2700 beats per minute have been recorded.[91]

Crustacean appendages which beat in a rotary fashion include the exopodites of Anostraca, already mentioned, the antennae, mandibles, and maxillules of calanoids,[20] the antennae and mandibles of calanoid nauplii,[150] perhaps the swimming pereiopods of Parasellidae,[80] and the thoracic exopodites of many Malacostraca.[23,43,64,119,181] Details of the limb movements and of the currents produced have been described for calanoid copepods,[20,91,151] and for one of the Mysidacea.[23]

In both the simple rowing beat and in the rotary type the pressure exerted on the water is greater during the propulsive part of the beat than it is during the recovery. Resistance to the water during the latter phase may be reduced in a number of ways. The limbs and their parts may be drawn close together, as in the thoracic legs of copepods[151] and the pleopods of Squilla[6]; or the flattened blade of the limb may be turned like a feathered oar, as in Emerita[143] and in crabs[78]; or the swimming setae may become pressed into a bundle resembling a folded fan, reported for Conchostraca,[86] Ostracoda,[135] Hemimysis,[23] and Haustorius[30]; or the setules which border the setae may slant so as not to offer much resistance; or perhaps the setae themselves may bend at particular joints, as has been claimed for the zoea larva of Uca.[71]

In a rotary beat the propulsive face of the appendage may be inclined at an angle to the direction of motion. As found in Anostraca and calanoid copepods, the resulting action has been compared to that of a propeller.[90,91] But since the direction of motion of the appendages is chiefly posterior during the more effective portions of their beat, the movement seems more appropriately described as having a modified oarlike action, a description which has been applied to the thoracic exopodites of Hemimysis.[23]

The swing of a true propeller is at right angles to the direction of locomotion, a condition which, judging from the interesting work of Kühl,[78] apparently occurs in the portunid crabs. According to Kühl, when a portunid swims sideways the two fifth pereiopods together beat backward and forward at right angles to the direction of locomotion. Their paddles are inclined like the blades of a propeller, and are rotated at the end of each half beat so as to provide a propulsive force during both the forward and the backward strokes. Special jointing of these legs to the body permits them to beat forward well above the carapace. The movement of the remaining legs is restricted to a level below the body although, as already noted, they may assist slightly in sideways swimming by paddling. The power provided by the fifth pereiopods is quite remarkable, some portunids being able to pursue and capture fast-swimming fish. Even with only one swimming leg, a portunid can swim quite effectively either sideways or backward.

Some interesting comparisons are possible with the wings of insects, which also act as propellers. From the ratio of forward speed to wing-tip speed in insects,[24,67] it may be supposed that the corresponding ratio in an aquatic animal would be about 3:4. At a forward speed of 1 meter per second, easily reached by portunids,[78] the tips of the paddles would then have to move at 1.33 meter per second. At a frequency of 10.5 beats per second, shown in some of Kühl's photographs,* each paddle would then have to cover about 13 cm during each full beat. This value appears reasonable and is in good agreement with the requirements of the mechanism involved.[78]

It would be of interest to know how the second paddle avoids acting in the turbulent wake of the leading paddle. Perhaps the situation will prove to be the same as that found for the locust *Schistocerca* in which the hind wings beat at a larger amplitude and slightly ahead of the forewings, thereby avoiding much of the turbulence created by the latter.[170] At any rate, the leading paddle in a portunid is reported to beat at a smaller amplitude than does the second one.[78]

When a swimming crab captures prey, its load is suddenly increased. A more gradual increase occurs when a species such as *Callinectes sapidus* enters fresh water. To support the extra load, the paddles might increase the frequency of their beat, increase their amplitude, or, like variable-pitch propellers, change their angle of attack. In *Schistocerca* this latter type of mechanism is said to be the most important[170]; a similar finding might be expected for portunids, in which the steering abilities of the paddles are certainly great.

In the most highly streamlined and most completely pelagic genera of portunids, such as *Portunus*,[130†] the swimming legs are relatively short. Presumably they beat at a correspondingly higher frequency. In

---

* Although his text gives a value of six beats per second.

† Confusion over the kind of swimming crabs cited is likely to arise from unfamiliarity with Opinion 394 (June 19, 1956) of the International Commission on Zoological Nomenclature. Following this ruling, species formerly referred to *Portunus* by European systematists and *Liocarcinus* by Americans are called *Macropipus;* those formerly called *Neptunus* by Europeans and *Portunus* by Americans are correctly called *Portunus*. These correct names then need to be carefully checked in comparing various species in the original papers. Thus in the work referred to here, Schäfer calls the most completely pelagic portunids *Neptunus*, here assigned to *Portunus* in conformity with Opinion 394.

all portunids the streamlining has to be such as to permit swimming to the left or to the right, which requires a spindle shape rather than that of a torpedo.[130] Perhaps the shape of the body is such as to provide some dynamic lift, as has been suggested,[67] rather uncertainly,[170] for certain insects.

In the fourth type of crustacean swimming mechanism, the animal is driven forward by single or repeated blows of the abdomen against the water. Sometimes the movements are more complex, as in the Cumacea, in which the abdomen executes vertical beats and undulations.[181] In the amphipod *Talitrus saltator* swimming is possible only when blows of the abdomen assist the reduced pleopods.[133] More frequently, however, the abdomen is used chiefly as a source of additional power for rising off the bottom, vertical climbing, or escape from enemies. Among crustaceans which employ the abdomen in this way are Anostraca,[86] many chydorid cladocerans,[149] Tanaidae,[80] Gammaridea,[68,81] Hyperiidea,[80] *Squilla*,[11] and the calyptopis larva of Euphausiacea.[128]

A peculiar case is that of the amphipod *Caprella*, which propels itself forward through the water by strong, ventroposterior flexion of the head and anterior part of the thorax, after which the body is once more slowly extended.[173]

3. *Feeding and respiration related to swimming.* The propulsive mechanisms used by crustaceans for swimming may also aid in feeding and respiration. Details will be found in Chapters 2 and 6, Vol. I, so that only brief mention of a few examples is necessary here. The Anostraca and the Conchostraca filter water which is drawn into their interlimb spaces.[22,37] When this water is expelled, it contributes to the propulsive current, and some of it also passes over the branchiae. In the case of the Anostraca, the amount of filtration may be less during hovering than when the animals are swimming forward.[86] Notostraca filter particles from a current of water created by the beating of their trunk limbs, but this filtration probably occurs only when the carapace is pressed against the substratum.[86] Many calanoid copepods have a filter-feeding mechanism associated with the slow, gliding type of locomotion. The beating of their cephalic appendages creates separate swimming and feeding vortexes.[20] Gliding without filtration frequently occurs, and some species of calanoids do not filter.[91]

In Mysidacea there has been an interesting evolution from forms with separate mechanisms for the feeding, respiratory, and swimming currents, to the Mysida in which the rotary beat of the thoracic exopodites contributes to all three functions.[99] In the nauplius larva of *Balanus* and probably of many other crustaceans a forward feeding current along the mid-line results from the swimming movements of the appendages,[85] and the swimming setae themselves perhaps also collect food.[115] In the protozoea larva of *Penaeus* the maxillipeds assist in producing both swimming and feeding currents.[119]

The use of pleopods in both swimming and respiration occurs in many Malacostraca, notably in Isopoda, Gammaridea, and Stomatopoda. The pleopods themselves may be respiratory, or they may contribute to the respiratory current. In the isopod families Sphaeromidae and Serolidae, the anterior three pairs of pleopods are adapted for swimming, while the posterior two pairs are adapted for respiration.

4. *Limb-beat rhythms in swimming.* Not much information is available concerning the swimming rhythms of Crustacea. Where series of appendages beat in a metachronal rhythm, the phase difference between successive limbs might be expected to be less than one half. Successive propulsive appendages would then diverge from each other, the turbulence produced by each would cause a minimum of interference with the limb immediately behind,[30] and the metachronal waves would appear to pass forward. A single metachronal rhythm is said to extend over both the pleopods and the thoracic exopodites of *Anaspides*[100] and of the shrimp *Acanthephyra*.[34] On the other hand, in *Paranaspides* the pleopods and the thoracic exopodites usually beat at different frequencies[100]; and when the portunid *Polybius* is swimming sideways, the fifth pereiopods do not beat at the same frequency as do the others.[78]

Some tentative values for phase differences can be derived from various published data. These generally confirm the notions that phase differences are less than one half and that at any given moment usually at least one metachronal wave is passing forward over the appendages involved. In most Anostraca, for example, the phase difference for the eleven pairs of trunk limbs appears to be about one tenth,[37,86] although the exact value is in dispute. Phase differences are less than one half in *Anaspides*[100] and in *Mysis*,[148] one eighth in the amphipod *Haustorius*,[30] one quarter in the amphipod *Bathyporeia*,[167] and slightly over one quarter in *Squilla*.[11] In the notostracan *Triops cancriformis* about six to eight metachronal waves pass forward at once over the 50–66 pairs[83] of trunk limbs, with the phase difference diminishing slightly as the waves pass anteriorly.[41,86,104] A similar progressive diminution of the phase difference seems to occur in the conchostracan *Leptestheriella*.[86]

In calanoid and cyclopoid copepods a peculiar rhythm has been reported for thoracic leg movement during jumping, apparently the phase difference between successive legs then being one half or slightly less during the backstroke, zero during the forestroke.[151] The rhythm in calanoids is also peculiar when they are gliding. In a diagram given by Cannon[20] for a gliding *Calanus* there appears to be a phase difference of about one quarter between the antennae and the mandibles, one twenty-fourth between the mandibles and the maxillules, and one sixth between the maxillules and the maxillipeds.

Phase differences of more than one half, with the metachronal wave passing posteriorly, have been reported for the second to fourth pereiopods of the portunid *Polybius*,[78] and for the second to fifth pleopods of *Palaemon*.[34] In *Polybius*, traveling sideways, such a rhythm would not occasion any difficulties, but for *Palaemon* the condition appears improbable.

Phase differences of zero have been reported, almost certainly erroneously, for the anostracans *Artemia* and *Branchipus*[109] and for the amphipod *Ampithoe*.[68] When only two successive pairs of appendages are involved, as in ostracods[72,135] and in portunids swimming backward,[78] the phase difference between the two pairs may be exactly one half. In the ostracods, the antennules and antennae, though in opposite phase, actually beat back together because of their position on the anterior end of the body.

Probably in most swimming Crustacea the appendages of each pair beat forward and backward together, although the alternation of the swimming paddles of portunids swimming backward[78] is an evident exception. A similar phase difference of one half between the two sides is reported for the antennules and antennae of ostracods during their first instar.[135] In the calanoid *Eurytemora*, when gliding forward, the phase difference between the two antennae is said to be seldom zero.[91]

The forestroke:backstroke ratio for crustacean swimming appendages has generally been assumed to be 1:1. But there are exceptions; probably the most striking concerns the thoracic legs of calanoid and cyclopoid copepods for which a forestroke:backstroke ratio of 1:5 has been suggested.[151] A ratio of 3:5 has been diagrammed for the pleopods of *Haustorius*,[30] while photographs of the anostracan *Pristicephalus*[131] reveal ratios of 1:1 and 3:2 for the trunk limbs.

5. *Body position while swimming.* While most crustaceans normally swim dorsal side up, a considerable number swim in other positions. Some regularly swim with the back down: anostracans[86,139];

various cladocerans such as *Holopedium, Simocephalus,* and perhaps some chydorids[80,86]; certain species of *Cyclops*[138]; larvae of the copepod *Lernaea*[175]; isopods like *Astacilla* and many Sphaeromidae[80]; the amphipod *Haustorius*[30]; and the shrimp *Lysmata.*[80] The cladocerans *Diaphanosoma* and *Limnosida*[80] tend to lean somewhat backward between antennal beats, and the amphipod *Corophium*[60] usually swims back down; this position is sometimes adopted by the conchostracans *Lynceus* and *Cyzicus*[105] and by the amphipods *Urothoe*[168] and *Ampithoe.*[68]

A few crustaceans swim with the longitudinal axis of the body in a vertical position, including *Cyclops leuckarti*[138] and several genera of deep-sea shrimps.[34,80] Some others swim with the body strangely bent at one or more joints, including the adult mysid *Praunus flexuosus*[156] and certain larvae of the shrimps *Sicyonia*[52] and *Sergestes,*[52] and of the lobsters *Nephrops*[43] and *Homarus.*[43,64]

6. *Control of swimming path and position.* The position in which a crustacean swims and the path followed may be controlled by purely mechanical means and by reflexes. To maintain a particular horizontal swimming position requires the control of rotations around the longitudinal and transverse axes, while for swimming head- (or tail-) first in a particular direction, rotations around the dorsoventral and transverse axes must be controlled. If the path is horizontal, rotations around the dorsoventral axis can be fully controlled by reflex responses only, but for other rotations the control may be either sensory or mechanical.

Mechanical control of the swimming position is maintained in a number of ways. If the animal's centers of gravity and buoyancy do not coincide, the former will tend to lie below the latter. If its specific gravity exceeds that of the water in which it lives, the body position may be regulated by forces of fluid resistance, either during passive sinking between jumps or perhaps during continuous swimming if a component of the fluid resistance supplies part of the lift.[89] The path followed during swimming will be influenced by the spatial position adopted by the body and by the interplay between the forces of propulsion, gravity, buoyancy, and fluid resistance. The sharpness of any turn will depend on the relation between the linear and angular velocity components.[15]

Body orientation and direction of movement may not have the same relation to an external stimulus. Thus a lobster larva may swim toward a weak light with its head directed away from it (positive taxis and negative orientation).[14] In some cases there may be a choice between two quite different types of response to the same stimulus. For instance, the anostracan *Artemia* usually swims at right angles to the rays of light with its ventral surface directed toward the source of illumination. The same animal, however, may display a negative orientation and taxis, swimming headfirst away from a source of light, parallel to its rays.[87] These two kinds of response obviously are mutually exclusive since their performance together is mechanically impossible.

Reflex control of the swimming path or position might involve sensory perception of any one or more of a variety of stimuli, such as light, gravity, angular acceleration, water currents, hydrostatic pressure, pressures or tensions arising from the support given by the water, pressures or tensions produced by movable internal organs or liquids, and tensions within appendages used for steering.[89]

Since the control of an animal's swimming path may involve so many factors, both mechanical and sensory, the experimental study of real cases raises many theoretical and practical problems.[89] Usually it would be necessary to determine at least the relative positions of the centers of gravity and buoyancy, the specific gravity of the animal, the lines of action of the propulsive force, and the lines of action of the fluid resistance both during passive sinking and during forward locomotion. In addition, means would have to be devised to eliminate, one by one, the various possible types of sensory control.

Such a complete experimental approach has rarely been attempted. Most investigators have emphasized only certain factors, neglecting others which might have proved equally important. A surprising number of investigators have attempted to show the relative positions of the centers of gravity and buoyancy by allowing a dead or narcotized crustacean to sink in water, entirely neglecting the important forces of fluid resistance which would then come into play.

There is an especially large literature concerning possible functions of the various spines and processes found on the body and appendages of many Crustacea. These outgrowths have been variously claimed to serve for flotation by slowing the rate of sinking,[172] for stabilizing the direction of locomotion when placed parallel to the line of action of the propulsive force,[140,166,176,177] for deflecting the swimming path away from that of the propulsive force,[140,176,177] for shifting the position of the center of gravity,[172,176] for increasing the amount of surface acted on by currents,[172] for improving sensory control during turns by magnifying the difference in fluid resistance on the two sides,[43] and for ensuring a floating position from which escape can best be made.[92]

These functions are all possibilities, but evidence for them in specific instances has rarely been adequate. The work of Woltereck[176] on Cladocera was perhaps the most brilliant in this field, yet a recent statement claims that all of his work was wrong.[70] The argument will not be settled until the several possibilities have been adequately tested for each animal.

Mechanisms controlling the swimming path and the body position have been most studied in the cladoceran *Daphnia*. This animal swims in characteristic jumps, sinking passively between each one, with the antennae extended as a sort of parachute. If there is a sufficient pause between jumps, the body rotates until it hangs vertically from the antennae. The path taken during an actual jump will vary, depending on the body position attained during sinking and on the direction of the antennal propulsive force. Early, careful observations[138,176] indicated that the antennae beat back dorsoposteriorly, but a recent report[57] states that they beat back parallel to the longitudinal axis of the animal, no reference being made to the earlier findings.

In any case, the precise action of the antennae can be controlled by a reflex operating through the fused compound eyes. Ocular muscles rotate the eye in response to changes in the intensity or position of the light. Descriptions vary as to which part of the eye is normally directed toward the light.[36,125,163,176] Presumably in response to proprioceptors in the ocular muscles, the antennae correct any displacements of the animal's orientation so that the eye can return toward its normal position. This complex response keeps the dorsal surface of the animal directed toward the light, usually slanted with the head end up.[176] Normally the mechanism also serves to keep the animal swimming at a particular depth in the water.[58]

Opinions differ concerning the alterations in antennal action responsible for these changes in orientation. Woltereck attributed the effect mainly to the independent control of exopodite and endopodite of each antenna.[176] On the other hand, Harris states[57] that changes in the attitude assumed by the whole antenna are involved. Perhaps the differences between these two descriptions can be attributed to the fact that the species observed were not the same.

Below a certain light intensity, rotations of the eye in response to light no longer occur.[57,176] But the animal may still stay close to one level in the water, alternately swimming up and sinking down, because of a periodic reversal between positive photokinesis during which light adaptation occurs and negative photokinesis during which dark adaptation occurs.[58,59]

This photokinesis does not involve the compound eye; but the suggestion has been made that if the eye differs enough in specific gravity from the surrounding blood it may exert a pull on the ocular muscles whenever the body is tilted.[57] Thus, even in the dark, the eyes could exert some reflex control of the antennae by a mechanism similar to that found at higher light intensities. It is also possible that during the pauses between jumps the position of the antennae may be regulated in direct response to tensions in their muscles occasioned by the pull of gravity.[9,57,59]

During each jump the propulsive force as well as the forces of gravity, buoyancy, and fluid resistance must influence the path followed and the position adopted. Woltereck[176] was the first investigator to state clearly the principles here involved but, as noted above, his detailed suggestions have not been universally accepted. The complete path which *Daphnia* follows depends not only on the length and direction of each jump but also on the amount of sinking between jumps. The net direction can be regulated either by changing the mode of action of the antennae or by altering their frequency of beat. Obviously to swim horizontally, the animal must progress upward at each jump as much as it sinks downward between jumps.[176]

Daphnia magna has been reported to swim horizontally by horizontal strokes of the antennae, parallel to the long axis of the body, the line of action of the fluid resistance then being nearly horizontal also.[57] But in such a case the antennae must beat at a frequency sufficient to prevent sinking between jumps, and some vertical lift must be provided, either by the propulsive force or from a component of the fluid resistance.

Some Cladocera, such as *Bosmina* and most chydorids,[176] by beating the antennae at a high frequency do regularly swim in a continuous fashion rather than in the more usual series of jumps. Here the antennae beat back ventroposteriorly in contrast to the situation in *Daphnia*.[176] In *Bosmina* the eye rotates in response to light, and there is presumably an associated reflex control of the antennae. In *Chydorus*, on the other hand, swimming with the back directed upward may continue even when the animal is illuminated from below.[86] Some other Cladocera, such as *Sida* and *Leptodora*, show no eye movements in response to light, yet do maintain a particular body position with respect to the source of illumination.[38]

Many other Crustacea orient to light in the same way without accompanying movements of the eyes. Particularly persistent in this type of orientation is the anostracan *Artemia* which nearly always swims with its ventral surface directed toward the light source,[139] even in dim red light and after the removal of any two of the three eyes.[87] When both compound eyes are removed, control of rotations around the transverse axis is impaired, presumably because the median eye contains only a single cup in the sagittal plane. Removal of all three eyes abolishes the response to light,[87] and the operated animals then usually swim in all possible positions, easily changing from one to another.[88] If, however, the animal is lethargic, it swims lying on the back, doing so whether its brine environment has a specific gravity the same as or different from that of the individual. These findings are at least partially explained by the fact that in *Artemia* the center of gravity lies just slightly dorsal to the center of buoyancy.[88] In fresh-water Anostraca the ventral light response is much less persistent, and the centers of gravity and buoyancy appear to be farther apart.[86,113,139]

The conchostracan *Leptestheriella* usually swims with its back directed toward the source of light, but this response is not strongly persistent. In the dark or when not orienting to a light, the animal swims with the back up and the head end highest. This position seems to be determined mechanically by the interacting forces of gravity, buoyancy, and propulsion.[86]

The use of statocysts in the control of orientation is discussed in Chapter 2. In animals without statocysts, reflex responses to gravity are still theoretically possible, as has been noted already for the cladoceran *Daphnia*. Von Buddenbrock[162] believed that the swimming position of *Leptomysis*, *Hemimysis*, and *Palaemon* is in part controlled through some form of "proprioception." His experiments were not conclusive,[89] but more convincing evidence for this type of control is available from some work of Demoll[29] on *Squilla*. Although Demoll thought from his results that *Squilla* must possess statocysts, none have been found, and the data can perhaps be explained best by assuming the presence of receptors which respond to the movements of internal organs or liquids.[89]

Sensitivity to currents acting on the swimming appendages perhaps often influences the steering of Crustacea. The perception of echo currents, or of the pattern of currents around the body while sinking, might serve for the maintenance of a particular body position, although no crustacean examples of such mechanisms seem to have been reported.[89] Hydrostatic pressure receptors serve for controlling the spatial orientation of certain insects, but the receptors of this kind found in some crustaceans are not nearly sensitive enough for such a purpose, responding only to depth changes in excess of 76 mm.[9]

7. *Steering.* In an animal swimming forward or backward, steering is necessary for turning around the dorsoventral and transverse axes. The swimming appendages themselves or other special structures effect this steering. Turns to the right or left are probably achieved in most Crustacea by the swimming appendages on the two sides beating in different directions or, perhaps, as in certain mysids,[8] at different rates. Differences in the amplitude seem not to have been reported for any crustacean, although such differences play an important part in some flying insects.[24] Complete reversal in the direction of beat on one side has been reported for *Artemia*,[109] but this claim must surely be incorrect. In most cases, at least, any changes in the direction of beat involve only the angle at which the appendages exert their thrust against the water. Probably it is by such changes that nearly all crustaceans steer. For instance, portunid crabs can control the directive action of their swimming paddles when going either backward or sideways,[78] and *Daphnia* can alter the action of its antennae in ways discussed in the preceding section.

In some crustaceans, steering to the left or right may be accomplished by structures other than the swimming appendages. Examples of such rudders include the abdomen of Anostraca[113] and of copepods when swimming in jumps,[151] the third uropods of the amphipods *Bathyporeia* and *Urothoe*,[168] the last pereiopods of the amphipods *Haustorius*[30] and *Ampithoe*,[68] the antennal scales of *Squilla*,[6] and possibly the winglike extensions of the cephalothorax in *Argulus*.[172]

Turns around the transverse axis cannot be achieved by differential steering action on the two sides. If the swimming appendages are used, they therefore can become effective only by altering the direction of their propulsive thrust. Conchostraca, Cladocera, and Ostracoda do this with their antennae. In the Conchostraca the trunk limbs and the antennae combine to produce the net propulsive force.[86] A similar situation is more strikingly evident in many ostracods which swim by means of both the antennae and the antennules. After the antennae have been removed the swimming path of these animals curves downward, and after amputation of the antennules it curves upward.[172] However, in some ostracods only the antennae are used for swimming,[135,140] and in at least one species the role of the antennules is in dispute.[18,72] In portunid crabs upward and downward turns are readily controlled by the swimming paddles when going either backward or sideways.[78]

Perhaps the most usual method of controlling rotations around the transverse axis is by the action of flattened structures at the end of the abdomen. Such a mechanism is found in the Anostraca,[113] Copepoda,[151] Branchiura,[174] and many Malacostraca. Sometimes the whole body may be curved or straightened, as in many amphipods.[68] Steering devices at the anterior end, such as the antennal scales of many Malacostraca, may also be important.[119] A special type of steering already described for *Daphnia* involves changes in the duration of the pauses between jumps. When these pauses are long the net swimming path is downward. If the pauses are short, the path may be upward.[176]

8. *Swimming backward.* The ability to swim backward seems to be especially characteristic of crustaceans which swim by a rotary type of appendage beat, as in some Anostraca,[90] the copepods *Calanus* and *Diaptomus*,[91] the mysid *Praunus flexuosus*,[156] isopods of the Family Parasellidae,[80] and many decapod larvae.[14,43] In some of the larvae, going backward is the most usual mode of progression, as is also the case in the Parasellidae which can not only glide backward but can leap in the same direction, using some of the more posterior pereiopods for both types of locomotion. The zoea larva of *Porcellana*, while normally swimming forward, virtually has to swim backward at times, being almost unable to turn because of its very long spines.[43] Portunid crabs quite frequently swim backward by the rowing action of their swimming paddles described in an earlier section. The backward leaps so characteristic of many Malacostraca are described below under "Escape mechanisms" (page 353).

9. *Surface-film swimming.* A number of crustaceans have special, unwettable setae or other parts by means of which they sometimes hang from the surface film. While suspended in this position they can continue to swim, apparently by the same mechanisms as are used at greater depths. Crustaceans reported to have this habit include the notostracan *Triops*,[41] the cladocerans *Scapholeberis*[137] and *Dadaya macrops*,[45] the ostracods *Notodromas monacha*,[137] *Cyprinotus incongruens*, *Cyprois marginata*,[74] and *Oncocypris mülleri*,[45] and various copepods[137] including the calanoid *Labidocera aestiva*.[116]

10. *Swimming speeds.* The rate of limb beat and the speed of swimming are much influenced by various factors, particularly temperature, as has been noted earlier. However, records taken at normal habitat temperatures provide some data of comparative interest.

Probably the fastest of swimming Crustacea are the portunid crabs, which may swim sideways at a rate of 1 meter per second with only moderate exertion.[78] Among crustaceans which use the appendages in an oarlike fashion, perhaps the fastest reported speeds are achieved by calanoid copepods, despite their small size. *Diaptomus gracilis* is said to leap at over 20 cm per second.[90] In more prolonged swimming, the megalops larvae of certain crabs are especially fast, the megalops of *Cancer magister* being able to maintain its position against a current of 17.8 cm per second.[98] Among fish parasites, prodigious speeds have been claimed for the larvae of Gnathiidea[110] and of *Caligus*,[61] which must secure attachment to a fish, but no actual rates appear to have been published.

Crustaceans which glide by a rotary beat of the appendages progress much more slowly. The copepod *Centropages typicus* glides forward at about 2 mm per second,[91] and a speed of 11.5 mm per second has been determined for the zoea of the crab *Pinnotheres*, gliding toward a light at 18.5°C.[171]

When swimming vertically upward, the speed maintained for two minutes may vary between about 6 mm per second for the nauplii of *Balanus* and nearly 5 cm per second for a euphausiid, *Meganyctiphanes*.[55] Over longer periods the average speeds are slower.* *Daphnia longispina* can swim upward at nearly 6 cm per second,[26] although this speed is probably exceptional.[55,169] Interesting records have been published for a number of copepods, but unfortunately without any clear statement as to the type of swimming involved.[55]

The frequency of limb beat is least in forms which sink between jumps, but even *Daphnia magna* at 20°C, beats its antennae 95–225 times per minute, depending on the number of eggs or embryos carried.[42] Fairly typical frequencies for limbs being used like oars are those reported for *Paranaspides*,[100] namely, 120 per minute for the pleopods, and 250–300 per minute for the thoracic exopodites. However, some of Kühl's photographs indicate a frequency of 630–780 beats per minute for the second to fourth pereiopods of *Polybius*, a rate slightly exceeding that of the propellerlike fifth pereiopods.[78] Limb-beat frequency in the notostracan *Triops* at 24.5°C has been reported to decrease from 180–230 per minute posteriorly to 150–170 per minute anteriorly,[104] a situation that seems unlikely since at intervals it would result in successive appendages beating too much toward each other. The highest limb-beat frequencies reported, up to about 2700 per

---

* For diurnal migrations of planktonic forms, average speeds of 1.7–34.7 mm per second are cited in Chapter 12.

minute, are for some copepod appendages which beat in a rotary fashion, as noted above.

Where sufficient data are available it is of interest to estimate the swimming speeds that might be expected. Thus in the calanoid copepod *Diaptomus* an entire beat of all the thoracic legs is reported to occupy $\frac{1}{60}$ of a second.[151] If we accept the tentative suggestion that each leg swings back in one sixth of this time ($\frac{1}{360}$ sec), and if the distance covered in each swing is about 1 mm (half the body length), then speeds for each jump in excess of the reported 20 cm per second[90] should certainly be possible. A similar calculation is presented above for the sideways swimming of portunids.

G. ESCAPE MECHANISMS

Many Crustacea can flee from danger by sudden movements of the abdomen. In some cases considered in Section III,F,2, the abdomen is suddenly extended and the animal propelled forward. On the other hand, in many Malacostraca the abdomen is strongly flexed ventrally, and the animal shoots rapidly backward. As a part of this latter type of reaction, many of the appendages are pointed forward to secure a streamlined effect. The entire response is coordinated through the giant fibers in the central nervous system (Chapter 7).

Usually a single stimulus elicits only one backward leap, achieved by just one flip or a few successive flips of the tail. But in some forms like certain shrimps, *Homarus*,[63] *Panulirus*,[82] and *Galathea*, the animal may speed backward for some distance, flexing the abdomen repeatedly, and steering with great skill.

The leaps are so powerful that certain shrimps, mysids,[156] anaspidaceans,[100] and others often jump right out of the water. There are even reports of two crustaceans which fly considerable distances through the air, one a copepod, *Pontella mediterranea*,[117] and the other an unknown creature 15–25 cm long, said to be shrimplike and to sail into the wind 15 meters or more.[178] Unfortunately no specimens of the latter have been taken.

Details of the mechanism used for backward leaps under water and of the path which is followed have been best described for *Astacus*[161] and for *Panulirus*.[82] The abdominal segments are hinged on a rocker principle at points above and below which the cross-sectional area is equal. This arrangement permits flexion and extension to occur without any loss of energy occasioned by changes in internal volume.[153,154] The infolding of the intersegmental membranes is also important in this connection, and it appears to be controlled by special muscles.[47] Interesting modifications occur in female shrimps, which must use the abdomen both for locomotion and for carrying the eggs.[179]

Although powerful muscles and a large tail fan are needed for fast, backward jumps, the inertia of the cephalothorax must exceed that of the abdomen if the mechanism is to be effective. In the larva of a thalassinidean, *Jaxea*, the body flexes at a point which divides it into portions almost equal in size and in the surface offered to the water. As a result neither flexion nor extension of the abdomen produces much locomotory effect.[43]

The speed attained by malacostracans in their backward leaps is generally thought to be great. About 8 meters per second was claimed for *Homarus*,[63] but 0.9–1.2 meters per second for *Panulirus*[82] seems to be the only reliable record available.

IV. *COMPARISON WITH OTHER ANIMALS*

Although the locomotion of Crustacea has long excited the interest of naturalists, no adequate studies of the mechanics involved have been made by physiologists. Present data suggest some interesting probable mechanisms but usually do not provide any detailed evidence.

Future investigators in this field would do well to make a comparative approach. Crustaceans walk, climb, jump, and sometimes dig in ways comparable with the mechanisms used by terrestrial arthropods and vertebrates. In both of these groups, studies of locomotion have been made far in advance of anything attempted with Crustacea. The various swimming mechanisms used by crustaceans can likewise be compared with some of the types of swimming found in other animals. The use of appendages as oars occurs in certain insects, turtles, and numerous other vertebrates. The creation of vortexes and a gliding type of movement by a rotary action of the appendages can perhaps be compared with the type of swimming often found in ciliated organisms. The propellerlike action of the paddles in portunid crabs may have much in common with the actions of insect wings and of the caudal fin in fish. The high standards attained in recent investigations of these latter two mechanisms should serve as a guide for future crustacean research.

V. *SUMMARY AND CONCLUSIONS*

Crustacean locomotion is a varied and complex function, and each of the many types of walking, burrowing, running, climbing, jumping, and swimming involves adaptations in the exoskeleton, the muscles, the neuromuscular system, various sensory receptors, and the central nervous system. Although some components of these mechanisms have been intensively studied, the actual mechanics of the various types of propulsion have not been sufficiently investigated. As in other arthropods and in vertebrates, jointed appendages for locomotion are usually well developed. Their number is often large, being exceeded only among the myriapods. Frequently the limbs move in a characteristic metachronal rhythm which ordinarily is transmitted posteriorly in the central nervous system, but in one case is said to pass anteriorly. Usually both the rhythm and the individual movements are subject to a high degree of plasticity, but the relation of locomotion to the central nervous pathways is complex and not well understood. The body may remain rigid during locomotion, or in some crustaceans may perform movements important for jumping, steering, or other activities.

The power of walking is often well developed, particularly among the Malacostraca. Usually three or more pairs of legs are used, so that the body is always well supported, and sudden shifts in speed or direction can be made easily. At least in the case of crabs, a leg can share in the walking rhythm only if it can touch the substratum. Some species can run backward as easily as they go forward, and the habit of walking sideways is well developed among the crabs. Surprising speed and agility is attained in the latter type of progression which avoids any problems of overlapping between successive limbs.

Many Crustacea burrow, employing a wide variety of methods. Often the various appendages are specialized for different tasks. Thus, different pairs of appendages may loosen the substratum, brace the body, rake the loosened particles toward the rear, throw clear the material thus accumulated, and push the body down into the excavation. In some cases loads of material are carried out of the burrow at intervals; in others certain appendages create a water current which carries the loosened material away.

A sudden extension of the abdomen provides most of the power for highly effective jumping in talitrid amphipods, and for forward spurts through the water in a number of free-swimming forms. A quick, powerful flexion of the abdomen is used by many aquatic Malacostraca for leaping backward when alarmed. Sometimes these leaps carry the animal right out of the water, and two crustaceans have been claimed to sail through the air like flying fish.

Use of the appendages for swimming takes place in many different ways which may be distinguished under three main types. When the appendages beat back more or less directly, their action can be compared to that of oars. Swimming of this type is often encountered.

Many copepods, for example, are able to spurt through the water at speeds perhaps exceeding 20 cm per second, apparently by beating back the five pairs of thoracic appendages one after the other, then returning them all forward together. A second, rather different type of mechanism is found when the appendage beat is rapid and rotary, producing a system of vortexes in the water. A slow gliding type of swimming results, and usually the animal can hover or even move slowly backward. The third type of mechanism involves using the appendages rather like propellers, beating at right angles to the direction of locomotion. Such an action has been reported only for the fifth pereiopods of portunid crabs swimming sideways. The paddles of these legs are fringed with sensory setae and apparently can be slanted to provide a propulsive force when beating either forward or backward. They also serve for steering and probably can act like variable-pitch propellers to accommodate different loads. The power which they provide is considerable since portunids can swim at speeds well in excess of 1 meter per second.

To control rotations around the three major body axes, crustaceans may modify the beat of their swimming appendages, or they may employ special rudders located near one end of the body. The body position and the swimming path may be regulated by reflex responses to light, gravity, angular acceleration, and possibly other stimuli, or by purely mechanical interactions between the forces of gravity, buoyancy, propulsion, and fluid resistance.

REFERENCES

1. Andrews, C. W. 1909. Exhibition of a photograph of the robber crab (*Birgus latro*) on Christmas Island, with an account of its habits. *Proc. Zool. Soc. London* 1909:887–889.
2. Atkins, D. 1955. The post-embryonic development of British *Pinnotheres* (Crustacea). *Proc. Zool. Soc. London* 124:687–715.
3. Baldi, E. 1935. Moti di maneggio per lesioni cerebrali nel gambero. *Arch. sci. biol.* (*Italy*) 21:533–569.
4. Baldi, E. 1936. Ricerche sulla fisiologia del sistema nervoso negli artropodi. I. La meccanica deambulatoria normale del gambero. *Arch. zool. ital.* 23:47–80.
5. Balss, H. 1926. Decapoda. *In:* "Die Tierwelt der Nord- und Ostsee" (G. Grimpe and E. Wagler, eds.), Lfg. 6, Teil Xh2, pp. 9–112. Akademische Verlagsges., Leipzig.
6. Balss, H. 1938. Stomatopoda. *In:* "Bronn's Tierreich," Bd. 5, Abt. 1, Bch. 6, Teil II, pp. 1–173. Akademische Verlagsges., Leipzig.
7. Balss, H. 1956. Decapoda. VI. Ökologie. *In:* "Bronn's Tierreich," Bd. 5, Abt. 1, Bch. 7, Lfg. 10–11, pp. 1285–1476. Akademische Verlagsges., Leipzig.
8. Bauer, V. 1908. Über die reflektorische Regulierung der Schwimmbewegungen bei den Mysiden mit besonderer Berücksichtigung der doppelsinnigen Reizbarkeit der Augen. *Z. allgem. Physiol.* 8:343–370.

9. Baylor, E. R., and Smith, F. E. 1957. Diurnal migration of plankton crustaceans. *In:* "Recent Advances in Invertebrate Physiology" (B. T. Scheer, ed.), pp. 21–35. Univ. of Oregon Publications, Eugene.

10. Berkeley, A. A. 1928. The musculature of *Pandalus danae. Trans. Roy. Can. Inst.* 16:181–231.

11. Bethe, A. 1897. Vergleichende Untersuchungen über die Funktion des Zentralnervensystems der Arthropoden. *Arch. ges. Physiol. Pflüger's* 68:449–545.

12. Bethe, A. 1897–1898. Das Centralnervensystem von *Carcinus maenas. Arch. mikroskop. Anat. u. Entwicklungsges.* 50:460–546, 589–639; 51:382–452.

13. Bethe, A. 1930. Studien über die Plastizität des Nervensystems. I. Mitteilung. Arachnoideen und Crustaceen. *Arch. ges. Physiol. Pflüger's* 224:793–820.

14. Blum, H. F. 1934. Le mécanisme d'orientation de la larve de *Homarus vulgaris* sous l'influence de la lumière. *Bull. inst. océanog. No.* 660:1–4.

15. Blum, H. F. 1935. An analysis of oriented movements of animals in light fields. *Cold Spring Harbor Symposia Quant. Biol.* 3:210–223.

16. Bohn, G. 1902. Des mécanismes respiratoires chez les Crustacés Décapodes. *Bull. sci. France et Belg.* 36:178–551.

17. Brenner, H. 1939. Die Beziehung zwischen Muskelreaktion und Querstreifung. *Z. Zellforsch. u. mikroskop. Anat.* 29:251–276.

18. Cannon, H. G. 1926. On the feeding mechanism of a freshwater ostracod, *Pionocypris vidua* (O. F. Müller). *J. Linnean Soc. London Zool.* 36:325–335.

19. Cannon, H. G. 1927. On the feeding mechanism of *Nebalia bipes. Trans. Roy. Soc. Edinburgh* 55:355–369.

20. Cannon, H. G. 1928. On the feeding mechanism of the copepods, *Calanus finmarchicus* and *Diaptomus gracilis. Brit. J. Exptl. Biol.* 6:131–144.

21. Cannon, H. G. 1931. Nebaliacea. *Discovery Repts.* 3:199–222.

22. Cannon, H. G. 1933. On the feeding mechanism of the Branchiopoda. *Phil. Trans. Roy. Soc. London* B222:267–352.

23. Cannon, H. G., and Manton, S. M. 1927. On the feeding mechanism of a mysid crustacean, *Hemimysis lamornae. Trans. Roy. Soc. Edinburgh* 55:219–253.

24. Chadwick, L. E. 1953. The motion of the wings. Aerodynamics and flight metabolism. *In:* "Insect Physiology" (K. D. Roeder, ed.), pp. 577–636. Wiley, New York.

25. Cochran, D. M. 1935. The skeletal musculature of the blue crab. *Smithsonian Inst. Publs. Misc. Collections* 92(9):1–76.

26. Cushing, D. H. 1955. Some experiments on the vertical migration of zooplankton. *J. Animal Ecol.* 24:137–166.

27. Daniel, R. J. 1933. Comparative study of the abdominal musculature in Malacostraca. Part III. *Proc. Trans. Liverpool Biol. Soc.* 47(Appendix):71–133.

28. Dembowski, J. B. 1926. Notes on the behavior of the fiddler crab. *Biol. Bull.* 50:179–201.

29. Demoll, R. 1909. Über die Augen und die Augenstielreflexe von *Squilla mantis. Zool. Jahrb. Abt. Anat. u. Ontog. Tiere* 27:171–212.

30. Dennell, R. 1933. The habits and feeding mechanism of the amphipod *Haustorius arenarius* Slabber. *J. Linnean Soc. London Zool.* 38:363–388.

31. Dennell, R. 1937. On the feeding mechanism of *Apseudes talpa*, and the evolution of the peracaridan feeding mechanisms. *Trans. Roy. Soc. Edinburgh* 59:57–78.

32. Dietrich, W. 1915. Die Metamorphose der freilebenden Süsswasser-Copepoden. I. *Z. wiss. Zoöl.* 113:252–324.

33. Dixon, A. Y. 1944. Notes on certain aspects of the biology of *Cumopsis goodsiri* (Van Beneden) and some other cumaceans in relation to their environment. *J. Marine Biol. Assoc. United Kingdom* **26**:61–71 .

34. Doflein, F. 1910. Lebensgewohnheiten und Anpassungen bei dekapoden Krebsen. "Festschrift zum 60 Geburtstag Richard Hertwigs," Vol. 3, pp. 215–292. Fischer, Jena.

35. Drach, P. 1949. Principales données sur les relations entre la glande du sinus, la mue et le métabolisme des Crustacés Décapodes. *Bull. biol. France et Belg.* Suppl. 33, 164–173.

36. Eckert, F. 1935. Die positiv phototaktische Einstellreaktion des Komplexauges von *Daphnia pulex* im Zweilichterversuch. *Lotos* **83**:1–30.

37. Eriksson, S. 1934. Studien über die Fangapparate der Branchiopoden nebst einigen phylogenetischen Bemerkungen. *Zool. Bidr. Uppsala* **15**:23–287.

38. Ewald, W. F. 1910. Über Orientierung, Lokomotion und Lichtreaktionen einiger Cladoceren. *Biol. Zentr.* **30**:1–16; 49–63; 379–399.

39. Flückiger, E. 1951. Die Wirkung von 1-Adrenalin an *Daphnia magna* Str. *Kgl. Fysiograf. Sällskap. Lund Förh.* **21**:63–68.

40. Forsman, B. 1938. Untersuchungen über die Cumaceen des Skageraks. *Zool. Bidr. Uppsala* **18**:1–161.

41. Fox, H. Munro. 1949. On *Apus:* its rediscovery in Britain, nomenclature and habits. *Proc. Zool. Soc. London* **119**:693–702.

42. Fox, H. Munro, and Mitchell, Y. 1953. Relation of the rate of antennal movement in *Daphnia* to the number of eggs carried in the brood pouch. *J. Exptl. Biol.* **30**:238–242.

43. Foxon, G. E. H. 1934. Notes on the swimming methods and habits of certain crustacean larvae. *J. Marine Biol. Assoc. United Kingdom* **19**:829–849.

44. Foxon, G. E. H. 1936. Notes on the natural history of certain sand-dwelling Cumacea. *Ann. Mag. Nat. Hist.* [10] **17**:377–393.

45. Fryer, G. 1956. A cladoceran *Dadaya macrops* (Daday) and an ostracod *Oncocypris mülleri* (Daday) associated with the surface film of water. *Ann. Mag. Nat. Hist.* [12] **9**:733–736.

46. Gebler, K. 1955. Über die Verwendung von *Daphnia magna* in pharmakologischen Versuchen. *Arch. Hydrobiol. Suppl.* **22**:306–309.

47. George, C. J., Reuben, N., and Muthe, P. T. 1955. The trunk muscles of *Panulirus polyphagus*. *J. Animal Morphol. Physiol. Bombay* **2**:65–72.

48. Ginet, R. 1956. Études sur la biologie d'Amphipodes troglobies du genre *Niphargus*. I. Le creusement de terriers; relations avec le limon argileux. *Bull. soc. zool. France* **80**:332–349.

49. Gislén, T. 1947. Conquering terra firma. The transition from water to land-life. *Kgl. Fysiograf. Sällskap. Lund Förh.* **17**:216–235.

50. Gravier, C. 1922. Observations sur la locomotion chez l'Ocypode chevalier. *Ann. sci. nat. Zool.* [10] **5**:119–124.

51. Green, J. 1956. The structure and function of the post-abdomen of *Camptocercus* (Crustacea: Cladocera). *Proc. Zool. Soc. London* **126**:283–290.

52. Gurney, R. 1943. The larval development of two penaeid prawns from Bermuda of the Genera *Sicyonia* and *Penaeopsis*. *Proc. Zool. Soc. London* **B113**:1–16.

53. Hanko, B. 1926. *Iliocryptus balatonicus*, eine neue Cladocere aus der Gyttja des Balaton-Sees. *Arch. Balatonicum Budapest* **1**:97–115.

54. Harding, J. P. 1953. The first known example of a terrestrial ostracod. *Ann. Natal Museum* **12**:359–365.

55. Hardy, A. C., and Bainbridge, R. 1954. Experimental observations on the vertical migrations of plankton animals. *J. Marine Biol. Assoc. United Kingdom* 33:409–448.

56. Harms, J. W. 1937. Lebensablauf und Stammesgeschichte des *Birgus latro. Jena. Z. Naturw.* 71:1–34.

57. Harris, J. E. 1953. Physical factors involved in the vertical migration of plankton. *Quart. J. Microscop. Sci.* 94:537–550.

58. Harris, J. E., and Mason, P. 1956. Vertical migration in eyeless *Daphnia. Proc. Roy. Soc.* B145:280–290.

59. Harris, J. E., and Wolfe, U. K. 1955. A laboratory study of vertical migration. *Proc. Roy. Soc.* B144:329–354.

60. Hart, T. J. 1930. Preliminary notes on the bionomics of the amphipod, *Corophium volutator. J. Marine Biol. Assoc. United Kingdom* 16:761–789.

61. Heegaard, P. 1947. Contribution to the phylogeny of the arthropods. Copepoda. *Skrifter Univ. Zool. Mus. København* 8:1–227.

62. Hempel, G. 1952. Die Energetik des Feldheuschrecken-Sprunges. *Z. vergleich. Physiol.* 34:26–40.

63. Herrick, F. H. 1895. The American lobster, a study of its habits and development. *Bull. U. S. Fish Comm.* 15:1–252.

64. Herrick, F. H. 1911. Natural history of the American lobster. *U. S. Bur. Fisheries Bull.* 29:149–408.

65. Herter, K. 1927. Reizphysiologische Untersuchungen an der Karpfenlaus (*Argulus foliaceus*). *Z. vergleich. Physiol.* 5:283–370.

66. Herter, K. 1932. Beiträge zur Zentrenfunktion zehnfüssiger Krebse. *Z. vergleich. Physiol.* 17:209–266.

67. Hocking, B. 1953. The intrinsic range and speed of flight of insects. *Trans. Roy. Entomol. Soc. London* 104:223–345.

68. Holmes, S. J. 1901. Observations on the habits and natural history of *Amphithoe longimana. Biol. Bull.* 2:165–193.

69. Hughes, G. M. 1952. The co-ordination of insect movements. I. The walking movements of insects. *J. Exptl. Biol.* 29:267–284.

70. Hutchinson, G. E. 1953. Turbulence as random stimulation of sense organs. *Josiah Macy, Jr. Foundation, Trans. 9th Conference Cybernetics:* 155–158.

71. Hyman, O. W. 1922. Adventures in the life of a fiddler crab. *Smithsonian Inst. Publs. Repts.* 1920:443–459.

72. Kesling, R. V. 1951. The morphology of ostracod molt stages. *Illinois Biol. Monographs* 21:1–324.

73. Kesling, R. V. 1956. The ostracod, a neglected little crustacean. *Turtox News, Chicago* 34:82–86; 90–94; 114–115.

74. Klie, W. 1926. Ostracoda. *In:* "Biologie der Tiere Deutschlands" (P. Schulze, ed.), Lfg. 22, Teil 16, pp. 1–56. Borntraeger, Berlin.

75. Koepcke, H. W., and Koepcke, M. 1953. Contribucion al conocimiento de la forma de vida de *Ocypode gaudichaudii. Rev. cienc. (Peru)* 55:157–202.

76. Kühl, H. 1931. Beitrag zur Plastizität des Nervensystems bei Brachyuren. *Z. vergleich. Physiol.* 14:450–461.

77. Kühl, H. 1932. Beobachtungen zur Plastizität des Nervensystems bei langschwänzigen Krebsen (Hummer, Flusskrebs). *Arch. ges. Physiol. Pflüger's* 229:636–641.

78. Kühl, H. 1933. Die Fortbewegung der Schwimmkrabben mit Bezug auf die Plastizität des Nervensystems. *Z. vergleich. Physiol.* 19:489–521.

79. Kühl, H. 1953. Über das Aufsuchen des Siedelplatzes durch die Cyprislarven von *Balanus improvisus. Verhandl. deut. zool. Ges.* 1952:189–200.

80. Kükenthal, W., and Krumbach, T. (eds.) 1926. Crustacea. *In:* "Handbuch der Zoologie," Bd. 3, Hälfte 1, pp. 277–1158. de Gruyter, Berlin.

81. Kunkel, B. W. 1918. The Arthrostraca of Connecticut. *Conn. State Geol. and Nat. Hist. Survey Bull. No.* 26:1–261.

82. Lindberg, R. G. 1955. Growth, population dynamics, and field behavior in the spiny lobster, *Panulirus interruptus. Univ. Calif. (Berkeley) Publs. Zoöl.* 59:157–248.

83. Linder, F. 1952. Contributions to the morphology and taxonomy of the Branchiopoda Notostraca. *Proc. U. S. Natl. Museum* 102:1–69.

84. List, T. 1895. Morphologisch-biologische Studien über den Bewegungsapparat der Arthropoden. I. Theil: *Astacus fluviatilis. Gegenbaurs morphol. Jahrb. Leipzig* 22:380–440.

85. Lochhead, J. H. 1936. On the feeding mechanism of the nauplius of *Balanus perforatus. J. Linnean Soc. London Zool.* 39:429–442.

86. Lochhead, J. H. 1937. The feeding mechanism of Crustacea Branchiopoda. Doctoral thesis, Cambridge University, England.

87. Lochhead, J. H. 1939a. Functions of the two types of eye in the brine shrimp, *Artemia. Anat. Record* 75, Suppl.: 64.

88. Lochhead, J. H. 1939b. Mechanical factors controlling swimming positions in aquatic invertebrates and particularly in the brine shrimp, *Artemia. Anat. Record* 75, Suppl.: 65.

89. Lochhead, J. H. 1942. Control of swimming position by mechanical factors and proprioception. *Quart. Rev. Biol.* 17:12–30.

90. Lowndes, A. G. 1933. The feeding mechanism of *Chirocephalus diaphanus* Prévost, the fairy shrimp. *Proc. Zool. Soc. London* 1933:1093–1118.

91. Lowndes, A. G. 1935. The swimming and feeding of certain calanoid copepods. *Proc. Zool. Soc. London* 1935:687–715.

92. Lowndes, A. G. 1942. The displacement method of weighing living aquatic organisms. *J. Marine Biol. Assoc. United Kingdom* 25:555–574.

93. Lundblad, O. 1920. Vergleichende Studien über die Nahrungsaufnahme einiger schwedischer Phyllopoden, nebst synonymischen, morphologischen und biologischen Bemerkungen. *Arkiv Zool.* 13(16):1–114.

94. Luntz, A. 1929. Weitere Untersuchungen über die Sinkgeschwindigkeit von Süsswasserorganismen. *Zool. Jahrb. Abt. Allgem. Zool. Physiol. Tiere* 46: 465–482.

95. MacGinitie, G. E. 1930. The natural history of the mud-shrimp, *Upogebia pugettensis. Ann. Mag. Nat. Hist.* [10] 6:36–44.

96. MacGinitie, G. E. 1934. The natural history of *Callianassa californiensis. Am. Midland Naturalist* 15:166–177.

97. MacGinitie, G. E. 1935. Ecological aspects of a California marine estuary. *Am. Midland Naturalist* 16:629–765.

98. MacKay, D. C. G. 1943. The behavior of the Pacific edible crab *Cancer magister. J. Comp. Psychol.* 36:255–268.

99. Manton, S. M. 1928. On some points in the anatomy and habits of the lophogastrid Crustacea. *Trans. Roy. Soc. Edinburgh* 56:103–119.

100. Manton, S. M. 1930. Notes on the habits and feeding mechanisms of *Anaspides* and *Paranaspides. Proc. Zool. Soc. London* 1930:791–800.

101. Manton, S. M. 1952a. The evolution of arthropodan locomotory mechanisms. Part 2. General introduction to the locomotory mechanisms of the Arthropoda. *J. Linnean Soc. London Zool.* 42:93–117.

102. Manton, S. M. 1952b. The evolution of arthropodan locomotory mechanisms. Part 3. The locomotion of the Chilopoda and Pauropoda. *J. Linnean Soc. London Zool.* 42:118–167.

103. Manton, S. M. 1953. Locomotory habits and the evolution of the larger arthropodan groups. *Symposia Soc. Exptl. Biol. No.* 7:339–376.

104. Margalef, R. 1951. Observaciones sobre *Triops* (= *Apus*) *cancriformis* de una localidad catalana. *Publs. inst. biol. apl. (Barcelona)* 9:247–254.

105. Mathias, P. 1937. Biologie des Crustacés Phyllopodes. *Actualités sci. et ind. No.* 447:1–109.

106. Matula, J. 1912. Die Regulation der Atemrhythmik bei *Squilla mantis. Arch. ges. Physiol. Pflüger's* 144:109–131.

107. Matula, J. 1917. Untersuchungen über die Leistungen der Nervenzentren bei Dekapoden. *Arch. ges. Physiol. Pflüger's* 169:503–516.

108. Mead, H. T. 1917. Notes on the natural history and behavior of *Emerita analoga. Univ. Calif. (Berkeley) Publs. Zoöl.* 16:431–438.

109. Menner, E. 1938. Studien über die Bewegung von *Artemia salina* und *Branchipus stagnalis. Zool. Anz.* 122:49–65.

110. Monod, T. 1926. Les Gnathiidae. Essai monographique. *Mém. soc. sci. nat. Maroc* 13:1–668.

111. Moore, G. M. 1939. A limnological investigation of the microscopic benthic fauna of Douglas Lake, Michigan. *Ecol. Monographs* 9:537–582.

112. Müller, G. W. 1893. Über Lebensweise und Entwickelungsgeschichte der Ostracoden. *Sitzber. kgl. preuss. Akad. Wiss.* 1893:355–381.

113. Müller, R. T. 1918. *Tanymastix lacunae* (Guérin) aus dem Eichener See (südl. Schwarzwald). *Z. Biol.* 69:141–274.

114. Needham, A. E. 1947. Excessive hydration in an animal with an open type of circulation. *Nature* 160:755.

115. Norris, E., and Crisp, D. J. 1953. The distribution and planktonic stages of the cirripede *Balanus perforatus* Bruguière. *Proc. Zool. Soc. London* 123:393–409.

116. Parker, G. H. 1901. The reactions of copepods to various stimuli, and the bearing of this on daily depth migrations. *Bull. U. S. Fish Comm.* 21:103–123.

117. Parker, T. J., and Haswell, W. A. 1940. "A Text-Book of Zoology," Vol. I, 6th ed., 770 pp. Macmillan, London.

118. Pearse, A. S., Humm, H. J., and Wharton, G. W. 1942. Ecology of sand beaches at Beaufort, N. C. *Ecol. Monographs* 12:135–190.

119. Pearson, J. C. 1939. The early life histories of some American Penaeidae. *U. S. Bur. Fisheries Bull.* 49(30):1–73.

120. Pennak, R. W. 1953. "Freshwater Invertebrates of the United States," 769 pp. Ronald, New York.

121. Peters, N., and Panning, A. 1933. Die chinesische Wollhandkrabbe (*Eriocheir sinensis,* H. Milne-Edwards) in Deutschland. *Zool. Anz.* 104, Erganz. Bd.: 1–180.

122. Pravda, O. 1950. Fluorescence-analysis of some Crustacea. *Věstnik Českoslov. zool. společnosti Praze* 14:267–319.

123. Prosser, C. L. 1935. Action potentials in the nervous system of the crayfish. III. Central responses to proprioceptive and tactile stimulation. *J. Comp. Neurol.* 62:495–505.

124. Prosser, C. L. 1946. The physiology of nervous systems of invertebrate animals. *Physiol. Revs.* 26:337–382.

125. Rádl, E. 1902. Ueber die Lichtreaktionen der Arthropoden auf die Drehscheibe. *Biol. Zentr.* 22:728–732.

126. Reid, D. M. 1938. Burrowing methods of *Talorchestia deshayesii* (Audouin) (Crustacea, Amphipoda). *Ann. Mag. Nat. Hist.* [11] 1:155–157.

127. Remane, A. 1952. Die Besiedelung des Sandbodens im Meere und die Bedeutung der Lebensformtypen für die Ökologie. *Verhandl. deut. zool. Ges.* 1951: 327–359.

128. Sars, G. O. 1898. On the propagation and early development of Euphausiidae. *Arch. Math. Naturvidenskab* 20(11):1–41.

129. Sars, G. O. 1901. Contributions to the knowledge of the freshwater Entomostraca of South America, as shown by artificial hatching from dried material. Part I. Cladocera. *Arch. Math. Naturvidenskab* 23(3):1–102.

130. Schäfer, W. 1954. Form und Funktion der Brachyuren-Schere. *Abhandl. senckenberg. naturforsch. Ges. No.* 489:1–65.

131. Schäferna, K. 1931. Studien über Phyllopoda Anostraca. *Věstník králov. Ceské společnosti nauk Třida Mat.-přirod.* 2(17):1–32.

132. Schallek, W. 1942. Some mechanisms controlling locomotor activity in the crayfish. *J. Exptl. Zool.* 91:155–167.

133. Schellenberg, A. 1929. Körperbau und Grabweise einiger Amphipoden. *Zool. Anz.* 85:186–190.

134. Schlick, W. 1943. *Haustorius arenarius* (Slabber). Ein merkwürdiger Flohkrebs als "Schwimmgraber" im feuchten Sandstrande der Nordsee. *Zool. Anz.* 142:160–172.

135. Schreiber, E. 1922. Beiträge zur Kenntnis der Morphologie, Entwicklung und Lebensweise der Süsswasser-Ostracoden. *Zool. Jahrb. Abt. Anat. u. Ontog. Tiere* 43:485–538.

136. Schuster-Dieterichs, O. 1956. Die Makrofauna am sandigen Brandungsstrand von El Salvador. *Senckenbergiana Biol.* 37:1–56.

137. Scourfield, D. J. 1894. Entomostraca and the surface-film of water. *J. Linnean Soc. London Zool.* 25:1–19.

138. Scourfield, D. J. 1900. On the swimming peculiarities of *Daphnia* and its allies. *J. Quekett Microscop. Club* [2] 7:395–404.

139. Seifert, R. 1932. Raumorientierung und Phototaxis der anostraken Euphyllopoden. *Z. vergleich. Physiol.* 16:111–184.

140. Skogsberg, T. 1920. Studies on marine ostracods. *Zool. Bidr. Uppsala Suppl.* 1: 1–784.

141. Smallwood, M. E. 1903. The beach flea: *Talorchestia longicornis. Cold Spring Harbor Monographs* 1:1–27.

142. Smallwood, M. E. 1905. The salt-marsh amphipod: *Orchestia palustris. Cold Spring Harbor Monographs* 3:1–21.

143. Snodgrass, R. E. 1952. The sand crab *Emerita talpoida* (Say) and some of its relatives. *Smithsonian Inst. Publs. Misc. Collections* 117(8):1–34.

144. Snodgrass, R. E. 1956. Crustacean metamorphoses. *Smithsonian Inst. Publs. Misc. Collections* 131(10):1–78.

145. Sollmann, T., and Webb, W. 1941. Pharmacologic responses of *Daphnia magna*. *J. Pharmacol. Exptl. Therap.* 71:261–267.

146. Spandl, H. 1926. Copepoda. *In:* "Biologie der Tiere Deutschlands" (P. Schulze, ed.), Lfg. 19, Teil 15, pp. 1–73. Borntraeger, Berlin.

147. Sperry, R. W. 1945. The problem of central nervous reorganization after nerve regeneration and muscle transposition. *Quart. Rev. Biol.* 20:311–369.

148. Stålberg, G. 1934. Beitrag zur Kenntnis der Biologie von *Mysis relicta* des Vättern. *Arkiv Zool.* 26A:1–29.

149. Storch, O. 1925. Cladocera. *In:* "Biologie der Tiere Deutschlands" (P. Schulze, ed.), Lfg. 15, Teil 14, pp. 23–102. Borntraeger, Berlin.

150. Storch, O. 1928. Der Nahrungserwerb zweier Copepodennauplien (*Diaptomus gracilis* und *Cyclops strenuus*). *Zool. Jahrb. Abt. Allgem. Zool. Physiol. Tiere* 45:385–436.

151. Storch, O. 1929. Die Schwimmbewegung der Copepoden, auf Grund von Mikro-Zeitlupenaufnahmen analysiert. *Verhandl. deut. zool. Ges.* 33:118–129.

152. Tait, J. 1917a. Experiments and observations on Crustacea: Part III. Limb-flexures and limb-taxis in the Peracarida. *Proc. Roy. Soc. Edinburgh* 37:69–94.

153. Tait, J. 1917b. Experiments and observations on Crustacea: Part IV. Some structural features pertaining to *Glyptonotus*. *Proc. Roy. Soc. Edinburgh* 37:246–303.

154. Tait, J. 1917c. Experiments and observations on Crustacea: Part V. A functional interpretation of certain structural features in the pleon of macrurous decapods. *Proc. Roy. Soc. Edinburgh* 37:304–305.

155. Tait, J. 1927. Experiments and observations on Crustacea: Part VII. Some structural and physiological features of the valviferous isopod *Chiridotea*. *Proc. Roy. Soc. Edinburgh* 46:334–348.

156. Tattersall, W. M., and Tattersall, O. S. 1951. "The British Mysidacea," 460 pp. Ray Society, London.

157. Templeman, W. 1940. The life history of the lobster. *Newfoundland Dept. Nat. Resources Govt. Service Bull. (Fisheries)* 15:1–42.

158. Valente, D., and Edwards, G. A. 1955. The regulation of the activity rhythm of the crab (*Trichodactylus petropolitanus*). *Univ. São Paulo, Fac. filosof. ciênc. e letras Bol. No. 207, Zool. No.* 20:5–17.

159. Veil, C. 1934. Différenciation structurale, chronaxie de constitution et de subordination des fléchisseurs et extenseurs des pattes de la crevette grise. *Compt. rend. soc. biol.* 115:845–846.

160. Verwey, J. 1949. Habitat selection in marine animals. *Acta Biotheor. Leiden (B)* (= *Folia Biotheor.*) 4:1–22.

161. Voelkel, H. 1922. Die Fortbewegungsarten des Flusskrebses. *Arch. ges. Physiol. Pflüger's* 194:224–229.

162. von Buddenbrock, W. 1914. Über die Orientierung der Krebse im Raum. *Zool. Jahrb. Abt. Allgem. Zool. Physiol. Tiere* 34:479–514.

163. von Frisch, K., and Kupelwieser, H. 1913. Über den Einfluss der Lichtfarbe auf die phototaktischen Reaktionen niederer Krebse. *Biol. Zentr.* 33:517–552.

164. von Holst, E. 1943. Über relative Koordination bei Arthropoden. *Arch. ges. Physiol. Pflüger's* 246:847–865.

165. von Holst, E. 1948. Von der Mathematik der nervösen Ordnungsleistung. *Experientia* 4:374–381.

166. Wagler, E. 1927. Über die "Schwebefortsätze" der Daphnien. *Zool. Anz.* **74:** 284–302.
167. Watkin, E. E. 1939. The swimming and burrowing habits of some species of the amphipod Genus *Bathyporeia. J. Marine Biol. Assoc. United Kingdom* **23:**457–465.
168. Watkin, E. E. 1940. The swimming and burrowing habits of the amphipod *Urothoë marina. Proc. Roy. Soc. Edinburgh* **60:**271–280.
169. Wautier, J. 1950. Réponses de quelques invertébrés aux actions combinées de la pesanteur et d'un courant d'eau vertical. *Bull. mens. soc. linnéenne Lyon* **19:**199–201.
170. Weis-Fogh, T. 1956. Biology and physics of locust flight. II. *Phil. Trans. Roy. Soc. London* **B239:**459–510.
171. Welsh, J. H. 1932. Temperature and light as factors influencing the rate of swimming of larvae of the mussel crab, *Pinnotheres maculatus. Biol. Bull.* **63:** 310–326.
172. Wesenberg-Lund, C. 1939. "Biologie der Süsswassertiere. Wirbellose Tiere," 818 pp. Springer, Vienna.
173. Wetzel, A. 1932. Studien über die Biologie der Caprelliden. I. Bewegung, Nahrungserwerb, Aufenthaltsort. *Z. wiss. Zoöl.* **141:**347–398.
174. Wilson, C. B. 1902. North American parasitic copepods of the Family Argulidae. *Proc. U. S. Natl. Museum* **25:**635–742.
175. Wilson, C. B. 1917. The economic relations, anatomy, and life history of the Genus *Lernaea. U. S. Bur. Fisheries Bull.* **35:**163–198.
176. Woltereck, R. 1913. Über Funktion, Herkunft und Entstehungsursachen der sogen. "Schwebe-Fortsätze" pelagischer Cladoceren. *Zoologica Stuttgart* **26:** 475–550.
177. Woltereck, R. 1929. Sinkgeschwindigkeit, Ernährungszustand und pelagische Form. *Zool. Jahrb. Abt. Allgem. Zool. Physiol. Tiere* **46:**209–213.
178. Worcester, D. C. 1914. Note on the occurrence of a flying crustacean in the Philippine Islands. *Philippine J. Sci.* [D] **9:**57.
179. Yonge, C. M. 1955. Egg attachment in *Crangon vulgaris* and other Caridea. *Proc. Roy. Soc. Edinburgh* **B65:**369–400.
180. Zimmer, C. 1933. Mysidacea. *In:* "Die Tierwelt der Nord- und Ostsee" (G. Grimpe and E. Wagler, eds.), Lfg. 23, Teil Xg₃, pp. 29–69. Akademische Verlagsges., Leipzig.
181. Zimmer, C. 1941. Cumacea. *In:* "Bronn's Tierreich," Bd. 5, Abt. 1, Bch. 4, pp. 1–222. Akademische Verlagsges., Leipzig.

CHAPTER 10

L. PARDI

F. PAPI

KINETIC AND TACTIC RESPONSES

I. *INTRODUCTION*

Tactic responses are oriented reactions to external stimuli. In nature they combine with locomotion to lead animals directly to particular environmental conditions. Kinetic responses are nonoriented reactions, but they may also bring about the same result indirectly by physiologically simpler mechanisms. Both types of reaction, therefore, are of notable biological importance since they make it possible for the animal to reach and maintain its normal ecological niche. Moreover, they are a relatively simple part of the complex mechanisms involved in instinctive behavior. Their significance in crustaceans has repeatedly been the subject of investigation.[38,54,61,65,99–101,113–115,117,120]

Kinetic and tactic responses may be classified on several different bases. One of these depends on the nature of the effective stimuli, each usually with its corresponding type of sense organ. Accordingly, there are responses to photic, chemical, thermal, or mechanical stimuli. A second classification depends on the stimulating field concerned.[87] This may be of four kinds: 1) without directionality and without gradient (e.g. uniformly diffuse light); 2) without directionality but with gradient (e.g. a chemical diffusion gradient); 3) with directionality but without gradient (e.g. sunlight); 4) with directionality and with gradient (e.g. an unfocused point light source). Finally there is the classification of these responses based on the underlying mechanisms.

II. *FUNDAMENTAL MECHANISMS*

A. KINESES

Kineses are locomotor responses whose intensity is related to that of the stimulus and which involve movements not oriented either to the gradient or source of the stimulus if these exist. They constitute the only possible response when the stimulus lacks both gradient and directionality; but they occur in any case when the receptors, either because of their structure or the nature of the stimulus or both, cannot

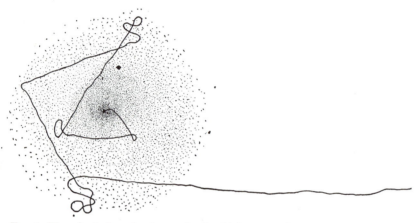

FIG. 1. Hypothetical path of an animal which approaches the center of diffusion of a favorable stimulus klinokinetically. The trail is straight if the stimulation is constant or increasing; it twists if the stimulation decreases. (From Wigglesworth.[134])

directly establish the position of the source of stimulation. Orthokinetic responses may be distinguished from klinokinetic[44] (= phobotactic)[61] responses although in fact they are combined.

Orthokinesis is a change in activity or the rate of locomotion or both induced by variations in stimulus intensity. Ordinarily this response is maximal to unfavorable stimuli and minimal under favorable stimulation. Hence in a gradient the animal remains longer in the regions favorable to it.

Klinokinesis (Fig. 1) is an alteration in the frequency of changes in direction effected by stimuli of variable intensity. When an animal which is proceeding linearly or with a low, constant angular velocity encounters an unfavorable environmental zone, the rate of direction change may be increased by klinokinesis. Random directional changes decrease in frequency as soon as the animal happens once again into a favorable zone so that this response is reduced. If perchance the animal comes to the center of an extensive unfavorable zone, it does not become trapped there; instead, adaptation intervenes to reduce the angular velocity so that the linear segments in its path become longer until it leaves the unfavorable zone. Flight or escape reactions (Schreckreaktionen) may be considered a special type of klinokinesis.

B. TAXES

In considering taxes it is necessary to distinguish the oriented turning (the taxis sensu strictu[54]) with which the animal reaches and/or maintains a particular position of the body axes with respect to the stimulus source or its gradient, and the locomotion which can follow this orientation.

A descriptively convenient classification of oriented responses may be based on the animal's rotation about its three main reference axes in relation to the stimulus.[71] 1) There may be turning about the dorsoventral axis (spin or yaw). When the longitudinal axis is turned toward the stimulus source, orientation is said to be direct. From this position a spin of less than 180° leads to transverse alignments. 2) There may be turning around the longitudinal axis (roll). Orientation is perpendicular when the dorsoventral axis is directed toward the source. Rolling leads to an oblique orientation. 3) Finally there may be turning around the transverse axis (pitch, Neigung); this alters direct or perpendicular orientation to inclined positions. Of course, any combination of these three kinds of rotation is possible in an animal's response.

Locomotion toward the source in a directional field may be defined as positive and that away from the source, as negative. Since crustaceans frequently may have retrograde, lateral, or oblique (in decapods) locomotion, various species may move toward or away from the stimulus with different orientations of their longitudinal axis. Consequently the receptors involved may be turned toward or away from the source at various angles.

The underlying mechanisms of oriented turning, following Kühn's analysis,[61,62] are of three well-known types: tropotaxis, telotaxis, and menotaxis.

Tropotaxis results from the maintenance of equal receptor excitation on the two sides of the body. If the symmetrical receptors are stimulated with different intensities, reflex turning takes place until equal stimulation is again attained. The turning may be toward either the more or the less intensely stimulated side depending on internal conditions. As a result, the animal will turn toward or away from the stimulus. Inactivating one of the bilateral receptors causes continuous circling (circus movement) until adaptation intervenes.

In telotaxis, the receptor concerned has an area whose localized stimulation does not provoke turning reflexes. This area therefore constitutes a sort of fixation zone. In contrast, stimulation of other areas of the sensory surface initiates turning movements which bring the stimulus back into the fixation zone. This kind of orientation, unlike a tropotaxis, can be effected by one sense organ of a bilateral pair, and removal of its opposite member does not evoke circus movements.

Finally, menotaxis is a transverse orientation to a directional stimulus; different particular patterns of stimulation are maintained on the receptors of the two sides.

This analysis of taxes has been criticized a number of times and the difficulty of accounting for all the known facts on its basis has been stressed. The concepts involved were based originally on a rigidly reflex-dominated analysis of behavior and on the assumption that the key to such taxes lay in peculiarities of receptor organization. At the same time the central nervous system was treated as if a given input automatically gave rise to a fixed predetermined output.[127]

Principally through the work of von Holst and his school, a different conception has recently been advanced to explain results obtained in crustaceans[99-101] as well as in insects[71,98] and fish.[126] An important aspect of these investigations is the experimental demonstration that an animal's orientation does not automatically follow reflex predictions based on the sensory input of a single receptor modality. On the contrary, the central nervous system is shown to govern the organism's position in space on the basis of all the information which reaches it as a result of the total pattern of peripheral stimulation. Therefore, it is centrally, rather than peripherally, determined moment by moment, which position the animal will assume in a stimulating field and which aspects of peripheral stimulation will or will not evoke overt behavior.[126]

Where the receptors are simple and the nature of the stimulus permits, its unequal effects on bilateral receptors may differentially by their afferent impulses activate two correspondingly inferior hemicenters in the central nervous system. If the higher centers do not intervene, reflex turning may then take place until an orientation is achieved which, at that moment, represents the physiologically neutral position in the field. Such behavior corresponds descriptively to the tropotaxis of Kühn. But the same mechanism may, for example, govern transverse orientation if a stimulating bias coming from higher nervous centers compensates the lack of equilibrium in the lower ones. In more complex systems an additional capacity to evaluate differentially the intensity of stimulation in specific zones of the same receptor may be present. This permits a more precise orientation in the stimulating field.

If the structure of the receptors and the type of stimuli permit, orientation may be regulated by the central evaluation of the localization of peripheral excitations on the sensory surface, rather than on their intensity alone. In such a case the stimulus, depending on its direction, would supposedly create a quantitatively different imbalance of excitation in the hemicenters concerned. With this mechanism, too, the animal could assume different orientation (direct, normal, transverse, oblique, or inclined) with respect to the stimulus under the influence of central compensation acting on the excitation established peripherally.

Thus, Kühn's classification of responses appears outmoded, at least in its original form and for the higher animal groups. Yet adequate analysis of individual cases has not progressed to the point where a more satisfactory analysis of all the known facts can be formulated according to mechanism. Therefore, this review will be mainly descriptive and organized according to the nature of the stimuli.

III. *RESPONSES TO LIGHT*

A. Directional Responses to Light

If a light field has a gradient or a directionality or, as most frequently occurs in laboratory experiments, both these characteristics, individual animals often move toward or away from the source, toward the more or less luminous region of the gradient. Here one speaks of photopositive or photonegative reactions without regard to mechanism. Where both gradient and directionality are present, there has been some discussion as to which of the two guides the animal's locomotion. For various planktonic Copepoda[106] and Cladocera,[113] for example, the direction of the source is of decisive importance (Fig. 2). In *Daphnia*, progression toward the light is possible also without eyes;[103] presumably this is based on a general dermal light sensitivity[113] (see Chapter 1).

There is an enormous literature both on the internal conditions which control the general direction of the light reactions in crustaceans and on the environmental factors which can modify it. Most Crustacea show positive or negative light responses so that indifference to light is relatively rare. Examples of photic responses in a variety of forms which do react are shown in Table 1. A few Crustacea have reactions of the same sign over wide limits of intensity; these may be either positive (Type 1) or negative (Type 2). However, the great majority of species react either positively or negatively depending on the intensity level. Of these, all are ordinarily positive in dim light and

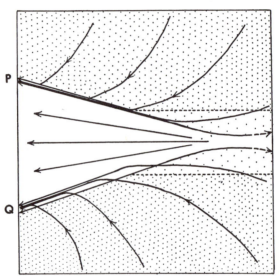

Fig. 2. Trails of photopositive marine planktonic crustaceans in a converging beam of light. The ray enters at *PQ*; animals moving toward the light reach zones of lower light intensity. (From Spooner.[106])

negative in very bright light. But at medium radiant energy levels some are positive (Type 3) and others negative (Type 4).

In addition to such relatively stable patterns of light response, many are known which vary with the physiological state of the organism. Thus in *Artemia*,[105] Cladocera,[21,34,114] Copepoda,[89] and nauplius larvae of Cirripedia,[42,89] a population of animals at medium intensities may consist of two groups of individuals, one photopositive and one photonegative. A specific individual shows continual alternation between them. Such changes in the sign of photic reactions can be correlated in many cases either with additional environmental factors or with various physiological changes.

TABLE 1

DIRECTIONAL LIGHT RESPONSES AT VARIOUS STIMULATING INTENSITIES[a]

Group	Examples	Type of response	Low intensities	Medium intensities	High intensities
Anostraca	*Chirocephalus*[105]	1	+	+	+
Copepoda	*Acartia clausi*[89]	1	+	+	+
Isopoda	Generally[1,10,24]	2	−	−	−
Decapoda	*Carcinus*	2	−	−	−
	Astacus	2	−	−	−
	Cambarus	2	−	−	−
Anostraca	*Eubranchipus serratus*	3	+	+	−
Cladocera	*Scapholeberis*	3	+	+	−
	Simocephalus	3	+	+	−
Ostracoda	*Cypridopsis*	3	+	+	−
Copepoda	*Labidocera*	3	+	+	−
Mysidacea	Several	3	+	+	−
Cumacea	*Diastylis*	3	+	+	−
Isopoda	*Idotea*	3	+	+	−
	Ligia	3	+	+	−
Amphipoda	*Gammarus*	3	+	+	−
	Talorchestia	3	+	+	−
	Podocerus	3	+	+	−
Decapoda	*Pagurus*	3	+	+	−
	Uca	3	+	+	−
	Galathea	3	+	+	−
	Several juvenile and larval forms	3	+	+	−
Anostraca	*Artemia salina*	4	+	−	−
Cladocera	*Alona*	4	+	−	−
Ostracoda	*Cypris*	4	+	−	−
Cirripedia	*Balanus improvisus* (larvae)	4	+	−	−
Isopoda	Many[128]	4	+	−	−
Amphipoda	*Niphargus*	4	+	−	−
	Ampithoe	4	+	−	−

[a] + = positive reaction toward the source or greater intensity; − = negative reactions away from source or greater intensity.[48]

Among the external factors influencing photic behavior the following may be cited. The albedo of the bottom is one of these. *Praunus flexuosus* and *P. inermis*, *Palaemon squilla* and *P. serratus*[86] are photopositive on a dark bottom and photonegative on a light one; the opposite is true of *Palaemon* zoeas.

For many forms, an increase in temperature at equal light intensities results in photonegativity and a decrease provokes photo-positive reactions (*Daphnia*,[86,89] Copepoda,[64,89] larvae of Cirripedia[86,91] and *Squilla*[38]). Opposite reactions take place in others (*Artemia*,[105] *Gammarus mucronatus, Orchestia*,[86] and *Armadillidium cinereum*[47]).

In terrestrial Isopoda (*Porcellio*,[1] *Armadillidium*,[47] *Oniscus asellus*[22,130]) and in Amphipoda (*Orchestia*[20]), a decrease in relative humidity or drying tends to render the animals more photopositive. Positive reactions are exhibited by terrestrial isopods (*Porcellio scaber, Oniscus asellus*) upon immersion also.[36]

Lowering the salinity of the medium generally results in photo-negative reactions by marine crustaceans, while increased concentration of the medium produces photopositive reactions in Copepoda,[64,89] larvae of Cirripedia[34,118] and *Palaemonetes*.[86] Dilution leads to negative reactions in nauplius larvae of *Artemia;* adult *Artemia*, on the other hand, appear indifferent within wide limits of salt content.[105]

Chemical modifications of the environment may also affect the direction of light reactions. In CO_2-rich and O_2-poor water there is generally an appearance or reinforcement of positive reactions (Anostraca, Cladocera, Mysidacea, *Palaemonetes*[48]). Marine *Gammarus*, in contrast to the fresh-water forms, do not modify their reaction at all in the face of such changes. The addition of acids, alcohols,[65] alkaloids (strychnine, caffeine), or water impurities[16] in general cause photopositivity, while bases usually have the opposite effect.[89] Finally, it should be recalled that mechanical stimuli (shaking, contact) in some cases strengthen positive reactions and in others, negative ones.[48] These are essentially escape or flight reactions.

Similarly, various internal changes within the animal can modify the sign of its light responses. For example in amphipods, as in insects, the sign of the photic responses is correlated with metabolic level.[85] Also light adaptation affects the sign of light responses in *Artemia*,[125] Cladocera,[52,53,125] Copepoda,[89] and *Homarus* larvae.[15] After light adaptation, an increase in the stimulus intensity tends to produce negative reactions, whereas an intensity decrease gives rise to positive ones. Also if animals live for long periods at given intensities their light reactions may change. After long exposure to light *Armadillidium* becomes photopositive.[73] *Oniscus asellus*, on the other hand, becomes photopositive after exposure to darkness.[23]

The nutritional state of the animal and also its stage in the sexual cycle may also influence photoreaction. In *Armadillidium cinereum*, fasting causes strongly positive reactions on which age and sex have little influence.[47] On the other hand, ovigerous females of *Daphnia* are particularly negative.[89]

Variations in light reactions occur in the course of diurnal cycles (Chapter 11), particularly in relation to periodic vertical migrations (Chapter 12). These have been explained on the basis of an endogenous physiological periodism in phase with the daily alternation between dark and light. But such an explanation is presumably not required in those cases where complete cycles of migration can be reproduced in the laboratory, merely by varying the intensity of illumination (*Acartia*[95] and *Daphnia*[46]). In the latter case external rather than internal factors provide the critical control.

Securely based on internal physiological phenomena is the alternation of positive and negative phases in constant intensity (polyphasic light reaction). This is displayed in the continuous migration from one end of a directional light field to the other (Cladocera,[21,113] Copepoda, nauplii of Cirripedia,[89] and Mysidacea[38,107]).

Ontogenetic changes in light responses are common. In general there is a greater photopositive tendency in younger, as compared to adult, stages. Thus in *Artemia* the nauplius larvae are photopositive, the adults negative;[12] the nauplii of *Tanymastix lacunae* (Anostraca) are photopositive until their fifth day and then become negative or indifferent;[74] those of *Trypetesa* (Cirripedia) are initially more strongly photopositive;[59] nauplius larvae of *Balanus* are more strongly positive at hatching than later.[89] Cyprids of *Balanus improvisus*, *B. amphitrite*, and *Chthamalus fragilis* are more generally photopositive but become clearly negative before fixation.[116] In larvae of *Homarus americanus* the reaction to light reverses at the same time the method of locomotion is altered. The first three instars are almost always photopositive and swim toward the light with the abdomen turned to it; the fourth stage may be equally photopositive but swims with the head toward the light; the fifth and the following stages live on the bottom and are always strongly photonegative.

B. PHOTOKINESES

1. *Orthokinesis.* It is well known that a sudden variation in light intensity can reduce the rate of locomotion. Abrupt illumination produces such an effect in *Oniscus asellus*, *Asellus communis*, *Hyalella knickerbockeri*, *Cambarus* sp.,[108] and *Uca pugnax*.[50] The interval between stimulation and reaction is inversely proportional to the light intensity.[108] Similarly, in *Daphnia* a sudden exposure to sunlight induces a characteristic oscillating motion[34]; red light is ineffective in inducing this reaction in *Leptodora*.[34] *Argulus foliaceus* begins to move following slight or transitory variations in illumination intensity.[49]

Under laboratory conditions a sudden passage from darkness into light may arrest the swimming movement of some Copepoda.[89] A similar response occurs in the nauplius larvae of *Balanus* at particularly high levels of irradiance.[34]

Acceleration of limb movement in fixed animals exposed to increasing illumination has been well documented in *Branchipus*,[69] *Triops*,[104] and *Hemimysis lamornae*.[40] In *Cambarus*[58] illumination of one eye increases the frequency and amplitude of the pereiopod movement on the same side of the body.

The same relation between light intensity and rate (or frequency) of limb movements in a fixed animal can be seen in variations in the speed of locomotion of free specimens. If *Daphnia* is exposed successively to different intensities in a light field without gradient, the speed of locomotion increases as a function of the logarithm of the intensity (log *I*).[114] *Daphnia pulex* "hops" with greater frequency in light than in the dark or in red light,[103] and a progressive diminution of intensity reduces the amplitude of the rowing movements of the antennae until complete immobility is reached. Recently, the greatest importance has been given to photo-orthokinetic responses to explain the ascent at low light intensities which characterizes the cycle of vertical migration of *Daphnia magna* produced in the laboratory by periodic variations in radiant intensity[46] (Chapter 12).

Even more frequently than pure orthokinesis, the kinetic components of phototaxis have been studied in many Crustacea. Essentially similar results have been obtained in Cladocera,[34,113,114,139] Ostracoda,[139] Copepoda,[132] nauplius larvae of Cirripedia[34] and Decapoda (*Pinnotheres*, *Hippa*),[132] as well as outside the Crustacea, e.g. in *Limulus*.[25] Accurate measurements of the locomotion of single *Daphnia* show that its velocity toward the light increases as a function of log *I*.[113] The speeds of oriented displacement away from the light, on the other hand, are independent of intensity at all the medium and low values of the latter but increase abruptly starting at a certain level, reaching their highest values almost at once.[113] With decreasing wavelengths of monochromatic light, the positive photokinetic influence of illumination grows, in *Daphnia*, along a sigmoid curve from red to violet. In *Acartia tonsa* (Copepoda),[96] the velocity of locomotion is independent of intensity in a horizontal light beam. A linear relation between light intensity and locomotor velocity occurs in larvae of the anostracan *Tanymastix lacunae* up to a critical intensity level which is lowered with decreased temperature and increased age.[74] Above this critical light intensity some other factor apparently limits speed of locomotion.

2. *Klinokinesis.* Much less well documented is the existence of photoklinokinetic responses, partly because less frequent use has been made of the proper experimental conditions for their best demonstration, which requires a light gradient in the complete absence of directionality. Of course, this is not proof that for the natural aggregation of animals in a zone of optimal light intensity, the klinokinetic mechanism alone or, more frequently, combined with orthokinesis, is unimportant.

To give only a few examples, the assembling of *Daphnia* in the optimal zone of an experimental horizontal light gradient[139] presumably is both ortho- and klinokinetic. The swarming of *Argulus* into the lightest region of an aquarium by avoidance responses to regions of lower light intensities[49] has been described as klinokinetic. An extensive series of experiments with a pure intensity gradient between 0.5 and 3500 lux has been carried out on various species of invertebrates[10] including the crustaceans *Porcellio scaber*, *Oniscus asellus*, and *Armadillidium cinereum*. All three species behave, in general, in a photophobic manner, assembling where the light is weakest (zone between 0.5 and 10–30 lux). Within this intensity range they remain at rest or moving without any orientation with respect to the gradient; this is a phenomenon common to many other species in their optimal zone.[27] Attainment and maintenance of the preferred location are brought about both by orthokinetic effects (lower velocity in the optimal zone) and klinokinetic effects (returning reactions at its margins). In *Porcellio* and *Armadillidium* there are also photophilic individuals which aggregate within the 400–600 lux zone.

Another reaction of *Armadillidium cinereum* generally attributable to photo-orthokinesis combined with klinokinesis is its aggregation in the dark part of a field which is half light and half dark.[47] Photoklinokinesis has also been described in the myrmecophilous isopod *Platyarthrus hoffmannseggi*.[19]

C. Phototaxes

Every oriented reaction in a light field is a phototaxis. Since reactions related to equilibrium are referred to in Chapter 13, the following discussion will deal principally with orientation by turning around the dorsoventral axis, i.e. orientation in azimuth. Most of our knowledge of such phototaxes comes from experiments carried out with single or multiple artificial lights, which establish directional fields having an intensity gradient.

1. *Direct orientation.* In terrestrial isopods (*Cylisticus, Oniscus, Trichoniscus, Armadillidium, Porcellio*)[47,73] direct orientation toward the light may occur apparently through a mechanism based on the evaluation of stimulus intensities reaching the photoreceptors of both sides. In diffuse light, photopositive animals which have been blinded unilaterally rotate toward the intact eye; photonegative animals rotate in the opposite direction. In a horizontal light beam, the positive individuals describe a curved path toward the intact side. In such cases the animals are presumably adjusted centrally to a direct orientation. If so, the turning movements represent attempts to compensate the central imbalance due to sensory excitation by turning. In these cases, compensation by higher nervous centers does not appear possible, at least within the time limits of the experiments. However, in some Isopoda (*Oniscus asellus*)[28] and Amphipoda (*Orchestia*)[20] central compensation apparently is possible, since even unilaterally blinded animals succeed, sooner or later, in moving toward the stimulating light in a straight line.

An analysis of the mechanism of light orientation has often been attempted by testing the orienting effects of two lights of equal or different intensities. The four major response patterns encountered in various Crustacea are shown in Table 2. In Type 1 responses, the

TABLE 2

RESPONSES TO TWO STIMULATING LIGHTS

Group	Examples	Type	Behavior
Cladocera	*Daphnia*[5,35]	1	Orient toward intermediate point between the lights
Copepoda	*Phyllothalestris mysis*[37]	1	
Cirripedia	*Lepas* larvae[67]	1	
Amphipoda	Caprellidae[133]	1	
	Corophium[37]	1	
Mysidacea	*Hemimysis lamornae*[39]	2	Orients directly to one of the two lights
Copepoda	*Calanus helgolandicus*[41]	3	Either intermediate or direct
Isopoda	*Armadillidium*[73]	3	
	Oniscus[28]	3	
Decapoda	Larvae[137]	3	
Isopoda	*Aega*[38]	4	Intermediate, direct, or alternating from one light to the other
Decapoda	*Carcinus*	4	
	Pagurus	4	

photopositive animals sooner or later exhibit a "point or zone of decision,"[121] often characterized by searching movements, beyond which the animal turns toward one of the two lights (e.g. *Daphnia*[5]). *Corophium* and *Phyllothalestris*,[38] having reached approximately the level of the two lights, stop swimming and fall to the bottom, where they then move in a straight line toward one light. With two lights of different intensities, the photopositive animals deviate more or less toward the side of the brighter light; similar behavior may occur with Type 3 responses also.[47] In certain cases (*Phyllothalestris mysis*) the orientation is the resultant of a parallelogram of forces determined by the direction of the lights and their intensities.[37]

Attempts to interpret these various behavior patterns have given rise to a vast and often contradictory literature. At present, a reinterpretation would be so hypothetical as to be premature. However, the variability in the behavior of some forms, even in successive tests with the same animal, demonstrates how much weight should be assigned to central factors and how inadequate any attempt at explanation would be if it depended purely on reflexes.

According to Kühn's terminology those forms, like certain Isopoda,[47,73] are considered tropotactic which upon unilateral blinding show noncompensated circus movements, whereas those forms are considered telotactic which can direct themselves with one eye toward the light or orient toward one source in a two-light field. Direct orientation by "fixation" toward an object and the so-called scototaxis, i.e. an orientation toward dark surfaces, described in *Carcinus*[6] and in Isopoda (*Oniscus* and *Porcellio*),[28] are telotactic responses.

2. *Transverse orientation.* Transverse orientation, or light compass movement, also occurs frequently among the crustaceans. A plausible neurophysiological mechanism for such behavior has already been postulated above (page 369).[14]

In a light beam consisting of parallel or almost parallel rays originating from the sun, moon, or other distant light sources, the maintenance of a constant angle of orientation will lead an animal to follow a straight-line course. But for a nearby source the constant angle path is a spiral which leads to the source or away from it depending on whether the angle of orientation is less or greater than 90°. The maintenance of such a menotactic angle can be demonstrated easily either with the mirror experiment of Santschi,[93] where the sun is shielded and its reflected image is projected on the animal, or with a rapid displacement of a stimulating light source either directly to a different azimuth or stroboscopically.[119] In either case the animal changes its orientation, rotating on its vertical axis so that the original angle of orientation is maintained relative to the new stimulus direction.

In forms with compound eyes experiments have shown that the minimum angular variation in the position of the light source with respect to the animal which can produce a change in the orientation is related to the angle between ommatidial axes. Thus the larger this ommatidial angle, the greater must be the change in the stimulus position required to alter the animal's course. This suggests that in such

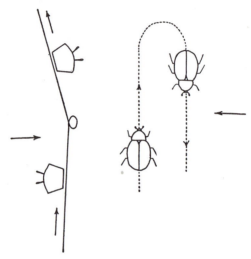

Fig. 3. Different behavior of *Carcinus* and of an insect upon a 180° change in the direction of incident light. (From Wolter.[138])

orientation the image of the light is fixated by a particular ommatidium.[121]

Transverse orientation of this type has been demonstrated in *Carcinus maenas*[138] (Fig. 3). But in this case, the possibility of lateral locomotion with either the right or left side leading may allow the animal to reorient itself with respect to the displaced source without changing its direction of motion significantly. In *Carcinus*, furthermore, the mobility of the eyestalks permits the animal within certain limits to maintain a given image position on its retinas with respect to the experimentally displaced light without rotating its body. Thus changes in stimulus position of less than 20° usually are compensated solely by ocular movements without changes in course. If ocular compensation is prevented by immobilizing the eyes, a full 100% compensating course change occurs even with variations of 20° in the position of the source.[138]

The actual angle of transverse orientation maintained by an animal is surely controlled by internal factors,[14,79] but ordinarily it does not exhibit any systematic variation. Different courses may succeed each other at longer or shorter intervals during experiments, but they seem unrelated to each other and at the "volition" of the crustacean.

A different state of affairs exists in the astronomical orientation of *Talitrus saltator*, other beach-inhabiting amphipods,[77,81–84,121] and the isopod *Tylos latreillei*.[80,81]

If, for example, *Talitrus saltator*, which lives in wet sand on the seashore, accidentally finds itself in dry sand or falls into the water, it can return directly to the beach zone it normally inhabits. The direction of its return is approximately perpendicular to the shore and constant during the course of the day. On a shore facing the ocean toward the west, *Talitrus* will orient itself toward the west if it falls into dry sand and toward the east if it finds itself in water. Specimens living on differently oriented shores have different directions of such flight movements. The direction taken is independent of nearness to the sea or the land and hence cannot, as has been postulated,[136] depend on optical stimuli coming from the shore. Instead it is based on the sight of the sun and the sky.

By reflecting sunlight on the animal from different azimuths one can cause its flight direction to be changed at will. Since the direction of these escape movements toward the ocean or inland remains constant in the course of the day, the angle of orientation to the sun evidently must vary in a continuous and regular manner during the day. And, naturally, this takes place in different ways for populations which live on shores with other geographical orientations. Thus, to cite a simplified example, animals on a beach with the ocean to the west will have on dry sand an angle of orientation of 180° around dawn (sun to the east), of 90° around noon, and 0° around sunset (Fig. 4).

Such regular variation in the angle of orientation to the sun is conditioned by rhythmical internal phenomena which persist in the dark within certain time limits (an internal "clock"). The course of this endogenous rhythm is controlled in turn by the daily alternation of light and darkness. By subjecting the animals to a day which is artificially retarded by 6 hr with respect to the normal day (illumination from noon to midnight), predictable deviations in the direction of flight are obtained; the treated animals assume at true noontime the same angle with respect to the sun which they normally would have assumed at six o'clock in the morning.[82] By transporting the animals in the dark to a different longitude, it has likewise been proved that the angle of orientation with respect to the sun is determined on the basis of an internal clock and not by external stimuli. This is clearly so because the animals regulate themselves in synchrony with the hour prevailing in the place from which they came.[76]

Recently it has been demonstrated[111] that *Hemigrapsus oregonensis* and *H. nudus* placed in a circular receptacle, and seeing only the sun and sky, are mainly distributed in directions parallel to the water line of the beach from which they are taken. This behavior presumably depends on sight of the sun, since uniform distribution is observed with an overcast sky. Quite probably similar methods of astronomical orientation can also be found in other littoral crustaceans. For example, oriented reactions under the name of hydrotropism have been described for *Carcinus*[32] and *Cambarus*,[109] which, when brought on land, can orient and return toward the water. It is significant that in blinded *Cambarus* this orientation is absent. In *Ligia* an oriented return either from the sea to the land or from the land to the sea has been described,[8,9] but the explanations suggested are not entirely satisfactory, and the involvement of astronomical factors has not been excluded.

D. SPECIAL CASES

1. *Responses to polarized light.* The transverse orientation which certain crustaceans assume in polarized light (Chapter 1) must be considered a particular form of phototaxis. The capacity of Crustacea to perceive polarized light was discovered in *Daphnia*.[94,112] The behavior of various other Cladocera, in addition to *Daphnia*, has been studied in vertical beams of polarized light entering the top of the experimental vessel. All these entomostracan species respond by swimming to and fro at right angles to the plane (*e* vector) of polarization. If the plane is rotated by 90°, the animals change their direction of swimming correspondingly.

Quantitative measurements have shown that *Mysidium gracile* in a similar vertical beam of linearly polarized light is also capable of

FIG. 4. Results of three experiments at different times with *Talitrus saltator* from a beach with the ocean to the west. The animals are placed in a glass receptacle whose dry bottom is divided into sixteen sectors. At any hour of the day these amphipods distribute themselves in the sectors toward the ocean by assuming a different angle with respect to the sun at the different times of day. The arrow indicates the azimuth of the "resultant direction" of this flight response. (Original.)

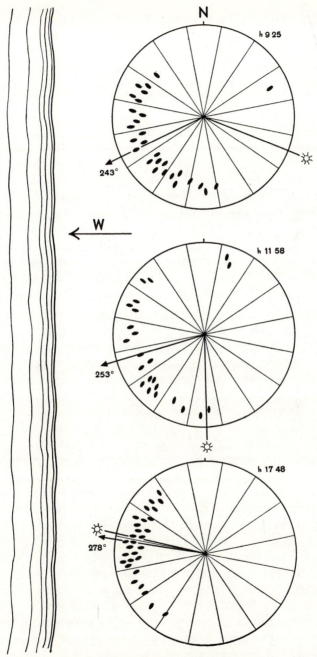

FIG. 4 (See legend on opposite page.)

orienting relative to the *e* vector of the polarization.[7] A significant preference is shown for orienting perpendicular to the plane with a minor peak parallel to it; orientation on an average was random 40% of the time. At present little is known concerning the actual importance of these behavior patterns in nature[11,33] although underwater illumination, like that of the blue sky, is linearly polarized in patterns mainly determined by the sun's position.[131] These matters are discussed further in Chapter 1.

The function of an orientation to polarized light in the blue sky, where the animal uses astronomical clues for orientation, is more readily demonstrated. Since *Talitrus* and *Tylos* can also orient themselves correctly in the shade, they are probably able, like the bees and other insects, to utilize the polarized light of the sky. This notion is supported further by the fact that in a fully overcast sky which completely depolarizes the sky light, disorientation occurs. Indeed, by rotating a sheet of Polaroid over the animal it has been possible to obtain in *Talitrus* significant deviations of the average direction of the escape reaction, corresponding to the rotation of the plane of polarization.[84]

2. *Optomotor reactions.* These reactions to movement in the visual field are well known in higher crustaceans, primarily Decapoda (*Carcinus,*[13,30,121–123,138] *Palinurus*[29,30]) and Stomatopoda.[97] They consist of motor responses which compensate for retinal image displacement caused either by movement of an optically heterogeneous environment with respect to the animal or by the passive displacement of the animal itself in such an environment.[30] Such responses are best demonstrated experimentally by rotating a cylindrical pattern of vertical stripes around the animal or by turning the animal on a rotating disk. The optomotor response itself consists of rotation around the dorsoventral body axis in the same direction as the displacement of the visual field. In stalk-eyed forms there is also typically a series of nystagmus movements of the eyes. These comprise first horizontal swiveling of the eye stalks in the same direction as the optomotor turning of the body. When this slow phase of eye movement has reached a certain limit, the eyestalks then flick rapidly back to their starting position symmetrical with the anteroposterior body axis. Body turning and eyestalk nystagmus may occur either together or separately. It has been postulated that optomotor reactions may result from retinal image dislocations produced by active movement of the animal itself, but apparently the evidence does not support this for the intact animal under natural conditions.[30]

Two biological functions may be attributed to optomotor reactions. One consists of increasing the precision of visual perception by maintaining a more stable visual field, and the other, probably more important in nature, consists of helping the animal maintain its position in space. Optomotor reactions accompanied by locomotion do tend, in fact, to compensate passive dislocations caused by external agents such as water currents.[30]

IV. RESPONSES TO CHEMICAL STIMULI

Chemical stimulation may be due to variations of any kind in the chemical composition of the environment. The stimulating field may have the character of a gradient but is never otherwise directional. The responses to these stimuli will be considered independently of the receptors concerned, which are discussed in Chapter 3.

Because of the nature of the stimulating field, the response mechanisms to chemical stimuli are commonly kinetic ones. But among tactic reactions one based on the comparison of the stimulus intensities by receptors on the two sides of the body is at least theoretically possible. However, it appears unlikely that natural differences in stimulus intensity are often pronounced enough to make this evaluation possible. Nevertheless, oriented responses may take place when the propagation of a chemical substance through the medium first reaches the receptors on one side.

In terrestrial isopods[43,130] and terrestrial amphipods[135] there are kinetic responses to variations in atmospheric humidity (hygrokineses). These are of three kinds: 1) variations in amount of activity, 2) variations in speed of locomotion, 3) variations in the number of changes of direction per unit time (Fig. 5). The first two of these are orthokineses, the third is a klinokinesis. All three types of response may be present and combined in the same species, e.g. *Porcellio scaber*, and, in every case, at least the second is always present. Likewise, the number and nature of the periods of inactivity are often affected by stimulus intensity.

All these responses result in an accumulation of specimens in the optimal zones of an environment with a gradient, here specifically, the most humid region. Among the various species of isopods, differences in the intensity of these responses are apparently related to the animal's resistance to drying.[130] Other factors may also influence the intensity of the response; in *Oniscus asellus*, for example, it is different in the dark and in the light.[22] It has been postulated[130] that there are no special hygroreceptors but that the reaction concerned depends merely on the drying out of the animal's body (Chapter 3).

Oniscus asellus and *Porcellio scaber* react to various odorous substances, moving away from the stimulating source probably by a

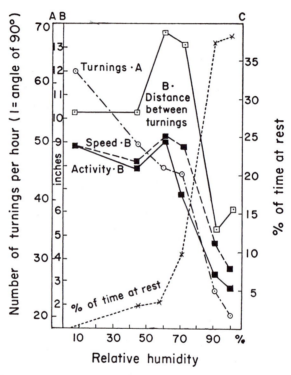

FIG. 5. Behavior of the wood-louse *Porcellio scaber* in constant humidities calculated from the average of 30 specimens. The number of turnings are shown on ordinate *A*. The average distance between turnings, the activity and the speed per minute on ordinate *B*. The percentage of time at rest is read from ordinate *C*. (From Waloff.[130])

klinokinetic mechanism. They appear unable to distinguish whether the stimulating source approaches them from the front or from the rear, but if the stimulus reaches them laterally, an oriented turning takes place so that the animal turns away from the side stimulated. This reaction apparently results from differential stimulation of receptors situated on the second antennae. In fact, after removal of one of these appendages the animals turn mainly toward the operated side, regardless of the direction of the stimulating source.[36]

On the other hand, the myrmecophilous isopod *Platyarthrus hoff-mannseggi* reacts positively to formic acid vapors.[19,70] This reaction, which undoubtedly has an important function in the search for anthills, probably is based on nontactic mechanisms, like most crustacean chemical responses. *Platyarthrus* also can follow a formic acid trail on the ground.

Daphnia magna and *D. pulex*[110] move into more highly oxygenated regions of the environment when the O_2 tension where they are drops below optimum. Although the mechanism of this response is unknown, similar reactions are certainly widespread among aquatic crustaceans. Likewise, reactions which permit animals to remain in zones of optimal salinity must be widely distributed. The decapod *Jasus lalandei*, for example, can perceive variations in salinity with sense organs located at the tip of the antennules. Escape reactions appear when the salinity is reduced merely to 75% of normal, and their intensity grows with further dilution of the sea water, an effect which has been shown electrophysiologically to originate peripherally.[56]

The positive responses of aquatic crustaceans to chemical gradients originating from food are quite familiar. Lobsters, crabs, and crayfish are well known by fishermen to be attracted to fish heads and other bait. But the mechanism of orientation has been analyzed only in a few cases; moreover, it is often clear that other sense organs in addition to those of chemical sense may assist in directing the animal toward the bait. For example, the water currents which carry chemical stimulations certainly serve for such orientation. *Carcinus maenas*, when excited by the diffusion of substances coming from bait, moves against a current as soon as one is produced.[13,68] In *Palaemon* the chemical stimulus seems to evoke only nonoriented kinetic reactions, while food is found principally by sight.[31]

Nevertheless, responses clearly oriented toward the stimulating source may occur even in the absence of water currents and visual stimulation, for example in *Carcinus maenas*,[13,68] *Maja verrucosa*, and *Eriphia spinifrons*.[17] Apparently this is possible because the crustaceans test their respiratory water currents for the presence and position of sources of chemical stimulation in the environment. Thus the hermit crab *Dardanus arrosor* can direct water currents coming from various directions toward its antennular chemoreceptors. If they carry chemical stimuli, a preliminary alert response is generally followed by an oriented turning of the animal toward the stimulus direction. The succeeding search for the food, however, is of three types (Fig. 6), to judge from the paths which are followed. 1) If the respiratory currents have not established a definite pattern of stimulation, or if the animal is distracted by other stimuli, the search is unorganized and the animal

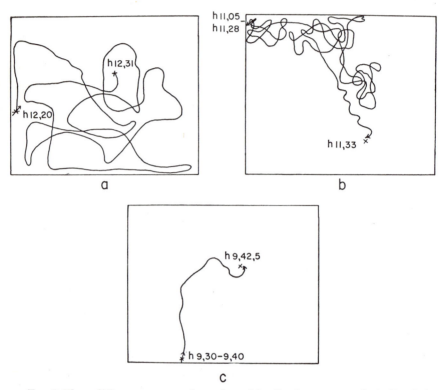

Fig. 6. Three different patterns of search used by *Dardanus arrosor* in finding bait. The experimental receptacle has its bottom covered with small cement blocks which are all alike (not drawn). Below one of these at the point indicated by *x* the bait (meat, fish, or mollusks) is placed with care while the animal is at the periphery. In (a) the search is of the so-called "irregular" type, in (b) it is of the "sectorial" type, in (c) there is a linear trail. The times indicate the start of the experiment, the start of the search, and the finding of the bait. (Modified from Brock.[17])

explores its surroundings in an apparently aimless manner. 2) If, on the other hand, a region of higher concentration is found between the animal and the bait, the organism explores this zone with more or less curving paths, showing avoidance behavior when it passes out of the stimulating zone. 3) Finally, if a particularly narrow stimulating zone has been produced, the trail is linear, but this does not necessarily prove the presence of a taxis since the capacity to follow such a path may actually be based on a klinokinetic mechanism.

V. *RESPONSES TO MECHANICAL STIMULI*

A. RHEOTAXIS AND ANEMOTAXIS

Water or air currents can evoke oriented responses in crustaceans. The reaction is almost always positive and the animals orient themselves by turning upcurrent, moving or not moving against it. The rheotactic reactions of *Asellus, Gammarus,* and some other aquatic crustaceans are well known. In *Asellus,* various external conditions such as light, temperature, and O_2 tension may influence the rheotactic response.[2-4] Since high O_2 content augments the taxis, it is easily explained that *Asellus communis* in slowly running water exhibits a more pronounced reaction than the same species in stagnant water.[140]

Cladocera likewise show positive rheotaxis, which may help to avoid impoverishment of lake populations by loss through their outlets.[129] The copepod *Euterpina acutifrons* shows similar distinct rheotactic behavior.[89]

The mechanism of rheotactic orientation has been little studied in crustaceans. Nonetheless, orientation against a current probably is an optomotor reaction which compensates visually for passive transport. Experiments on *Homarus americanus*[45] and on Mysidacea[38] support this conclusion.

In populations of various species of Balanomorpha, the beak-carina axis is found predominantly to have one particular orientation which may be modified during growth and which does not necessarily correspond to the original orientation of the cyprid larvae at the moment of fixation. A persistent current, or light direction, and tactile features of the fixation surface are apparently responsible for such orientation. Larvae of *Balanus improvisus* var. *assimilis* first align themselves parallel to the current. Then, after metamorphosis, their longitudinal axis is placed transversely in the flow of current.[72] *B. improvisus* and *B. amphitrite* always grow so that their cirriform feet beat against the direction of water flow.[26]

Rheotactic responses of a part of the body occur in many species of Brachyura and Anomura, in which the resistance of the water stimulates the antennules to be oriented in the direction toward which the animal is moving, even if it walks sideways. At rest, the antennules are also directed against the current if there is one present. In opposing lateral currents the antennules diverge, each one being directed laterally against the corresponding flow of water.[18] It is of interest that these responses are identical whether the stimulus arises as a consequence of locomotion, or whether it results from a current flowing past an immobile animal.

The only known case of a crustacean anemotaxis, oriented by air currents, is in *Talitrus saltator*, which, in the absence of other orienting stimuli, heads in the direction toward which the air current is blowing.[79]

B. THIGMOKINESIS

Among the varied, often specific, responses evoked by contact stimuli on the body surface, only those which tend to turn the body away from the stimulus (negative reactions) or to maintain or extend the stimulation (positive reactions) will be mentioned here. The most frequently used term for such reactions, thigmotaxis, is improper in most cases since by the very nature of the stimulus, the reaction can be oriented only with great difficulty.[39] A more proper term is thigmokinesis.

Flight reactions from tactile stimuli are widely distributed and have been recorded particularly in pelagic larvae and copepods. Also of frequent occurrence among crustaceans is the opposite tendency to bring as much as possible of the body surface into contact with foreign bodies. This was called stereotropism by Loeb.[65] Thus, *Asellus aquaticus* prefers to assume positions of rest which permit contact with solid surface even for the back, antennae, and cerci.[36] Such reactions are particularly evident in forms which habitually find refuge in crevices and under stones or which dig hiding places in the ground. If *Hemigrapsus* is placed in a dry receptacle, it moves in a circular path while maintaining its anterior or posterior margin in contact with the vessel's vertical wall; if several specimens are placed in the receptacle they tend to group together.[111] Some species seek primarily to maintain some particular portion of the body in contact with the surroundings. Thus, *Porcellio scaber* placed in a receptacle often moves so that one antenna is kept in contact with the wall. If this antenna is amputated, the animal orients so that this contact is established by the other antenna. This thigmokinetic response increases with humidity.[130]

Hermit crabs deprived of their shell tend to establish a tactile stimulation of the abdomen by taking refuge in the sand, often to such an extent that they leave only a limited portion of the anterior extremity of the body uncovered or by causing their abdomen to touch solid bodies over as large a surface as possible.[88] Similarly, the marine isopod *Zenobiana prismatica* deprived of the plant stalk in which it lives promptly attaches itself to any substratum offered to it, but the reaction is stronger if woody material is involved.[51]

C. Geotaxis

The field of stimulation by gravity is a directional one practically devoid of variations in intensity. Gravitational orientation is always a taxis. A sense of gravity is postulated in most crustaceans. In certain forms the receptors are statocysts, while in others they are less obvious and not precisely localized. The static sense functions in the maintenance of equilibrium (Chapters 2 and 13) as well as in the geotactic control of vertical movements (Chapter 12). Only this second aspect of the subject will be treated here.

Recently[102] a function in the vertical migrations of planktonic crustaceans has again been attributed to geotaxis, although many analyses of this behavior pattern depend largely on responses to changes in light intensity.[27,46] Likewise, in all the forms (Amphipoda, Decapoda) which dig vertical tunnels in sand or mud, one obviously must postulate control by means of a sense of gravity. Thus, if the isopod *Cyathura carinata* is deprived of its statocysts, it loses the capacity to dig vertically but does not remain completely disoriented, since it is able somehow to find the surface again.[63] The sensory basis for geotaxis mediated by statocysts is considered in Chapter 2 and the complex behavioral patterns resulting are discussed in Chapter 13. Since normal orientation is possible in many decapods with statocysts after unilateral extirpation, the taxis concerned must be controlled by the impulses coming from a single organ.[117,121] The statocysts of crustaceans operate not only in the resumption of the normal position[100,101] when the animal has been forced out of it, but also in the attainment and maintenance of any other position in space. The effective stimulus is the shearing force of the statolith acting to deform the organ's sensory hairs in a plane parallel to the surface from which they arise. On the basis of the direction and intensity of this shearing force the animal can evaluate the direction and degree of postural deviations from a horizontal orientation. *Crangon* and *Palaemonetes*, under constant environmental conditions, swim down or up along trajectories making a particular angle with the horizontal. It has been demonstrated that the animal chooses a particular position so that its statocysts produce impulses at a constant rate.[101] Experiments where a centrifuge in effect increases the force of gravity support this interpretation (Fig. 7).

They show that $\alpha g = k$, where α is the angle of inclination and k is the traction on the statolith.[101]

In common with many species of other groups, some crustaceans assume a particular orientation when they walk on an inclined plane. With inclination (α) of the plane between 15° and 70°, *Uca pugnax* walks sideways along a line which makes an angle δ with the horizontal; this angle increases with the slope of the plane according to the formula $\delta = k \sin \alpha$.[57] In male *Uca* an influence of the asymmetry caused by the different weights of the chelae on the value of the angle

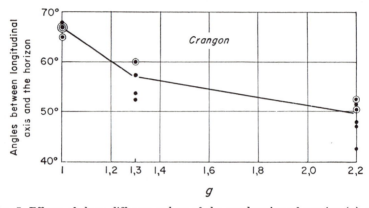

FIG. 7. Effects of three different values of the acceleration of gravity (g) on the angle which the longitudinal axis of a swimming *Crangon* makes with the water surface as it descends toward the bottom. Each point represents one measurement. (From Schöne.[101])

δ has been ascertained. In the crab *Coenobita cavipes* an influence due to the nature of the substratum and of the shell has been demonstrated.[60] The physiological interpretation of such behavior is still controversial.

VI. *RESPONSES TO THERMAL STIMULI*

Oriented responses to thermal stimuli are little known among the crustaceans (Chapter 3). In a temperature gradient, *Daphnia magna* moves away from regions where the water reaches 28°C, with a klinokinetic, but not a tactic, mechanism.[53] *Argulus foliaceus* also exhibits a klinokinetic reaction at temperatures of 30–31°C. The preferred temperature of *Eubranchipus serratus* in diffuse light is between 14° and 17°C; that of *Tanymastix lacunae*, between 9° and 16°C.[74]

VII. *RESPONSES TO ELECTRICAL STIMULI*

Locomotor responses to electric currents in the medium have been studied in various aquatic crustaceans. Such galvanotaxes may cause the animal to approach either the anode or the cathode. Anodal or positive reactions occur in *Triops cancriformis*,[92] *Palaemonetes, Uca*, and *Astacus*.[66] Cathodic or negative reactions are reported in Cyclopidae[75] and various Ostracoda.[92] It is noteworthy in *Palaemonetes* that the displacement toward the anode is not necessarily preceded by oriented turning of the body. If the animal has its head toward the cathode when the stimulus starts, it will move backwards; if it is transverse to the electrical field, it will move sideways. The sign of such taxes may furthermore depend on the voltage of the electric field employed. Thus fresh-water *Gammarus* move to the anode when the potential range is between 6 and 9 volts, but to the cathode at higher or lower voltages.[90]

VIII. *CONCLUSIONS*

Kineses and taxes obviously are fundamental components in every activity of crustaceans relating to their environment. As cited above, for example, hygrokineses allow the animals to attain optimum conditions of humidity; chemotaxes permit the capture of food. Phototaxes guide the animal either in avoiding unfavorable situations or in finding favorable ones. The positive photoreaction of juvenile forms aids in their dispersal, and both kinetic and tactic photoreactions in general certainly play a pre-eminent part in vertical migrations. Also evident is the biological importance of light compass orientation in keeping the animal in its proper niche, particularly when correlated with a time sense as in littoral amphipods and isopods.

If in some instances the biological significance of certain observed reactions is not apparent at first sight, this often results from the artificiality of experimental conditions frequently used and misused in this field, as, for example, pin-point light sources in dark chambers in the study of phototaxes. Laboratory experiments have undoubtedly aided the analysis of the physiological mechanisms underlying such behavior, but it is the merit of many of the more recent investigations to study the animal under conditions which conform more closely to natural situations. This often provides greater insight into the biological significance of the responses obtained.

Kinetic and tactic responses are quite a general attribute of animals. The uniformity of their fundamental mechanisms has already been

emphasized a number of times (e.g. reference[55]), and recent researches
have confirmed this point of view even in distantly related groups of a
high level of organization. The functioning of statocysts in fish[126] is
practically the same as in crustaceans, whether for maintenance of
equilibrium or for the control of movement in space.[100,101] The same
can be said of the laws which describe the orientation of insects and
crustaceans in a light field. The mechanism which accounts for the
light compass movement of *Geotrupes*[14] is applicable also to crustaceans.
And in order to explain the astronomical orientation common to
crustaceans, arachnids,[78] and insects[124] it is sufficient to postulate that
the maintenance of a particular nonequilibrium condition of sensory
excitation is regulated by cyclical internal factors in phase with the
alternation of day and night.

Whether the same fundamental unity of mechanism is present even
in animal groups of quite divergent levels of structural and functional
organization, as has been held in the past, appears more doubtful. In
fact, recent studies, by emphasizing the importance of central nervous
centers for animal orientation rather than the organization of the
peripheral receptors, must necessarily lead to a fresh examination of
the problem.

IX. *SUMMARY*

The kinetic and tactic responses of crustaceans have been surveyed
mainly from three points of view: 1) the stimuli which give rise to
them, 2) the characteristics of the stimulating field, and 3) the
mechanisms by which they are brought about. In harmony with
modern analyses, the inadequacy of rigidly reflex-dominated schemes
has been emphasized for Crustacea. More plausibly, orientation appears
to be governed continuously by the higher nervous centers utilizing
the information on the intensity and/or localization of the stimuli provided by the receptors.

Movement in a light field, regardless of the mechanism with which
it operates, depends in various cases not only on the intensity and
quality of the light, but also on the temperature and the chemical properties of the environment, as well as on a number of internal factors.

Photo-orthokinesis as well as photoklinokinesis, often in combination
with each other, are of widespread occurrence among crustaceans. Of
the phototaxes, a particularly clear biological function is played by
the one which is the basis for astronomical orientation. Special forms
of light-oriented responses are the reactions to polarized light and

optomotor reactions; the natural usefulness of the latter in compensating for passive displacement is particularly evident.

Responses to chemical stimuli have the most varied biological significance; in crustaceans, they are predominantly kineses. The maintenance of a particular orientation in a water current may be based on optical as well as mechanical stimuli. In many forms, a state of minimum locomotor activity occurs when tactile stimulation occurs on the largest surface of the body. Responses to gravitational stimuli are at present among the best-analyzed reactions, whereas little is known about the causation or biological significance of crustaceans' responses to thermal and electrical stimuli.

REFERENCES

1. Abbott, C. H. 1918. Reactions of land isopods to light. *J. Exptl. Zool.* **27**:193–246.
2. Allee, W. C. 1916a. The effect of certain ions on rheotaxis in *Asellus*. *Science* **43**:142–143.
3. Allee, W. C. 1916b. Chemical control of rheotaxis in *Asellus*. *J. Exptl. Zool.* **21**:163–198.
4. Allee, W. C., and Tashiro, S. 1914. Some relations between rheotaxis and the rate of carbon dioxide production of isopods. *J. Animal Behavior* **4**:202–214.
5. Alverdes, F. 1924. Das Verhalten positiv-phototaktischer Daphnien gegen eine doppelte Lichtquelle. *Z. wiss. Zoöl.* **123**:359–371.
6. Alverdes, F. 1930. Tierpsychologische Analyse der intracentralen Vorgänge welche bei dekapoden Krebsen die lokomotorischen Reaktionen auf Helligkeit und Dunkelheit bestimmen. *Z. wiss. Zoöl.* **137**:403–475.
7. Bainbridge, R., and Waterman, T. H. 1957. Polarized light and the orientation of two marine Crustacea. *J. Exptl. Biol.* **34**:342–364.
8. Barnes, T. C. 1932. Salt requirements and space orientation of the littoral isopod *Ligia* in Bermuda. *Biol. Bull.* **66**:109–117.
9. Barnes, T. C. 1935. Salt requirements and orientation of *Ligia* in Bermuda. III. *Biol. Bull.* **66**:259–268.
10. Bauers, C. 1953. Über die Orientierung wirbelloser Tiere zum Licht. *Zool. Jahrb. Abt. Allgem. Zool. Physiol. Tiere* **64**:348–390.
11. Baylor, E. R., and Smith, F. E. 1953. The orientation of Cladocera to polarized light. *Am. Naturalist* **87**:97–101.
12. Bellisai, I. 1929. Variazioni della fototassi in *Artemia salina*. *Monit. zool. ital.* **40**:227–230.
13. Bethe, A. 1897–1898. Das Nervensystem von *Carcinus maenas*. *Arch. mikroskop. Anat. u. Entwicklungsmech.* **50**:462–546; 589–640; **51**:382–452.
14. Birukow, G. 1954. Photo-Geomenotaxis bei *Geotrupes silvaticus* Panz. und ihre zentralnervöse Koordination. *Z. vergleich. Physiol.* **36**:176–211.
15. Blum, H. F. 1934. Le mécanisme d'orientation de la larve de *Homarus vulgaris* sous l'influence de la lumière. *Bull. inst. océanog.* No. 660:1–4.
16. Bohn, G. 1940. "Actions Directrices de la Lumière," 74 pp. Gauthier Villars, Paris.

17. Brock, F. 1926. Das Verhalten des Einsiedlerkrebses *Pagurus arrosor* Herbst während der Suche und Aufnahme der Nahrung. *Z. Morphol. Ökol. Tiere* 6:415–552.

18. Brock, F. 1930. Das Verhalten der ersten Antennen von Brachyuren und Anomuren in Bezug auf das umgebende Medium. *Z. vergleich. Physiol.* 11: 774–775.

19. Brooks, J. L. 1942. Notes on the ecology and the occurrence in America of the myrmecophilous sowbug, *Platyarthrus hoffmanseggi* Brandt. *Ecology* 23: 427–438.

20. Brundin, T. M. 1913. Light reactions of terrestrial amphipods. *J. Animal Behavior* 3:334–352.

21. Clarke, G. L. 1932. Quantitative aspects of the change of phototropic signs in *Daphnia. J. Exptl. Biol.* 9:180–211.

22. Cloudsley-Thompson, J. L. 1952a. Diurnal rhythms. *Trans. Ninth Intern. Congr. Entomol.* 1:305–310.

23. Cloudsley-Thompson, J. L. 1952b. Studies in diurnal rhythms. II. Changes in the physiological responses of the woodlouse *Oniscus asellus* to environmental stimuli. *J. Exptl. Biol.* 29:285–303.

24. Cloudsley-Thompson, J. L. 1956. Studies in diurnal rhythms. VII. Humidity responses and nocturnal activity in woodlice (Isopoda). *J. Exptl. Biol.* 33:576–582.

25. Cole, W. H. 1923. Circus movements of *Limulus* and the tropism theory. *J. Gen. Physiol.* 5:417–426.

26. Crisp, D. J. 1953. Changes in the orientation of barnacles of certain species in relation to water currents. *J. Animal Ecol.* 22:331–343.

27. Cushing, D. H. 1951. The vertical migration of planktonic Crustacea. *Biol. Revs. Cambridge Phil. Soc.* 26:158–192.

28. Dietrich, W. 1931. Die lokomotorischen Reaktionen der Landasseln auf Licht und Dunkelheit. *Z. wiss. Zoöl.* 138:187–232.

29. Dijkgraaf, S. 1955. Die Augenstielbewegungen der Languste (*Palinurus vulgaris*). *Experientia* 11:329–330.

30. Dijkgraaf, S. 1956. Kompensatorische Augenstieldrehungen und ihre Auslösung bei der Languste (*Palinurus vulgaris*). *Z. vergleich. Physiol.* 38:491–520.

31. Doflein, F. 1910. Lebensgewohnheiten und Anpassungen bei dekapoden Krebsen. "Festschrift zum 60 Geburtstag Richard Hertwigs," Vol. 3, pp. 215–292. Fischer, Jena.

32. Drzewina, A. 1908. De l'hydrotropisme chez les crabes. *Compt. rend. soc. biol.* 64:1009–1011.

33. Eckert, B. 1953. (The orienting effect of polarized light on *Daphnia*.) *Československ. biol.* 2:76–80. (In Czech.) Cited in *Ber. wiss. Biol.* 89:198.

34. Ewald, W. F. 1910. Über Orientierung, Lokomotion und Lichtreaktionen einiger Cladoceren und deren Bedeutung für die Theorie der Tropismen. *Biol. Zentr.* 30:379–399.

35. Ewald, W. F. 1914. Versuche zur Analyse der Licht- und Farbenreaktionen eines Wirbellosen (*Daphnia pulex*). *Z. Sinnesphysiol.* 48:285–323.

36. Fischbach, E. 1954. Licht- Schwere- und Geruchsinn bei Isopoden. *Zool. Jahrb. Abt. Allgem. Zool. Physiol. Tiere* 65:141–170.

37. Fraenkel, G. S. 1927. Phototropotaxis bei Meerestieren. *Naturwiss.* 5:117–122.

38. Fraenkel, G. S. 1931. Die Mechanik der Orientierung der Tiere im Raum. *Biol. Revs. Biol. Proc. Cambridge Phil. Soc.* 6:36–87.

39. Fraenkel, G. S., and Gunn, D. L. 1940. "The Orientation of Animals," 352 pp. Oxford Univ. Press, London and New York.

40. Franz, V. 1914. Die phototaktischen Erscheinungen im Tierreich und ihre Rolle im Freileben der Tiere. *Zool. Jahrb. Abt. Allgem. Zool. Physiol. Tiere* 33:259–286.

41. Friedrich, H. 1931. Mitteilungen und vergleichende Untersuchungen über den Lichtsinn einiger mariner Copepoden. *Z. vergleich. Physiol.* 15:121–138.

42. Groom, T. T., and Loeb, J. 1890. Der Heliotropismus der Nauplien von *Balanus perforatus* und die periodischen Tiefenwanderungen pelagischer Tiere. *Biol. Zentr.* 10:160–177.

43. Gunn, D. L. 1937. The humidity reactions of the wood-louse, *Porcellio scaber* (Latr.). *J. Exptl. Biol.* 14:178–186.

44. Gunn, D. L., Kennedy, J. S., and Pielou, D. P. 1937. Classification of taxes and kineses. *Nature* 140:1064.

45. Hadley, P. B. 1906. The relation of optical stimuli to rheotaxis in the American lobster, *Homarus americanus. Am. J. Physiol.* 17:326–343.

46. Harris, J. E., and Wolfe, U. K. 1955. A laboratory study of vertical migration. *Proc. Roy. Soc.* B144:329–354.

47. Henke, K. 1930. Die Lichtorientierung und die Bedingungen der Lichtstimmung bei der Rollassel *Armadillidium cinereum* Zenker. *Z. vergleich. Physiol.* 13:534–625.

48. Herter, K. 1927a. Taxien und Tropismen der Tiere. *Tabulae Biol.* 4:348–381.

49. Herter, K. 1927b. Reizphysiologische Untersuchungen an der Karpfenlaus *Argulus foliaceus* L. *Z. vergleich. Physiol.* 5:283–370.

50. Holmes, S. J. 1908. Phototaxis in fiddler crabs and its relation to theories of orientation. *J. Comp. Neurol. Psychol.* 18:493–497.

51. Issel, R. 1912. Biologia neritica mediterranea. Ricerche di etologia sull'Isopodo tubicolo *Zenobiana prismatica* (Risso). *Arch. zool. exptl. et gén.* 51:479–500.

52. Kikuchi, K. 1938. Studies on vertical distribution of the plankton Crustacea II. The reversal of phototropic and geotropic signs of the plankton Crustacea with reference to vertical movement. *Records Oceanogr. Works Japan* 10:17–41.

53. Koehler, O. 1924. Über das Farbensehen von *Daphnia magna* Strauss. *Z. vergleich. Physiol.* 1:84–174.

54. Koehler, O. 1931. Die Orientierung von Pflanze und Tier im Raum. 2. Zoologischer Teil. *Biol. Zentr.* 51:36–58.

55. Koehler, O. 1950. Die Analyse der Taxisanteile instinktartigen Verhaltens. *Symposia Soc. Exptl. Biol.* 4:269–304.

56. Krijgsman, B. J., and Krijgsman, N. E. 1954. Osmoreception in *Jasus lalandii. Z. vergleich. Physiol.* 37:78–81.

57. Kropp, B., and Crozier, W. J. 1928. Geotropic orientation in Arthropods. III. The fiddler crab, *Uca. J. Gen. Physiol.* 12:111–112.

58. Kropp, B., and Enzmann, M. 1933. Photic stimulation and leg movements in the crayfish. *J. Gen. Physiol.* 16:905–910.

59. Krüger, P. 1940. Cirripedia. *In:* "Bronn's Tierreich," Bd. 5, Abt. 1, Bch. 3, pp. 1–560. Akademische Verlagsges., Leipzig.

60. Kubo, I. 1937. On the geotropic orientation of a terrestrial hermit crab, *Coenobita cavipes* Stimpson. *J. Imp. Fisheries Inst.* (*Japan*) 32:105–113.

61. Kühn, A. 1919. "Die Orientierung der Tiere im Raum," 71 pp. Fischer, Jena.
62. Kühn, A. 1929. Phototropismus und Phototaxis der Tiere. *In:* "Handbuch der Normalen und Pathologischen Physiologie" (A. Bethe, ed.), Vol. 12 (1), Receptionsorgane II: pp. 17–35. Springer, Berlin.
63. Langenbuch, R. 1928. Über die Statocysten einiger Crustacean. *Zool. Jahrb. Abt. Allgem. Zool. Physiol. Tiere* 44:575–622.
64. Loeb, J. 1893. Über künstliche Umwandlung positiv heliotropischer Tiere in negativ und umgekehrt. *Arch. ges. Physiol. Pflüger's* 54:81–107.
65. Loeb, J. 1913. Die Tropismen. *In:* "Handbuch der Vergleichende Physiologie" (H. Winterstein, ed.), Vol. 4, pp. 451–519. Fischer, Jena.
66. Loeb, J., and Maxwell, S. S. 1896. Zur Theorie des Galvanotropismus. *Arch. ges. Physiol. Pflüger's* 63:121–144.
67. Loeb, J., and Northrop, J. H. 1917. Heliotropic animals and photometers on the basis of the validity of the Bunsen-Roscoe Law for heliotropic reactions. *Proc. Natl. Acad. Sci. U. S.* 3:539–544.
68. Luther, W. 1930. Versuche über die Chemorezeption der Brachyuren. *Z. vergleich. Physiol.* 12:177–205.
69. McGinnis, M. 1911. Reactions of *Branchipus serratus* to light, heat and gravity. *J. Exptl. Zool.* 10:227–240.
70. Mathes, I., and Strouhal, H. 1954. Zur Ökologie und Biologie der Ameisenassel *Platyarthrus hoffmannseggii* Brdt. *Z. Morphol. Ökol. Tiere* 43:83–93.
71. Mittelstaedt, H. 1950. Physiologie des Gleichgewichtssinnes bei fliegenden Libellen. *Z. vergleich. Physiol.* 32:422–463.
72. Moore, H. B. 1933. Change of orientation of a barnacle after metamorphosis. *Nature* 2:969–970.
73. Müller, A. 1926. Über Lichtreaktionen von Landasseln. *Z. vergleich. Physiol.* 3:113–144.
74. Müller, R. T. 1918. Zur Biologie von *Tanymastix lacunae* Guerin. *Biol. Zentr.* 38:257–268.
75. Nagel, W. A. 1895. Über Galvanotaxis. *Arch. ges. Physiol. Pflüger's* 59:603–642.
76. Papi, F. 1955a. Experiments on the sense of time in *Talitrus saltator* (Montagu) (Crustacea-Amphipoda). *Experientia* 11:201.
77. Papi, F. 1955b. Orientamento astronomico di alcuni Carabidi. *Atti. soc. toscana sci. nat. Pisa Mem. Ser. B* 62:83–97.
78. Papi, F. 1955c. Ricerche sull'orientamento astronomico di *Arctosa perita* (Latr.) (Araneae-Lycosidae). *Pubbl. staz. zool. Napoli* 27:76–103.
79. Papi, F., and Pardi, L. 1953. Ricerche sull'orientamento di *Talitrus saltator* (Montagu) (Crustacea-Amphipoda). II. Sui fattori che regolano la variazione dell'angolo di orientamento nel corso del giorno. L'orientamento diurno di altre popolazioni. *Z. vergleich. Physiol.* 35:490–518.
80. Pardi, L. 1954. Über die Orientierung von *Tylos latreillii* (Aud. & Sav.) (Isopoda terrestria). *Z. Tierpsychol.* 11:175–181.
81. Pardi, L. 1955. L'orientamento diurno di *Tylos latreillii* (Aud. & Sav.) (Crustacea-Isopoda terrestria). *Boll. Ist. Mus. Zool. Univ. Torino* 4:167–196.
82. Pardi, L., and Grassi, M. 1955. Experimental modification of direction finding in *Talitrus saltator* (Montagu) and *Talorchestia deshayesei* (Aud.) (Crustacea-Amphipoda). *Experientia* 11:202–203.

83. Pardi, L., and Papi, F. 1952. Die Sonne als Kompass bei *Talitrus saltator* (Montagu) (Amphipoda, Talitridae). *Naturwiss.* **39**:262–263.

84. Pardi, L., and Papi, F. 1953. Ricerche sull'orientamento di *Talitrus saltator* (Montagu) (Crustacea-Amphipoda). I. L'orientamento durante il giorno in una popolazione del litorale tirrenico. *Z. vergleich. Physiol.* **35**:459–489.

85. Phipps, C. F. 1915. An experimental study of the behavior of amphipods with respect to light intensity, direction of rays and metabolism. *Biol. Bull.* **28**:210–223.

86. Plate, L. 1924. Die Sinnesorgane der Tiere. *In:* "Allgemeine Zoologie und Abstammungslehre," Teil 2, 806 pp. Fischer, Jena.

87. Precht, H. 1942. Das Taxis-Problem in der Zoologie. *Z. wiss. Zoöl.* **156**:1–127.

88. Rabaud, E. Le stéréotropisme des pagures. *Compt. rend.* **202**:350–352.

89. Rose, M. 1925. Contribution à l'étude de la biologie du plankton. *Arch. zool. exptl. et gén.* **64**:387–542.

90. Rose, M. 1927. Sur le galvanotropisme des *Gammarus* d'eau douce. *Compt. rend. assoc. franç. avanc. sci.* **51**:251–252.

91. Runnström, S. 1925. Zur Biologie und Entwicklung von *Balanus balanoides* (Linné). *Bergens Museums Arbok, Naturv. Rekke.* **1925**:1–46.

92. Ruttner-Kolisko, A. 1943. Das Verhalten niederer Süsswasserkrebse im elektrischen Felde. *Intern. Rev. ges. Hydrobiol. Hydrog.* **43**:82–97.

93. Santschi, F. 1911. Observations et remarques critiques sur le mécanisme de l'orientation chez les fourmis. *Rev. suisse zool.* **19**:303–338.

94. Ščerbakov, A. P. 1955. (Recent work on photo- and geotaxis in the lower crustaceans.) *Uspekhi Sovremennoĭ Biol.* **40**:88–93. (In Russian.) Cited from *Ber. wiss. Biol.* **101**:85.

95. Schallek, W. 1942. The vertical migration of the copepod *Acartia tonsa* under controlled illumination. *Biol. Bull.* **82**:112–126.

96. Schallek, W. 1943. The reaction of certain Crustacea to direct and diffuse light. *Biol. Bull.* **84**:98–105.

97. Schaller, F. 1953. Verhaltens- und sinnesphysiologische Beobachtungen an *Squilla mantis. Z. Tierpsychol.* **10**:1–12.

98. Schöne, H. 1951. Die Lichtorientierung der Larven von *Acilius sulcatus* L. und *Dytiscus marginalis* L. *Z. vergleich. Physiol.* **33**:63–98.

99. Schöne, H. 1952. Zur optischen Lageorientierung ("Lichtrückenorientierung") von dekapoden Krebsen. *Naturwiss.* **39**:552–553.

100. Schöne, H. 1954. Statocystenfunktion und statische Lageorientierung bei dekapoden Krebsen. *Z. vergleich. Physiol.* **36**:241–260.

101. Schöne, H. 1957. Kurssteuerung mittels der Statocysten (Messungen an Krebsen). *Z. vergleich. Physiol.* **39**:235–240.

102. Schröder, R. 1956. Simultane Photo- und Geotaxis bei der Vertikalwanderung von *Daphnia longispina* O.F.M. und *Bosmina coregoni* Baird. *Naturwiss.* **43**:285.

103. Schulz, H. 1928. Uber die Bedeutung des Lichtes im Leben niederer Krebse. *Z. vergleich. Physiol.* **7**:488–552.

104. Seifert, R. 1930. Sinnesphysiologische Untersuchungen am Kiemenfuss (*Triops cancriformis Bosc*). *Z. vergleich. Physiol.* **11**:386–436.

105. Seifert, R. 1932. Raumorientierung und Phototaxis der anostraken Euphyllopoden. *Z. vergleich. Physiol.* **16**:111–184.

106. Spooner, G. M. 1933. Observations on the reaction of marine plankton to light. *J. Marine Biol. Assoc. United Kingdom* 19:385–438.
107. Stålberg, G. 1934. Beitrag zur Kenntnis der Biologie von *Mysis relicta* des Vättern. *Arkiv Zool.* 26A:1–29.
108. Stehr, W. C. 1931. The activating influence of light upon certain aquatic Arthropoda. *J. Exptl. Zool.* 59:297–335.
109. Turner, C. H. 1924. A new field method of investigating the hydrotropism of fresh-water invertebrates. *Biol. Bull.* 46:35–54.
110. Ubrig, H. 1952. Der Einfluss von Sauerstoff und Kohlendioxyd auf die taktischen Bewegungen einiger Wassertiere. *Z. vergleich. Physiol.* 34:479–507.
111. van Tets, G. F. 1956. A study of solar and spatial orientation of *Hemigrapsus oregonensis* (Dana) and *Hemigrapsus nudus* (Dana). A thesis submitted to the Department of Zoology. The University of British Columbia. April, 1956. 30 pp. Typescript, Vancouver.
112. Verkhovskaya, I. N. 1940. The influence of polarized light on the phototaxis of certain organisms. (In Russian with French summary and figure legends.) *Bull. Moscow Nat. Hist. Soc., Biol. Sect.* 49:101–113.
113. Viaud, G. 1948. "Le Phototropisme Animal. Aspects Nouveaux de la Question," 99 pp. J. Vrin, Paris.
114. Viaud, G. 1951a. Le phototropisme chez les Cladocères, les Rotifères et les Planaires. *Année biol.* 27:365–378.
115. Viaud, G. 1951b. "Les Tropismes," 124 pp. Presses Universitaires, Paris.
116. Visscher, J. P., and Luce, R. H. 1928. Reactions of the cyprid larvae of barnacles to light with special reference to spectral colors. *Biol. Bull.* 54:336–350.
117. von Buddenbrock, W. 1914. Über die Orientierung der Krebse im Raum. *Zool. Jahrb. Abt. Allgem. Zool. Physiol. Tiere* 34:479–514.
118. von Buddenbrock, W. 1924. "Grundriss der Vergleichenden Physiologie." 1. Sinnesorgane und Nervensystem, 143 pp. Bornträger, Berlin.
119. von Buddenbrock, W. 1931. Beiträge zur Lichtkompassorientierung (Menotaxis) der Arthropoden. *Z. vergleich. Physiol.* 15:597–612.
120. von Buddenbrock, W. 1945. Physiologie der Dekapoden. *In:* "Bronn's Tierreich," Bd. 5, Abt. 1, Bch. 7, Lfg. 7, pp. 863–1006. Akademische Verlagsges., Leipzig.
121. von Buddenbrock, W. 1952. "Vergleichende Physiologie," Bd. 1, Sinnesphysiologie, 504 pp. Birkhäuser, Basel.
122. von Buddenbrock, W., and Friedrich, H. 1933. Neue Beobachtungen über die kompensatorischen Augenbewegungen und den Farbensinn der Taschenkrabben (*Carcinus maenas*). *Z. vergleich. Physiol.* 19:747–761.
123. von Buddenbrock, W., Moller-Racke, I., and Schaller, F. 1954. Neue Experimente über die Augenstielbewegungen von *Carcinus maenas. Experientia* 10: 333–334.
124. von Frisch, K. 1950. Die Sonne als Kompass im Leben der Bienen. *Experientia* 6:210–221.
125. von Frisch, K., and Kupelwieser, H. 1913. Über den Einfluss der Lichtfarbe auf die phototaktischen Reaktionen niederer Krebse. *Biol. Zentr.* 22:517–552.
126. von Holst, E. 1950. Die Arbeitsweise des Statolithenapparates bei Fischen. *Z. vergleich. Physiol.* 32:60–120.
127. von Holst, E., and Mittelstaedt, H. 1950. Das Reafferenzprinzip. *Naturwiss.* 37:464–476.

128. von Kaulbersz, G. 1913. Biologische Beobachtungen an *Asellus aquaticus* nebst einigen Bemerkungen über *Gammarus* und *Niphargus*. *Zool. Jahrb. Abt. Allgem. Zool. Physiol. Tiere* **33**:287–360.

129. Wagler, E. 1927. Branchiopoda. *In:* "Handbuch der Zoologie" (W. Kükenthal and T. Krumbach, eds.), Bd. 3, Hälfte 1, pp. 305–398. de Gruyter, Berlin.

130. Waloff, N. 1941. The mechanisms of humidity reactions of terrestrial isopods. *J. Exptl. Biol.* **18**:115–135.

131. Waterman, T. H., and Westell, W. E. 1956. Quantitative effect of the sun's position on submarine light polarization. *J. Marine Research (Sears Foundation)* **15**:149–169.

132. Welsh, J. H. 1932. Temperature and light as factors influencing the rate of swimming of larvae of the mussel crab *Pinnotheres maculatus* Say. *Biol. Bull.* **63**:310–326.

133. Wetzel, A. 1933. Studien über Caprelliden. II. Raumorientierung, Farbanpassung und Farbwechsel. *Z. wiss. Zoöl.* **143**:77–125.

134. Wigglesworth, V. B. 1950. "The Principles of Insect Physiology," revised ed., 544 pp. Methuen, London.

135. Williamson, D. I. 1951. Studies in the biology of Talitridae (Crustacea, Amphipoda): Effects of atmospheric humidity. *J. Marine Biol. Assoc. United Kingdom* **30**:73–90.

136. Williamson, D. I. 1951. Studies in the biology of Talitridae (Crustacea, Amphipoda): Visual orientation in *Talitrus saltator*. *J. Marine Biol. Assoc. United Kingdom* **30**:91–99.

137. Wojtusiak, R. J. 1932. Versuche mit Hummer und *Maja* Larven bei doppelter Belichtung. *Acta Biol. exptl. (Warsaw)* **7** (1): 1–25. (In Polish with German summary.)

138. Wolter, H. 1936. Beiträge zum Lichtsinn von *Carcinus maenas*. *Zool. Jahrb. Abt. Allgem. Zool. Physiol. Tiere* **56**:581–612.

139. Yerkes, R. M. 1900. Reaction of Entomostraca to stimulation by light. II. Reaction of *Daphnia* and *Cypris*. *Am. J. Physiol.* **4**:405–422.

140. Zimmer, C. 1927. Isopoda. *In:* "Handbuch der Zoologie" (W. Kükenthal and T. Krumbach, eds.), Bd. 3, Hälfte 1, pp. 697–766. de Gruyter, Berlin.

CHAPTER 11

FRANK A. BROWN, JR.

PHYSIOLOGICAL RHYTHMS

I. *GENERAL INTRODUCTION*

Organisms dwell in a rhythmic environment, in which there are a number of natural frequencies. Twenty-four-hour daily cycles are associated with such conspicuous changes as in the intensity of illumination, in temperature, in humidity, and in a number of such less obvious factors as barometric pressure, ionizing radiations, and gravitation. Lunar-day cycles of 24.8 hours also exist, but for the terrestrial environment the concomitant cyclic physical changes are relatively small compared with those in oceanic, and particularly littoral, regions. Intertidally lunar cycles, with either two (12.4-hr) or one (24.8-hr) high and low tides each lunar day, effect substantial changes in the depth of overlying water with its light- and heat-absorbing action, in pressure, in periodic desiccation, anoxia, and enforced inactivity for numerous inhabitants of this zone. Superimposed on these solar- and lunar-day cycles are the lunar-related, fortnightly and synodic monthly periods involving changes in nocturnal illumination and tidal rhythms in the oceans and atmosphere. Finally the annual cycle of the seasons with its extensive illumination and temperature changes should be mentioned.

In response to such rhythmic changes in their external physical environment organisms show corresponding frequencies of cyclic activities initiated by reasonably well-understood mechanisms of physiological response to stimuli. But, in addition, during the past sixty or so years it has become increasingly evident that numerous living organisms can maintain physiological cycles of very closely the same frequencies as the natural physical ones, even when they are kept in conditions constant with respect to all factors generally conceded to influence them.

Among the general reviews including the subject of such persistent rhythmicity are those of Welsh,[75] Park,[58] Kleinholz,[49] Brown,[4] Kleitman,[52] and Caspers.[25] Korringa[53] has reviewed lunar periodisms in animals.

The Crustacea, as well as Mammalia and Insecta, are among the groups of animals whose persistent rhythmicities have probably been most extensively investigated. Comparative studies have strongly suggested that the basic mechanisms of persistent rhythmicity of all organisms are fundamentally similar to one another.

II. *PERSISTENT RHYTHMS*

A. CHROMATOPHORES AND COLOR CHANGE

One of the earliest described persistent diurnal rhythms of color change in Crustacea was that observed by Gamble and Keeble in 1900.[37] They found that the prawn, *Hippolyte varians*, whether kept in constant light or constant darkness, may exhibit a daily fluctuation in color. During the day pigments are dispersed to give the animals their color patterns adaptively mimicking the water plants with which they are normally associated. At night all the pigments become withdrawn to the chromatophore centers; a blue pigment may pervade the tissues, which become highly transparent. The animal in its nocturnal phase is more active than in the diurnal. Later re-examination of this species[50] failed to confirm the original observations, suggesting that a daily rhythm of color change need not invariably be present. A persistent rhythm of the chromatophore system in *Praunus* has also been reported.[43]

A similar chromatophore periodicity continuing in constant darkness for at least two months was described[55] for the isopod *Idotea balthica*. This was later confirmed[60] and extended to the other isopods, *Ligia baudiniana*[46,51] and *Ligia exotica*.[33] In all the isopods the diurnal state is a darkened integument, the nocturnal state, a blanched one. Although the diurnal rhythmicity generally persists in darkness, *Ligia* has its color-change cycles partly or completely inhibited in constant illumination.[28,33,46]

A persistently rhythmic color change in constant conditions was described[41] for the crayfish *Astacus*. Since the rhythm was abolished by removal of the eyestalks, it was assumed that the rhythmic centers lie in these organs. Similar periodic color change occurs in constant darkness in *Uca*, which is dark by day and pale by night (Fig. 1). This rhythm of color change is abolished by removal of the animal's eyestalks.[1,23,24,54] These observations, initially pertaining to the melanophore responses,[1,23] were extended to include the red chromatophores of *U. pugilator*.[5]

Following the demonstration of eyestalk hormones which regulate the integumentary pigments (see Chapter 4) it was presumed that the

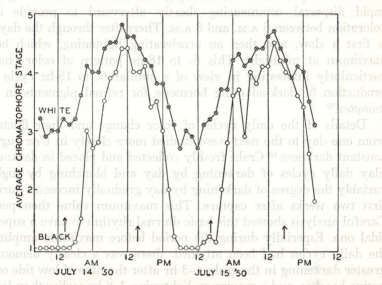

FIG. 1. Changes in the degree of dispersion of the black and white pigment of *Uca pugnax* during a 48-hr period in darkness. The arrows indicate the times of low tide in the native habitat of the crabs. Stage 1 denotes fully concentrated, and stage 5 fully dispersed pigment. (From Brown, Fingerman, Sandeen, and Webb.[13])

rhythmic dispersion and concentration in chromatophores are a consequence of periodic liberation into the blood of chromatophorotropic substances in the eyestalks.[1,23,24] The pigmentary rhythm of *Ligia* was similarly considered due to a cyclic secretion,[41,46] but no rhythm could be found either in the hormonal content of the eyestalk of *Uca* or of the head of *Ligia*. It was assumed, therefore, that production and liberation of hormone must occur at the same rates and that the rhythm arose from periodic rate changes. However, the demonstration of a clear diurnal rhythm in the degree of pigment dispersion in melanophores of legs 60 min after their autotomy from crabs which had been as long as 48 hr without eyestalks proves that these phenomena are not exclusively controlled by eyestalk hormones.[67] In this cycle the pigment was minimally dispersed at about 8 A.M. and maximally so about midnight. It was postulated that this rhythm reflects a daily secretory cycle of a body-lightening hormone, which normally antagonizes the darkening hormone from the eyestalk.

Among all the preceding investigations of diurnal rhythm of color change, only two[28,33] attempted to describe the form of the daily color cycles in some detail. Both were studies of *Ligia exotica*. In this animal minimum dispersion of the dark pigment occurs about midnight, with rapid dispersal commencing shortly afterward to provide darkest coloration between 6 A.M. and 8 A.M. Thereafter through the day, there is first a slow, and then an accelerating lightening, which becomes maximum at midnight. This 6- to 18-hr pattern of color change is particularly interesting in view of a similar 6- to 18-hr cycle in the production of dark-adapting hormone for retinal pigments in *Palaemonetes*.[69]

Details of the daily cycles of color change and their fluctuations from one day to the next were studied more closely in *Uca pugnax* in constant darkness.[13] Crabs freshly collected and placed in darkness display daily cycles of darkening by day and blanching by night. Invariably the degree of darkening by day gradually increases during the first two weeks after capture. This maximum value then persisted. Careful analysis showed this basic diurnal rhythm to have a superposed tidal one. Especially during the period before maximum amplitude of the daily cycles had been attained, there was a clearly demonstrable greater darkening in the crabs 1–3 hr after the time of low tide on their native beaches, and a maximum lightening 3–6 hr earlier than low tide. Comparison of crabs collected from beaches where the tides were out of phase by about 4 hr showed that these tidal modifications of the daily cycle are quite precisely adjusted to their own local tidal times. Such differences persisted during the 2–4 weeks they were observed under constant conditions. Thus in *U. pugnax* the degree of body darkening for any given hour of a particular day is explicable through mutual periodic reinforcement of the solar and lunar cycles discussed.

A similar instance of a persistent 12.4-hr rhythm of color change superimposed upon a regular diurnal one has been reported[32] for *Callinectes sapidus*. This case is particularly interesting because in the Gulf of Mexico, where these studies were made, there is only a single high and low tide per lunar day instead of two as occur where the earlier studies of *Uca pugnax* were made. Despite this, *Callinectes* exhibited maximum darkening at 12.4-hr intervals, correlated in time with both high and low tides.

Uca pugilator and *U. speciosa* of the Gulf of Mexico also possess 12.4-hr cycles of color change despite the 24.8-hr normal tidal cycles of that region.[34] This rhythm was observed to persist in *U. pugilator* for at least 48 days without alteration of its original frequency. An interesting phase difference of about 5 hr was noted between the two species. Since the two forms typically occupied different tidal levels of the beach, this apparently is correlated with the time interval between the tidal covering and uncovering of the two species' burrows. Further study of the problem[35] using only *U. speciosa* has given additional support for this correlation. Crabs occupying burrows at two tidal levels differing in uncovering time by 1.6 hr were found to have a corresponding phase difference of their persistent rhythms. A lunar-tidal cycle superimposed on the diurnal rhythmicity in *U. pugnax* has also been found in the state of the melanophores of legs 30 min after they were autotomized.[40] Maximum concentration of the pigment in the isolated legs occurred about 1 hr before high tides; minimum concentration occurred 2–3 hr before times of low tides.

B. RETINAL PIGMENT MIGRATION

The earliest report of a clear persistent diurnal rhythm in retinal pigment migration among Crustacea was made by Welsh in 1930[72] for the fresh-water shrimps, *Macrobrachium olfersii* and *M. acanthurus*.* Under continuous illumination the distal retinal pigment of these forms still moves distally to occupy its typical nocturnal position at about sunset and returns to the daytime position at about sunrise. No comparable rhythmic changes are known for the proximal retinal pigment. Soon afterward the proximal retinal pigment of *Orconectes virilis*[3] was found to continue its daily proximal nocturnal and distal diurnal movements in darkness at constant temperature. No such rhythmic movement of the proximal pigment occurs in constant illumination, thus agreeing with *Macrobrachium*. Both of the preceding studies emphasize the remarkable correspondence in the time of pigment movement with the normal changes in external illumination.

During 2 weeks in continuous darkness the distal and reflecting pigments of the caridean *Anchistioides antiguensis* were observed not only to maintain high-amplitude cycles showing no reduction, but also to remain strictly in phase with the time of day from beginning to end.[74] But in a similar period of constant illumination, the retinal pigments

---

* The visual significance of retinal pigment migration is discussed in Chapter 1, the mechanisms of its control in Chapter 4.

of the same prawn display a comparable cycle, although of low amplitude, and apparently with its period lengthened to about 26 hr. In the latter case the pigment movements become about 180° out of phase with normal day-night after about 6 days and return briefly to normal phase relations by the end of about 12 days.

Further studies on several species (Table 1) re-emphasized 3 things: 1) Persistent rhythmicity of retinal pigments is widespread among

TABLE 1

STUDIES ON DIURNALLY RHYTHMIC MOVEMENTS
OF RETINAL PIGMENTS

Species	Pigment	Constant condition
Macrobrachium olfersii[72]	Distal	Light
Macrobrachium acanthurus[72]	Distal	Light
Latreutes fucorum[73]	Reflecting; proximal	Light; dark
Leander tenuicornis[73]	Reflecting	Light; dark
Palaemon northropi[73]	Reflecting; distal	Light; dark
Palaemon paucidens[57]	Distal	Light; dark
Penaeopsis goodei[73]	Proximal	Dark
Anchistioides antiguensis[74]	Distal; reflecting	Dark
Sicyonia sp.[47]	Distal	Light
Trachypeneopsis mobilispinis[47]	Distal	Light
Palaemonetes[69]	Distal	Light
Hippolyte pleuracantha[48]	Distal	Dark
Heptacarpus geniculatus[57]	Distal	Light; dark
Paratya compressa[57]	Distal	Light; dark
Orconectes virilis[3]	Proximal	Dark
Cambarus bartonii[77]	Proximal; distal	Dark
Calappa flammea[47]	Distal; proximal	Dark
Parthenope serrata[47]	Distal; proximal	Dark
Portunus anceps[47]	Distal; proximal	Dark
Portunus depressifrons[47]	Distal; proximal	Dark

crustaceans. 2) Any one retinal pigment, or combination of two or more depending upon species, may participate in these rhythmic movements. 3) The persistent migration can occur, in any given instance, in constant darkness, or constant light, or in both constant light and darkness. There appears to be no single systematic scheme that will describe the observed species differences.

The great persistence of retinal pigment rhythms was spectacularly established in *Cambarus bartonii*;[77] the cycles may continue in constant darkness in phase with external day-night cycles for as long as 4 months at 21–23°C and 5 months at 6.8°C.

In general, efferent nerve fibers supplying the retinal pigment elements have never been demonstrated in Crustacea, and a number of experiments and observations strongly suggest that a hormonal mechanism regulates the retinal pigments (see Chapter 4). Consequently, all investigators have postulated that the persistence of rhythmic movements under constant conditions are a direct consequence of comparable rhythmic secretion of an active principle into the blood stream. Such a substance is apparently present in the sinus glands of the eyestalks because injection of extracts from this structure will move into the daytime disposition 1 or 2 of the 3 retinal pigments, depending upon species and dosage.[44,45,76]

Some understanding of the tremendous variety of retinal-pigment rhythms as a function of species and of the kind of constant conditions has been provided by studies on *Palaemonetes*.[11,22,69] This species has no persistent rhythm of a retinal pigment either in continuous bright illumination or in continuous darkness, but in the dark the response of the distal retinal pigment to brief light stimuli shows a clear persistent diurnal rhythm.[69] When a 1-min, 2700-lux exposure to light is given, the magnitude of the resulting light adaptation is a clear function of the time of day (Fig. 2). The response is minimal, small, and of short duration at midnight. Maximal response appears at about 5 A.M., or near daybreak when the pigment moves to a completely light-adapted state in response to a single brief light flash and returns to the fully dark-adapted state slowly, achieving it only about 12 hr later. Groups of prawns left in darkness overnight and, beginning at 8 A.M., exposed to 2700 lux for varying lengths of time through the day before being returned to darkness, show a progressively increasing initial rate of dark adaptation throughout the day.

Substantial evidence suggests that this observed diurnal fluctuation in rate of re-dark-adaptation is due to changes in the production of a dark-adapting hormone which antagonizes the light-adapting one previously described from the sinus glands. Probably a diurnal rhythm was not observed in either constant darkness or constant bright light because in light there was always an excess of the light-adapting hormone and in darkness, fluctuations in dark-adapting hormone could obviously produce no change in the already dark-adapted eye. Supporting this hypothesis is the demonstration that when *Palaemonetes* is kept in a particular low, constant illumination, a clear persistent diurnal rhythm is evident. This could be due to an altering ratio of the two hormones, which holds the retinal pigment in an intermediate degree of light adaptation.

Furthermore the form of the diurnal cycle of secreting dark-adapting hormone is much altered if the animals are exposed to the normal,
initially very low, dawn illumination which gradually increases.[22] Such
an extended period of dim illumination in the early morning apparently
induces a physiological state involving the secretion and storage of dark-
adapting hormone. This enables the animals to re-dark-adapt at maximal rate at any time after exposure to about a half hour of such natural

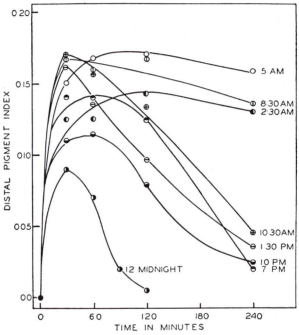

Fig. 2. Responses of the distal retinal pigment of *Palaemonetes* in continuing
darkness to a 1-min, 2700-lux light exposure at various hours of the solar day. The
pigment index of a fully light-adapted eye is about 0.18. (From Webb and Brown.[69])

low illumination or an experimentally produced equivalent. It should
be recalled in this connection that an abrupt change from darkness to
2700 lux at about daybreak yields animals incapable of complete re-
dark-adaptation until evening.

C. Spontaneous Motor Activity

The first clear evidence that the daily activity cycle of a crustacean
would persist under constant conditions was presented by Kalmus in
1948.[42] He showed that during several weeks in constant darkness the

crayfish, *Astacus astacus*, was active only at night. A similarly persistent daily rhythm was later described for *Orconectes virilis*.[61] In this organism and in *Procambarus clarkii*, and *Cambarus diogenes*, these diurnal rhythms persist at least 5 weeks in darkness.[62] Such cycles become most evident after the animals have been in darkness for about a week. In the American crayfish the daily pattern of activity was observed to possess either of two forms: about half the animals studied exhibited a unimodal cycle with a maximum at midnight or noon, the other half displayed a bimodal cycle with maxima at dawn and dusk. However, a single individual could show an abrupt shift from a unimodal to a bimodal cycle, or the reverse.

In all three of the preceding investigations removal of the eyestalks abolished the diurnally rhythmic character of locomotor activity, but opinions differed on the explanation of this disappearance. Since total activity in *Astacus* diminishes after stalk removal and injection of eyestalk extract increases activity, the rhythm was postulated[42] to result from a periodic liberation by the eyestalk of an activity-exciting hormone. But in *Orconectes*,[61,62] on the contrary, increased and continuous activity follows eyestalk removal. In this case, transection of the optic nerves which left the rest of the stalk intact demonstrated[62] that the inhibitory influence coming from the eyestalks is nervous in character.

The blind cave crayfish, *Orconectes pellucidus*, shows no significant diurnal rhythm of activity in either constant light or darkness[59]—presumably an adaptation to its relatively stable cave environment.

Spontaneous locomotor activity in *Orconectes virilis* in constant darkness has been reinvestigated recently, utilizing automatic recording apparatus which permits a more quantitative study and, simultaneously, indicates the mean activity of a number of animals.[39] Average daily cycles were determined over fortnightly periods. Lowest activity occurs in the early morning hours and highest activity in the late afternoon and early evening. The cycles have a form generally similar to those reported earlier[61] for the same species. The mean cycle observed resembled suggestively the mirror image of the concurrently recorded average daily changes in barometric pressure. When the mean activity was analyzed in terms of lunar days, using the same data, cycles were obtained which were also similar to the concurrent mean lunar-day cycles of barometric pressure. Pressure was not directly concerned since these cycles occurred essentially as before even when hydrostatic pressure on the crayfish was experimentally kept constant by compensating for atmospheric pressure changes with a regulated height of water above the animals.

The spontaneous locomotor activity of the crayfish, *Orconectes cly-peatus*, in continuous low illumination displays two general types of cycles. About half the animals have daily cycles basically like those of *Orconectes virilis*;[39,61] the remainder exhibit cycles which are mirror images of these latter, in other words with highest activity during the early morning hours. Two nervous centers of endogenous rhythmicity were postulated to account for this, one exercising a rhythmic inhibitory, and the other a rhythmic excitatory, influence on activity, and both employing blood-borne factors as their mediating agents.

Spontaneous motor activity has also been investigated in two species of the marine crustacean *Uca*, *U. pugnax* and *U. pugilator*.[10,27] Using single crabs in ordinary laboratory illumination, two kinds of cycles like those in *Orconectes*, *Procambarus*, and *Cambarus* (page 409) are obtained,[27] one a bimodal diurnal cycle, and the other a unimodal one. The bimodal cycle generally has activity correlated with dawn and dusk; the unimodal shows a nocturnal maximum. In contrast, the mean activity of 10 or 20 isolated crabs in constant, low, illumination has a lunar tidal cycle as its predominant rhythmic component.[2,10] The two daily maxima clearly move over the hours of the solar day at a tidal rate of about 50 min a day (Fig. 3). Maximum activity occurs about 2–4 hr before the time of low tide upon the beach from which the crabs were collected. This lunar rhythm persists in these same phase relations at least 10–12 days, with completely independent samples of crabs showing high hourly correlations with one another.

The *Uca* activity patterns in constant conditions also possess a solar-day rhythmic component, exhibiting a maximum in the early morning hours and minimum in the afternoon. This is evident both in single-day fluctuations and in mean daily cycles for fortnights. In the latter, a reduction in the height of the tidal peaks occurs as they move toward and into the afternoon.

D. Metabolic Rate

The occurrence of a persistent daily rhythm of metabolic rate in Crustacea was first suggested by Gamble and Keeble in 1900.[37] In *Hippolyte varians* these investigators noted an accelerated heart rate at night when the animals were in the nocturnal, transparent, blue phase of their daily color change. In *Praunus*,[43] a diurnal change in acidity of muscle and liver was found with the pH being lower in the nocturnal phase. Following these leads a number of later workers[32,55,60,72,75] postulated that a rhythm in general metabolism was in some manner responsible for the persistent cycles of integumentary color changes and retinal-pigment movements.

The first systematic study of O_2 consumption in a crustacean was that of Gompel who in 1937[38] made hourly determinations for the

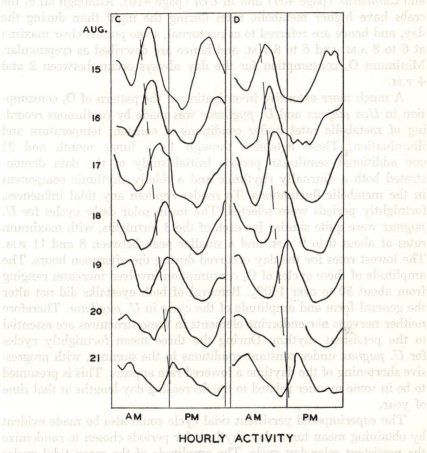

Fig. 3. Average locomotor activity of two independent groups of *Uca pugnax*, *C* and *D*, during a week in constant conditions. A tidal, or lunar, frequency of rhythmic activity is clearly evident. (From Brown.[6])

crab, *Xantho*, kept in the laboratory up to several weeks. These crabs apparently possess a persistent tidal rhythm, with maximum rate of O_2 consumption occurring at about the time of the local high tides and minimum rate at about the time of low tide. In contrast, the rates of O_2 consumption in the fiddler crab, *Uca pugilator*, were reported to reveal only a diurnal rhythm.[27] Presumably both these studies were made in the normal laboratory conditions of changing illumination. Under these conditions two kinds of metabolic cycles occur in patterns reminiscent of spontaneous motor activity in *Orconectes, Procambarus*, and *Cambarus* (page 409) and in *Uca* (page 410). Although all of the crabs have higher metabolic rates during the night than during the day, and hence are referred to as nocturnal, some possess clear maxima at 6 to 8 A.M. and 6 to 8 P.M. and hence are described as crepuscular. Minimum O_2 consumption for the day always occurs between 2 and 4 P.M.

A much more extensive investigation of the pattern of O_2 consumption in *Uca pugnax* and *U. pugilator* was made by continuous recording of metabolic rate[9] under conditions of constant temperature and illumination. These extended through 1) a lunar month and 2) one additional semilunar period. Initial study of the data demonstrated both a diurnally rhythmic and a tidally rhythmic component in the metabolic fluctuations. To render random any tidal influences, fortnightly periods were selected. The mean solar daily cycles for *U. pugnax* were quite similar for each of the 3 fortnights, with maximum rates at about 6 to 9 A.M. and a smaller peak between 8 and 11 P.M. The lowest rates for the day occurred during the afternoon hours. The amplitude of these cycles of O_2 consumption involved increases ranging from about 50 to over 150%. Removal of both eyestalks did not alter the general form and amplitude of the cycle in *U. pugilator*. Therefore neither nervous nor endocrine elements in these structures are essential to the persistent rhythm. During the three mean fortnightly cycles for *U. pugnax* under constant conditions in the summer, with progressive shortening of the daytime a lowered rate appears. This is presumed to be in some manner related to the decreasing day-lengths at that time of year.

The superimposed persistent tidal cycle could also be made evident by obtaining mean lunar-day rhythms for periods chosen to randomize the persistent solar-day cycle. The amplitude of the mean tidal cycles involves a 50–70% increase from lowest to highest values. The former are reached near the time of high tide on the beaches from which the crabs were collected, and the latter an hour or two before the time of low tide. Unlike the diurnal solar rhythm, removal of the eyestalks abolished the persistent tidal rhythm of metabolism in *U. pugilator*.

An attempt was made during the next summer to repeat these results in both *Uca pugnax* and *U. pugilator*.[20] Four consecutive fortnightly mean daily cycles were obtained for both species. All of them are essentially mirror images of those obtained during the preceding summer, the maximum rates in the present case occurring between 2 and 4 P.M. (Fig. 4). Apparently also there is a persistent cycle about a month in length exhibited in the form of high-amplitude daily cycles for the fortnights centered on a full moon and low-amplitude cycles for those centered upon a new moon. A persistent lunar tidal cycle was also evident in this second set of data. It is similar for both the two species

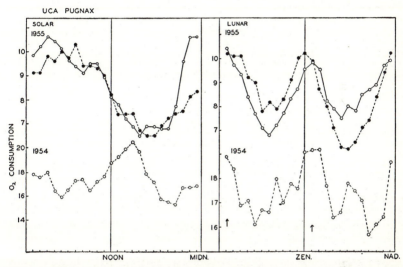

Fig. 4. Mean solar- and lunar-day rates of O₂ consumption in *Uca pugnax* in constant conditions in one summer month of 1955 and the corresponding month of 1954. The solid circles of 1955 show the cycle for a sample of crabs subjected to daily fluctuations of barometric pressure; the open circles indicate the cycle for an independent parallel sample of crabs hermetically sealed in barostats.

and the two months. Minimal values in the tidal cycles occurred 4–6 hr prior to lunar zenith and lunar nadir.

The next summer, 1955, a third study of the fluctuations in O₂ consumption was made using *Uca pugnax*.[8] Now, not only were temperature and illumination kept constant, but so too was pressure, through having continuous recording respirometers hermetically sealed in barostats (Fig. 4). Clear mean solar-day and lunar-tidal cycles were once more apparent, but this time the solar-day cycles were again of the general form of those obtained in the first summer.

The dwarf crayfish, *Cambarellus shufeldtii*, also possesses a mean daily rhythm of O₂ consumption with the maximum at about 6 A.M.[31]

The rhythm persists in specimens from which the eyestalks have been removed. Daily cycles in O_2 consumption have been described as well for the crayfish, *Orconectes clypeatus*.[36] The cycles occur in either of two distinct patterns 180° out of phase. About half the animals display maximum metabolic rate between noon and midnight, the other group, minimum rate at this time. Both types of rhythm continue following eyestalk-removal.

E. OTHER PHENOMENA

1. *Diurnal planktonic migrations.* Esterly[29,30] suggested that a persistently rhythmic physiological mechanism might be involved in the well-known vertical migrations of planktonic copepods. *Acartia* kept in constant darkness tend to move to higher levels in tall cylindrical vessels during the evening, a time when in nature their migration was surfaceward. A further suggestion that such a mechanism might be operative comes from field studies[78] on the movements of planktonic copepods under natural conditions. There was some indication that the animals tend to anticipate the dawn illumination change in their daily migration. If these migrations are, in part, a consequence of a physiological rhythmic mechanism, it would still not be clear whether the rhythm was one of general motor activity or of response to some other physical factor such as gravity or hydrostatic pressure. This matter is discussed further in Chapter 12.

2. *Miscellaneous.* A daily rhythm in molting has been described[63] for *Orconectes*. In animals whose molting process has been accelerated by extirpation of the eyestalks, the forming gastroliths are stratified. This results apparently from a diurnal rhythm of calcium deposition, which occurs chiefly at night. Some evidence was obtained that this cyclic change was regulated by an extra-eyestalk, molt-accelerating hormone. Since these observations were not made in constant conditions, it cannot be concluded on their basis that the physiological rhythm involved a persistent component.

A lunar rhythm of swarming in *Anchistioides antiguensis* at Bermuda occurs throughout the year at the times of new moon.[80] The swarming could not be correlated with the fluctuations in any of the commonly suspected factors such as lunar illumination, sex and reproduction, surface temperature, wind and weather, nor even state of the tides during several months' observations. Further study[79] confirmed earlier data that the synodic monthly cycles display two maxima, one centering on the second day, and the other on the twenty-sixth day, after new moon. Each of these two peaks of swarming is preceded by a peak in molting frequency. Prawns kept in captivity through three generations over a period of more than two years continue to show the same exact lunar relationships in their molting cycles.

Luminescent copepods kept in constant darkness for as long as 12 days show a greater tendency to luminesce during the period 6 P.M. to 6 A.M. than during the remainder of the day.[56] The time of daily reduction in light production correlates with the arrival of dawn.

A persistent tidal rhythmicity in phototaxis of a hermit crab has been described.[26]

III. *PROPERTIES OF THE RHYTHMIC MECHANISM*

A. TEMPERATURE RELATIONS

All the observations of solar and lunar rhythmicity persisting in constant conditions imply that the frequency of the rhythms must be to a large measure independent of temperature. The constant temperature of the experimental conditions could only quite coincidentally have been that of the organism's natural habitat. And, furthermore, to possess adaptive significance for the organism a considerable degree of temperature independence would be needed to permit the cycles to retain their normal lengths when exposed to natural temperature fluctuations.

The diurnal rhythm in retinal-pigment movements of *Cambarus* was found to persist for several months in constant darkness and with the natural diurnal frequency whether the animals were retained at 7°C or 21°C.[77] A few years later the 24-hr rhythm of color change in *Uca* was shown[16] to persist in darkness in synchrony with solar day-night for several weeks whether the constant temperature was 6°C, 16°C, or 26°C (Fig. 5). Although the temperature coefficient of their frequency was, therefore, approximately 1.00, the amplitude of the daily cycles was directly related to the temperature as would be expected of a metabolic process.

A frequency thus independent of temperature is also characteristic of the tidal rhythm of integumentary color change in *Uca*.[19] No observable acceleration of retardation of the changes in a single tidal cycle occurs in crabs subjected to constant temperatures within the temperature range, 13–30°C.

Temperatures within 2–3° of freezing, however, do exert a profound change in the cyclic mechanism.[16] Crabs, in constant darkness, held at such low temperatures for 6 hr were still found, upon rewarming, to possess clear 24-hr cycles of color change, but these now lagged

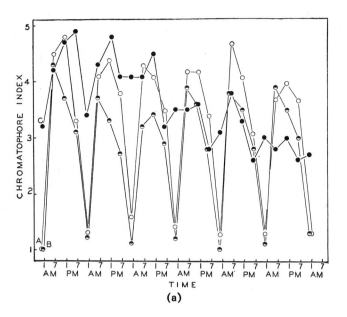

(a)

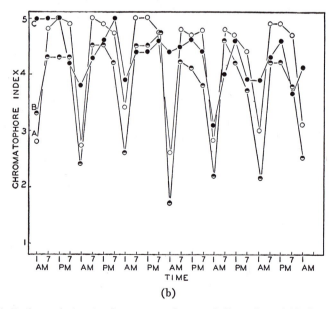

(b)

Fig. 5. Daily variation in the average degree of dispersion of black pigment (a) and white pigment (b) in *Uca pugnax* in constant darkness for 6 days at (A) 26°C, (B) 16°C, and (C) 6°C. (From Brown and Webb.[16])

behind the untreated controls by about 6 hr. This altered state persisted during 5 days of observation under constant conditions. The low temperature appears to inhibit an endogenous cyclic mechanism. In a further study at low temperature,[68] the degree of rhythm inhibition was found to be a function of the time of day of chilling for 2- or 6-hr exposures to temperatures of 5°C. For the four consecutive 6-hr periods of chilling during a day commencing at midnight, the percentages of inhibition in sample groups were 72, 56, 63 and 78. When 2-hr chilling periods were employed, the maximum inhibition, 79%, was found from 8 to 10 P.M., and the minimum, 24%, was seen from 10 to 12 A.M.

Quite another effect of temperature on persistent daily rhythmicity has been described for *Uca pugnax*.[65] In this case the temperatures concerned are well above the range which inhibits the endogenous cycles. Persistent alterations in phase relations of the diurnal color changes result from lowering the temperature below a critical point lying in the range 9.5–18°C and chilling the crabs for a minimum of 6, but not more than 12, hours prior to returning them to the initial higher temperature. The resulting amount of phase shift is independent of the time spent at the reduced temperature and of the amount of temperature drop to the critical point. On the other hand, it is dependent upon the times of day when the animals are chilled and when they are returned to higher temperatures. Repeated exposures to low temperature at suitable intervals result apparently in a simple summation of the cycle shift due to each chilling. These daily cycles of susceptibility to shift by temperature changes did not follow the changing phase relations of the color-change cycles. This suggests that the daily rhythm of response to temperature is less labile than the color-change rhythm. This latter observation provides further support for the hypothesis[17] that more than one kind of rhythmic center exists in the organism.

B. RELATIONSHIPS TO LIGHT

Many years ago[55] it was demonstrated that the diurnal rhythm of color change in *Idotea* could have its phase relationships shifted about 180° by illuminating the animals at night and keeping them in darkness during the daytime for 9 days. The resultant inverted color cycles persist about a week. A similar 180°-phase shift in chromatophore cycles is found in *Uca pugnax*.[71] The number of reversed cycles of light and dark needed to effect the shift is an inverse function of the brightness of the illumination. An illumination of 1600 lux brings about the change in a single cycle. With 850 lux, 3 cycles, and with 425 lux, 4 cycles, are required. Once shifted, the rhythm in constant darkness appears as stable as that of controls having the original phase relations to solar day-night (Fig. 6).

When *Uca* are subjected to alternating 6-hr periods of light and darkness, with illuminated periods from 7 A.M. to 1 P.M. and 7 P.M. to 1 A.M., the phase relations of their 24-hr cycles shift at once to about a quarter cycle earlier than normal, a condition which persists as long as the short light cycles continue. When the crabs are returned to constant darkness, the outcome depends upon the time of day of the last light period. When it is in the morning there is immediate reversion to the normal phase relations. When the last light period is

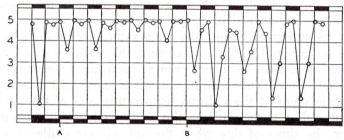

Fig. 6. The shifting by 180° of the daily rhythm of melanin dispersion in *Uca pugnax* otherwise in continuing darkness by five cycles of illumination by night (commencing at *A* and terminating at *B*). Note the gradual character of the shift. (From Webb.[66])

in the evening, the alteration persists for a time, drifting gradually back to the normal phase relations over about a 5-day period. Chiefly to account for such transient phase alterations, in contrast with those which are quite stable, a two-center hypothesis for the mechanism of endogenous rhythmicity was advanced.[17] According to this, only conditions which effect an alteration in the more basic of the two centers would result in a permanently shifted rhythm (Fig. 7).

The foregoing results indicate that there is an underlying 24-hr cycle in sensitivity to phase-shifting stimuli. Illumination from 7 A.M. to 1 P.M. is not the physiological equivalent of illumination from 7 P.M. to 1 A.M. In crabs whose rhythmic changes have been persistently shifted 180° by several periods of illumination at night, the times of greatest sensitivity to shift by light are altered to the same extent.

Further studies[66] showed that the time of the light-to-dark or dark-to-light change, rather than duration of exposure, is the chief factor determining the extent of phase shifts induced by light. Crabs exposed to illumination beginning at 1 A.M. had their cycles persistently shifted a quarter cycle earlier whether the duration of the light was 6 or 12 hr. Any time thereafter, as long as the crabs remained in continued darkness, a second shift to a 6-hr earlier time could be produced by a 6-hr period of illumination now commencing at 7 P.M. The first shift had rendered 7 P.M. the physiological equivalent of the former 1 A.M. Furthermore, crabs with normal cycles kept in constant darkness and exposed to a single light period beginning anytime

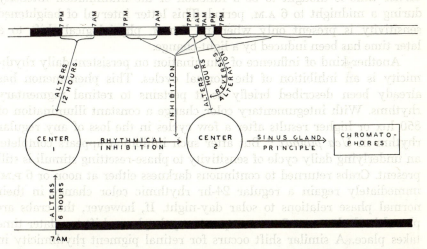

FIG. 7. A diagram of a two-center hypothesis for the regulation of daily rhythmicity in the crabs, together with some of the kinds of light changes which appear to alter the phase relations of each. Center 1 is a more basic, less labile center than 2 and appears capable of dominating over the latter. (From Brown and Webb.[7])

in the daytime period and terminating at 7 A.M. show a persistent phase shift of a quarter-cycle later. Apparently the maximum possible phase shift produced by a *single* light change is about one quarter-cycle (6 hr).

The mechanism of such shifts in phase relationships induced by light in the rhythm of color change of *Uca pugnax* was investigated.[12] Five daily cycles of various combinations of higher illuminations by night and lower ones by day produce a whole spectrum of induced persistent shifts ranging from 12 hr later to 6 hr earlier. The maximum shift to 12 hr later occurs only when the nighttime illumination has a minimum brightness of 540 lux and the daytime illumination is

22 lux or lower. Similarly the maximum shift to 6 hr earlier is obtained only when the minimum nighttime brightness is 540 lux, but now with 110 lux or higher illumination by day. Otherwise, for any given brightness by night, the amount of forward shift is an inverse function of the brightness of day. These observations can be interpreted in terms of two kinds of response in a 6–18-hr asymmetrical cycle of sensitivity to resetting by light. The phase shift to a later time is thought to be due to the strength of the light-increase stimulus at the 7 P.M. transition from "day" to "night" illumination. The phase shift to an earlier time is thought to be a function of the illumination intensity during a midnight to 6 A.M. period. This latter interval of heightened sensitivity is present only when no 7 P.M. physiological shift to a later time has been induced by a light-change.

Another kind of influence of illumination on persistent daily rhythmicity is an inhibition of the normal cycles. This phenomenon has already been described briefly as it pertains to retinal pigmentary rhythms. With integumentary color change a constant illumination of 850 lux or higher results after a few cycles in the loss of any regular rhythm in *Uca pugnax*.[17] But after such inhibition appears complete, an underlying daily cycle of sensitivity to phase-resetting stimuli is still present. Crabs returned to continuous darkness either at noon or 6 P.M. immediately regain a regular 24-hr rhythmic color change in their normal phase relations to solar day-night. If, however, the crabs are placed in darkness at 7 A.M., a quarter-cycle phase shift to a later time takes place. A similar shift occurs for retinal pigment rhythmicity in *Hemigrapsus* when the crabs are placed in darkness at about 6 A.M.[64]

Continuous illumination has been found to influence the amplitude of the diurnal color change in *Uca pugnax*.[14] Within an illumination range from 22 to about 1100 lux the amplitude of the persisting cycles is an inverse function to the intensity. The effects of the light on the rhythms are of two types, 1) a direct inhibition reversible at once when the crabs are returned to a much lower illumination or darkness, and 2) a persistent diminution in rhythm amplitude in subsequent low illumination or darkness. The latter effect is clearly apparent after crabs are kept in a continuous illumination of 2700 lux for periods varying from 1 to 16 days and then tested in an illumination of 22 lux. The amplitude decreases with the number of days' exposure to 2700 lux, at first rapidly, then more slowly, finally reaching a steady level after about 2 weeks when the cycles are of quite low amplitude.

Another kind of modification in the daily cycles is induced by experimentally altering the photoperiods within the 24-hr framework.[15]

Light exposures of 6 and 18 hr have been used. These may induce some alterations in the rhythms of color change which later persist in constant darkness. Nonpersistent as well as transient alterations are also observed. The latter disappear during about a week in constant darkness, at the end of which time the cycles stabilize in a form different from previous ones. These observations, like some described above (page 410) point clearly to at least two rhythmic centers in *Uca* possessing different properties of stability and lability.

The frequency of the daily cycles in *Uca* color change may be altered by exposure to continuous illumination. In one particular experiment constant low illumination gave rise to cycles about 25.3 hr long.[71]

The lunar tidal cycles of color change in *Uca pugnax* may also have their phase relationships reset by light-changes.[13] When the phases of the diurnal color cycle are set to a 4.5–5.5 hr earlier time of solar day by three successive midnight to 6 A.M. periods of illumination of animals otherwise in darkness, the phases of the tidal cycles are simultaneously altered to an earlier time of lunar day by a corresponding number of hours. There seems, therefore, to be some definite functional interrelationship between the resetting mechanisms for both cycles in these crabs.

C. OTHER PROPERTIES

A social factor in the maintenance of the diurnal rhythm of color change has been reported.[70] Fiddler crabs in constant conditions show gradually decreasing amplitude of their rhythms following their isolation into individual containers. By the tenth to thirteenth day the average daily amplitude is very low and many of the individuals exhibit no measurable change. The diurnal rhythm is restored at once to normal amplitude if the crabs are replaced in a common container. Even two crabs, both of which have ceased to show daily changes, redevelop the cycles at once when put into a common vessel.

IV. *THE NATURE OF THE FREQUENCY-REGULATING MECHANISM*

Despite the substantial amount of descriptive work which has been done on persistent rhythmicity in crustaceans, relatively little light has been cast to date upon the mechanism by which the relatively precise 12.4-hr, 24-hr, 24.8-hr, 14.8-day, or 29.5-day cycles can be maintained for extended periods and can exhibit the remarkable property of temper-ature-independence. Theoretically there would seem to be two possi-bilities. The rhythmicity could be a consequence of a wholly autono-mous metabolic clock within the organism, in other words be completely endogenous. On the other hand, the cycles could be dependent upon some type of external physical pace-setting stimulus still able to affect the organisms in the presumed constant conditions.

The plasticity of the forms, amplitudes, and phase relations of the cycles which have been described above argue eloquently in favor of an endogenous cyclic mechanism. This may be set in motion and adap-tively modified to fit some pattern of obvious external stimuli such as light or temperature, and then, in constant conditions, be independently continued with the aid of a precise endogenous clock.*

The animals do appear, however, to possess a deeply ingrained 24-hr cyclicity. Prolonged attempts by Webb in 1950[66] to impose a per-sistent 32-hr "day" on fiddler crabs met with complete failure. The *Uca* tend to develop a 96-hr (the smallest common denominator of the im-posed and natural periods) fluctuation while the artificial illumination changes are continued but revert at once to a precise 24-hr rhythmicity when returned to constant darkness. Furthermore, crabs whose overt rhythm of color change appeared completely abolished after 10 days of continuous high illumination, revert at once to a regular 24-hr cycle when placed in darkness.[17]

To determine whether the fiddler crab can produce an accurate 24-hr cycle independent of all known and unknown external physical cycles which are a consequence of a particular geographical locus, *Uca* were transported by airplane from Woods Hole, Massachusetts, to Berkeley, California (a distance of about 51° of longitude) in light-tight containers; a duplicate control was left in Woods Hole.[18] The cycles of color change were then carefully followed under constant conditions for the succeeding 6 days in the two locations (Fig. 8). The two samples showed no significant mean difference from one another in their phase relations, nor was there any suggestion during the 6-day period that the crabs in California altered their cycles toward the sun-time of their new location. Evidently, at least during the westward trip, the crabs must have maintained rather precise solar-day and lunar-day cycles independently of any external cycles whose length was deter-mined by the earth's rotation on its axis.

The foregoing investigation while thus demonstrating an autono-mous cyclicity, at the same time yielded evidence that single cycles

---

* But further support for the dependence of animal rhythms on subtle geophysical ones has been presented.[6a]

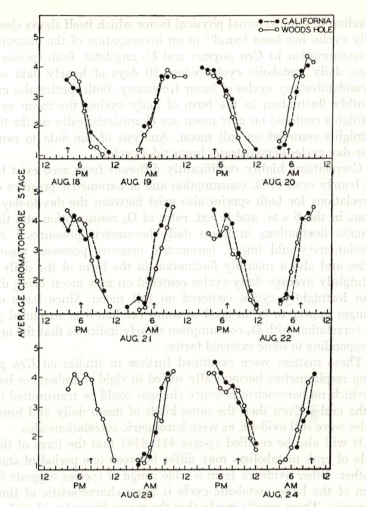

Fig. 8. The cycles in degree of dispersion of melanin in *Uca pugnax* transported in constant darkness to Berkeley, California (approximately 122°W.; 38°N.) compared with a duplicate sample kept in Woods Hole, Massachusetts (approximately 71°W.; 42°N.). The cycles were determined under similar constant conditions. All times are Eastern Standard. The arrows indicate the times of low tide at the place of collection of the crabs. (From Brown, Webb, and Bennett.[18])

even of large crab samples varied considerably in length from one day to another; only the mean cycle length during several days was quite accurately 24 hr in length. Furthermore, this study did not prove that the cycles of the crabs in either location could continue with their precise mean frequencies without some external, rhythmic pacemaker.

Evidence that fiddler crabs in "constant conditions" are still responding to some external physical factor which itself shows clear mean daily cycles has been found[20] in an investigation of the fluctuations in O_2 consumption in *Uca pugnax* and *U. pugilator*. Both species possess mean daily metabolic cycles when 30 days of hourly data are used to randomize any cycles of lunar frequency. Both species also exhibit a monthly fluctuation in the form of daily cycles; the mean cycles for fortnights centered on new moon are characteristically unlike those for fortnights centered on full moon. Analysis of the data to randomize solar-day cycles demonstrates lunar tidal cycles.

Correlations highly significantly different from zero exist between the hourly rates of O_2 consumption and of barometric pressure change. Correlations for both species also exist between the day-to-day fluctuations in the 6 A.M. and 6 P.M. rates of O_2 consumption and the large climatic fluctuations in mean daily barometric pressures.[21] As such correlations would imply, barometric pressure possesses mean daily cycles and also a monthly fluctuation in the form of the daily cycles, fortnightly average daily cycles centered on new moon being different from fortnightly cycles centered on full moon. Since large climatic changes appear to be in good measure random over extended periods, the correlation with O_2 consumption clearly indicates that the organism is responding to some external factor.

These matters were examined further in studies on *Uca pugnax*, using respirometers hermetically sealed in rigid chambers, or barostats, in which no barometric pressure changes could be transmitted directly to the crabs. Even then the same kinds of mean daily and lunar tidal cycles were still evident, as were barometric correlations also.

It will also be recalled (pages 411–414) that the form of the daily cycle of crab metabolism may differ between one period of study and another. Other evidence from a wide range of species suggests that the form of the basic metabolic cycle is more characteristic of time than of species. These results imply that the mean diurnal cycles of metabolism are at least partly determined by some factor outside the crabs.

Apparently crabs in "constant" laboratory conditions are responding in part to fluctuations in some external physical factor which is correlated with barometric pressure changes, but not actually to this pressure itself. One such possible factor with this characteristic is high-energy radiation of cosmic-ray origin. To test this notion color changes were studied in *Uca pugnax* placed beneath lead plates. Crabs under lead sheets are significantly darker during the day and early evening than control animals[7] and also are paler during the early morning. These results have been interpreted to suggest that the crabs display a measureable response to changes in intensity of some cosmic-ray-derived radiation as small as those known to be effected by 2cm-thick lead plates.

The foregoing observations encourage a hypothesis that there are mean daily, lunar day, and monthly cycles of metabolic rate in crabs which are of exogenous origin and that these cycles constitute the pace-making system for persistent endogenous rhythmicities. This view suggests that in the schema[77] for the daily series of events, namely: nervous → humoral → metabolic → nervous, etc., the "metabolic" would be partly exogenous even though the organism clearly can reproduce from one to a few reasonably accurate cycles independently. Such a mechanism not only would provide the crustacean with an insurance factor for brief periods when the exogenous factor was irregular, but would also yield an endogenous mechanism capable of generating the commonly observed regular cycles in the face of the day-to-day irregularities in all known external, physical periodic factors.

V. GENERAL CONCLUSIONS AND SUMMARY

Numerous instances are known of persistent diurnal rhythmicity in crustaceans kept in conditions constant with respect to all external factors known to influence them. Among the most regular and striking are those of retinal pigment migrations, integumentary color changes, and spontaneous locomotor activity. Some of these rhythms may persist as long as several months without alteration of their phase relationships relative to the external day-night cycles.

The rhythmic color changes have been the most intensively investigated in an attempt to learn something of the underlying rhythm-determining mechanism. The 24-hr frequency appears to be very deeply ingrained in the animals. No attempt to impose cycles of other than the diurnal frequency has given any persistent element, even in those few instances where an induced alteration was evident, as long as the stimulus was rhythmically applied. If temperatures are constant the frequency is independent of this factor through a wide range.

In contrast with such a relatively stable frequency of the rhythm, its phase relationships to the natural solar-day cycle may be shifted to any degree. These phase shifts may be effected by 1) illumination changes at sensitive times in the daily cycle, 2) temperature alterations having appropriate ranges and frequencies, and 3) temporary inhibition of rhythms by temperatures near 0°C. Depending upon how the shift is induced, the animals may, when replaced in constant conditions, 1) revert at once to the former phase relations, 2) drift gradually back during a 4 to 5 day period to the original phase relations, 3) shift to a new relation and become stabilized, or 4) remain indefinitely stable and persistent in the shifted state.

The cycles may also be persistently altered both in amplitude by extended periods of continuous bright illumination and in form by the particular pattern of daily changes in illumination. Experimental alteration of photoperiods will induce corresponding and persisting changes in the relative lengths of the day and night phases in color change.

The substantial stability in frequency of persistent daily cycles suggests strongly the possession of an endogenous 24-hr cyclicity in crustaceans, despite the modifiability of its form and phase relationships. This has been made even more convincing by the observation that rather precise 24-hr cycles may persist during rapid east-west geographic translocation of animals in otherwise constant conditions.

Regular lunar tidal cycles have been reported chiefly for some instances of color change and of spontaneous locomotor activity, where such rhythms are commonly superimposed upon a diurnal cyclicity. The tidal periods, like the daily ones, are relatively temperature-independent as to their frequency and labile in their phase relationships, with clear indication that these are set by the tidal timetable of the local habitat.

All crustaceans whose metabolic rate or spontaneous activity has been measured continuously for a sufficient period exhibit rhythmic components of solar-day and lunar-day frequencies and also of fortnightly and synodic monthly cycles. The rates of O_2 consumption correlate with barometric-pressure change. Also the correlations still persist even when the O_2 consumption is measured in animals in barostats, where pressure cannot be a direct mediating factor. But, since clear mean daily, mean lunar-tidal, and synodic monthly cycles of barometric pressure exist, it appears highly probable that metabolic cycles of these mean frequencies, exogenous in character, occur in so-called constant conditions.

Whatever the nature of these strikingly precise cyclic mechanisms, they are presumably highly adaptive and constitute an indispensable clock regulating such periodic activities as feeding, tidal migrations, and breeding, thus enabling the animals to maintain optimal adaptive relations to the regular changes in their environment.

REFERENCES

1. Abramowitz, A. A. 1937. The chromatophorotropic hormone of the Crustacea: Standardization, properties and physiology of the eye-stalk glands. *Biol. Bull.* **72:** 344–365.

2. Bennett, M. F., Shriner, J., and Brown, R. A. 1957. Persistent tidal cycles of spontaneous motor activity in the fiddler crab, *Uca pugnax*. *Biol. Bull.* 112:267–275.

3. Bennitt, R. 1932. Diurnal rhythm in the proximal pigment cells of the crayfish retina. *Physiol. Zoöl.* 5:65–69.

4. Brown, F. A., Jr. 1944. Hormones in the Crustacea, their sources and activities. *Quart. Rev. Biol.* 19:32–46, 118–143.

5. Brown, F. A., Jr. 1950. Studies on the physiology of *Uca* red chromatophores. *Biol. Bull.* 98:218–226.

6. Brown, F. A., Jr. 1958. Studies of the timing mechanisms of daily, tidal, and lunar periodicities in organisms. *In:* "Perspectives in Marine Biology." (A. A. Buzzati-Traverso, ed.), pp. 269–282. Univ. California Press, Berkeley.

6a. Brown, F. A., Jr. 1959. Living clocks. *Science* 130:1535–1544.

7. Brown, F. A., Jr., Bennett, M. F., and Ralph, C. L. 1955. Apparent reversible influence of cosmic-ray-induced showers upon a biological system. *Proc. Soc. Exptl. Biol. Med.* 89:332–337.

8. Brown, F. A., Jr., Bennett, M. F., Shriner, J., Webb, H. M., and Brown, R. A. 1956. Mean cycles of O₂-consumption in fiddler crabs and sea-weed under constant conditions including pressure. *Anat. Record* 125:614.

9. Brown, F. A., Jr., Bennett, M. F., and Webb, H. M. 1954. Persistent daily and tidal rhythms of O₂-consumption in fiddler crabs. *J. Cellular Comp. Physiol.* 44:477–506.

10. Brown, F. A., Jr., Brown, R. A., Webb, H. M., Bennett, M. F., and Shriner, J. 1956. A persistent tidal rhythm of locomotor activity in *Uca pugnax*. *Anat. Record* 125:613.

11. Brown, F. A., Jr., Fingerman, M., and Hines, M. N. 1952. Alterations in the capacity for light and dark adaptation of the distal retinal pigment of *Palaemonetes*. *Physiol. Zoöl.* 25:230–239.

12. Brown, F. A., Jr., Fingerman, M., and Hines, M. N. 1954. A study of the mechanism involved in shifting of the phases of the endogenous daily rhythm by light stimuli. *Biol. Bull.* 106:308–317.

13. Brown, F. A., Jr., Fingerman, M., Sandeen, M. I., and Webb, H. M. 1953. Persistent diurnal and tidal rhythms of color change in the fiddler crab, *Uca pugnax*. *J. Exptl. Zool.* 123:29–60.

14. Brown, F. A., Jr., and Hines, M. N. 1952. Modifications in the diurnal pigmentary rhythm of *Uca* effected by continuous illumination. *Physiol. Zoöl.* 25:56–70.

15. Brown, F. A., Jr., and Stephens, G. C. 1951. Studies of the daily rhythmicity of the fiddler crab, *Uca*. Modifications by photoperiod. *Biol. Bull.* 101:71–83.

16. Brown, F. A., Jr., and Webb, H. M. 1948. Temperature relations of an endogenous daily rhythmicity in the fiddler crab, *Uca*. *Physiol. Zoöl.* 21:371–381.

17. Brown, F. A., Jr., and Webb, H. M. 1949. Studies of the daily rhythmicity of the fiddler crab, *Uca*. Modifications by light. *Physiol. Zoöl.* 22:136–148.

18. Brown, F. A., Jr., Webb, H. M., and Bennett, M. F. 1955. Proof for an endogenous component in persistent solar and lunar rhythmicity in organisms. *Proc. Natl. Acad. Sci. U. S.* 41:93–100.

19. Brown, F. A., Jr., Webb, H. M., Bennett, M. F., and Sandeen, M. I. 1954. Temperature-independence of the frequency of the endogenous tidal rhythm of *Uca*. *Physiol. Zoöl.* 27:345–349.

20. Brown, F. A., Jr., Webb, H. M., Bennett, M. F., and Sandeen, M. I. 1955. Evidence for an exogenous contribution to persistent diurnal and lunar rhythmicity under so-called constant conditions. *Biol. Bull.* **109**:238–254.

21. Brown, F. A., Jr., Webb, H. M., and Macey, E. J. 1957. Lag-lead correlations of barometric pressure and biological activity. *Biol. Bull.* **113**:112–119.

22. Brown, F. A., Jr., Webb, H. M., and Sandeen, M. I. 1953. Differential production of two retinal pigment hormones in *Palaemonetes* by light flashes. *J. Cellular Comp. Physiol.* **41**:123–144.

23. Carlson, S. P. 1935. The color changes in *Uca pugilator*. *Proc. Natl. Acad. Sci. U. S.* **21**:549–551.

24. Carlson, S. P. 1936. Color changes in Brachyura crustaceans, especially in *Uca pugilator*. *Kgl. Fysiograf. Sällskap. Lund Förh.* **6**:1–18.

25. Caspers, H. 1951. Rhythmische Erscheinungen in der Fortpflanzung von *Clunio marinus* (Dipt. Chiron.) und das Problem der lunaren Periodizität bei Organismen. *Arch. Hydrobiol. Suppl.* **18**:415–594.

26. Drzewina, A. 1907. Les variations périodiques du signe phototropisme chez les Pagures misanthropes. *Compt. rend.* **145**:1208–1209.

27. Edwards, G. A. 1950. The influence of eyestalk removal on the metabolism of the fiddler crab. *Physiol. Comparata et Oecol.* **2**:34–50.

28. Enami, M. 1941. Melanophore responses in an isopod crustacean, *Ligia exotica*. I. General responses. *Japan. J. Zoöl.* **9**:497–514.

29. Esterly, C. O. 1917. The occurrence of a rhythm in the geotropism of two species of plankton copepods when certain recurring external conditions are absent. *Univ. Calif. (Berkeley) Publs. Zoöl.* **16**:393–400.

30. Esterly, C. O. 1919. Reactions of various plankton animals with reference to their diurnal migrations. *Univ. Calif. (Berkeley) Publs. Zoöl.* **19**:1–83.

31. Fingerman, M. 1955a. Factors influencing the rate of oxygen consumption of the dwarf crawfish, *Cambarellus shufeldtii*. *Tulane Studies in Zool.* **3**:103–116.

32. Fingerman, M. 1955b. Persistent daily and tidal rhythms of color change in *Callinectes sapidus*. *Biol. Bull.* **109**:255–264.

33. Fingerman, M. 1956a. The physiology of the melanophores of the isopod *Idothea exotica*. *Tulane Studies in Zool.* **3**:139–148.

34. Fingerman, M. 1956b. Phase difference in the tidal rhythms of color change in two species of fiddler crabs. *Biol. Bull.* **110**:274–290.

35. Fingerman, M. 1957. Relation between position of burrows and tidal rhythm of *Uca*. *Biol. Bull.* **112**:7–20.

36. Fingerman, M., and Lago, A. D. 1957. Endogenous twenty-four hour rhythms of locomotor activity and oxygen consumption in the crawfish, *Orconectes clypeatus*. *Am. Midland Naturalist* **58**:383–393.

37. Gamble, F. W., and Keeble, F. W. 1900. *Hippolyte varians:* a study in colour-change. *Quart. J. Microscop. Sci.* **43**:589–698.

38. Gompel, M. 1937. Recherches sur la consommation d'oxygène de quelques animaux aquatiques littoraux. *Compt. rend.* **205**:816–818.

39. Guyselman, J. B. 1957. Solar and lunar rhythms of locomotor activity in the crayfish, *Cambarus virilis*. *Physiol. Zoöl.* **30**:70–87.

40. Hines, M. N. 1954. A tidal rhythm in behavior of melanophores in autotomized legs of *Uca pugnax*. *Biol. Bull.* **107**:386–396.

41. Kalmus, H. 1938a. Über einen latenten physiologischen Farbwechsel beim Fluss-krebs, *Potamobius astacus*, sowie seine hormonale Beeinflussung. *Z. vergleich. Physiol.* 25:784–797.

42. Kalmus, H. 1938b. Das Aktogram des Flusskrebses und seine Beeinflussung durch Organextrakte. *Z. vergleich. Physiol.* 25:798–802.

43. Keeble, F. W., and Gamble, F. W. 1904. The colour-physiology of higher crus-taceans. *Phil. Trans. Roy. Soc. London* B196:295–388.

44. Kleinholz, L. H. 1934. Eye-stalk hormone and the movement of the distal retinal pigment in *Palaemonetes*. *Proc. Natl. Acad. Sci. U. S.* 20:659–661.

45. Kleinholz, L. H. 1936. Crustacean eye-stalk hormone and retinal pigment migra-tion. *Biol. Bull.* 70:159–184.

46. Kleinholz, L. H. 1937a. Studies in the pigmentary system of Crustacea. I. Color changes and diurnal rhythm in *Ligia baudiniana*. *Biol. Bull.* 72:24–36.

47. Kleinholz, L. H. 1937b. Studies in the pigmentary system of Crustacea. II. Diurnal movements of the retinal pigments of Bermudan decapods. *Biol. Bull.* 72:176–189.

48. Kleinholz, L. H. 1938. Studies in the pigmentary system of Crustacea. IV. The unitary versus the multiple hormone hypothesis of control. *Biol. Bull.* 75:510–532.

49. Kleinholz, L. H. 1942. Hormones in Crustacea. *Biol. Revs. Cambridge Phil. Soc.* 17:91–119.

50. Kleinholz, L. H., and Welsh, J. H. 1937. Colour changes in *Hippolyte varians*. *Nature* 140:851.

51. Kleitman, N. 1940. The modifiability of the diurnal pigmentary rhythm in isopods. *Biol. Bull.* 78:403–406.

52. Kleitman, N. 1949. Biological rhythms and cycles. *Physiol. Revs.* 29:1–30.

53. Korringa, P. 1947. Relations between the moon and periodicity in the breeding of marine animals. *Ecol. Monographs* 17:347–381.

54. Megušar, F. 1912. Experimente über den Farbwechsel der Crustaceen. *Arch. Entwicklungsmech.* 33:462–665.

55. Menke, H. 1911. Periodische Bewegungen und ihr Zusammenhang mit Licht und Stoffwechsel. *Arch. ges. Physiol. Pflüger's* 140:37–91.

56. Moore, B. 1909. Observations of certain marine organisms of (a) variations in reactions to light, and (b) diurnal periodicity of phosphorescence. *Biochem. J.* 4:1–29.

57. Nagano, T. 1950. Physiological studies on the pigmentary system of Crustacea. IV. Studies on the diurnal rhythm of the eye pigments of the shrimps. *Science Repts. Tôhoku Univ. Fourth Ser.* 18:286–297.

58. Park, O. 1940. Nocturnalism—The development of a problem. *Ecol. Monographs* 10:487–536.

59. Park, O., Roberts, T. W., and Harris, S. J. 1941. Preliminary analysis of activity of the cave crayfish, *Cambarus pellucidus*. *Am. Naturalist* 75:154–171.

60. Piéron, H. 1914. Recherches sur le comportement chromatique des Invertébrés et en particulier des Isopodes. *Bull. sci. France et Belg.* 48:30–79.

61. Roberts, T. W. 1942. Behavior of organisms. *Ecol. Monographs* 12:339–412.

62. Schallek, W. 1942. Some mechanisms controlling locomotor activity in the cray-fish. *J. Exptl. Zool.* 91:155–166.

63. Scudamore, H. H. 1947. The influence of the sinus glands upon molting and asso-ciated changes in the crayfish. *Physiol. Zoöl.* 20:187–208.

64. Smith, R. I. 1948. The role of the sinus glands in retinal pigment migration in grapsoid crabs. *Biol. Bull.* 95:169–185.

65. Stephens, G. C. 1957. Influence of temperature fluctuations on the diurnal melanophore rhythm of the fiddler crab *Uca. Physiol. Zoöl.* 30:55–69.

66. Webb, H. M. 1950. Diurnal variation of response to light in the fiddler crab, *Uca. Physiol. Zoöl.* 23:316–337.

67. Webb, H. M., Bennett, M. F., and Brown, F. A., Jr. 1954. A persistent diurnal rhythm of chromatophoric response in eyestalkless *Uca pugilator. Biol. Bull.* 106:371–377.

68. Webb, H. M., Bennett, M. F., Graves, R. C., and Stephens, G. C. 1953. Relationship between time of day and inhibiting influence of low temperature on the diurnal chromatophore rhythm of *Uca. Biol. Bull.* 105:386–387.

69. Webb, H. M., and Brown, F. A., Jr. 1953. Diurnal rhythm in the regulation of distal retinal pigment in *Palaemonetes. J. Cellular Comp. Physiol.* 41:103–122.

70. Webb, H. M., Brown, F. A., Jr., Bennett, M. F., Shriner, J., and Brown, R. A. 1956. An alteration of the persistent daily rhythm of the fiddler crab. *Anat. Record* 125:615.

71. Webb, H. M., Brown, F. A., Jr., and Sandeen, M. I. 1954. A modification in the frequency of the persistent daily rhythm of the fiddler crab. *Anat. Record* 120:796.

72. Welsh, J. H. 1930. Diurnal rhythm of the distal pigment cells in the eyes of certain crustaceans. *Proc. Natl. Acad. Sci. U. S.* 16:386–395.

73. Welsh, J. H. 1935. Further evidence of a diurnal rhythm in the movement of pigment cells in eyes of crustaceans. *Biol. Bull.* 68:247–252.

74. Welsh, J. H. 1936. Diurnal movements of the eye pigments of *Anchistioides. Biol. Bull.* 70:217–227.

75. Welsh, J. H. 1938. Diurnal rhythms. *Quart. Rev. Biol.* 13:123–139.

76. Welsh, J. H. 1939. The action of eyestalk extracts on retinal pigment migration in the crayfish, *Cambarus bartoni. Biol. Bull.* 77:119–125.

77. Welsh, J. H. 1941. The sinus glands and 24-hour cycles of retinal pigment migration in the crayfish. *J. Exptl. Zool.* 86:35–49.

78. Welsh, J. H., Chace, F. A., Jr., and Nunnemacher, R. F. 1937. The diurnal migration of deep-water animals. *Biol. Bull.* 73:185–196.

79. Wheeler, J. F. G. 1944. Lunar periodicity in animals. *Rev. agr. de l'Ile Maurice* 23:151–156.

80. Wheeler, J. F. G., and Brown, F. A., Jr. 1936. The periodic swarming of *Anchistioides antiguensis* (Schmitt) (Crustacea Decapoda) at Bermuda. *J. Linnean Soc. London Zool.* 39:413–428.

CHAPTER 12

RICHARD BAINBRIDGE

MIGRATIONS

I. *INTRODUCTION*

All crustaceans undertake persistent oriented locomotor movements which may be considered migrations; although sometimes, as with the free-swimming larvae of parasitic forms, it is only one particular stage in the life history that does so. There are few records of movements as spectacular as those recorded for certain insects, fish, and birds, but it is quite possible that such migrations occur and have yet escaped detection. There is, however, a great deal of information concerning more modest movements. This relates to two major categories: 1) migrations free in the medium and 2) those migrations involving more or less continuous contact with the substratum. In the following account, pelagic, benthic, and terrestrial migrations will be considered in this order.

II. *PELAGIC MIGRATIONS*

Pelagic animals contrast strongly with benthic, terrestrial, and even aerial forms in their freedom and ease of three-dimensional movement. While both horizontal and vertical movements occur, however, it is with the latter that investigators have, understandably, been particularly preoccupied; for it is these that distinguish so completely life in the sea from that on land. Vertical migrations will therefore be considered first and then horizontal migrations in the body of the water.

431

A. Vertical Migration

The vertical movements of crustaceans in both fresh water and the sea have attracted much interest and their importance in the life of the animals concerned is undeniable. Various authors distinguish diurnal, ontogenetic, and seasonal migrations, but I have preferred to consider ontogenetic and seasonal changes as mere variations imposed on the theme of diurnal vertical migration. Russell[129] and Cushing[30] have published extensive reviews, particularly of the descriptive aspect of the

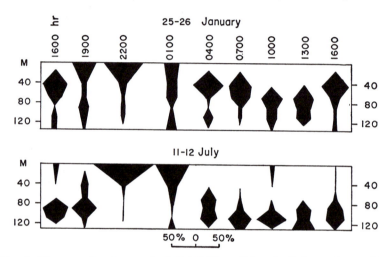

Fig. 1. Diagram showing vertical distribution of female *Calanus finmarchicus* at 3-hr intervals on 25–26 January (sunset 1627 hr, sunrise 0837 hr) and on 11–12 July (sunset 2007 hr, sunrise 0358 hr). From Nicholls.[113]

subject; Kikuchi[86] has a general review; and Marshall and Orr,[104] a particular but very full account of the vertical migrations of *Calanus*.

1. Description

a. *Time and space parameters.*   One example must suffice to show the pattern of migration common to most planktonic Crustacea. Nicholls[113] took vertical hauls every 3 hr with a closing net in 130 meters of water in Loch Fyne, Scotland, dividing the total depth into 6 sections, and showed marked vertical movements on the part of some stages of the copepod *Calanus finmarchicus*. Figure 1 illustrates the upward movement of female *Calanus* at sunset, a more even distribution in the middle of the night, and a collecting at one level followed by descent in the early morning. The upper part of the figure represents obserrations in January, the lower in July. A seasonal difference in depth distribution is apparent from a comparison of these two.

Table 1 lists the principal observations reporting such migrations and illustrates their widespread incidence. Any attempt to correlate the detailed behavior of different species, however, or of one species at different times, reveals at once an astonishing variety of performance. In an attempt to rationalize such diversity the diurnal cycle has been considered to comprise: 1) ascent from the day depth, 2) midnight sinking, 3) dawn rise, and 4) descent to the day depth.[30] Although admitting that this pattern may be modified by a variety of factors, Cushing claims it to be the basic one and relates it to a postulated mechanism of aggregation in a band of optimum light intensity.[128] But this ideal cycle is in fact revealed by field observation only upon the rarest of occasions. It would seem more consonant with the facts to admit the existence of various behavior patterns and to recognize that no single species or stage of a species can be expected to behave entirely consistently either upon successive nights or even in the same night.

Ascent from the day depth generally begins about 2 hr before sunset, but marked deviation may be found in exceptional cases. Thus it may start as early as 10 hr before sunset (*Acanthephyra purpurea*,[163] *Calanus propinquus*[101]), or may start as late as 2.5 hr after sunset (*Ctenocalanus vanus*[71]). Upward migration continues for a period partly dependent upon the depth from which it began. In the majority of cases it continues until about midnight, but it may be prolonged until dawn (*Diaphanosoma excisum*[170]). In other species it may be completed in a short time either over a long distance (*Euphausia frigida*[71]) or over a short distance (*Polyphemus*[86]). Downward migration commences either at dawn or some time before. Frequently this may be as early as midnight and sometimes even 2000 hr (*Vibilia antarctica*[101]).

The spatial extent of such migrations varies from about 2 meters (*Polyphemus*[86]) to 600–1000 meters (*Gennadas elegans*,[143] *Thysanopoda acutifrons*, and *Acanthephyra purpurea*[163]). Such extended movement does not always carry the animals right to the surface. These bathypelagic crustaceans especially, even at the upper limit of their migration, always remain below 200 meters. More generally however, the extent of crustacean migration is related to the normal day depth of the animal since most species come right up to, and accumulate at, the surface. Because of the extraordinary variability of this day depth, both in time and space, no meaningful figure for the average extent of vertical migration can be given. However, the three most substantial

TABLE 1

A LIST OF THE PRINCIPAL FIELD OBSERVATIONS ON THE VERTICAL MIGRATIONS
OF CRUSTACEA[a]

Subclass Branchiopoda
  Order Diplostraca
    Suborder Cladocera
      Cladocera in general[83]
      Daphniidae in general[34,92]
      Bosmina coregoni[95,157,169]
      Bosmina longirostris[87,122,147,157,158]
      Bosminopsis deitersi[87]
      Bythotrephes longimanus[95,143,169]
      Ceriodaphnia sp.[147,158,169]
      Daphnia cucullata[157]
      Daphnia longispina[b]
      Daphnia lumholzi[169]
      Daphnia pulex[31,62,122]
      Diaphanosoma brachyurum[87,169]
      Diaphanosoma excisum[170]
      Evadne sp.[87]
      Evadne nordmanni[64]
      Holopedium gibberum[87,89,161]
      Leptodora kindtii[87,95,143,164,169]
      Moina brachiata[170]
      Moina dubia[170]
      Podon polyphemoides[64]
      Polyphemus pediculus[87]
Subclass Copepoda
  Copepoda in general[83,132]
  Order Calanoida
    Acartia clausi[47,50,86,134]
    Acartia longiremis[10,134]
    Acartia spinata[22]
    Acartia tonsa[47]
    Anomalocera patersoni[9,127,130]
    Calanoides acutus[71,101,102]
    Calanopia americana[22]
    Calanus finmarchicus[c]
    Calanus hyperboreus[57,141]
    Calanus propinquus[71,101]
    Calanus simillimus[71,101]
    Candacia sp.[101,127]
    Centropages hamatus[65]
    Centropages typicus[9,20]
    Chirundina streetsii[50]
    Clausocalanus laticeps[71]
    Diaptomus sp.[101]
    Diaptomus banforanus[170]

Order Calanoida (Cont'd)
    Diaptomus birgei[124]
    Diaptomus gracilis[103,144,147,169]
    Diaptomus japonicus[86]
    Diaptomus laciniatus[169]
    Diaptomus leptopus[62]
    Diaptomus minutus[89]
    Diaptomus oregonensis[89]
    Diaptomus pacificus[86]
    Diaptomus shoshone[122]
    Drepanopus pectinatus[71]
    Eucalanus sp.[101]
    Eucalanus elongatus[42,43,101]
    Euchaeta acuta[50]
    Euchirella sp.[101]
    Euchirella curticauda[50]
    Euchirella galeata[43]
    Eurytemora velox[144]
    Gaetanus unicornis[43]
    Haloptilus ocellatus[101]
    Heterorhabdus sp.[101]
    Limnocalanus grimaldii[37]
    Limnocalanus macrurus[84,89]
    Lophothrix frontalis[43]
    Lucicutia flavicornis[108]
    Lucicutia lucida[108]
    Metridia gerlachei[71,101]
    Metridia longa[10]
    Metridia lucens[10,20,21,43,50,51,71]
    Microcalanus pusillus[10]
    Microcalanus pygmaeus[10,71]
    Paracalanus parvus[50]
    Pareuchaeta sp.[101]
    Pareuchaeta antarctica[71]
    Pareuchaeta gracilis[50]
    Pareuchaeta tonsa[43]
    Pleuromamma abdominalis[43,50,108]
    Pleuromamma gracilis[50,108]
    Pleuromamma robusta[50,71,101,105]
    Pleuromamma xiphias[50,108]
    Pseudocalanus elongatus[10,134]
    Rhincalanus gigas[71,101,102]
    Scaphocalanus echinatus[50]
    Scaphocalanus magnus[43]
    Scolecithricella dentata[50]

TABLE 1 *(Continued)*

Order Calanoida *(Cont'd)*
    Scolecithricella ovata[50]
    Sinocalanus sinensis[86]
    Temora longicornis[9]
    Thermodiaptomus galeboides[169]
    Undeuchaeta major[50]
    Undeuchaeta minor[50]
Order Harpacticoida
    Harpacticus superflexus[10]
Order Cyclopoida
    Cyclops sp.[84,89,169]
    Cyclops bicuspidatus[103,122,124]
    Cyclops hyalinus[170]
    Cyclops leuckarti[169,170]
    Cyclops oithonoides[147]
    Cyclops strenuus[86,95,144,159,169]
    Mesocyclops oithonoides[87]
    Oithona frigida[71]
    Oithona nana[65,87]
    Oithona similis[10,50]
    Oncaea borealis[65]
Subclass Malacostraca
  Order Mysidacea
    Acanthomysis longicornis[127]
    Anchialina agilis[127]
    Antarctomysis sp.[101]
    Boreomysis microps[163]
    Eucopia unguiculata[163]
    Leptomysis gracilis[127]
    Mysis mixta[116]
    Mysis relicta[32,85,142,144]
    Schistomysis sp.[127]
  Order Cumacea
    Diastylis sp.[127]
  Order Amphipoda
    Suborder Gammaridea
      Apherusa clevei[134]
      Cyphocaris anonyx[163]
    Suborder Hyperiidea
      Parathemisto gaudichaudi[71,101]
      Parathemisto gracilipes[127]
      Primno macropa[101]

Order Amphipoda *(Cont'd)*
    Vibilia propinqua[163]
Order Euphausiacea
    Euphausia brevis[108]
    Euphausia frigida[71,101,102]
    Euphausia hemigibba[108]
    Euphausia krohnii[79]
    Euphausia pacifica[44]
    Euphausia superba[55,71,79,101]
    Euphausia tenera[108]
    Euphausia triacantha[71,101,102]
    Euphausia vallentini[101,102]
    Meganyctiphanes norvegica[78]
    Nematoscelis megalops[163]
    Nyctiphanes couchii[65,78,90,134]
    Nyctiphanes simplex[44]
    Stylocheiron suhmii[79]
    Thysanoessa sp.[78,101]
    Thysanoessa gregaria[108]
    Thysanoessa inermis[57]
    Thysanoessa raschii[57]
    Thysanopoda acutifrons[163]
    Thysanopoda aequalis[108]
    Thysanopoda obtusifrons[108]
Order Decapoda
    Various decapod larvae[127]
  Suborder Natantia
    Acanthephyra purpurea[110,163,165]
    Funchalia woodwardi[110]
    Gennadas elegans[146,163]
    Hymenodora glacialis[110,163]
    Parapandalus richardi[110]
    Parapasiphae sulcatifrons[110,163]
    Sergestes arcticus[163]
    Sergestes atlanticus[165]
    Sergestes corniculum[165]
    Sergestes prehensilis[111]
    Sergestes sargassi[165]
    Solenocera membranaceum[146]
  Suborder Reptantia
    Panulirus interruptus (phyllosoma)[139]
    Panulirus longipes (phyllosoma)[137]

---

  [a] For ease of reference the genera and species in this table are listed alphabetically within the larger systematic groups.

  [b] For *Daphnia longispina* see refs. 87, 89, 122, 142, 143, 144, 157, 158, 169.

  [c] For *Calanus finmarchicus* see refs. 9–11, 20, 21, 41, 43, 51, 52, 56, 57, 61, 65, 113, 127, 128, 134, 141, 148, 168.

sets of data available show that the fresh-water Cladocera have migrations of the order of 30–50 meters; the marine Copepoda, of 50–150 meters; and the bathypelagic Decapoda, of 300–400 meters.

When the extent and duration of the movement of a population are known, the average speed of migration of a typical member of it can be computed. Such figures for ascending and descending *Labidocera aestiva* are approximately 6 meters and 20 meters per hour respectively;[120] for fresh-water Cladocera and Copepoda, of the order of 10 to 15 meters per hour;[160] for pelagic Decapoda, from 25 to 125 meters per hour;[163] and for marine Copepoda, about 60 meters per hour, with indications of much higher figures for *Scolecithricella minor* and for some euphausiids.[71]

The information given above merely indicates the extent of the variability of a natural behavior pattern differing from species to species and from time to time. Figures concerning various particular animals are available in the literature (Table 1), but they obviously relate only to a particular time and place and cannot necessarily be reproduced. Nevertheless, the basic pattern within which this great variability occurs is clearly a movement up toward the surface, starting in the afternoon or evening and continuing for a varying time into the night; to be followed by a return movement to deeper waters, starting either at the completion of the upward migration, at dawn, or sometime between. If there is a gap between the completion of the upward, and the start of the downward, movement, then the animals may either remain close to their upper level or become more randomly distributed around that level. In the latter case, downward movement at dawn may occasionally be preceded by a second slight upward rise.

b. *Systematic and ontogenetic occurrence.* All the major crustacean orders living where the phenomenon can be manifest have members performing diurnal vertical migrations (Table 1). In particular, they are most thoroughly recorded for Copepoda and for Cladocera, and to a certain extent for some Mysidacea, Isopoda, Amphipoda, Euphausiacea, and Decapoda. Even with the most widespread general sampling, both on the bottom and in the water mass, the number of observations of vertical movement seems to be directly related to the likelihood of the animals performing such migrations rather than to their abundance. For example, it is the pelagic hyperiid amphipods that are recorded as migrating, not the bottom-living forms, and similarly the natant forms among the Decapoda. Normally benthic and parasitic forms such as the reptant Decapoda or the Cirripedia frequently have free-swimming larvae, however, which indulge in vertical migrations while in their planktonic phase.

The records make it clear that members of all these groups can perform definite migrations up and down in the water. With one or two exceptions, however, the Mysidacea are bottom-living animals during the day, and the records of their nightly incursions into the plankton have more the appearance of random exploratory wanderings about in the body of the water rather than vertical migrations directly to and from the surface.

Some authors distinguish two types of vertical migration: the diurnal one considered so far and a second seasonal one.[104,128] But it is not always easy to distinguish migrational changes dependent upon season from those resulting from the age of the migrants. Both age and season may contribute to depth changes in some instances. Thus in temperate latitudes overwintering *Calanus* remain in deep water in a preadult stage and do not undertake vertical migrations. In the Clyde Sea area the Stage V copepodites molt into adults in deep water, and the resulting females engage in a diurnal migration while the males remain in deep water.[104] But in the Arctic the Stage V copepodites come up to the surface layers in January and February, simultaneously molting to the adult stage preparatory to breeding. While near the surface they may or may not undertake a certain amount of vertical migration. In both these cases a marked seasonal change coincides with a recognizable ontogenetic change. The importance of the seasonal change in the north, where it is a restoration of alternating periods of dark and light after the constant darkness of the polar night, has been emphasized. On the other hand the apparent importance of the ontogenetic change is supported by the participation of *Calanus* from below 1000 meters in the spring migration to the surface, when the changes in light intensity at such depths are negligible biologically. Whether such a seasonal change in depth distribution can rightly be considered a migration at all, however, is doubtful. It is more probably a gradual upward drift of the optimum distribution level with the seasonal change, rather than an active, oriented, and persistent directional swimming.

Discussing depth distribution, Cushing[30] concludes that surface-living animals (*Daphnia, Diaptomus, Bosmina*) have young that live in deep water and that animals living in deep water (*Calanus*) have young that live nearer the surface. Since they come up to the surface, the extent of the diurnal migration of such animals is directly related to their day depth. But detailed data concerning the behavior of various stages occurring together are confusing. All stages of *Calanus*, for example, seem to migrate on some occasions while any stage may not on others. Such data cannot yet be rationalized. Where information is less extensive, however, it is possible to find some regularity in the observations. Thus in *Euphausia superba* from the Antarctic, the metanauplii remain in deep water, the later larval stages migrate diurnally, and the adolescents stay permanently at the surface.[55] The migrating stages all come from 100–250 meters, and the time of their arrival at the surface is directly related to their swimming capacity: 3rd (oldest) calyptopis from 1800–2200 hr; 2nd, from 2200–0200 hr; and 1st, from 0200–0600 hr. Similar ontogenetic differences are apparent in *Bosmina coregoni* whose adults remain at the surface while the young migrate to and from a depth of 50 meters. Such permanent occurrence at the surface could of course be considered the extreme of a variable day depth. The effect of day depths upon the surfacing of various animals has been reviewed elsewhere.[30]

   c. *Anomalies.* In spite of the variability of migrational behavior, some kinds of anomalies may be recognized. Vertical movement occurs in some forms apparently in the reverse manner to that commonly met. Such reversed migrations are known for *Acartia clausi, A. longiremis, Nyctiphanes couchii,*[134] *Evadne* sp., *Oithona nana,*[87] *Daphnia lumholzi,*[169] Stages IV, V, and adult of *Calanus finmarchicus,*[56] *Diaptomus banforanus,*[170] and *Cyclops bicuspidatus.*[103] An echo-producing layer, which the authors think probably consists of euphausiids, has also been described as, in part, regularly moving in a reverse manner.[77] Most of these records are well substantiated and involve whole populations rather than aberrant individuals. But normal movements have been reported also for the same species in the case of five of these examples and for other species in the same genera for the remaining *Evadne, Daphnia,* and *Diaptomus.*

   Many forms sometimes migrate and on other occasions do not, but a few appear to remain permanently at one level. Considering the widespread incidence of migration in the groups concerned, these may be considered as anomalous. The most clearly substantiated case is that of the copepod *Anomalocera patersoni,* which remains permanently at the surface.[9,127,130] Among other copepods *Rhincalanus gigas,*[71,101,102] *Calanoides acutus,*[71,101] *Microcalanus pygmaeus, Oithona frigida,*[71] and *Centropages typicus*[9] are all reported as showing no migration. The predaceous cladoceran *Bythotrephes longimanus* also remains at one level, about 10 meters down.[169]

   In view of its well-known normal migration, the occurrence of

Calanus finmarchicus in the summer at the surface in bright sunlight may justly be considered anomalous. This phenomenon has nevertheless been recorded many times,[104] and such surface *Calanus* may be present in enormous numbers, breaking the surface into small circular ripples like raindrops. Observed underwater, two zones of differing behavior were recognized:[5] an upper one about 30 cm in depth, in which the *Calanus* swam up and down repeatedly, frequently bumping on the undersurface of the water, and a lower one of indeterminate depth in which animals swam directly up or down. It seems likely that a continuous interchange was taking place between the population at the surface and that in deeper water.

A second group whose normal vertical migration is sufficiently well known to make daytime occurrence at the surface rank as anomalous is the Euphausiacea. There are numerous records of euphausiids swimming at the surface in bright sunshine, with particular mention of their shoaling behavior under these circumstances.[9,56,71,78]

2. *Mechanisms.* The majority of vertical migrations undoubtedly result from active swimming although passive movement through the water has been suggested on various grounds. For example, transport in vertical currents resulting from temperature differences has been proposed;[2] differences in water viscosity after temperature changes have also been suggested as a cause of movement,[115] and passive movement could possibly result from changes in the specific gravity of the animals as a result of feeding.[49] Any or all of these mechanisms might apply under particular circumstances, but the evidence in favor of active swimming is overwhelming. Indeed, deep-living *Calanus* may even keep its level during the arctic night by active migration against such vertical water movements as do occur.[10] The rapidity of some vertical movements has led to the supposition that the animals must have had passive assistance,[71] but measurements of swimming speeds[70] prove that even the most extensive and rapid vertical movement is within the capabilities of the animals performing it (Table 2).

Evidence[30] has been presented for a supposed randomness in the movement of plankton animals. If valid, this implies that migrations involve kineses rather than taxes (Chapter 10). However, the data cited in support of this idea comprise without exception observations made in the laboratory. A kinesis resulting in an upward movement by *Daphnia* has also been demonstrated in the laboratory at particularly low light intensities, but otherwise swimming in these experiments was directional in relation to the light source.[74] Such observations as have been made in the sea[5] indicate that the predominant movement of copepods is directional. Although a random movement may occur close to the surface, this results from the restriction imposed by the boundary itself. The speeds of ascent calculated for some forms in the sea make it further improbable that the mechanism of ascent is a kinesis; a directional taxis would seem more probable. Downward movement may in some forms start as a passive sinking, especially when it occurs

TABLE 2

DISTANCES TRAVELED AND SPEEDS OF VERTICAL SWIMMING OF SOME CRUSTACEANS
MEASURED IN THE PLANKTON WHEEL[a]

Organism	Up			Down		
	Dura-tion (min)	Dis-tance (meters)	Speed (meters/ hr)	Dura-tion (min)	Dis-tance (meters)	Speed (meters/ hr)
Calanus finmarchicus	2	2.2	66	2	3.57	107
	30	17.8	35.6	30	29.9	59.8
	60	15	15	60	47	47
Acartia clausi	2	1.12	33.6	2	0.57	17.1
	30	4.43	8.86	8	1.61	12.1
	60	8.81	8.81	—	—	—
Balanus nauplius	2	0.75	22.5	—	—	—
	30	7.63	15.26	—	—	—
	60	14.9	14.9	—	—	—
Zoea (Brachyura)	1	1.17	70.2	—	—	—
	2	1.95	58.5	—	—	—
	10	4.89	29.34	—	—	—
Meganyctiphanes norvegica	2	5.77	173.1	2	7.17	215.1
	30	62.21	124.4	30	68.2	136.4
	60	92.8	92.8	60	128.8	128.8

[a] Hardy and Bainbridge.[70]

before dawn; but this must almost certainly be replaced by the head-first downward swimming observed in the field.[5]

3. *Initiating, controlling, and orienting factors.* The primary dependence of diurnal migrations upon changes in light intensity is beyond doubt. Yet in spite of a great amount of work, the detailed causal relationship remains one of confused complexity. Loeb[93] first suggested the importance of light as the governing factor but combined its influence with that of gravity. Later authors, in particular Rose,[126] have proposed that light alone can provide an adequate mechanism if the animals have, and select by exploration, a zone of optimum light intensity. This view has been enlarged[129] with a suggestion that both

phototaxes and geotaxes may play a part in keeping animals near their optimum.

Experimental work[70,72] largely performed on *Calanus*, however, has failed to make clear the relative importance of light and gravity in this context. A plankton population held in glass tubes at a particular depth in the sea resolves itself into two components, one swimming up and the other down.[72] The proportion swimming up increases with increasing depth. Experiments using light reflected up against gravity showed that here the reaction to light predominates. Yet other experiments in the dark showed that the population still segregated into one group swimming up and another swimming down. Hardy and Bainbridge[70] have been able to remove the confusing experimental factor of a limited vertical range with their plankton wheel. Their tentative conclusion is that upward migration is generally a positive movement toward a source of low light intensities. Little upward movement can be obtained by blacking out during the day, except with *Daphnia*. Their results leave little doubt that downward migration is not sinking as the result of an inhibition of movement but is a strong, rapid, and direct downward swimming away from light. The complete absence of light does not generally result in a downward sinking but rather in station-keeping maintained by a characteristic hop-and-sink behavior comprising alternate phases of upward swimming and downward sinking. In *Daphnia*, migratory behavior results from the interaction of both phototactic and geotactic responses.[18] Furthermore, the direction of phototactic movement is dependent upon the postural angle of the antenna and not the orientation of the body.[19] A reversible photochemical system has been proposed to account for the photic responses, and this requires a minimal rate of change in light intensity to induce response; but the rates of change in the sea may be too low for this.[21]

An important experimental advance has been made by Harris and Wolfe,[74] who studied the behavior of *Daphnia magna* in a tank filled with India ink suspension and illuminated by an overhead light of variable intensity. This technique has allowed for the first time sufficient change in intensity over limited distances for dependent behavioral changes to be seen in the laboratory. Despite a compressed time scale these authors have obtained an extraordinarily close simulation of migratory behavior in nature. A complete cycle of vertical migration can be demonstrated in a vessel 30 cm high. As well as strong naturally-characteristic individual variations, this includes a midnight sinking and a dawn rise. At high light intensities the animals keep station at their optimum by a vertical hop-and-sink behavior and this confirms earlier observations on station-keeping in *Balanus* nauplii.[48] At low light intensities this is replaced by a kinetic response independent of the light direction. The dawn rise is a manifestation of this. In complete darkness all movement is inhibited and a sinking results. Harris and Wolfe stress the importance of a sensory adaptation in the photoreceptor system when interpreting their results and suggest that animals in the sea could follow prolonged slight changes without being affected by rapid large changes.

In imposing directionality upon the movement of vertically migrating animals, gravity must be second only to light. Preoccupation with the idea of kinetic movement and an overemphasis of the incidence of midnight sinking have led some authors to dismiss gravity as of no consequence.[30] Yet it must in fact be of the utmost importance in many cases. Parker[120] first proposed "geotropism" as one of the factors in vertical migration, and his ideas have since been enlarged by many authors. The continued ascent of crustaceans in total darkness, which seems substantiated in a good many instances, and the experimental evidence[19,70,72] showing *Calanus* keeping station in the dark and *Daphnia* ascending, strongly imply an orientation dependent upon gravity.

Pressure has been suggested as having some influence upon migration, especially of *Calanus*.[72] But experiments expressly designed to test this[69] have not revealed any change in the behavior of this species under pressures up to the equivalent of 20 meters depth. Striking results were obtained, however, with zoea and megalopa stages of *Portunus* and *Carcinus*. A high proportion of these swam up for periods of up to 3 hr when subjected to pressures equivalent to 5, 10, 15, and 20 meters depth. These findings have since been confirmed in studies of *Acartia* and *Centropages*,[8] the megalopas of *Carcinus maenas* and *Galathea* as well as adults of the copepod *Caligus rapax*,[88] still without any success in eliciting a response from *Calanus*. There is as yet no morphological evidence for a pressure-sensitive organ in any of these forms, and the mechanism of perception is quite uncertain. The unequivocal demonstration of a sensitivity to pressure in some of the deep-migrating copepods or decapods would be a valuable contribution to the whole problem of vertical migration. But at the moment, light must remain the chief factor by which most forms may gauge depth.

There is evidence that phytoplankton may have some effect on the vertical migration of crustacean zooplankton. Hardy[71] first laid real emphasis on this possibility. Observations on the inverse distribution of plants and animals in the sea suggested that many forms must be prevented from coming up or must come up for only a short time in the presence of high concentrations of phytoplankton. There is some evidence possibly supporting this idea[96] although this relates only to horizontal movement; on this basis the concept of external metabolites as affecting animal-plant relationships in the sea has been developed by Lucas.[97,99] But later laboratory experiments indicate that greater numbers of *Calanus* swim up in the presence of a variety of pure and mixed phytoplankton cultures than in unenriched water, only one culture, of *Chlorella*, depressing the number swimming up.[6]

The mechanism underlying this increase in upward migration has not been investigated, but probably reduction in light intensity by the plant cells is not the intermediate factor. In other instances this might however be effective: for example, blue-green algae in Lake Windermere may reduce the light intensity at 4.3 meters by more than 50%.[121] This must surely affect the responses of animals. Experimental work on the influence on horizontal migration of filtrates from growing diatom and flagellate cultures implies that the factor concerned here may also sometimes be a substance secreted into the water and sometimes the actual physical presence of the plant cells.[4,6] Possibly a more direct effect of diatoms could result from the mucus they secrete. It has been suggested that such mucus may alter the viscosity of the water sufficiently to slow down considerably the sinking rate of eggs.[103] If so, it could presumably also affect the locomotion of other stages.

Besides such physical effects of phytoplankton as reduction in light intensity, chemical influences, e.g. the secretion of repellent or attractive substances, the production of mucus, and the possible effect of consumption or release of O_2 or CO_2, must be borne in mind. The conclusion has been drawn that excess or lack of O_2 has little effect upon the phototaxis or geotaxis of *Daphnia pulex*, but there is little critical evidence concerning the influence of this factor in general.[34] Carbon dioxide and pH have been more carefully studied. Loeb[94] reported that copepods, *Daphnia*, *Balanus* nauplii, and *Gammarus* became positively phototactic in the presence of CO_2, but this finding has not been confirmed for either CO_2 or HCl,[107] and other workers have not been able to reproduce all the results.[34,126] Some consequently maintain that natural changes of pH can be of little consequence in affecting reaction to light. However, pH may have an effect upon geotaxis, as *Daphnia* swim up in the dark at a pH of 9.0 but down at a pH below 7.0.[8]

Although temperature changes have been considered as another initiating factor[17] in diurnal vertical migration, this seems unlikely but not perhaps for the so-called seasonal migrations. Their important role is more probably as a controlling factor for animals swimming through water layers of different temperatures. Thus on some occasions the movement of *Calanus finmarchicus* is limited by the thermocline,[51,114,134] although on others this species climbs through marked discontinuity layers.[21,43] A good deal of information about the thermocline and fresh-water Cladocera is admirably summarized by Cushing.[30] Various species and stages remain above or below the thermocline on different occasions, and he concludes that temperature is an effective limiting factor to migration at the extremes of an animal's range.

A decrease in temperature has been shown experimentally to induce positive phototaxis,[34] and an upward movement by animals upon sinking from water of 10°C into water of 8° to 9°C has also been demonstrated.[45,46] The latter observation is quite consistent with the occurrence of female *Calanus* in Oslo Fjord only within the discontinuity layer, except when migrating to the surface around midnight; males here also remained within the thermocline but did not migrate, while Stage V *Calanus* were unaffected.[65] There can be little doubt in this case that temperature was materially affecting migrational behavior, but there are equally well-substantiated cases where it has no discernible effect.

The possibility that diurnal vertical movements result from a physiological rhythm (Chapter 11) rather than from reaction to changes in the environment was proposed by Esterly.[45] He observed an apparent persistence of vertical migration by *Acartia* kept in complete darkness in the laboratory. This has not been confirmed[135] and may have been fortuitous, but such a rhythm could explain the movement of deep-water forms which cannot be following changes in light intensity. The possibility of a rhythmical change in the capacity to react to light might also be borne in mind. This could account for the failure in some experiments to induce upward movement with artificial darkness during the day, while such movement was obtained during the evening.[70]

In conclusion, the basic cycle of crustacean vertical migration and its controlling factors may be summarized as follows: a rise occurs in the late afternoon which is a positive swimming toward a source of weak or decreasing light intensity. This is continued into or through the night with an orientation dependent upon gravity and is replaced either by a station-keeping behavior or by sinking as a result of inhibition of activity. With the increase of light at dawn the station-keeping or sinking may be followed by upward movement which may be kinetic at the low intensities involved. Later this is superseded under the rapidly increasing intensity by a downward movement away from the light. At the day depth this is in turn replaced by an exploratory hop-and-sink behavior which keeps the animal within a zone of optimum illumination. With advancing afternoon the upward part of this hop-and-sink activity must become gradually extended until finally a continuous upward swimming takes place again as a directional taxis toward the rapidly dimming light.

This cycle of behavior can be markedly affected to the extent of complete distortion by many factors including effects of the phytoplankton, pH, temperature, and apparently also by various known and unknown features of the animal's physiological state.

4. *Value to the animal.* The widespread occurrence of diurnal migration, not only in the Crustacea but among all pelagic groups, and the expenditure of energy that these movements must require, implies a place of some significance in the welfare of the animals concerned. Recognition of this has led to considerable speculation as to the nature of this place.

For many marine pelagic animals the region of normal daytime occurrence is below the euphotic zone. This is true even in inshore waters where light penetration is much less and the photosynthetic zone correspondingly shallower. It follows that, except for a rain of dying, dead, and decaying phytoplankton, herbivorous crustaceans must move into the upper layers in order to feed, although it is not clear what proportion of their normal requirements might derive from the sinking phytoplankton. This implies that the migration is essentially a feeding response.[169] In *Calanus* feeding is certainly confined to the hours of darkness and to the upper layers when vertical migration takes place.[58] Return to deeper layers might then be an escape from the harmful effects of sunlight[80] and of toxic products from plants[71,97,98] or from the attacks of predators better able to detect their prey in the light.[109] Evidence supporting the latter possibility is found in *Eucalanus elongatus*, which is especially well adapted by its absolute transparency for invisibility in the upper layers and shows no vertical migration.[42] Vertical migration might also be of value in allowing an animal to exploit a greater body of water than would be possible if it remained only at the surface or at great depths.[164] It seems likely that any of these factors might provide a selective advantage which could result in the evolution of vertical migration.

The most ingenious suggestion of its value in the life of the animal is that it subserves the performance of planktonic navigation.[66-68,71] This concept, originated by Hardy, postulates that vertically migrating animals mediate their horizontal distribution by varying the amount of time they spend in water layers moving in different directions or at different speeds. This mechanism is the basis of his theory of animal exclusion. There can be little doubt as to the potentialities of such navigation as a means for moving animals about horizontally in the sea. In contrast to the theory of exclusion, however, navigation could be the means by which animals congregate in areas rich in food rather than escape from them.[6]

As a result of his experimental work on *Daphnia*,[73] Harris suggests that vertical migration is merely an inescapable consequence of maintaining a certain level within the photic zone. He considers it thus to be a secondary manifestation of the depth-maintaining mechanism depriving it of much immediate significance in the life of the animal.

B. HORIZONTAL MIGRATION

1. *Description.* The usual techniques used to demonstrate vertical migration are not adapted to detecting any horizontal movement that may occur. Coupled with this, the tacit inclusion of all pelagic Crustacea among the plankton has resulted in a neglect of the problem of horizontal migration. Many of the larger pelagic Crustacea probably should be considered nektonic, and there is evidence that some Mysidacea, Euphausiacea, and Decapoda may effect considerable horizontal movements.

Three types of horizontal migration have been reported by various authors for mysids: 1) a daily active swimming upstream in estuaries with the rising tide, 2) a seasonal migration to deeper water in the summer, followed by a return in the winter, and 3) a migration inshore after dark by animals normally living further out.[153] As already mentioned (p. 437), much of the evidence for the vertical migration of mysids gives the impression of a combination of horizontal and vertical movements. A uniform distribution in the water column after dark rather than an aggregation at the surface is sometimes mentioned,[131,142,144] although an exception appears to be the vigorous swimmer *Anchialina agilis*, which does reach the surface in large numbers.

The euphausiids *Meganyctiphanes* and *Thysanoessa* are usually oceanic in habitat but approach the coast to breed, while *Nyctiphanes* is truly neritic.[91] The considerable data concerning swarming by the truly pelagic euphausiids provides strong evidence for horizontal movements since shoals[133] are always sharply circumscribed horizontally and the animals can often be seen making considerable horizontal excursions.[71]

Many Decapoda Natantia make extensive horizontal movements, but it is difficult to know whether these are really pelagic or whether they involve walking over the bottom. A migration of two species of the shrimp *Crangon* out into deeper water has been described in San Francisco Bay.[81] Similar data are known also for *Penaeus setiferus*.[166] This species migrates inshore after wintering in deeper water and later returns to depths over 15 fathoms for spawning, while *P. duorarum* "retires to deeper water after a littoral youth."[16] Shoreward migrations of *P. setiferus* also occur seasonally,[1,12] and this same species has been reported as being a shy, active animal, constantly moving about from place to place.[145] Adult littoral Penaeinae have been described as generally migrating to deeper water, while some abyssal Solenocerinae and Aristaeinae may sometimes be benthonic and sometimes nektonic.[14] Obligatory recourse to the bottom by usually pelagic species is proved by the nature of the statolith, which in *Sicyonella* for example contains bottom debris.[15] There is little information on carideans, especially those living fully pelagic lives in deep mid-water, but evidence from catches of these suggests that they also swarm and hence probably swim horizontally, in addition to their extensive vertical migrations. Recent work in Bermuda[7] suggests considerable horizontal movements by the shrimp *Palaemon northropi*.

There remains the possibility of horizontal migration in the hyperiid amphipods, but the data could be accounted for either by this or by a chance horizontal aggregation into swarms.

2. *Mechanisms*. The mechanisms used in performing horizontal migrations have been little studied, but most of the observations imply an active swimming by the animal, although occasionally tidal movements may assist, and at other times obstruct, migration. While pelagic animals are basically free to move in any plane, the form of their body and the site of their center of gravity must, however, impose some limitations upon the direction in which locomotion, at least, starts. For example, a copepod hangs naturally in a vertical position as if suspended from its antennae. Any movement of its swimming feet must therefore start it traveling upward. Even if the swimming is to be downward, it first starts in an upward direction, loops over, and then goes headfirst down.[70] On the other hand a mysid or a euphausiid lies naturally in a horizontal posture so that any swimming movement must first result here in horizontal movements. When animals thus naturally adapted for horizontal movement do swim up, they often do

so in a helix with some forward component, e.g. *Meganyctiphanes*. The first larva of *Munida rugosa* rests horizontally in the water and swims in line with the long axis of the body.[53] Similar relations hold for *Homarus gammarus* larvae but brachyuran zoeas show no such resting orientation.[167] Unlike *Meganyctiphanes*, *Munida* directs its swimming by tipping the whole body. In contrast to the general rule, horizontal movement may not always be dependent upon the position of the body. It is often so in *Daphnia*,[74] but this animal can also control its direction of movement solely by altering the postural angle of the antennae.[19]

It is perhaps possible to separate pelagic Crustacea into two great groups, the one fitted naturally for vertical, and the other for horizontal, movement. The differences in behavior between members of these two groups could readily be seen in the plankton wheel.[70]

3. *Initiating, controlling, and orienting factors.* In contrast to vertical migration there are few data concerning the factors which govern horizontal movement. Field observations lead us to suppose that initiation may sometimes arise from the daily changes from light to dark,[38,39] sometimes from tidal movement,[123] but more often from some physiological change associated with growth or development. The latter would seem to be the factor initiating most of the onshore-offshore migrations, although the temperature changes associated with the seasons might be effective, directly or through related physiological changes.

Little work has yet been done on the orientation of such animals, but some form of navigation would seem to be essential. This could be either directly by the sun or possibly by means of the polarized light which is now known to occur in the sea. Preliminary work[7,8] suggests that both these factors may be involved and, further, that in *Daphnia* the color of the incident light may determine the proportions of time spent swimming either vertically or horizontally.[8] Besides orientation in the horizontal plane some control over depth is required. This may be accomplished using either pressure or light intensity, but most probably the latter. *Palaemon* can be observed to swim roughly in a vertical sine wave when moving horizontally close to the surface as if sampling alternately deeper and shallower positions. This behavior may perhaps be the counterpart of the hop-and-sink station-keeping of vertically migrating animals with a horizontal component imposed upon it.

4. *Value to the animal.* Horizontal movements that result in shoaling have clear value to the participants so far as reproduction is concerned and possibly also for survival of the individual, but the latter

depends partly upon the nature and size of the predators involved. The inshore-offshore movements of littoral Crustacea are less simply accounted for. Some clearly result in the deposition of eggs in a place more suitable for the development of the young than is the adult environment. The latter, with its accumulation of detritus and rich littoral fauna and flora, may fulfill the food requirements of the adults most satisfactorily, as these are generally omnivorous bulk feeders. The young however require the clean suspensions of phytoplankton only found further out to sea. Without more knowledge of the individual requirements of species it is not possible to go further, for *Penaeus duorarum* apparently behaves in the reverse manner during its inshore-offshore migrations (p. 447). Apart from such spawning and feeding movements some migrations are probably purely for feeding, as those of mysids toward the shore, while others may be movements into the protection of quiet and thermally stable deeper water, as the winter migration of *P. setiferus*.

III. *BENTHIC AND TERRESTRIAL MIGRATIONS*

A. DESCRIPTION

Because of their commercial importance more is known of the movements of the spiny lobsters than of any other bottom-living crustacean. In *Panulirus argus* and *P. interruptus* off southern Florida both trapping and marking[27,33,139,140] have demonstrated regular and extensive migrations. The animals collect in special shallow areas for mating, move out to deep water to spawn and then return inshore. In winter they generally move out into deep water again and, when about to molt, return to shallow regions. They are gregarious and often migrate in clusters or long columns from one feeding place to another. Alongshore movements may be quite extensive (Fig. 2) but are often only a random wandering of the order of 8 km or less. They may be northward in the summer and southward in the winter.

P. argus in Bermuda shows a breeding migration of about 13 km out across the lagoon to the edge of the reefs,[149,150] but *P. guttatus* in the same place apparently does not.[151] Off the Cape of Good Hope *Jasus lalandei* shows a sort of slow wandering in search of food, a "trekking" of whole populations, and movements into shelter for molting.[59,160] At times males and females congregate exclusively in certain areas. This has been confirmed for the same species in Australia, and apparently oriented movements of up to 30 miles in 2 or 3 months have been shown to occur there in *P. longipes*.[137]

A general movement into shallower water with the approach of maturity also appears to be substantiated. Off Florida and Australia this is an inshore migration; off Bermuda it is offshore but from the deeper lagoon to the shallower reefs. After mating and a period of incubation there may be a movement of females back into deeper water for the release of larvae, but this is not entirely substantiated. The possibility of a homing instinct has been suggested on the basis of the recapture of tagged lobsters at the point of original capture after release

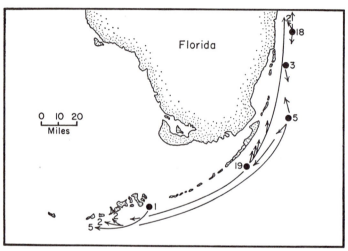

Fig. 2. Movements of tagged spiny lobsters, 1946. Figures beside black circles indicate number of animals recaptured within 5 miles of the place of tagging; arrows indicate resultant direction and distance traveled (when over 5 miles) of either single specimens or the number given. After Dawson and Idyll.[33]

at distances up to 8 km.[28] W. H. Sutcliffe, Jr. (unpublished), however, has failed to confirm these results with lateral transfers along the shore.

An inshore movement in the spring and an offshore one in the autumn have been described in *Homarus americanus*.[76,154–156] However the tagging of 2209 lobsters in the Gulf of St. Lawrence also showed that alongshore movements are here limited to directionless wanderings.[154] In the European lobster there is little sign of movement except possibly a contranatant one by mature females.[106] The likelihood of such movement against the prevailing current has been enlarged upon by Graham.[60]

Information concerning other decapods is sparse. In *Callinectes sapidus* mating occurs in shallow water and is followed by a migration to deep water for egg-laying and a return migration of young larvae inshore.[29,75,112,125] There are also movements into deeper water in winter as well as localized feeding ones. *Uca pugilator* can return to its holes from as far as 12 meters and habitually migrates from its burrows to feed on the edge of the receding tide. *Emerita analoga* exhibits a more dramatic migration. It lives and feeds on sandy beaches[100] in a few centimeters of water. As this restricted feeding zone moves up and down the shore *Emerita* moves with it, generally in quick mass movements of all the population lasting less than 10 sec and occurring every hour or so. A seasonal migration into deeper water is undertaken by the European crab (*Cancer*) in winter, with a return in the summer; there is also a contranatant movement along the coast by females.[105] Verbal reports of extensive breeding migrations from inland down to the sea by the land crabs in Miami (*Cardisoma*) seem unrecorded in the literature as do the movements of *Birgus*, the coconut crab.

There appears to be a seasonal migration of the little wood-boring isopod *Limnoria lignorum*, at a maximum in March and April and consisting of a centrifugal swimming over a distance of several meters followed by release of the young.[82] Apart from this, there is probably a constant slow crawling migration away from centers of high population density to fresh but contiguous wood.

Talorchestia longicornis, the beach flea, comes out of its burrows only after dark to feed.[138] It runs down to the tide line as the water recedes and migrates up the beach again as the tide comes in, finally burrowing when overtaken by the tide higher up the beach. If surprised by daylight apparently "all hasten up the beach" and within 10 min have burrowed. Another amphipod, *Talitrus saltator*, has an extraordinary capacity of migrating back to the sea after removal to a drier place and some analysis of the orienting mechanism has been made[119] (Chapter 10).

The Isopoda contain most of the terrestrial Crustacea (Chapter 11, Vol. I), but little is known of their migratory movements. Wood lice generally burrow from 8 to 20 cm into soil on the approach of winter; some may go into the burrows of earthworms, while others hide under old logs,[25] and similar lateral movements to the shelter of compost heaps, cellars, or other overwintering places has been reported.[162] No evidence for a homing instinct was found by marking and releasing wood lice,[26] although specimens disturbed in a long greenhouse would migrate 6–7 meters back to the darker end after being disturbed. Both a downward migration from low surface temperatures and an upward one into trees away from very wet soil have been demonstrated in

Tracheoniscus rathkei.[24] *Porcellio scaber* and *Ligia oceanica* show a vertical migration of single adults up a cliff face into the sunlight from among the shingle beneath.[35] Finally a return migration to shelter in the morning is apparently shown by nocturnally wandering wood-lice,[23] although *Armadillidium vulgare* is an exception since it leaves shelter in the morning and runs about in the sunshine, returning to cover after noon.[3]

B. Mechanisms

While passive transport by water currents might account for the return of larvae to shallower water in some cases, the outward spawning migration of adults and any contranatant alongshore migrations must involve active movement. Considering the nature of most rocky bottoms and the abilities of the animals, both walking and swimming are probable. *Callinectes sapidus* actively walks on the bottom and swims normally with a striking rate from 20 to 40 strokes per minute of its paddlelike posterior legs.[75] It can move forward, backward or sideways when walking, backward or sideways when swimming. Walking on the tips of the claw is given as the usual mode of locomotion in *Panulirus*,[27] but flexures of the abdomen may be used for rapid swimming. The speeds calculated from recaptures (necessarily minimal) appear within the capacity of such mechanisms. *Homarus americanus* may travel 6 km in 1 day, while several animals have been found to move 3 km per day for several days.[154] One animal is described as having traveled 19 km in 3 days,[13] and the recapture of a marked female shore crab 260 km away after 3 years and 5 months is also reported.[105]

C. Initiating and Controlling Factors

The initiating factors governing the benthic migrations described are probably primarily physiological and in response to the necessities of breeding, molting, and feeding. The state of the animal in these respects may of course be secondarily affected by light, temperature, and the presence or absence of food. Also temperature change, and possibly light, as well as the state of the weather may be directly responsible for the deep-water and alongshore winter movements. Molting, mating, and temperature change have been most emphasized in the literature.[27]

Control of a movement once initiated must be complex and variable according to the organism and to the circumstances. For instance, *Emerita* probably keeps position in its feeding zone by a combination of clues deriving from currents, depth, slope of the beach, and light intensity, but the direct stimulus for the sudden mass movement of these animals up or down the beach is unknown.[100] Movement out into deep water and alongshore could be controlled by either diminishing or constant light intensity or by the depth or the slope of the bottom. No pressure-sensitive organ is known in these forms, but well-developed statocysts exist (Chapter 2) and could presumably be used in the detection of slopes. Use of light gradients as a control seems unlikely in *Panulirus argus* as it is most active in complete darkness, movement being suppressed even by moonlight.[152] Many other animals showing benthic and terrestrial migrations are also nocturnal, but they may occasionally engage in impressive daytime treks when light could be used. Sensitivity to currents may also account for the contranatant movements of crabs (Chapter 10), since benthic animals must be subject to strong and persistent current action both on shores and in estuaries. Movements of estuarine forms may be governed by salinity changes. Thus sensitivity to salinity (Chapter 3) could be a factor controlling the movements of species of *Gammarus*,[40] although *G. chevreuxi* is not affected by great changes in salinity.[136]

The land migrations of isopods seem to comprise both direct taxes and kineses. Edney[36] admirably summarizes our knowledge of the factors controlling these movements. The isopods are largely adapted to terrestrial life by behavioral mechanisms rather than by structure. The control mechanisms are chiefly a response to moisture combined to a certain extent with temperature[35] and also light.[54] *Porcellio scaber* moves toward moisture by orthohygrokinesis[63] and negative phototaxes occur in various wood lice.[54] These differences in reaction may depend upon the nature of the receptor mechanisms involved. A refinement of such reactions to light is seen in *Talitrus* and *Talorchestia*, which appear to possess a physiological clock which enables them to steer by the position of the sun at different times of the day;[117,118] they are also sensitive to the plane of polarization of sky light (Chapters 1 and 10).

D. Value to the Animal

The movements enumerated can, without exception, be interpreted as valuable in placing the animal under conditions more suitable for its particular phase of life history. The benthic movements to deep water in winter, the molting migrations to rocky or weedy ground, and the hygrokinesis of isopods all result in their protection, either from harmful conditions or at times when they are vulnerable. The various shore movements of crabs and the alongshore and trekking movements of lobsters subserve feeding, as probably also do the inshore movements of young after a planktonic existence. Finally the deep-water breeding migrations, as with the shrimps, generally allow release of the young in circumstances favorable for growth, and the contranatant movements of crabs, while not doing this so well, do enable the young to return more easily to the adult habitat.

W. H. Sutcliffe, Jr. (1956, personal communication) describes how settlement of the *Panulirus* phyllosoma does not occur indiscriminately after a certain time but only on reaching a suitable substrate. The phyllosoma larval life of 6–8 months combined with the prevailing currents means consequently that all Bermuda larvae are lost and recruitment of these islands is entirely from the Bahamas by the Gulf Stream. Under these circumstances the offshore breeding migration of Bermudan adults can be of little value and shows perhaps that these animals are here at the limit of a population sequence stretching from the Gulf of Mexico.

IV. *CONCLUSIONS*

Since Crustacea are primarily aquatic, the quantitative study of their migratory movements involves a medium man can enter only most superficially without great danger and expense. This must in part account for the present rather unsatisfactory state of our studies. A large body of both observational and experimental data has nevertheless been accumulated. Its analysis, if not producing a clear and concise picture, does at least outline the major features and show where more quantitative information is required.

While we can never hope to have a single simple exposition of the mechanisms and functions of so complex a behavioral cycle as that of vertical migration, many more accurate field observations are clearly necessary. Wherever possible these should be coupled with measurements of light and taken in one body of water at time intervals sufficiently short to demonstrate the presence or absence of midnight sinking and the dawn rise. Similarly, experimental work should be continued especially upon the effects of combining other factors with, rather than separating them from, light. Pelagic horizontal migration stands in great need of more field observation and of experimental analysis of the problems of underwater navigation. Also observations on any common benthic or littoral forms in the field will greatly assist the planning of apposite experimental work on their movements. The preoccupation with vertical migration must not be allowed to preclude a study of horizontal movements in open water. Whether this be by direct swimming or by planktonic navigation, it allows animals to sample new and possibly more advantageous regions of a very variable environment and merits more attention than hitherto accorded it.

To say thus that the whole field of migrations needs more accurate work is not to belittle that already done, but rather to emphasize the vastness and the complexity of the problems involved. It is not perhaps too much to expect that the current application of modern techniques, such as that of echo-sounding combined with limited sampling of the reflecting layer to vertical migration, or underwater frogman observation to the behavior of littoral animals, will produce just those data and ideas necessary to integrate what is yet a rather amorphous mass of information.

REFERENCES

1. Anderson, W. W., King, J. E., and Lindner, M. J. 1949. Early stages in the life history of the common marine shrimp, *Penaeus setiferus* (Linn.). *Biol. Bull.* 96:168–172.
2. Apstein, C. 1896. "Das Süsswasserplankton," 200 pp. Lipsius and Tischer, Leipzig.
3. Arthur, D. R., Cloudsley-Thompson, J. L., and Sankey, J. H. P. 1951. Some aspects of the fauna of the district around Juniper Hall, Mickleham, Surrey. *Entomol. Monthly Mag.* 87:275–278.
4. Bainbridge, R. 1949. Movement of zooplankton in diatom gradients. *Nature* 163:910–911.
5. Bainbridge, R. 1952. Underwater observations on the swimming of marine zooplankton. *J. Marine Biol. Assoc. United Kingdom* 31:107–112.
6. Bainbridge, R. 1953. Studies on the interrelationships of zooplankton and phytoplankton. *J. Marine Biol. Assoc. United Kingdom* 32:385–447.
7. Bainbridge, R., and Waterman, T. H. 1957. Polarized light and the orientation of two marine Crustacea. *J. Exptl. Biol.* 34:342–364.
8. Baylor, E. R., and Smith, F. E. 1957. Diurnal migration of plankton crustaceans. *In:* "Recent Advances in Invertebrate Physiology" (B. T. Scheer, ed.), pp. 21–35. Univ. of Oregon Publications, Eugene.
9. Bigelow, H. B. 1926. Plankton of the offshore waters of the Gulf of Maine. *Bull. U.S. Bur. Fisheries* 40:1–509.
10. Bogorov, B. G. 1946. Peculiarities of diurnal vertical migrations of zooplankton in polar seas. *J. Marine Research (Sears Foundation)* 6:25–32.
11. Brady, G. S. 1883. Report on the Copepoda obtained by H. M. S. Challenger during the years 1873–1876. *Rept. Sci. Results Challenger, Zoology* 8:1–142.
12. Broad, C. 1950. Results of shrimp research in South Carolina. *Proc. Gulf and Caribbean Fish Inst.* 1950:27–35.
13. Bumpus, H. C. 1901. On the movement of certain lobsters liberated at Woods Hole during the summer of 1898. *Bull. U.S. Fish Comm.* 19:225–230.
14. Burkenroad, M. D. 1936. The Aristaeinae, Solenocerinae and pelagic Penaeinae of the Bingham Oceanographic Collection. *Bull. Bingham Oceanog. Collection* 5 (2):1–151.

15. Burkenroad, M. D. 1937. Some remarks on the structure, habits and distribution of the benthonic sergestid *Sicyonella* Borradaile (Crustacea, Decapoda). *Ann. Mag. Nat. Hist.* [10] **19**:505–514.

16. Burkenroad, M. D. 1939. Further observations on Penaeidae of the northern Gulf of Mexico. *Bull. Bingham Oceanog. Collection* **6** (6):1–62.

17. Chun, C. 1888. Die pelagische Thierwelt in grosseren Meerestiefen und ihre Beziehungen zu der Oberflächenfauna. *Bibliotheca zool.* **1**:1–66.

18. Clarke, G. L. 1930. Change of phototropic and geotropic signs in *Daphnia* induced by changes of light intensity. *J. Exptl. Biol.* **7**:109–131.

19. Clarke, G. L. 1932. Quantitative aspects of the change of phototropic sign in *Daphnia. J. Exptl. Biol.* **9**:180–211.

20. Clarke, G. L. 1933. Diurnal migration of plankton in the Gulf of Maine and its correlation with changes in submarine illumination. *Biol. Bull.* **65**:402–436.

21. Clarke, G. L. 1934a. Further observations on the diurnal migrations of copepods in the Gulf of Maine. *Biol. Bull.* **67**:432–455.

22. Clarke, G. L. 1934b. The diurnal migration of copepods in St. George's Harbor, Bermuda. *Biol. Bull.* **67**:456–460.

23. Cloudsley-Thompson, J. L. 1952. Studies in diurnal rhythms. II: Changes in the physiological responses of the woodlouse *Oniscus asellus* to environmental stimuli. *J. Exptl. Biol.* **29**:295–303.

24. Cole, L. C. 1946. A study of the Cryptozoa of an Illinois woodland. *Ecol. Monographs* **16**:50–86.

25. Collinge, W. E. 1941. Notes on the terrestrial Isopoda (woodlice) No. 2. *Northwestern Naturalist* **16**:247–256.

26. Collinge, W. E. 1942. Notes on the terrestrial Isopoda (woodlice). No. 3. *Northwestern Naturalist* **17**:5–11.

27. Crawford, D. R., and de Smidt, W. J. J. 1922. The spiny lobster, *Panulirus argus*, of southern Florida: Its history and utilization. *Bull. U.S. Bur. Fisheries* **38**:281–310.

28. Creaser, E. P., and Travis, D. 1950. Evidence of a homing instinct in the Bermuda spiny lobster. *Science* **112**:169–170.

29. Cronin, L. E. 1949. Comparison of methods of tagging the blue crab. *Ecology* **30**:390–394.

30. Cushing, D. H. 1951. The vertical migration of planktonic Crustacea. *Biol. Revs. Cambridge Phil. Soc.* **26**:158–192.

31. Cuvier, G. 1833. Annelida, Crustacea and Arachnida. *In:* "The Animal Kingdom Arranged in Conformity with Its Organisation." Vol. 13: 540 pp. Whittaker Treacher, London.

32. Dakin, W. J., and Latarche, M. 1913. The plankton of Lough Neagh. A study of the seasonal changes in the plankton by quantitative methods. *Proc. Roy. Irish Acad.* **B30**:20–96.

33. Dawson, C. E., and Idyll, C. P. 1951. Investigations on the Florida spiny lobster, *Panulirus argus* (Latreille). *Marine Lab. Univ. Miami Tech. Ser.* No. **2**:1–39.

34. Dice, L. R. 1914. The factors determining the vertical movement of *Daphnia. J. Animal Behavior* **4**:229–265.

35. Edney, E. B. 1953. The temperature of woodlice in the sun. *J. Exptl. Biol.* **30**:331–349.

36. Edney, E. B. 1954. Woodlice and the land habit. *Biol. Revs. Cambridge Phil. Soc.* **29**:185–219.

37. Ekman, S. 1914. Studien über die marinen Relikte der nordeuropäischen Binnengewässer. iii: Uber das Auftreten von *Limnocalanus grimaldii* (de Guerne) und *Mysis oculata* (Fabre) im Meere, besonders im Ostseebecken. *Intern. Rev. ges. Hydrobiol. Hydrog.* **6**:493–517.

38. Elmhirst, R. 1931. Studies in the Scottish marine fauna—The Crustacea of the sandy and muddy areas of the tidal zone. *Proc. Roy. Soc. Edinburgh* **B51**:169–175.

39. Elmhirst, R. 1932. Quantitative studies between tide marks. *Glasgow Naturalist* **1932**:1–8.

40. Elmhirst, R. 1935. The occurrence of *Gammarus* in Scottish waters. *Scot. Naturalist* **1935**:17–21.

41. Esterly, C. O. 1911a. Diurnal migrations of *Calanus finmarchicus* in the San Diego region during 1909. *Intern. Rev. ges. Hydrobiol. Hydrog.* **4**:140–151.

42. Esterly, C. O. 1911b. The vertical distribution of *Eucalanus elongatus* in the San Diego region during 1909. *Univ. Calif. (Berkeley) Publs. Zoöl.* **8**:1–7.

43. Esterly, C. O. 1912. The occurrence and vertical distribution of the Copepoda of the San Diego region, with particular reference to nineteen species. *Univ. Calif. (Berkeley) Publs. Zoöl.* **9**:253–340.

44. Esterly, C. O. 1914. The vertical distribution and movements of the Schizopoda of the San Diego region. *Univ. Calif. (Berkeley) Publs. Zoöl.* **13**:123–145.

45. Esterly, C. O. 1917. The occurrence of a rhythm in the geotropism of two species of plankton copepods when certain recurring external conditions are absent. *Univ. Calif. (Berkeley) Publs. Zoöl.* **16**:393–400.

46. Esterly, C. O. 1919. Reactions of various plankton animals with reference to their diurnal migrations. *Univ. Calif. (Berkeley) Publs. Zoöl.* **19**:1–83.

47. Esterly, C. O. 1923. Preliminary statistical report on the occurrence of marine Copepoda in the plankton at La Jolla, California. *Univ. Calif. (Berkeley) Publs. Zoöl.* **22**:417–433.

48. Ewald, W. F. 1912. On artificial modification of light reactions and the influence of electrolytes on phototaxis. *J. Exptl. Zool.* **13**:591–612.

49. Eyden, D. 1923. Specific gravity as a factor in the vertical distribution of plankton. *Biol. Revs. Biol. Proc. Cambridge Phil. Soc.* **1**:49–55.

50. Farran, G. P. 1926. Biscayan plankton collected during a cruise of H. M. S. Research, 1900. Pt. XIV: The Copepoda. *J. Linnean Soc. London Zool.* **36**:219–310.

51. Farran, G. P. 1947. Vertical distribution of plankton (*Sagitta, Calanus* and *Metridia*) off the south coast of Ireland. *Proc. Roy. Irish Acad.* **B51**:121–136.

52. Filteau, G. 1948. Recherches sur les Copépodes marins de la Baie des Chaleurs. *Rappt. sta. biol. St. Laurent* **7**:69–76.

53. Foxon, G. E. H. 1934. Notes on the swimming methods and habits of certain crustacean larvae. *J. Marine Biol. Assoc. United Kingdom* **19**:829–850.

54. Fraenkel, G. S., and Gunn, D. L. 1940. "The Orientation of Animals," 352 pp. Oxford Univ. Press, London and New York.

55. Fraser, F. C. 1936. On the development and distribution of the young stages of krill (*Euphausia superba*). *Discovery Repts.* **14**:1–192.

56. Gardiner, A. C. 1933. Vertical distribution in *Calanus finmarchicus*. *J. Marine Biol. Assoc. United Kingdom* **18**:575–610.

57. Gardiner, A. C. 1934. Variations in the amount of macroplankton by day and night. *J. Marine Biol. Assoc. United Kingdom* 19:559–567.
58. Gauld, D. T. 1953. Diurnal variation in the grazing of planktonic copepods. *J. Marine Biol. Assoc. United Kingdom* 31:461–474.
59. Gilchrist, J. D. F. 1918. Crawfish investigations including experimental hauls, artificial rearing and migratory movements of the Cape crawfish (*Jasus lalandii*). *Union S. Africa Marine Biol. Rept.* 4:1–43.
60. Graham, M. 1949. A note on the theory of a dwarf race of lobsters on the Norfolk coast. *J. Marine Biol. Assoc. United Kingdom* 28:481–487.
61. Gran, H. H. 1902. Das Plankton des norwegischen Nordmeeres von biologischen und hydrographischen Gesichtspunkten behandelt. *Rept. Norweg. Fishery Invest.* 2 (5):1–222.
62. Grover, W. W., and Coker, R. E. 1940. A study of the depth distribution of certain net plankters in Mountain Lake, Virginia. *Ecology* 21:199–205.
63. Gunn, D. L. 1937. The humidity reactions of the woodlouse, *Porcellio scaber* (Latreille). *J. Exptl. Biol.* 14:178–186.
64. Halme, E. 1937. Eine neue Methode zur Bestimmung der relativen Wanderungsintensität des Zooplanktons. *Acta Soc. Fauna Flora Fennica* 60:347–373.
65. Hansen, K. V. 1951. On the diurnal migration of zooplankton in relation to the discontinuity layer. *J. conseil, Conseil permanent intern. exploration mer* 17:231–241.
66. Hardy, A. C. 1938. Change and choice: a study in pelagic ecology. *In:* "Evolution" (G. R. deBeer, ed.), pp. 139–159. Clarendon Press, Oxford.
67. Hardy, A. C. 1953. Some problems of pelagic life. *In:* "Essays in Marine Biology" (S. M. Marshall and A. P. Orr, eds.), pp. 101–121. Oliver and Boyd, Edinburgh.
68. Hardy, A. C. 1956. "The Open Sea, its Natural History: The World of Plankton," 335 pp. Collins, London.
69. Hardy, A. C., and Bainbridge, R. 1951. Effect of pressure on the behaviour of decapod larvae (Crustacea). *Nature* 167:354–355.
70. Hardy, A. C., and Bainbridge, R. 1954. Experimental observations on the vertical migrations of plankton animals. *J. Marine Biol. Assoc. United Kingdom* 33:409–448.
71. Hardy, A. C., and Gunther, E. R. 1935. The plankton of the South Georgia whaling grounds and adjacent waters, 1926–1927. *Discovery Repts.* 11:1–456.
72. Hardy, A. C., and Paton, W. N. 1947. Experiments on the vertical migration of plankton animals. *J. Marine Biol. Assoc. United Kingdom* 26:467–526.
73. Harris, J. E. 1953. Physical factors involved in the vertical migration of plankton. *Quart. J. Microscop. Sci.* 94:537–550.
74. Harris, J. E., and Wolfe, U. K. 1955. A laboratory study of vertical migration. *Proc. Roy. Soc.* B144:329–354.
75. Hay, W. P. 1905. The life history of the blue crab (*Callinectes sapidus*). *Rept. U.S. Bur. Fisheries* 1904:397–413.
76. Herrick, F. H. 1896. The American lobster; a study of its habits and development. *Bull. U.S. Fish Comm.* 15:1–252.
77. Hersey, J. B., and Moore, H. B. 1948. Progress report on scattering layer observations in the Atlantic Ocean. *Trans. Am. Geophys. Union* 29:341–354.
78. Hickling, C. F. 1925. Notes on euphausids. *J. Marine Biol. Assoc. United Kingdom* 13:735–745.

79. Holt, E. W. L., and Tattersall, W. M. 1905. Biscayan plankton. Part V: The Schizopoda, with an appendix by G. H. Fowler. *Trans. Linnean Soc. London Zool.* 10:103–129.
80. Huntsman, A. G. 1924. Limiting factors for marine animals. I. The lethal effect of sunlight. *Contr. Can. Biol. and Fisheries* [N.S.] 2:83–88.
81. Israel, H. R. 1936. A contribution towards the life histories of two California shrimps, *Crago franciscorum* (Stimpson) and *Crago nigricauda* Stimpson. *Calif. Div. Fish and Game, Fish Bull.* 46:1–28.
82. Johnson, M. W. 1935. Seasonal migrations of the wood-borer, *Limnoria lignorum* (Rathke) at Friday Harbour, Washington. *Biol. Bull.* 69:427–438.
83. Jolly, V. H. 1952. A preliminary study of the limnology of Lake Hayes. *Australian J. Marine and Freshwater Research* 3:74–91.
84. Juday, C. 1904. The diurnal movement of plankton Crustacea. *Trans. Wisconsin Acad. Sci.* 14:534–568.
85. Juday, C., and Birge, E. A. 1927. *Pontoporeia* and *Mysis* in Wisconsin Lakes. *Ecology* 8:445–452.
86. Kikuchi, K. 1930a. Diurnal migration of plankton Crustacea. *Quart. Rev. Biol.* 5:189–206.
87. Kikuchi, K. 1930b. A comparison of the diurnal migration of plankton in eight Japanese Lakes. *Mem. Coll. Sci. Kyoto Imp. Univ.* B5:27–74.
88. Knight-Jones, E. W., and Qasim, S. Z. 1955. Responses of some marine plankton animals to changes in hydrostatic pressure. *Nature* 175:941–942.
89. Langford, R. R. 1938. Diurnal and seasonal changes in the distribution of the limnetic Crustacea of Lake Nipissing. *Univ. Toronto Studies Biol. Ser.* 45:1–142.
90. Lebour, M. V. 1924. The Euphausidae in the neighbourhood of Plymouth and their importance as herring food. *J. Marine Biol. Assoc. United Kingdom* 13:402–432.
91. Lebour, M. V. 1926. The Euphausidae in the neighbourhood of Plymouth. III. *Thysanoessa inermis. J. Marine Biol. Assoc. United Kingdom* 14:1–21.
92. Leydig, F. 1862. "Naturgeschichte der Daphniden (Crustacea, Cladocera)," 252 pp. Laupp and Siebeck, Tübingen.
93. Loeb, J. 1893. On the influence of light on the periodical depth migrations of pelagic animals. *Bull. U.S. Fish Comm.* 13:65–68.
94. Loeb, J. 1906. Ueber die Erregung von positiven Heliotropismus durch Säure, insbesondere Kohlensäure und von negativen Heliotropismus durch ultraviolette Strahlen. *Arch. ges. Physiol. Pflüger's* 115:564–581.
95. Lozéron, H. 1902. Sur la répartition verticale du plankton dans le lac de Zürich de Déc. 1900 à Déc. 1901. *Vierteljahrsschr. naturforsch. Ges. Zürich* 47:115–198.
96. Lucas, C. E. 1936. On certain interrelations between phytoplankton and zooplankton under experimental conditions. *J. conseil, Conseil permanent intern. exploration mer* 11(3):343–362.
97. Lucas, C. E. 1947. The ecological effects of external metabolites. *Biol. Revs. Cambridge Phil. Soc.* 22 (3):270–295.
98. Lucas, C. E. 1949. External metabolites and ecological adaptation. *Symposia Soc. Exptl. Biol.* 3:336–356.
99. Lucas, C. E. 1955. External metabolites in the sea. *In:* "Papers in Marine Biology and Oceanography" (M. Sears, ed.), pp. 139–148. Pergamon Press, London.

100. MacGinitie, G. E. 1938. Movements and mating habits of the sand crab, *Emerita analoga. Am. Midland Naturalist* 19:471–481.
101. Mackintosh, N. A. 1934. Distribution of the macroplankton in the Atlantic sector of the Antarctic. *Discovery Repts.* 9:65–160.
102. Mackintosh, N. A. 1937. The seasonal circulation of the Antarctic macroplankton. *Discovery Repts.* 16:365–412.
103. Maloney, M. T., and Tressler, W. L. 1942. The diurnal migration of certain species of zooplankton in Caroga Lake, New York. *Trans. Am. Microscop. Soc.* 61:40–51.
104. Marshall, S. M., and Orr, A. P. 1955. "The Biology of a Marine Copepod *Calanus finmarchicus* (Gunnerus)," 188 pp. Oliver and Boyd, Edinburgh.
105. Meek, A. 1916. Migration of crabs. *Rept. Dove Marine Lab.* [N.S.] 5:7–10.
106. Meek, A. 1925. Experimental legislation with reference to the crab and lobster fisheries of the east coast of Britain. *J. Marine Biol. Assoc. United Kingdom* 13:755–768.
107. Moore, B. 1909. Observations on certain marine organisms of a) variations in reaction to light, and b) diurnal periodicity of phosphorescence. *Biochem. J.* 4:1–29.
108. Moore, H. B. 1949. The zooplankton of the upper water of the Bermuda area of the North Atlantic. *Bull. Bingham Oceanog. Collection* 12 (Art. 2):1–97.
109. Morgan, T. H. 1903. "Evolution and Adaptation," 470 pp. Macmillan, New York.
110. Murray, J., and Hjort, J. 1912. "The Depths of the Ocean," 821 pp. Macmillan, New York.
111. Nakazawa, K. 1915. On *Sergestes prehensilis* (Bate) and the Penaeidae of Japan. Cited in: *Knowledge* 13:108 (1916).
112. Newcombe, C. L. 1945. The biology and conservation of the blue crab, *Callinectes sapidus* (Rathbun). *Virginia Fisheries Lab. Educ. Ser. No.* 4:1–39.
113. Nicholls, A. G. 1933. On the biology of *Calanus finmarchicus.* III: Vertical distribution and diurnal migration in the Clyde Sea Area. *J. Marine Biol. Assoc. United Kingdom* 19:139–164.
114. Nikitine, B. 1929. Les migrations verticales saisonnières des organismes planktoniques dans la mer Noire. *Bull. inst. océanog. No.* 540:1–24.
115. Ostwald, W. 1902. Zur Theorie des Planktons. *Biol. Zentr.* 22:596–605.
116. Otterstrom, A. 1910. Beobachtungen über die Senkrechten Wanderungen des Mysisbestandes in der Ostsee bei Bornholm. *Medd. Komm. Havundersøgelser, Kjøbenhaven* 5 (9):1–10.
117. Papi, F. 1955. Experiments on the sense of time in *Talitrus saltator* (Montagu) (Crustacea-Amphipoda). *Experientia* 11:201–202.
118. Pardi, L., and Grassi, M. 1955. Experimental modification of direction finding in *Talitrus saltator* (Montagu) and *Talitrus deshayesei* (Aud.) (Crustacea-Amphipoda). *Experientia* 11:202–205.
119. Pardi, L., and Papi, F. 1953. Ricerche sull'orientamento di *Talitrus saltator* (Montagu) (Crustacea-Amphipoda). I. L'orientamento durante il giorno in una popolazione del litorale tirrenico. *Z. vergleich. Physiol.* 35:459–489.
120. Parker, G. H. 1901. Reactions of Copepoda and the bearing of this on daily depth migration. *Bull. U.S. Fish Comm.* 21:103–123.
121. Pearsall, W. H., and Ullyott, P. 1934. Light penetrations into fresh water. III. Seasonal variations in the light conditions in Windermere in relation to vegetation. *J. Exptl. Biol.* 11:89–93.

122. Pennak, R. W. 1944. Diurnal movements of zooplankton organisms in some Colorado mountain lakes. *Ecology* 25:387–403.

123. Percival, E. 1929. A report on the fauna of the estuaries of the River Tamar and the River Lynher. *J. Marine Biol. Assoc. United Kingdom* 16:89–108.

124. Plew, W. F., and Pennak, R. W. 1949. A seasonal investigation of the vertical movements of zooplankters in an Indiana Lake. *Ecology* 30:93–100.

125. Rathbun, M. J. 1895. The Genus *Callinectes*. *Proc. U.S. Natl. Museum* 18:349–375.

126. Rose, M. 1925. Contributions à l'étude de la biologie du plancton; le problème des migrations verticales journalières. *Arch. zool. exptl. et gén.* 64:387–649.

127. Russell, F. S. 1925. The vertical distribution of marine macroplankton. An observation on diurnal changes. *J. Marine Biol. Assoc. United Kingdom* 13:769–809.

128. Russell, F. S. 1926. The vertical distribution of marine macroplankton. IV. The apparent importance of light intensity as a controlling factor in the behaviour of certain species in the Plymouth area. *J. Marine Biol. Assoc. United Kingdom* 14:415–440.

129. Russell, F. S. 1927a. The vertical distribution of plankton in the sea. *Biol. Revs. Biol. Proc. Cambridge Phil. Soc.* 2:213–262.

130. Russell, F. S. 1927b. The vertical distribution of marine macroplankton. V. The distribution of animals caught in the ring trawl in the daytime in the Plymouth area. *J. Marine Biol. Assoc. United Kingdom* 14:557–608.

131. Russell, F. S. 1931. The vertical distribution of marine macroplankton. XI. Further observations on diurnal changes. *J. Marine Biol. Assoc. United Kingdom* 17:767–775.

132. Russell, F. S., and Colman, J. S. 1934. The Zooplankton. II. The composition of the zooplankton of the Barrier Reef lagoon. *Great Barrier Reef Exptl. Sci. Rept.* 2:159–176.

133. Rustad, D. 1930. Euphausiacea, with notes on their biogeography and development. *Sci. Results Norweg. Antarctic Expeditions* 5:1–83.

134. Savage, R. E. 1926. The plankton of a herring ground. *Ministry Agr. and Fisheries, Fishery Invest.* [Ser. II] 9 (1):1–35.

135. Schallek, W. 1943. The reaction of certain Crustacea to direct and to diffuse light. *Biol. Bull.* 84:98–105.

136. Sexton, E. W., and Matthews, A. 1913. Notes on the life history of *Gammarus chevreuxi*. *J. Marine Biol. Assoc. United Kingdom* 9:546–556.

137. Sheard, K. 1949. The marine crayfishes (spiny lobsters), Family Palinuridae, of Western Australia. *Australia Commonwealth Sci. Ind. Research Organization Bull. No.* 247:1–45.

138. Smallwood, M. E. 1903. The beach flea: *Talorchestia longicornis*. *Cold Spring Harbor Monographs* 1:1–27.

139. Smith, F. G. W. 1948. The spiny lobster industry of the Caribbean and Florida. *Caribbean Research Council Fisheries Ser. No.* 3:1–49.

140. Smith, F. G. W. 1950. Caribbean spiny lobster investigations. *Proc. Gulf and Caribbean Fisheries Inst.* 1950:128–134.

141. Sømme, J. D. 1934. Animal plankton of the Norwegian coastal waters and the open sea. I. Production of *Calanus finmarchicus* (Gunner) and *Calanus hyperboreus* (Krøyer) in the Lofoten area. *Fiskeridirektorat. Skrifter Ser. Havundersøk.* 4 (9):1–163.

142. Southern, R., and Gardiner, A. C. 1926a. The seasonal distribution of the Crustacea of the plankton in Lough Derg and the River Shannon. *Sci. Invest. Fish Ireland No.* 1:143.

143. Southern, R., and Gardiner, A. C. 1926b. A preliminary account of some observations on the diurnal migration of the Crustacea of the plankton of Lough Derg. *Intern. Rev. ges. Hydrobiol. Hydrog.* 15:323–326.

144. Southern, R., and Gardiner, A. C. 1932. The diurnal migrations of the Crustacea of the plankton in Lough Derg. *Proc. Roy. Irish Acad.* **B40**:121–159.

145. Spaulding, M. H. 1908. Preliminary report on the life history and habits of the "Lake Shrimp." *Gulf Biol. Sta. Bull.* **11**:1–24.

146. Stephensen, K. 1923. Decapoda-Macrura excl. Sergestidae. *Rept. Danish Oceanog. Expedition 1908–10 Mediterranean* **2**:1–85.

147. Steuer, A. 1902. Die Entomostrakenfauna der "Alten Donau" bei Wien. Eine ethologische Studie. Mit einem Anhang: Zur Frage über Ursprung und Verbreitung der Entomostrakenfauna des Süsswassers. *Zool. Jahrb., Abt. System. Geograph. Biol.* **15**:1–156.

148. Störmer, L. 1929. Copepods from the "Michael Sars" expedition, 1924. *Rappt. Conseil permanent intern. exploration mer* **56** (7):1–57.

149. Sutcliffe, W. H. 1952. Some observations of the breeding and migration of the Bermuda spiny lobster, *Panulirus argus. Proc. Gulf Caribbean Fish Inst. 4th Ann. Session* 64–69.

150. Sutcliffe, W. H. 1953a. Further observations on the breeding and migration of the Bermuda spiny lobster, *Panulirus argus. J. Marine Research (Sears Foundation)* **12**:173–183.

151. Sutcliffe, W. H. 1953b. Notes on the biology of a spiny lobster, *Panulirus guttatus*, in Bermuda. *Ecology* **34**:794–796.

152. Sutcliffe, W. H. 1956. Effect of light intensity on the activity of the Bermuda spiny lobster, *Panulirus argus. Ecology* **37**:200–201.

153. Tattersall, W. M., and Tattersall, O. S. 1951. "The British Mysidacea," 460 pp. Ray Society, London.

154. Templeman, W. 1935. Lobster tagging in the Gulf of St. Lawrence. *J. Biol. Board Can.* **1**:269–278.

155. Templeman, W. 1940a. Lobster tagging on the west coast of Newfoundland, 1938. *Research Bull. (Fish), Dept. Nat. Resources, St. John's, Newfoundland No.* **8**:1–16.

156. Templeman, W. 1940b. The life history of the lobster. *Newfoundland Govt. Service Bull. No.* **15**:1–42.

157. Ter-Poghossian, A. 1928. Über die räumliche und zeitliche Verteilung von *Daphnia longispina* und *cucullata*, sowie von *Bosmina coregoni* und *longirostris* im Klostersee bei Seeon. *Intern. Rev. ges. Hydrobiol. Hydrog.* **20**:73–88.

158. Thienemann, A. 1919. Über die vertikale Schichtung des Planktons im Ulmener Maar und die Planktonproduktion der anderen Eifelmaare. *Verhandl. Naturhist. Ver. Preuss. Rheinlande* **74**:103–134.

159. Ullyott, P. 1939. Die täglichen Wanderungen der planktonischen süsswasser Crustaceen. *Intern. Rev. ges. Hydrobiol. Hydrog.* **38**:262–284.

160. von Bonde, C., and Marchand, J. M. 1935. The natural history and utilisation of the cape crawfish, Kreef, or spiny lobster *Jasus (Palinurus) lalandii* (Milne-Edwards) Ortmann. *Fisheries and Marine Biol. Survey S. African Fish Bull. No.* **1**:1–55.

161. von Freidenfelt, T. 1920. Zur Kenntnis der Biologie von *Holopedium gibberum* Zaddach. *Arch. Hydrobiol.* **12**:725–749.
162. von Fritsche, H. 1934. Über Wanderungen von *Porcellio scaber* (Sars). *Zool. Anz.* **107**:62–64.
163. Waterman, T. H., Nunnemacher, R. F., Chace, F. A., Jr., and Clarke, G. L. 1939. Diurnal vertical migrations of deep-water plankton. *Biol. Bull.* **76**:256–279.
164. Weismann, A. 1874. Ueber Bau und Lebensercheinungen von *Leptodora hyalina* Lilljeborg. *Z. wiss. Zoöl.* **24**:349–418.
165. Welsh, J. H., Chace, F. A., Jr., and Nunnemacher, R. F. 1937. The diurnal migration of deep-water animals. *Biol. Bull.* **73**:185–196.
166. Weymouth, F. W., Lindner, M. J., and Anderson, W. W. 1933. Preliminary report on the life history of the common shrimp *Penaeus setiferus* (Linn.). *Bull. U.S. Bur. Fisheries* **48** (14):1–26.
167. Williamson, H. C. 1904. A contribution to the life history of the lobster (*Homarus vulgaris*). *Rept. Fishery Board Scot.* **23**:65–107.
168. With, C. 1915. Copepoda 1. Calanoida Amphascandria. *Danish Ingolf Expedition* **3** (Pt. 4): 1–248.
169. Worthington, E. B. 1931. Vertical movements of freshwater macroplankton. *Intern. Rev. ges. Hydrobiol. Hydrog.* **25**:394–436.
170. Worthington, E. B., and Ricardo, C. K. 1936. Scientific results of the Cambridge expedition to the East African lakes, 1930–1. No. 17. The vertical distribution and movements of the plankton in Lakes Rudolf, Naivasha, Edward and Bunyoni. *J. Linnean Soc. London Zool.* **40**:33–69.

CHAPTER 13

HERMANN SCHÖNE

COMPLEX BEHAVIOR

I. *INTRODUCTION*

During the days before molting, a lobster fights its companions with particular vehemence, driving them far away (page 477). Many shore crabs bury themselves in the mud just before the arrival of the incoming tide (page 468). In considering such behavior patterns, it is tempting to inquire first about their biological usefulness. But to perceive their purpose is not to understand the physiology involved, which obviously requires an analysis of causal relationships. However, teleological implications may provide fruitful points of departure for the latter (page 514).

Behavior is usually a link in an extensive chain of physiological events. Thus mating, egg deposition, care for young, and the endogenous maturation processes intimately connected with them are all essential parts of reproduction. In *Gammarus duebeni*, for example, molting and the egg-laying correlated with it are dependent on mating. Egg deposition can only take place if there is also a transfer of sperm during copulation; the only event required for the normal onset of the next molt, however, is the copulative act as such.[53] In Section II, a varied selection of typical examples of crustacean complex behavior is presented. In Section III, this descriptive material is used to document an analytical interpretation based on the results of experimental investigations.

II. *BEHAVIOR TYPES*

A. Individual Behavior

1. *Feeding and respiration.* In contrast to the relatively uniform behavior of the specialized filter feeders, with their complicated straining, filtering, and sorting structures (see Chapter 6, Vol. I), the behavior of omnivorous crustaceans is quite varied. *Birgus latro*, for instance, eats both fruits and dead animal matter. It locates food from a distance of many meters by means of olfactory organs and even climbs pandanus trees to reach their fruits. Then it often carries the food hundreds of meters into a hiding place.[39,44,45]

The hunting methods of predatory and raptorial forms range from close examination of the surface of the ground (*Ocypode ceratophthalma*,[98] *Eriocheir*[78]) to lying in ambush, stalking, and intensive

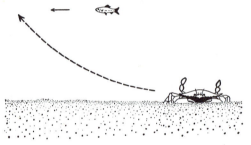

Fig. 1. Capture of prey by *Macropipus* (according to Schäfer[80]).

chase. *Lysiosquilla* lies in wait for prey in the entrance of its burrow and strikes out with raptorial claws when any passes.[40] *Carcinus*[10] and *Panulirus*[59] successfully chase swimming *Palaemonetes* or *Emerita*, while portunid crabs swim after and capture fish or other swimming forms[8,80] (Fig. 1). Some of the food-searching behavior of *Ocypode ceratophthalma* is reminiscent of that of birds. Thus this crab systematically turns over leaves lying on the beach and with its claws quickly seizes flies which are under them or starting to fly away (Altevogt, 1957, personal communication).

Pachygrapsus crassipes also is a clever hunter.[49] It may slowly emerge from a tide pool, carefully stalk the semiterrestrial isopod, *Ligia oceanica*, and then rush about in all directions in pursuit of the fleeing prey. Or this grapsoid crab may stealthily approach a hermit crab and try to catch it with a sudden lateral jump before the pagurid can retract into its shell. Species of *Squilla* may also stalk their prey, which they strike at with raptorial claws when within range. Some of the large decapods (*Cancer pagurus, Dardanus arrosor*) use their claws to break up the shells of snails; they will also smash small glass tubes containing pieces of meat.[80]

Birgus latro has been observed regularly to pursue the crab *Cardisoma* to its burrow, seize it, pull on the large claw which was sticking out defensively until the latter was autotomized, and then depart with this booty.[44] Aquarium specimens of *Palinurus elephas* may adopt a peculiar hunting custom. During a period of food scarcity they begin to attack and eat hermit crabs (*Pagurus bernhardus*) with which they have previously lived peacefully for months.[110] Thereafter they persist in this habit even when fed abundantly.

In terrestrial crustaceans, drinking and moistening the respiratory organs may be remarkable processes. *Gecarcoidea lalandei natalis*[39] and *Birgus latro*[44,45] dip the points of their claws into pools of water and then take up the water drops with their mouth parts. *Birgus* at the same time also moistens the brush-like fifth pereiopods and strokes them over the branchial tufts within its lung cavity.

2. *Body care.* Cleaning activity is developed to various degrees in different kinds of Crustacea. For instance, while *Squilla mantis* cleans itself untiringly and assumes every possible body position in the process,[40] and while the shrimps *Palaemonetes* (Schöne, 1956, unpublished) and *Palaemon*[35] also clean themselves frequently, one rarely sees *Carcinus*[10] thus occupied. Usually in Natantia and Macrura the second or third pairs of pereiopods serve especially in body care. However, the other ambulatory legs also may assist, rubbing against each other or stroking the abdomen. In Natantia such as *Palaemon*, the cleaning claws, which are equipped with a brush-like margin, move everywhere, rubbing and scouring the antennae, the region between the legs, the gill cavities and the abdomen, which is strongly flexed for this operation.[35]

A particularly thorough cleaning of the underside of the abdomen is carried out by female decapods in the days before spawning (*Cambarus*,[79,91] *Palaemon squilla*[50]). The species of *Uca* living on muddy shores often use the small claw to clean the large one when it becomes dirty with mud.[3] The eyes, too, are cleaned often. When emerging from its burrow, the animal places the endopodite of the third maxilliped over the orbital cavity, then the eyes flip up and are brushed.[101]

During the first days after a molt the small cleaning claws in many decapods pick up sand or other small particles from the bottom and introduce them with pushing and poking movements into the statocysts.

3. *Seeking and building shelter.* Many crustaceans seek a hiding place only temporarily. For example, *Crangon* after feeding digs into soft bottoms with lateral shoveling movements of the pleopods until only the eyes look out. The crabs *Grapsus grapsus*[28] and *Pachygrapsus crassipes*,[49] as well as the isopod *Ligia oceanica,* hide from danger in the nearest rock crevice while *Carcinus* retreat under shells or stones. In an aquarium, juvenile lobsters select for shelter a secure place to which they always return and in which they also hide the food they obtain.[6] Adult lobsters make suitable burrows between rocks by removing stones and gravel,[46] or in sandy ground they may dig a shelter under a stone.[46]

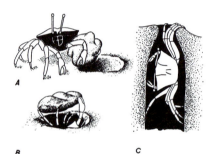

Fig. 2. Construction and closure of the burrow in *Uca* (slightly modified from Pearse[77]).

Numerous littoral, riparian, and terrestrial forms also can build burrows. *Cambarus diogenes* digs by pulling an armful of mud close to its body with both claws, carrying it to the surface of the hole, and depositing it on the rim; storage chambers may be built in lateral tunnels off the main shaft.[72] In *Uca pugilator,* the depth of the burrow is related to the groundwater level; the animal stops digging only when moist earth has been reached (regardless of whether it has been working for minutes or hours).[33] This fiddler crab digs by pushing the legs on the side of the small claw into the ground, pulling a lump of earth close to itself and carrying it away (Fig. 2A). In the beginning, the muddy sand is simply deposited in front of the entrance; later, balls of it are rolled away.

The walls of the terminal chamber are carefully smoothed. When the tide rises, the animal closes the entrance by first repeatedly pulling sections of the margin toward the inside with its feet (Fig. 2C) and fastening them in the opening until the entrance is closed by a thick plug. Now, additional lumps of earth brought from the bottom of the burrow are plastered underneath the plug. In this way, the entire air-filled section gradually moves deeper into the mud (aquarium experiments; see Fig. 9).[33] Other ocypodid crabs which also live in the intertidal zone similarly remain in a closed air-filled subterranean chamber during the period of high tide.[25,77,101] *Ocypode quadrata* like *Uca* closes its burrow by pulling in the margin.[24]

There are other ways of closing burrows as well. On solid ground, a lump of earth may be brought from outside the burrow and placed like a lid over the entrance (Fig. 2B).[77] The crab *Dotilla myctiroides* uses yet another method. In a semifluid sandy mud bottom it first makes a "shallow depression in which it turns on its side and quickly runs round backwards, pushing pellets of sand upwards and outwards. The semi-liquid pellets coalesce at first to form a circular wall"; this increases in height, arches inward and finally is closed to form a dome over the animal; the result is a bubble of sand enclosing the crab together with a quantity of air. If the crab continues to work in this way, the bubble, with the animal in it sinks into the substrate.[98]

The notion that these air chambers permit the crabs to continue breathing air while their burrow is covered by flood tide[98] has been denied on the basis of further observations on *D. myctiroides* and *D. blanfordi*. Apparently when built of relatively dry mud these crab "igloos" are quite permeable to air, and the animal must then depend on a second, pluglike structure which keeps the water out of its subadjacent burrow.[3a] However, it is not quite clear whether these igloos observed by Altevogt[3a] in India are the same structures as the air chambers described by Tweedie from Malaya.[98]

The males of a series of species of *Uca* build semicircular domed structures, more or less like umbrellas or shelters, over the entrance of their burrows.[25]

The macruran *Upogebia pugettensis* carries excavated mud from the shaft of its burrow with the basket-like first and second pairs of legs. Upon completing the construction of its U-shaped tunnel, the animal wedges itself firmly into the narrow, smooth shaft with its legs and back and, by beating the pleopods, creates a circulating current of water. With the basket-like legs acting as a sieve, it then separates out edible material from this current.[63] Similar behavior is encountered in the shaft-building amphipods (*Corophium*[89] and *Leptocheirus*[42]). Some isopods, such as *Zenobiana*, live in a hollow plant stem which they carry about with them as a protective shelter.[115]

The hermit crab *Clibanarius misanthropus* when deprived of its snail shell runs toward dark, contrasting objects and investigates them with its claws. If a concavity indicates an opening to the inside, it cleans this out and determines the size by probing with both claws. Finally if all is satisfactory the crab moves its abdomen in.[48] If *Pagurus bernhardus* seeking a shelter finds a suitable shell containing a sick snail, it eats the latter and empties the shell. It does not, however, touch healthy snails.[15] Several hermit crabs, e.g. *Diogenes pugilator*, may dig into the substratum even though they are already protected by a gastropod shell.[8]

Before settling and metamorphosis the cyprid larvae of the Balanomorpha, e.g. *Elminius*, explore the substratum with their antennules. They settle down preferentially on rough, dark surfaces at a certain distance from their fellows, and they always orient in such a way that when formed their carinal and tergal plates point toward the light.[9,29]

At present there is relatively little precise data on territoriality and homing in crustaceans. It may be recalled that *Alpheus dentipes*, *Upogebia*, and some other forms seldom leave their shelter. *Uca* often changes its burrow although sometimes* it occupies the same one for several days.[3,25] *Ocypode ceratophthalma* always returns to its own burrow within a radius of 100–200 m.[8] Marked specimens of *Panulirus* have been observed to remain in the same area for three years; another individual was found in the same burrow for 2–3 weeks.[59] Forty-four of sixty-six *Panulirus interruptus* which were caught and released again after marking were recaptured in the same area after one to six months; the others were found one to three miles away.[59] Similar evidence for territoriality has been obtained by analyzing *Homarus* catches.[46] Homing and other horizontal movements of Crustacea are discussed in Chapters 10 and 12.

4. *Masking, camouflage, and related behavior.* *Dardanus arrosor*, in a fixed sequence of separate operations, detaches the sea anemone *Calliactis parasitica* and places it on the gastropod shell in which the crab lives (Fig. 3).[16] *Pagurus prideauxii* shows closely similar behavior with another anemone *Adamsia palliata*.[8] When the crab moves into a new shell the anemones are transplanted from the old to the new one. *Dromia vulgaris* also sometimes carries anemones on its back.

---

* In species with highy developed courtship behavior, like *U. maracoani*, a particular burrow often is defended throughout the whole display phase.[28b] This is discussed further in Section III,C.

They are not attached to the carapace but instead are held in an expanded condition by the dorsally oriented fourth and fifth pereiopods.

Most of the time, however, this crab prefers to cover itself with pieces of the sponge *Suberites* which it shapes itself.[36] The methods of doing this vary and are adapted to the specific situation; for example, the crab may climb up on a sponge and cut a progressively deeper ellipsoidal groove around itself by pulling out small pieces of sponge with its claws. Finally, when there remains only a crab-shaped piece of sponge attached to the bottom by a stem, the crab then detaches the

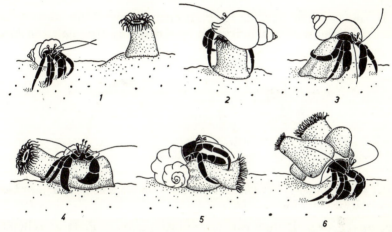

FIG. 3. Acquisition of an anemone by *Dardanus arrosor* (Table 3) (slightly modified from Brock[16]).

top. Six techniques for putting on this sponge covering have been observed.[31] These involve a variety of acrobatic movements which first bring the back of the crab and the concave surfaces of the sponge into their proper relationship and then heave the sponge up so that it can be held in position by the specialized pereiopods. The actual pattern of movement is highly dependent on circumstance such as the position of the piece of sponge on the bottom. If necessary, obstacles are removed and stones are cleaned out of the sponge; when the latter is attached to a wire hook the crab frees it by pulling away the sponge tissue surrounding the hook.[31]

Some other cases are known of symbiotic or commensal relations of crustaceans with animals from other phyla. Thus *Alpheus djiboutensis* typically has one or another of several species of gobiid fishes living together with it in its burrow;* both partners are believed to benefit from this association.[62a] Crustaceans are also known which live among the tentacles of certain sea anemones. *Heteromysis actiniae* is only known to occur among the tentacles and on the oral disc of the anemone *Bartholomea annulata.* The mysid seems to have immunity to the nematocysts of the coelenterate, but apparently prefers those individuals which lack these organelles near the bases of the tentacles.[23a] A species of caridean decapod, which seems not to have been described yet, has a similar habitat on the surface of a large anemone in Bermuda where both are common (T. H. Waterman, 1959, personal communication).

In some crustaceans, strong light elicits a search for some suitable covering material; this activity can be satisfied in *Dromia*[36] and *Ethusa*

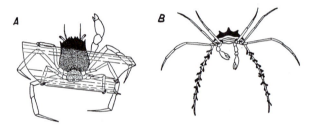

F ig. 4. Camouflage in: A) *Ethusa mascarone* (redrawn from Fenizia[37]), B) *Inachus dorsettensis* (redrawn from Schäfer[89]).

mascarone[37] even if they can only place pieces of glass or cellophane on top of themselves (Fig. 4A). The usual covering for *Ethusa* is one valve of a mussel shell.

Spider crabs, such as *Hyas araneus*, and species of *Maja*, mask themselves by placing such things as hydroid or bryozoan colonies on their carapaces or by covering themselves with pieces of algae; for this purpose, the algal filaments are torn off and either fastened to the back with an oral secretion or attached to small hooks on the dorsal surface or legs.[8,80] *Inachus dorsettensis* camouflages only the elongated first pair of walking legs (Fig. 4B).[80]

Behavior mimesis is shown by the amphipod *Caprella liparotensis* and the isopod *Astacilla.* While holding onto the branches of hydrozoan or bryozoan stems with the last pair of legs, they rigidly extend their oddly formed bodies and thus become almost indistinguishable from their surroundings.[89]

---

* A kind of symbiosis is known between *Hippolysmata* and various teleosts whose body surfaces are picked clean by the shrimp.[79a]

B. Behavior toward Others

1. *Behavior toward predators.* A bird flying at a distance of about 7 meters causes the members of a *Uca* colony to run to the entrance of their burrows. If the bird approaches to within 3–6 meters, or a human being to within 9 meters, the crabs all disappear into the burrows. The conspicuously colored males are the first to hide and the last to emerge again later.[25] When fleeing from pursuers, *Sesarma* can run with a speed up to 16 km/hr, *Pachygrapsus crassipes* merely up to 5 km/hr.

If pursued, the army crab *Mictyris longicarpus*, which lives in the moist mud of the intertidal zone, can penetrate about 25 cm into the mud within a few seconds by digging with its legs.[8] Hermit crabs run away, or, if threatened from close by, withdraw into their gastropod shells, obstructing the opening with their large claws. *Ethusa mascarone*, when in danger, pulls back under its shell with legs retracted; if the shell fits well all around, such behavior can effectively prevent the crab from being noticed by an octopus.[37]

Many brachyurans, especially running and beach-living forms, assume a defensive position* if they are surprised (*Eriocheir*,[78] *Uca*,[25] *Ocypode*,[24] *Pachygrapsus*[49]). *Carcinus maenas*, for instance, raises the anterior part of its body, as well as stretching out and bracing its legs. At the same time the crab raises its claws, which are also spread wide and opened. If the threatening object approaches to within a few centimeters, the animal quickly strikes at it with both claws.[10] *Ocypode* can fend off fish in this way.[24] On a rocky beach, *Menippe* (Brachyura) clings to a stone and boxes away with its claws while stridulating† with high-pitched chirps.[82] The crab *Lybia tesselata* carries the sea anemone *Bunodeopsis prehensa* in its claws and holds them out toward attackers in a defensive position.[8]

Defense reactions of brachyurans may turn into flight. *Carcinus* runs away with claws raised high; *Macropipus* raises its claws just for a few moments while swimming laterally backwards.[80] Many of the species which exhibit pronounced masking behavior can never, or only with difficulty, be made to assume a defensive position.[80] *Dromia* at first ducks down if its back is tapped, then rises slowly several seconds later and lifts its claws defensively.

The macruran decapods exhibit defensive behavior similar to that

---

* The neurophysiology of this reflex is discussed in Chapter 7.
† Crustacean sound production is discussed in Chapter 2.

of the brachyurans. They stretch out their legs threateningly toward the attacker (*Panulirus interruptus,*[59] *Palaemon*[35]). Frequently they are ready for flight at the same time with their abdomen extended so that they can dart off backward with a few vigorous beats of the tail. Smaller animals and females more readily take to flight than strong males. If a *Carcinus* is caught, it defends itself vigorously by biting with the claws and pushing with the legs.[10] *Panulirus* attempts to bite with its mouth parts and stridulates loudly.[59] *Pachygrapsus*[49] and *Cancer* (Schöne, 1951, unpublished) hold on to crevices by straddling their legs if one tries to pull them out.

Large specimens of crabs, like *Carcinus* and *Eriocheir,* when lifted by the carapace, extend all their extremities stiffly in a tonic contraction frequently lasting for minutes.[10,78] An octopus has been observed to release a *Carcinus* in such a spasm since the mollusk could not cope with it in this awkward posture.[10] Females of *Cancer* and *Carcinus* fold their claws and legs convulsively over the ventral side in what appears to be an "egg protection reflex."[10,80] A similar unwieldy position is assumed by *Cambarus* if it is picked up by hand; all the legs are extended and folded stiffly over the abdomen against which they are held convulsively.[79]

In many species, walking legs are autotomized if they are caught fast.* *Alpheus dentipes* shoots a stream of water toward an attacker by means of its snapping claw.[102]

2. *Social behavior.* Various kinds of stimuli provoke characteristic social behavior patterns in many Crustacea. Stridulation may be used for a sort of communication. Thus the noise made by a captured *Panulirus* apparently serves as a warning since all its companions within a range of 1–2 meters retire deep into their hiding places.[59] In *Uca pugilator,*[32] when one animal penetrates into the burrow of another and touches the owner sitting at the bottom, a noise is produced for 1–3 sec by the vibration of the merocarpopodite joint of the large claw at a frequency of 10–12 beats per second. Then both crabs climb out of the tunnel and if the owner is much smaller or a female, it then allows the interloper to re-enter the burrow without resistance; otherwise, both promptly begin to fight.

Optical or possibly tactile stimuli must serve as signals in the organized swarms, schools, or other communal feeding groups of malacostracans like Mysidae, *Ocypode ceratophthalma,*[98] *Mictyris longicar-*

---

* In the mangrove crab *Goniopsis cruentata* autotomy and rapid escape may occur while the cheliped still holds firmly to an attacking object (Schöne, 1959, unpublished).

pus,[s] and *Euphausia superba.*[116] In *Uca marionis,* several individuals suddenly start to move first, then others join in, until about fifteen to twenty males and females march single file to a new muddy feeding area[3] (Fig. 5A).

Social ties of a familial sort may be postulated when a large male is found to reside in a communal burrow with several females and a number of immature young animals as has been observed for *Panulirus*

A

B

Fig. 5A. Group migration in *Uca marionis* (from Altevogt[3]).
Fig. 5B. Male *Uca marionis* fighting his own image in a mirror (from Altevogt[3]).

interruptus[59] and *Xanthodius sternberghii.*[28] As in similar situations with many other kinds of animals, other adult males are not tolerated by the large dominant male.

A series of activity phases with increasing degrees of social significance has been found by Crane[28b] in male *Uca maracoani.* 1) In the "underground phase" each animal sits in its own burrow during the period of high tide. 2) With the receding tide, the "phase of maintenance activity" occurs during which feeding and repair of the burrow take place while aggressive or defensive behavior is lacking. 3) The "nonaggressive wandering phase" follows. During this period the animal walks continuously and apparently at random, feeding occasionally but still showing no aggressive or defensive behavior. 4) Then the appearance of attacks on other males in their burrows, plus the pursuit of females (without mating) added to phase 3 behavior, mark the "aggressive wandering phase." 5) In the "territorial phase" the male takes possession of a burrow which it defends against aggressors. Preliminary courtship behavior, without display, occurs as in phase 4. 6) Finally, in the "display phase," the male displays but only in the vicinity of his burrow.[28b] Perhaps the following curious fiddler crab behavior is part of a similar series of behavioral phases.

Strange types of behavior, described as "play," have been observed in fiddler crabs. Thus two males of different species, one *Uca marionis* and the other *Uca forcipata*, were seen to run around right next to each other for about half an hour in an area of approximately 12 meters' diameter.[77] In another case a male *Uca terpsichores* suddenly left its food and ran to the shelter of a neighbor's burrow, which it undermined and pushed over; a 15-min fight with the owner ensued. Suddenly, the troublemaker turned to the shelter of the next neighbor and a battle lasting 25 min then developed. Then as abruptly, the attacker hurried back to fight again with its first opponent, which unsuccessfully tried to escape into its hole. Finally the amuck crab ran to its own burrow, cleaned itself, and calmly started to eat.[25]

In decapods, fighting is particularly frequent among the males of communal species. In such battles the chelate legs are used as hitting or pinching weapons. Fights over bits of food are common. Thus individuals of *Palaemonetes varians* wield their chelate legs against any competitors (Schöne, 1956, unpublished); *Pachygrapsus crassipes* hit each other vigorously with their claws[49] and two *Pagurus longicarpus* without snail shells may fight until one of them is killed.[1]

In gregarious animals in general, behavior related to social contacts is often more or less ritualized. Thus in *U. maracoani*, entrance into a strange burrow, or into its own after an absence, is preceded by exploratory behavior. The large claw is inserted into the opening and thrust back and forth several times.[28b] Again in this same species, males in phases 4, 5, or 6 above, show threat behavior when approaching any burrow owner, or if another male or a female approaches. The movement consists of slightly raising the body and moving the large claw back and forth a little.

When a male in phase 5 or 6 threatens near his burrow, the movement pattern is like a low intensity display since the large claw is waved in a somewhat circular way.[28b] Phase 2 and 3 males show "submissive escape behavior" when attacked by another male. This consists of pressing the body and large claw flat against the ground and running away. The same behavior is observed in a male which loses a fight.

Fights between males of the same species tend to be ceremonial and are conducted in a fixed pattern which prevents serious damage to the opponents. In various species of *Uca*, fighting, which may last from a few seconds to several minutes, starts when one male invades the territory of another. The opponents approach each other with a stiff-legged gait and take turns hitting the large claws together (Fig. 6). In violent fights the large claws are locked together, and each contestant tries to push away or overturn the other.[2,3,25,28b] Before this happens, the weaker contestant usually gives up and flees into its burrow which it often plugs with the large claw. If the two opponents differ greatly in size, the larger one often simply stops fighting and disappears.[25,77] Large male specimens of *Pachygrapsus crassipes* also often do not fight much smaller ones.[49] Males and females rarely fight each other.[3] Females standing back to back sometimes try to push each other away or into a burrow.[3] On occasion, a victorious *Uca marionis* or *U. annulipes* after a fight may place a mud plug in the entrance of a burrow into which the loser has fled.[3,77] Similarly a crippled *Uca* with a damaged or missing claw may be tyrannized by a neighbor which repeatedly chases it back into its burrow, which is then plugged with mud by the attacker.[25]

After a fight between two male *Dotilla myctiroides,* the victor does a sort of triumphal dance, jumping up and down and drumming on the ground with its claws (Tweedie, according to Altevogt[3,3a]). A large captive male *Panulirus interruptus* has been seen to visit all the burrows in its tank one after the other. At each it tried to seize other males while stridulating with its antennae, but the females were ignored.[59] Lobsters chase their companions into the farthest corners of the aquarium before a molt (Schäfer, 1957, personal communication). Two specimens of *Alpheus dentipes* may react to one another by threatening with claws extended, touching each other with their antennae, shooting out streams of water with the snapping claws, and pinching with their claws.[102]

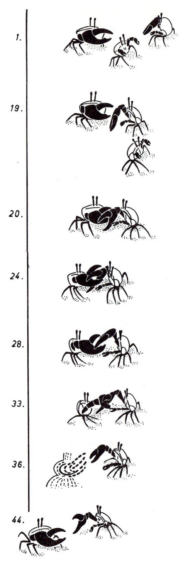

FIG. 6. Fight between two male *Uca marionis:* a female moves away. Single frames from a film strip; speed 16 frames per second (from Altevogt[2]).

The owner of a burrow usually is successful in fighting off members of its own species;* the amphipod *Talorchestia longicornis* for example struggles with its pereiopods in such encounters.[87] *Orconectes virilis,*[13] *Cambarellus shufeldtii,*[61] and *Alpheus dentipes*[102] can even vanquish larger opponents, the latter by using shots from the snapping claw.

In the crayfishes *Orconectes virilis,*[13] *Procambarus alleni,*[13] and *Cambarellus shufeldtii,*[61] the development of social dominance order has been observed among four equally large specimens in a series of vigorous fights (Fig. 19). Individuals of lower rank move out of the way of those of higher rank. Removal of the claws does not affect the position of the top-ranking specimen in a fixed dominance order (about 15 days old) of *Cambarellus;* indeed, even after an absence of 5 days such an individual can again assume its dominant position, although in a strange group it will have the lowest rank.[61] If the top-ranking individual is isolated for 5 days and then placed together with the next ranking specimen, a series of violent battles ensues until some order (usually the original one) is established again. Upon molting, a specimen drops into last place, but once the exoskeleton hardens, it usually fights its way back to its original position. Among animals of different sizes, the larger dominate; among specimens of equal size but of different sex, the males dominate in *Procambarus,*[14] the females in *Cambarellus.*[61]

3. *Sexual behavior.* In the search for a sex partner, special activity on the part of female crustaceans has been observed occasionally. Thus a female *Homarus gammarus* ready for mating was seen to walk about in the breeding pond until she ferreted out a male; then after mutual palpation, she turned over on her back.[81] Similarly a freshly molted female *Palaemon* ready for spawning approached a feeding male and touched him repeatedly with her antennae. However, the male copulated only after finishing its meal.[50]

Usually, however, the male crustacean is the more active sexual partner. In mate selection by the male, the behavior of the other individual is often decisive. In *Gammarus pulex*[47] and *Orconectes limosus,*[5] for example, any individuals which do not offer particularly vigorous resistance are seized and treated as females. In addition, some special "ripe" condition of the female often must be important. In *Gammarus duebeni,* only females with an ovary ready for spawning attract the males;[54] in *Palaemonetes,*[19] *Crangon crangon,*[70] and *Praunus flexuosus*[71]

---

* But in *Uca* this will depend on the animal's behavioral phase (page 476).

only females which have just molted into puberty are attractive for mating. This condition lasts only for about 20 minutes after the puberty molt in *Palaemonetes*. Definite chemical-mechanical stimuli emanating from mature females must be involved in this postmolt attractiveness.[19]

The females themselves are willing to mate only when they are ready for spawning. At other times, female *Carcinus maenas*[17] and

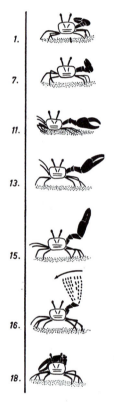

FIG. 7. Beckoning episode with bowing in *Uca annulipes*. Single frames from a film strip; speed 16 frames per second (from Altevogt[2]).

Homarus americanus[92] reject the males. In *Palaemonetes*,[19] *Palaemon squilla*,[50] and *Eriocheir*[78] females ward off further male approaches after a successful copulation.

Among shore-living forms, optical stimuli are often important. Male *Uca* intensify their claw-waving movements when a female approaches.[3,25] In such beckoning, the large claw, which usually becomes much paler with increasing mating excitement, is slowly opened laterally and upward and then retracted with a quick movement (Fig. 7). Frequently, particularly with strong excitation, the small claw carries out similar, but smaller-scale, movements at the same time.[25]

The beckoning behavior varies in its details from species to species.* Clawless males are treated as females, beckoned to in *Uca marionis*,[3] pursued and seized in *Sesarma taeniolata,* another shore crab.[101]

Comparable specific differences in the beckoning of 44 species of *Uca* from various parts of the world have been grouped into two main types of display which are correlated with two major morphological series. 1) The narrow-fronted species show vertical waving in which the large claw is moved up to about eye level and then down again without being extended. The male pursues the female or approaches her near her burrow, seizes her and attempts to copulate after briefly stroking her carapace with his walking legs. 2) On the other hand, the broad-fronted species wave with lateral movements in which the large cheliped moves laterally, is unflexed, and then returns to its original position through a high arc over the body. In addition, the male of this species group may court with specialized steps, curtsies or rapping the ground with the big claw. Thereafter he proceeds toward the opening of his burrow and attempts to lead her to it.[28a]

Female *Uca*, which at the beginning of mating approach first one male and then another as if quite unconcerned, eventually follow one specific male into its burrow after a particularly vigorous display (for example in *U. saltitanta, U. maracoani*[25,28b]). The male *U. annulipes* leads the female to his burrow with a sort of dance. While beckoning, it moves a few steps closer to the burrow, and bows repeatedly by bending its walking legs (Fig. 7, frame 11), as if indicating the intended descent into the burrow. The female follows the male after these gestures.[2,3] A similar bowing behavior is shown by male *U. pugilator*.[27]

Also in *U. maracoani* if the courtship takes place at the mouth of the male's burrow, an approaching female may, after the male has made an intensive waving display, follow him into his burrow. If, however, courtship occurs away from the male's burrow, he climbs on top of the female and with his small claw makes feeding and plucking movements at certain regions of her carapace. This is ritual behavior because no actual feeding takes place. In addition the male strokes the female's carapace with his walking legs. During this period the initially struggling female gradually relaxes into a quiescent condition. The male then turns her over in position for copulation.[28b] An unwilling *U. maracoani* female assumes a rejection posture at the approach of a male. Then she goes partly into her burrow leaving the legs on one side extending stiffly above the ground.[28b] The disappearance of a pair of fiddler crabs into a burrow is not necessarily always followed by

---

* Primitive forms of beckoning behavior are mentioned on page 513.

copulation. None of a number of pairs of *U. pugilator* which were dug up again were found to be copulating; while a series of copulating pairs were found above ground at night.[20] During copulation, the crabs are not easily disturbed,[3] and remain paired even when picked up.[20]

In *Eriocheir sinensis*, copulation is preceded by preliminary mating play. The male stands in front of the female in a stooped position and with claws hanging. From time to time she butts up against his claws. Then the male raises her frontally so that the pair stand sternum to sternum. The female uncovers her abdomen and the male inserts his own between the female's thorax and abdomen. Then the male embraces the female closely with his first pereiopods, raises his gonopods and pushes them into the female's sperm receptacles. There they probably move back and forth in the tube-like first pleopods and pump the sperm into the second pleopods. Following this, the union is terminated with a jerky movement. The entire copulation lasts about one hour.[78] Preliminary sex play also occurs in *Callinectes sapidus*.[100a] In these crabs the male dances from side to side in front of the female with his body raised and claws extended.

Except for the preliminaries, the copulation of most brachyurans (*Carcinus maenas*, various *Uca* species)[3,10,25,77] proceeds in a similar manner. In *Pachygrapsus crassipes* the male normally lies under the female.[49] Also a very large male *Callinectes sapidus*, copulating with a small female, lay on its back until the gonopods were inserted, in contrast to the usual habits of this species, and then turned over.[22] A male *Callinectes* or *Carcinus maenas* may carry a passive female around, clinging to his underside for several days before her puberty molt and subsequent copulation.[10,22]

The male penaeid *Sicyonia carinata* initiates mating by circling the female, using his rostrum to caress her sides and to tap her abdomen repeatedly when the female raises the latter (Fig. 8B).[73] Then he lies with his ventral side pressed at right angles against the female's ventral side, as do the males of *Palaemon squilla*[50] and other Natantia,[8,71] and transfers the sperm (Fig. 8C).

In *Orconectes limosus*, copulation proceeds as follows[5,79] (Fig. 8A). The male seizes the female, which at first fights back, throws her on her back, and then mounts the now passive female. In doing so he seizes her frontally extended claws and pereiopods with his own chelipeds, raises his gonopods and crosses over one of his fifth walking legs in front of them. Then he latches the hooks at the base of his third pereiopods in the corresponding depressions of the female and inserts the gonopods with several forward and backward movements and palpations. Now the male with his tail fan presses the female's abdomen firmly to his own and simultaneously pushes her cephalothorax away with his claws; as a consequence of the hook connection, the gonopods penetrate deeply into the female sperm receptacles. Sperm is transferred by pushing motions of the abdomen. Then male and female separate. The entire process lasts about nine hours.

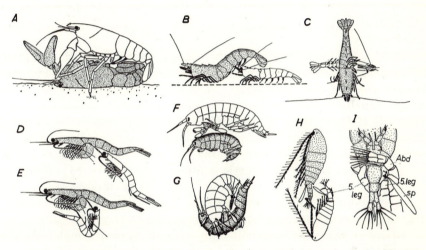

FIG. 8. Mating behavior: A, *Orconectes limosus*, stage just prior to hooking; see text; (the third to fifth pereiopods of the female have been omitted) (modified from Schellenberg[81]); B, preliminary play and C, copulation (seen from above) of *Sicyonia carinata* (modified from Palombi[73]); D, preliminary play and E, copulation of *Praunus flexuosus* (modified from Kinne[55]); F, precopulatory behavior and G, copulation of *Gammarus duebeni* (modified from Kinne[54]); H, seizure of the female by the grasping antenna of the male; and I, attachment of the spermatophore (*sp*) in *Diaptomus gracilis*; *Abd*, male abdomen (modified from Wolf[111]). In each pair the female is stippled to appear darker.

In mysids the male swims behind the female for several moments, with his long antennae placed against her brood pouch (Fig. 8D), then pushes his abdomen forward and inserts the long fourth pleopods into the brood space (Fig. 8E). In this way, the sperm which the pleopods have previously brushed from the penises is probably transferred to the female.[55]

Male gammarids carry females ready for spawning around on their ventral surface for some time before copulation ("precopulation,"

Fig. 8F). The females molt in this position (*Gammarus pulex*) and the male seeks out a hiding place a short time before she molts.* The anterior portion of the body molts first, the posterior portion later; the male always releases the molting part temporarily.[47] Copulation occurs immediately thereafter. The male *Gammarus duebeni* turns the female to lie across him at right angles and with several rapid strong thrusts of the abdomen transfers the sperm emitted by his genital papillae into the female marsupium. This transfer is effected with the pleopods, which are folded up in the form of a brush (Fig. 8G). In the course of 10–30 min, one to four such mating acts take place. Then the female is released.[53]

In the copepod *Diaptomus* the female is pursued; if the male *D. gracilis* succeeds in seizing the female's abdomen with his prehensile antenna, she immediately dashes through the water in a mad whirl. Finally when her attempts to free herself cease, the male flings his abdomen around (Fig. 8H) and clasps her abdomen with the right fifth foot which is developed as a prehensile claw. The rudimentary left fifth foot, which encloses the spermatophore neck, moves tentatively to and fro on the female genital segment (Fig. 8I), probably palpating with its long searching bristle, and then attaches the spermatophore to the genital orifice. The spermatophore emerges during the period when the female is being carried about.[111]

Many crustacean males will fight with rivals over females. At the approach of another male, a male *Orchestia mediterranea* drops its mate; the two rivals rear up and fight a wild duel with their gnathopods.[109] Similarly, a male *Pagurus* which holds his female with a claw and carries her about, releases her and fights when a rival comes near.[64] In the same way, two male *Homarus* fight each other in the presence of a female; even after copulation, rivals are kept away from the female.[92] After a fight the victor always takes possession of the female, unless as has been seen in *Orchestia*, she has meanwhile been taken over by a third male.

4. *Egg-laying and parental behavior.* Some crustaceans, like *Centropages, Argulus, Anaspides,* euphausiids and penaeids, do not retain their eggs at all. But more usually the mother holds them or attaches them somewhere to her body until hatching. In the days preceding oviposition, many female decapods clean the underside of their abdomens thoroughly. When spawning, female Natantia stand on their

---

* Concerning the relation between copulation and molting, see page 465.

legs (*Palaemon squilla*)[50] or lie on their side (*Crangon*),[8] the abdomen is flexed and the pleopods turned forward, so that a sort of pouch is formed. The emerging eggs are propelled into this abdominal space with the fifth pereiopods (*Athanas nitescens*)[71] or the first pleopods (*Palaemonetes*).[19] In *Palaemon*, the egg deposition takes 4 to 8 minutes.[50]

Female *Homarus*[93] and *Panulirus argus*[90] lie on their backs; the former raise the anterior end of the body from the bottom with their claws, the latter with the first antennae. *Panulirus interruptus* stands on its legs.[59] In all these animals, the abdomen is bent far forward and thus forms a pouch into which the eggs are guided. This is done by beating the pleopods in *Homarus gammarus*.[6] Female *Panulirus*, before ovipositing, scratch open the hard covering crust of the sperm mass with the fifth pereiopods.[90]

A female *Orconectes limosus* at first stands on its feet with the abdomen flexed far forward, and secretes into this cavity a mucus which hardens upon contact with fresh water and thus closes the pouch anteriorly. Then she turns on her back and deposits the eggs, pressing the fifth pereiopods close to the abdomen and thereby probably pushing sperm out of the receptacle. Then the female turns from one side to the other every 1–3 min for 3–5 hours; the eggs slide back and forth, eventually becoming glued to the beating pleopods by the solidifying mucus.[79]

The spawning female *Squilla* stands immobile for 4 hours with her body arched high, supported anteriorly on the walking legs, posteriorly by the telson. The spawn flows out to form an irregular egg mass which is picked up by the maxillipeds and kneaded continuously for hours with the aid of the cleaning legs.[40]

This mass of eggs, which in a female *Squilla* 14 cm long is about the size of a walnut, is carried about between the small maxillipeds. The females turn and roll it back and forth frequently and thereby clean it. During the brooding period they do not take any nourishment. If the egg mass is removed, they search for it, examining pieces of algae and other materials which they come across.[40]

In general, egg-carrying females usually are more timid than the other members of the species (*Orconectes immunis*,[91] *Cancer pagurus*[8]). *Eriocheir* and *Carcinus maenas* hide in the sand;[8] female *Uca pugilator* remain in their burrows during the day and emerge to feed only in the evening.[8] Female lobsters become more and more cautious as hatching time approaches.[6]

In decapods, the eggs are arranged and cleaned with the claws and walking legs, which move into the mass of eggs and poke about in it (Carcinus,[10] Upogebia,[63] Pachygrapsus[49]). The females of the macruran decapods from time to time move the egg-carrying pleopods back and forth; in Cambarus, this occurs more frequently in O_2-poor than in O_2-rich water.[8] Female Birgus latro care for the eggs with the fifth pereiopods, which otherwise lie in the lung cavity. The eggs are kept clean and moist while those which have become defective are picked out and eaten.[39] Female peracaridans carry eggs and young in a marsupium between their legs. Female Gammarus pulex from time to time drum vigorously on this brood pouch with their pleopods, thus whirling the eggs and larvae about and cleaning them.[47]

For the hatching and release of young, the females of the terrestrial and littoral crabs go to the ocean (Gecarcoidea lalandei).[39] Uca pugilator and Cardisoma carnifex[8] do this in the evening or at night. The female Birgus latro with her abdomen spread out holds on to a stone and shakes the eggs into a receding wave about twelve times, each time for 1–2 seconds.[44] Natantia and Macrura aid the hatching of young by vigorously beating the pleopods back and forth (Palaemon longirostris,[50] Homarus americanus[93]). Homarus does this in the evening, extending the claws horizontally forward and the abdomen obliquely upward.[93] The female Pagurus prideauxii partially emerges from her shell and carefully wipes over the eggs on the pleopods with the fifth pereiopods.[8] Frequently, the larvae themselves aid actively in rupturing the egg membrane, by jerking movements of the body (Copepoda),[65] or by pressing against it with abdomen and walking legs (Palaemon).[50]

After the eggs hatch, various amounts of brood care are provided by different crustaceans. Young specimens of Cambarus and Astacus use the small claws, which are bent to form a hook at the tip, to hold on to the egg stalk or the pleopods of the mother.[91] Young Orconectes immunis[91] remain with the mother up to the third molt; then they gradually become independent during the first 2 or 3 days, undertaking at first short and then more and more extended excursions. But even later, they still seek refuge with the mother if disturbed. Only the mother tolerates them. A brood of Orconectes limosus removed from their mother was placed in an aquarium into which the mother, a second female, and a male were transferred subsequently. The young animals sought refuge with all three. The male repelled them by striking them. After half an hour the young were distributed between the two females, but after 3 hr they were all assembled in contact with their own mother.[79] Young *Cambarus bartonii* and *Orco-nectes obscurus* remain in the mother's burrow until they themselves begin to dig.[72]

The isopod *Porcellio scaber* remains with its young in a nest which it has previously built of wilted leaves, under stones.[115] The female of *Phronima sedentaria* (Amphipoda) eats out tunicates, lives in their empty test within which she swims around and cares for her eggs and brood.[42] The young of the terrestrial potamonid crabs climb around on top of their mother but seek protection under the maternal abdomen in case of danger.[8]

III. *ANALYSIS OF BEHAVIOR*

In the study of orientation ability and learning, experimental methods have mainly been used, and up to the present these have particularly involved analyses of the effective external factors concerned. The results of older studies on the central nervous system described in Section III,A,2 below may be considered a first attempt at a direct investigation of the endogenous components of crustacean behavior. Detailed ethological studies dealing with Crustacea are not available, with a few exceptions. Consequently, we shall depend mainly on the descriptive material presented in Section II in dealing with the ethological questions and therefore shall often have to do without detailed analysis. The organization and terminology of the physiological-ethological problems presented here are based on recent work principally by E. von Holst, K. Lorenz, W. H. Thorpe, N. Tinbergen, and their followers.[7,60,96,97,105,108]

A. COMPONENTS OF BEHAVIOR

1. *Orientation mechanisms.* The term "orienting mechanism" will be applied only to the factors which control and adjust a sequence of movements; the sources or origins of the behavior are not significant in this connection. The simpler components of such activity and of the function of the sense organs are considered in detail in Chapters 2 and 10, while the sources of behavior are reviewed in Section III, A,4.

A specimen of *Birgus latro* in search of food sees a pandanus fruit and runs to it in a straight line.[44,45] Two different orientation processes participate in this behavior, as may be deduced from the observations: 1) the target orientation which enables the animal to recognize and run toward the fruit, and 2) the equilibrium and directional control of motor mechanisms by means of the statocysts.

a. *Target orientation.* This serves in the search for a goal. Eyes, olfactory organs, vibration or acoustic receptors, all may act as distance receptors, and principally eyes, taste receptors, tactile and vibration sense organs act as local receptors. Crustacean searching behavior usually involves several or many of these sensory modalities. The beach crab *Pachygrapsus crassipes* orients itself primarily with its eyes (see page 466) when seeking prey out of water but does so with its chemical receptors under water.[49] For further examples, see Part II.

b. *Equilibrium and directional orientation.* The pertinent mechanisms may be subdivided into three categories: Those which control body position and direction of movement in a vertical plane (i). Those which guide position and direction in the horizontal plane (ii). Those which control only turning movements (iii). The author has recently reviewed category (i) for both invertebrates and vertebrates.[84a]

i. *Orientation in a vertical plane.* The direction of digging in the building of burrows by *Uca pugilator,* whether they are level or steep, is oriented by the direction of gravity (Fig. 9).[33] The isopod

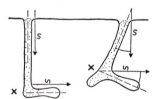

Fig. 9. Form of burrows made by two *Uca pugilator.* If the container was turned through 90° after the animal reached the point x, it then dug at the same angle in relation to the direction of the force of gravity (S) as before (modified from Dembowski[33]).

Cyathura after removal of its statocysts is no longer able to dig tunnels leading straight into the ground.[57] The swimming paths of *Palaemonetes varians* and *Crangon crangon* depend for their directions on the function of the statocysts or eyes (Fig. 10).[82,83] As a result of operative interference, the optical or gravity receptors may indicate the downward direction "ordered" by the central nervous system only when the path is much steeper than normal, or may fail to do so entirely. In the latter case their continuous turning beyond the normal downward direction causes the animals to follow curving or looping paths (Fig. 10:1b and 2b).

This interpretation has been confirmed by quantitative measurements of the positional and directional orientation with statocysts.[84] The inclination of the path of *Palaemonetes* and *Crangon* swimming downward was measured at 1 *g*, 1.3 *g*, and 2.2 *g* (Fig. 11). Orientation is such that the product of the sine of the angle of inclination* and gravitational force, the two factors determining the excitation of the statolith organs, remains constant (Fig. 11B, curve 2). This means

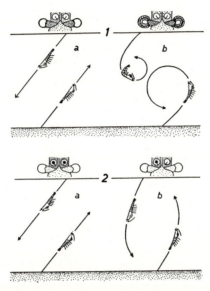

FIG. 10. 1) Directional orientation of swimming by *Palaemonetes* and *Crangon* with eyes but without statoliths: a) eyes normal, light coming from above; b) eyes darkened except for the dorsal region, light uniform and diffuse. 2) Directional orientation with statocysts and in uniform diffuse light: a) both statocysts normal, b) one statocyst without statolith. The upward paths were either spontaneous or induced by CO_2.

that the prawn orients itself so that its statolith organs furnish a constant pattern of excitation. The receptors act here like compasses which control the movement. The role of the statocysts and also of the eyes is therefore not restricted merely to the release of simple

---

* The angle of inclination should be measured relative to the surface bearing the sensory hairs since the effective stimulating process within the statocyst is the shearing force on the sensory hairs. This force is proportional to the sine of the angle of inclination relative to the horizon and, of course, to the magnitude of the force of gravity[84a] (see Chapter 2).

equilibrium reflexes or dorsal light reflexes evoked by disturbing the normal or resting position.

Orientation mechanisms may be considered as closed loop systems by analogy with engineering concepts of cybernetics or automatic regulation[68,107,108] (Fig. 12). In such a system a certain reference or

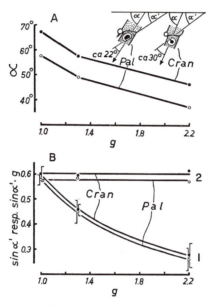

Fig. 11. Measurements of directional orientation by means of the statocysts in *Palaemonetes* (Pal) and *Crangon* (Cran): A) angle α between swimming path (corresponding to the longitudinal axis of the body) and the horizontal water surface, as a function of g ($1g$ is the normal gravitational acceleration); B) series 1: sine of the angle α' between the statocyst sensory surface and the surface of the water, as a function of g. The brackets delimit three times the standard deviation of the mean. Series 2: calculated from series 1 as sin α' times g (modified from Schöne[84]).

prescribed value for the sensory input from the statocyst is established in a dominant controlling center in the central nervous system. When the statocyst input actually has this reference value, a stable direction of locomotion ensues. But whenever 1) a disturbance by some external force changes the animal's orientation, or 2) some higher center alters the organism's motor pattern, this in turn affects the feedback input [in case 1) the "exafferent" input, in case 2) the "reafferent" input[108]] from the statocyst to the controlling center. The difference between this feedback input and the reference value thus produced gives rise to turning movements which reestablish the correspondence between feedback input and reference value required for a "steady state" of orientation. In case 1) when the feedback input is changed, the ensuing reflex turning movements restore and maintain the previous stable direction; in case 2) when the reference value is altered, the resulting change of the motor pattern leads to a new stable direction. Thus statocyst excitation serves in this manner to regulate the animal's movement through a central nervous system comparison of the prescribed and the actual sensory pattern concerned. The classic equilibrium responses as well as the dorsal light reflex are examples of corrective regulation of type 1 above, even though they are only part of the over-all orientation mechanism. Apparently all directional swimming is guided by

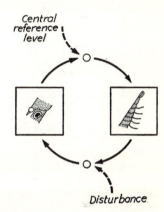

FIG. 12. Block diagram showing the regulation of directional orientation by the statocysts interpreted in terms of a feedback mechanism.

such feedback steering including upward, downward, positive, negative, and transverse tactic movements.

Interaction between gravitational and optical cues for position have been established in *Palaemon* and other decapods.[4,103] Recently, quantitative results have shown (Fig. 13) that light incident at a constant angle upon the eye releases a tendency to rotate in *Palaemonetes varians* (Schöne, 1955, unpublished). The magnitude of this turning movement, measured as angular deviation of the eyestalks from their normal position, depends on the animal's orientation in the gravitational field. When the statocyst is horizontal and therefore not affected by any shearing force (see footnote, page 489), the influence of light is strongest. It is weakest when the sensory hairs undergo maximal shearing by the statoliths. This effect of light is emphasized if the weight of the statoliths is experimentally increased in a centrifuge as shown in curve 2 of Fig. 13 (2.2g).

ii. *Orientation in a horizontal plane.* Probably orientation to light in a horizontal plane is effected in a similar regulated manner to that just described for positioning in a vertical plane (see Fig. 12). This would include the tactic behavior of *Asellus*,[34] *Carcinus*,[112] and of other so-called positive, negative, or menophototactic crabs.[103] In the escape orientation of *Talitrus* (Amphipoda), *Tylos* (Isopoda), and other beach inhabitants with the aid of the sun,* the actual reference direction is modified by endogenous, diurnally changing processes (the "internal clock")† so that the daily course of the sun through

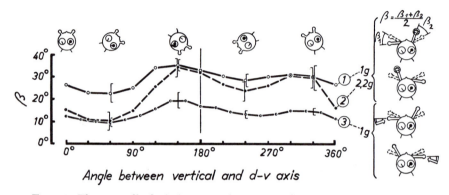

Angle between vertical and d-v axis

Fig. 13. The eyestalk deviation β produced in *Palaemonetes varians* (with one statocyst removed) by unilaterally directed illumination as a function of the crustacean's position in the gravitational field. In the schematic representation at the right the broken outline of the eyestalk shows the deviation produced by statocyst stimulation; the continuous outline of the eyestalk, the deviation produced by light stimulation in addition to that by the statocyst. The brackets delimit three times the standard deviation of the mean. The light was unilaterally directed either by darkening one entire eye (as in curves 1, 2) or by the unilateral presentation of a light beam at a constant angle to the eye (curve 3) (Schöne, 1955, unpublished).

the sky is compensated for‡ and a constant geographic direction, i.e. the direction toward the beach in the normal case, can be steadily maintained.[74,76]

iii. *Control of turning movements.* The fine adjustment of turning movements in locomotion is checked by optomotor mechanisms or by the statocyst function which resembles that of the semicircular canals of vertebrates. It also may be analyzed by analogy with a feedback system (Fig. 12).[69] According to such analysis, external

---

* For details see Chapters 1 and 10.
† Diurnal rhythms are discussed in Chapter 11.
‡ A similar orienting mechanism occurs in *Goniopsis* (Schöne, 1959, unpublished).

stimuli are distinguished from stimuli produced by movements of the animal itself. External stimuli which disturb the animal's position or direction induce corrective movements. Thus on a turntable, the receptors for angular acceleration or the optomotor apparatus are stimulated and cause the animal to run or turn in a direction opposite to the rotation.[10,83,112] On the other hand, the same stimuli resulting from the animal's own spontaneous movement serve merely to control the turning movements (see page 491).

The importance of the statocysts for complicated movement sequences is emphasized by the finding[10] that they are particularly large and well developed in soil species as well as in beach and terrestrial forms.

2. *Significance of central nervous system components.** The basic experiments of Bethe[10] on *Carcinus maenas* and the findings of several other authors have demonstrated the following general points (Table 1 and Fig. 14). Simple limb movements, such as those required for running, raising the anterior part of the body, assuming the threat position, take place even without the supraesophageal ganglion (SEG) (Table 1, column 5). The coordination center concerned with such activity lies in the subesophageal ganglion (column 6); this has been proved also for *Pagurus bernhardus*.[94]

The typical lateral walking of brachyurans cannot occur without the SEG (Db-5†) or without the neurons of the cellulae superiores mediales (Db, 14). Cutting one circumesophageal connective (Dc-4) or removal of an entire half of the SEG (Dc-10) results in circus movements in benthic brachyurans or swimming in a circle by portunid crabs.[56,86] If the operation has been on the right side, this circling always takes place counterclockwise, in locomotion to the right as well as to the left. Even after amputation of several legs the animal still tries to move in this direction with a new pattern of coordination‡ of the remaining legs.[11,86] In *Cancer* this effect of unilateral SEG deficiency can be decreased, removed, or reversed at will by appropriate electrical stimulation of the connective stump.[52] Raising the anterior body and the tonic convulsive posture occur more

---

* Physiology of the CNS is discussed in detail in Chapter 7. There it is emphasized that because of the functional organization of this system in Crustacea the results of surgical interference must be interpreted with great care.

† These symbols refer to behavior after operations on the supraesophageal ganglion specified in Table 1. The letters indicate the rows in the table, while the numbers refer to the columns and also to the cuts shown in Fig. 14.

‡ This is discussed further in Chapter 9.

TABLE 1

BEHAVIOR OF *Carcinus maenas* AFTER OPERATIONS ON THE CENTRAL NERVOUS SYSTEM
ILLUSTRATED IN FIG. 14 (COMPILED FROM BETHE[10])

The following operations (numbered in the vertical columns) affect various behavioral activities listed at the left as shown:

1 Darkening both eyes
2 Removal of right statocyst
3 Removal of both statocysts
4 Cutting right esophageal commissure
5 Cutting both esophageal commissures
6 Cutting fifth oral ganglion
7 Splitting anterior part of supraesophageal ganglion (SEG)
8 Splitting posterior part of SEG
9 Complete anteroposterior splitting of SEG
10 Sum of operations 4 and 9
11 Removal of right globulus
12 Removal of both globuli
13 Removal of cellulae superiores mediales on the right side
14 Removal of cellulae superiores mediales on both sides

Behavior	1	2	3	4	5	6	7	8	9	10	11	12	13	14
A. Eye movement in a) altered orientation relative to gravity	+	1 < r	−[a,l]	+v	+v		−	+	−		+	+	−	−
b) passive rotation around vertical axis	<n	<n	−[a,k]	r < l	<n		−	+	+	−	+	+		
c) running	+	+	+[b]	r < l	−		+	+			+	+		
B. Righting movements a) normal	+	+	±	r < l	+	−	+	+	+		+	+	+	+
b) overhead			+	r	+	−	+	−	+		+	+	−	−
c) legs on back[d]			+		+		−	±	±				−	−
d) somersaults					+		−		+	+				
C. Resting position normal	+			+[c]	−[l]		+	+	+v		+	+	+[e]	+
D. Walking a) right-left coordination	+	−	−	−		−[o]	−	+	−	−	−	−	+[e]	
b) lateral walking	+	+		+	−[g]	−[h]	+	+	+v	+	+	+	+	
c) circular walking				+		−							−[e]	−[g]

Behavior
Operation

Behavior		Operation													
		1	2	3	4	5	6	7	8	9	10	11	12	13	14
E. Defense	a) rearing up	+	r < 1		r < 1	< n		++		++		++	++	+[e]	< n
	b) directed defense				+	+[m]	+[p]	−	n	++		++	++	++	
	c) tonic convulsion					+[v]		++						+[e]	+[v]
F. Cleaning			r < 1		r > 1	++				+		+	+		
G. Feeding	a) directed grasping				+	+[n]		+[i]		++			i		
	b) eating					++									
H. Copulation					n	+++		++				++	+++	+	+
I. Muscle tone				< n	r < 1	<< n		++							
J. Flexor tension					r++	++									+
K. Assurance of movement				< n	< n	< n		+		< n	< n	+	+		
L. Light affects choosing a location		−				−		−		−	−	−[i]	−[i]		

Symbols:

n	normal	±	sometimes	>	more than
+	present	v	changed	<	less than
++	increased	r	right		
−	absent	l	left		

[a] Absent after 1; [b] still present after 1; [c] body inclined to the left; [d] when raised in normal position and in contact with the back; [e] up to the second and third day after operation, then like [d]; [f] same number and magnitude of steps of the right and the left side; [g] only a few steps forward; [h] does not walk at all; [i] but flees on optical stimulation; [j] food often refused; [k] not in all specimens; [l] lie on their backs or stand on their heads; [m] except when sense organs on the head are stimulated; [n] when there is the stimulus of food odor from about 4 cm distance; [o] no longer any coordinated walking movement; [p] upon local stimulation.

readily and more strongly than normal after splitting the two halves of the anterior part of the SEG (Ea, c-7) but the globuli are not involved in this (Ea, c-11, 12).

In addition to the obviously crucial central nervous connections with the receptors (columns 1, 2, 3) and effectors (columns 4, 5), the following central pathways are also important for various orientation processes. For orientation to gravity, the connection between anterior halves of the SEG and with the anterior neuropile are essential (Aa, Bc-7, 13, 14). The control of turning movements by the statocyst "semicircular canal" system also takes place without globuli (A, K-11, 12).* After sectioning of the anterior SEG into two halves and after removal of the globuli, light intensity no longer

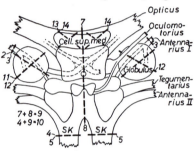

FIG. 14. Diagram of the supraesophageal ganglion of *Carcinus maenas*. Various cuts and operations described in the text and Table 1 are shown by broken lines labeled with the appropriate numbers (compiled from Bethe[10]).

influences the choice of a place to live (L-7, 11, 12) although defensive movements against visual stimuli still occur after the latter treatment (Eb-12).

Even without the entire SEG, local orientation by means of chemical and mechanical receptors is still possible for defense, feeding, and copulation (Eb, Ga, H-5). The capacity to discriminate food particles or mating partners and other objects likewise still is present. A *Pagurus* without its SEG will actually seize a snail shell after coming in contact with it, but such a crab does not examine or enter the shell.[94] A *Maja* without an SEG still camouflages itself with small pieces of paper if it happens to touch them.[67] Important inhibitory centers appear to be eliminated when the SEG is removed. Thus in its absence the animals sometimes feed until their stomachs burst, the males copulate for hours or days; a general pronounced restlessness appears as it may in other decerebrate arthropods.[104] The

---

* But it is disturbed after splitting the SEG (Ab, Bd, K-9).

globuli apparently are important for these SEG inhibitory processes (H-11, 12).

The habituation of the crayfish to having its back stroked is also based on inhibitory processes. But in this case peripheral inhibition is involved. Thus in the intact animal the defensive opening of the claws

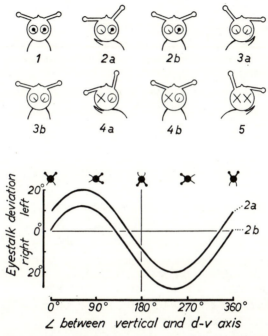

Fig. 15. Behavior after operations on the statocysts. The statoliths or whole statocysts were removed on one or both sides. The diagrams show the effects on eyestalk and leg motions while the body maintains a vertical dorsoventral axis; the curves, corresponding to diagrams 2a and 2b, show eyestalk deviation as a function of body position relative to the gravitational field; for details see text (data from Schöne[83]).

soon ceases; yet when the inhibitory axon of the opener muscle is cut, the claws are opened after each exposure to stroking.[104]

Finally, the central compensation processes which come into play after the elimination of sense organs should be mentioned. For example in *Palaemonetes, Crangon,* and other decapods[83] (Fig. 15:2a) unilateral statolith removal produces a tendency to rotate toward the deficient side which finds expression in movements of the extremities and in the deviation of the eyestalks from their normal position.

When the dorsoventral axis is vertical, the eyes are displaced toward the side from which the statoliths have been removed (Fig. 15:2a). In the course of several days, the position of the eyes moves back to the normal position (Fig. 15:2b). Correspondingly, the eyestalk positions are displaced to the side away from the deficiency by the same amount, if the crab is in other positions relative to gravity (Fig. 15: compare curves 2a and 2b). If one now also removes in series first the statolith of the opposite side, then the empty statocyst pocket on the first side, then the empty statocyst pocket on the other, the animal tends to rotate violently after each operation (Fig. 15:3a, 4a, 5) and then finally subsides* (Fig. 15:3b, 4b). These phenomena indicate that the absence of the statoliths or the entire sensory epithelium of one side is compensated centrally, by a sort of equalizing excitation. This becomes obvious, after compensation is complete, only if the same element on the other side is eliminated, too (Fig. 15:3a, 4a, 5).

3. *Behavior categories.* Behavior patterns may be fixed genetically or they may contain elements modifiable by experience and hence capable of adapting behavior to repeatedly occurring situations. The influence of experience is usually excluded from all actions which come into play in complete form immediately after attainment of a particular developmental stage. In this connection one might cite the hatching movements of embryos, the first locomotor actions of larvae, the clinging of young *Cambarus* (page 486), or the masking behavior of *Inachus dorsettensis* and *Macropodia longirostris* freshly molted to the bottom-living stage.[58]

Although conditioning or other environmental factors may affect the development of a certain behavior pattern, the direction of such an influence is dependent upon underlying innate features of central nervous structure and function (Section III,C). Other hereditary elements are certain species-specific components of movement such as grasping with the claws, carrying things to the mouth, chewing, cleaning, beckoning in *Uca*, swimming and running coordination, single movements in copulation, in defense, and the like. Such stereotyped elements of behavior seem to be quite rigid in form.

In contrast to this rigidity other components of behavior show a plasticity which is nevertheless also based on a fixed inherited pattern. These are, according to Bethe, related to the capacity of the central

---

* Effects of the wound itself disappear within a few minutes; they can be distinguished from the findings described here.

nervous system to effect a particular movement in several different ways. Thus in *Carcinus* and *Macropipus*, following leg amputation, the coordination of the remaining legs is reorganized so that the animal strives to achieve its original goal again immediately. A learning process seems out of the question.[11,56] After loss of the small claws,

TABLE 2

METHOD OF CUTTING OUT A PIECE OF CAMOUFLAGE FROM PAPER SHOWN BY *Dromia*. EACH OF 10 SPECIMENS (EXCEPT No. 7) WAS GIVEN TWENTY TRIALS[a]

Type of cut out[b]	Specimen										Totals
	1	2	3	4	5	6	7	8	9	10	
A	—	10	11	—	9	1	3	—	8	1	43
B	3	4	8	2	9	1	4	20	7	16	74
C	16	3	—	18	—	14	5	—	3	2	61
D	1	3	1	—	2	4	6	—	2	1	20

[a] Data from Dembowska.[31]
[b] The types of cut-out are illustrated in Fig. 16.

the large claw in *Uca* can be utilized in feeding.[25] In *Pachygrapsus*, the first pair of walking legs largely assumes the functions of claws if the latter are missing,[49] and the same is true for a *Pagurus bernhardus* which is examining shells.[94] Although basically hereditary, some of these plastic behavior patterns apparently may undergo a

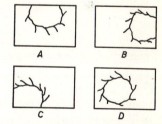

FIG. 16. Patterns of cutting out camouflage from a piece of paper by *Dromia vulgaris* (Table 2) (from Dembowska[31]).

certain degree of perfection by training. Thus the swimming of a *Macropipus*, from which one of its swimming legs has been removed, improves with time.[56]

The feeding behavior of *Palaemonetes*, *Carcinus*, and other decapods depends directly on the nature of the food, according to which the animal bites off pieces directly, plucks at it with its claws, braces itself with its legs, or tears pieces off by jerking back the body. In *Dromia*, six ways of donning a sponge for masking are known (page

471). Such variable types of behavior may involve components suscep-
tible to learning. The influence of experience may be recognized by the
peculiarities of individual animals, as does the proper cutting of a
piece of paper for masking by *Dromia* (Table 2 and Fig. 16). Such
matters are discussed further in the section on learning (page 506).

4. *Release and discharge of behavior*

a. *Appetitive behavior, sign stimuli, releasers and releasing
mechanisms.* A *Carcinus* reacts to contact of its taste receptors with
meat by reaching for the food and then eating it. A hermit crab runs toward empty snail shells and examines them. A crab flees when threatened. All these behavior patterns take place only under certain specific
conditions. The crab reaches for food only when it is hungry; the
hermit crab is interested in empty shells only when it has none of
its own; a crab sitting in its burrow does not flee.

In order for a particular behavioral response to occur, a readiness
for doing it, the so-called appetence, must be present to a sufficient
degree. This usually leads to a searching action (appetitive behavior)
which is directed toward the stimulatory situation which elicits the
behavior in question. Appetitive behavior is related to the releasing
mechanism (RM), a mechanism in the CNS, which, at the arrival of a
specific configuration of stimuli (sign stimuli), sets the final act,
the "consummatory" act,* into motion. With the completion of the last,
appetence disappears. So, after copulation, the females of various
decapods are no longer ready for mating (page 480). On the day after
vigorous and successful mating, a male *Uca* exhibits no mating behavior at all.[25]

Sign stimuli are specific. For example in *Macropipus*, an animal
swimming above it released pursuit behavior, but a *Crangon* crawling
between its legs was ignored (Schäfer, 1957, personal communication).
The sign stimuli may be determined in experiments with models. A
model for young *Cambarus*, to which they cling as to the pleopods of
their mother, may consist merely of a hollow piece of wire mesh.[91]
Since there is no influence of experience, we may speak of an innate
releasing mechanism (IRM) which evokes the clinging behavior. It
is typical of such mechanisms that they respond to elicitors which consist of one or a few sign stimuli.

The sign stimuli, which in *Uca pugilator* act as an "irresistible in-
vitation" to climb out of its burrow and to search for other members

---

* This term is discussed below (page 503).

of the species, consist of contact of its legs with those of an invading *Uca* and of a vibration of a certain intensity which it produces (page 474). The response can be initiated by a model consisting of a piece of wire whose free end is rubbed by a piece of corrugated wood.[32] The hermit crab *Clibanarius misanthropus* is induced to carry on intensive activity by a concavity in a snail shell model made of plaster of Paris; a bump within this concavity is worked over with the claws like a plug in the opening of a snail shell.[48]

In stridulating *Uca*, in *Panulirus* whose sound production warns its companions (page 474), in male *Uca* which will violently fight its image in a mirror as if it were a rival (Fig. 5B), and in finding of a

TABLE 3

BEHAVIORAL SEQUENCE IN THE ACQUISITION OF *Sagartia* BY *Dardanus arrosor*[a]

Level	Appetitive behavior	Releasing stimuli	Action (No. in Fig. 3)
1.	Searching	Optical stimuli	Approaching and examining (1)
2.	Approaching and examining	Chemical and tactile complex of stimuli	Climbing,[b] stroking, tapping (2)
3.	Climbing, stroking, tapping	Tactile stimuli (ridged pedal disk, etc.)	Detaching and laying down (3)
4.	Detaching and laying down	Stimuli of the horizontal anemone	Further tapping (4)
5.	Further tapping	Tactile stimuli (degree of softness)	Putting on and fitting close (5)

[a] Data from Brock.[16]
[b] First, if necessary, removing obstacles.

sexual partner, the sign stimuli derive from members of the same species. Species-specific sign stimuli (e.g. structural or behavioral characters), which have acquired during the evolutionary process the ability to elicit certain (innate) motor patterns in other members of the species, are called releasers or social releasers. For example, the appearance of the beckoning claw in the male *Uca* and its special movement pattern are specialized particularly to function as a social releaser.

b. *Sources of behavior.* Appetitive behavior may start spontaneously or may originate from other similar behavior. In the chain of events making up complex behavior (Table 3 and Fig. 3) the consummatory act of one step may represent simultaneously the appetitive behavior of the next step.[7] The appetitive activity which initiates a behavior complex may set in spontaneously, i.e. without direct external cause. For example, the search for food, the hiding impulse of crustaceans ready for molting or spawning, or the drive of barnacle larvae to settle on the substratum 24 hours before the last molt, are all initiated by endogenous processes, as are the various behavioral components of physiological rhythms in *Uca pugnax*[18] and many other forms (Chapter 11). There are several ways in which appetitive behavior may be induced; for example by enteroceptor stimuli of storage organs (stomach, etc.) or by hormones.[105] *Carcinus* in which the esophageal commissures are severed feeds until the stomach bursts (page 496). The fact that there are controlled fluctuations in this readiness to act, which apparently can only be explained by a central nervous activity, presents an unsolved problem.

Similarly, rhythmic movements of the extremities appear to be spontaneous or automatic, as for example the beat of the respiratory scaphognathites in Decapoda, of the cirri in barnacles, and of the filtering appendage of cladocerans (Chapter 2, Vol. I). The investigation on the nervous excitation of the lobster's heart (see Chapter 5, Vol. I) and the research on movement coordination in invertebrates and vertebrates (especially in fishes) done by von Holst[106] contradict the hypothesis that chains of reflexes are involved. The real nature of initiating factors in spontaneous behavioral patterns is not yet known. It has been suggested that they are produced by some cumulative processes which can by analogy be referred to in terms of certain action-specific substances or states of excitation.

In many cases, appetitive behavior often appears to become stronger and stronger. Thus in *Uca annulipes*, display activity is introduced by isolated hints of beckoning movement interpolated into the preceding feeding period; these hints gradually develop into increasingly distinct and extensive display movements.[3] The bowing of a male *Uca annulipes* leading a female to his burrow (page 481) may be considered to be such first hints or intention movements suggesting a behavioral act soon to follow. The longer the time interval elapsing since the performance of a certain consummatory act, the lower the threshold for the next one will be. In male *Gammarus*, individuals which have been kept isolated for a fairly long time accept females that were not noticed at all by males regularly provided with females. Finally, the consummatory behavior may be released by strong nonspecific stimuli. For instance, a male kept in isolation for 5 months seized a bit of leaf and carried it around for 4 days below its body as he would a female.[54]

The processes which help to diminish the appetence and are connected with the performance of the consummatory act have to be elucidated in every special case. For example some sort of fatigue may take place anywhere between the receptors receiving the sign stimuli and the motor organs performing the consummatory act; or some feedback stimuli of internal or external origin may be the causal factors.[7,105] One may perhaps consider as a stimulus-specific fatigue the results well represented (pages 511, 512 and Fig. 20) in experiments where hermit crabs were tested with shells of different snails. A feedback mechanism might terminate the digging behavior of *Uca* (page 468) or stop the reproductive migration of many land crabs to the sea.[39,44]

If the consummatory act cannot be performed because a second drive, incompatible with it, comes into action or because the consummatory act is prevented by other external factors, a third "unexpected" motor pattern called displacement activity often may appear. In *Uca inversa* displacement feeding occurs if the animals find themselves in a situation where they appear to hesitate between attack and flight or where the flight of a female from several closely crowding males is prevented. The displacement activity here consists of the claws carrying out hasty feeding movements which raise little or no mud.[43]

Similar feeding displacement* is known in other species of *Uca*, and even in other genera of displaying ocypodids such as *Ilyoplax*.[28a] Displacement claw cleaning also occurs in which the small claw moves as if to polish the large claw even though the latter is free of mud and the terminal brush of the small claw may not actually touch the other. Conflict between an urge to display and one to escape is especially likely to evoke this activity.[28a] Different species of *Uca* tend to show one or the other of these two types of displacement activity. Thus *U. festae*, *U. deichmanni*, and *U. cumulanta* seem prone to displacement claw cleaning while *U. lactea* and *U. leptodactyla* tend rather to have displacement feeding.[28a] In primitive species like *U. rhizophorae* no displacement behavior has been observed.[28a]

Another example of conflict behavior has been observed in an *Astacus astacus* (Schöne, 1950, unpublished). When the sensory hairs in a statocyst are so agitated with a fine water jet that their direction of bending changes too quickly for the reflex response movements of the eyes and extremities to keep pace, the animal suddenly begins to carry out feeding movements with the mouth parts, legs, and claws. Behavior apparently arising from a sort of conflict situation has also been observed in *Panulirus argus* (Schöne, 1959, unpublished). The lobsters, running in a two-choice maze, sometimes stop when a decision has to

---

* See also footnote page 513 concerning *Goniopsis*.

be made, then after a pause, suddenly show violent strokes of the abdomen and tail.

The endogenous sources of behavior are in turn connected to external factors. The internal clock of the solar orientation mechanism (Chapters 10 and 11) is ordinarily synchronized by the external rhythm of day and night and can be transposed by an experimental shift in the light-dark periods.[75] Food-seeking behavior often depends on the light intensity. Thus *Homarus*[46] and *Panulirus*[90] prefer to feed at night, whereas *Ocypode* and others may forage during the day.

A distinction should be made between external factors which 1) release a particular action, and those which 2) direct it.

1) When the CO_2 concentration of the water is increased, *Daphnia*, *Palaemonetes*, *Crangon*, and other Crustacea swim upward* (Fig. 10).[99,103] Certain changes in light intensity elicit the vertical migrations of many pelagic crustaceans and their larvae[23,30,36] (Chapter 12). The escape behavior of the beach inhabitants *Talitrus* and *Tylos* depends on the degree of moisture: on a dry substratum they flee toward the sea; on a wet substratum, toward the land.[74]

2) To be distinguished from these behavior-eliciting environmental factors are the external stimuli used by the orientation mechanisms to adjust and guide the course of the behavior. In the above examples, the upward swimming in CO_2-rich water as well as the vertical migration elicited by light intensity is guided by visual and gravitational mechanisms, the behavior of the beach crustaceans by solar orientation (Section III,A above). Similarly, in *Dromia* optical stimuli guide the searching activity, induced by bright light, to a suitable object (see also page 472).

But often releasing and orienting stimuli emanate from the same source as, for instance, in several of the above examples. Another case where the releasing and the orienting mechanism work hand in hand occurs in the crab *Dissodactylus mellitae*, whose search for its host, the sand dollar *Mellita quinquiesperforata*, is both elicited and oriented by means of an odorous substance emanating from the echinoderm.[51]

B. BEHAVIORAL CHANGES IN ONTOGENY

1. *Growth and maturation.* Many types of crustacean behavior develop in the course of ontogenetic growth, others appear as a consequence of periodic maturation of the gonads or other cyclic processes.[97] Thus lobster larvae in the third stage seize food with the maxillipeds;

---

* Related to the direction either of the gravitational field or of the light.

the claws are only auxiliary structures, held ventrally extended; after molting to the fourth stage, the claws are stretched forward and used as primary grasping organs.[6] In the transition to life on the bottom during the fourth stage, the previously pelagic larva develops the habit of seeking out dark corners and hiding.[6] Cypris larvae of barnacles when settling on a substrate at first align their anteroposterior body axis in relation to the predominant direction of incident light, but later change this alignment to accord with the pattern of current flow.[29a]

The elaboration of the mating behavior of adolescent male *Uca,* whose courtship behavior shows various degrees of perfection,[25] probably should also be attributed to endogenous differentiation and not to perfection by learning. An immature male *Uca beebei* beckoned and enticed a female into its burrow, but then he ran in and out "as if perplexed," apparently not yet capable of copulation. It is difficult to imagine how these young animals could learn their species-specific behavior exactly since they live in mixed populations in which individuals of different species often seem to live more closely together than members of the same species. Similar considerations hold for the behavioral differentiation of young animals which grow up separately from the adults. In *Procambarus alleni* "avoidance reactions" are the first to appear of the types of behavior which are important for the later formation of dominance orders; then "threat position" and finally "strike" and "fight" reactions are added.[14]

In these last examples, the young animals already resemble adults morphologically, but the differentiation of behavior, or more specifically of the endogenous causes of behavior, still lags behind. On the other hand, the development of the morphological and ethological protective devices of *Ocypode gaudichaudii* proceeds in parallel. The young animals are colored an inconspicuous brownish yellow and they hide by pressing themselves against the ground when in danger; in contrast, the adults are colored bright orange and when threatened they run away with lightning speed and try to reach a burrow.[26] In *Orchestia gammarellus,* the differentiation of behavior and of external morphology derives from a common dominant center. The implantation of the male androgenic glands into an immature female masculinizes the gonads and secondary sexual characters as well as the mating behavior (Chapter 13, Vol. I).[21]

One must distinguish maturation due to seasonal or other cycles from the differentiation processes connected with juvenile development. Reproductive behavior, for instance, may be correlated with the maturation of gonads and other endogenous processes. Thus at the beginning of the reproductive period, the beckoning and mating behavior of male *Uca* is considerably less well developed than in the middle of the season.[25]

2. *Learning.* "Many animals inherit predispositions to learn special things, and these dispositions to learn therefore belong to the innate equipment" (Tinbergen[97]). Further, this equipment determines the portions of the behavior which can be shaped by experience and the extent to which animals can learn things.[97] The innate behavior pattern forms a skeleton of animal behavior. This skeleton is completed by learning. The RM of the prey-catching behavior of the common toad becomes more selective by learning. While the young toad unselectively catches every small moving object, the adult has already learned to avoid stinging or unpalatable prey.[105] In principle, the same is true for crustaceans, e.g. *Panulirus* develops individual feeding habits as pointed out above (page 467).

The following categories[96] of learning may be distinguished for Crustacea: 1) habituation, 2) conditioning (classical conditioned reflex), and 3) motor learning. Subdivisions 2) and 3) together form trial-and-error learning; they may also be summed up by the term "association learning."[96]

"Habituation is a relatively persistent waning of a response as a result of repeated stimulation which is not followed by any kind of reinforcement."[96] In *Astacus,* habituation to stroking its back is related to the function of the inhibitory axon to the opener muscle of the claw (page 497). *Pagurus* grows accustomed to the initially frightening stimulus of being prodded with a stick (Fig. 17, curve 1). In becoming used to captivity, the susceptibility of a shrimp like *Palaemon* toward periodically recurring disturbances becomes progressively less. Such habituation involves the total situation since any changes in the environment can nullify it immediately.[35]

Adaptations to conditions of captivity often exceed the "waning" of a response. *Alpheus dentipes* gradually not only ceases the violent retraction into its tube as a result of a disturbance, but actually turns toward the hand feeding it and accepts proffered food.[102] Similar training processes have been observed in *Palaemon*[35] and *Palaemonetes* (Schöne, 1956, unpublished). Habituation and associative learning here merge into one another.

In conditioned learning the formation of associations takes place when a reward is offered simultaneously with or in immediate temporal proximity to the stimuli to be associated. If *Carcinus* and *Eriocheir* are repeatedly fed pieces of beef soaked in coumarin, the coumarin alone elicits typical food searching behavior even though it was originally foreign to the reward.[62] Hermit crabs continue for days to

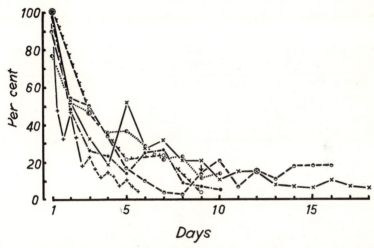

FIG. 17. Learning curves: 1, Habituation shown by the number of stimuli applied until a fright reaction disappears, in per cent of the initial average of 10.9 (data from Fink[38]). 2, Conditioned learning demonstrated by the number of hermit crabs (in per cent) which do not enter the dark feed box; from the point marked ↓ on, there was no food in this box (data from Spaulding[88]). 3, Conditioned learning shown by the time required to reach food through a gate; in per cent of the initial trial time of 15 min (data from Yerkes[113]). 4, Trial-and-error learning demonstrated by running time through a maze (Fig. 18D) in per cent of the period initially required, which was 62.8 min (data from van der Heyde[100]). 5, Learning through punishment, shown by the time during which a hermit crab had to be stimulated from behind through a hole in the shell before it crawled out, in per cent of the initial time of 9.8 min (data from ten Cate-Kazejewa[95]). 6, Trial and error learning demonstrated by per cent errors in runs through a maze (Fig. 18C) (data from Schwartz and Safir[85]).

KEY: × 30 *Pagurus longicarpus* mean; ◑ 27–30 *Pagurus longicarpus* mean; ● 2 *Carcinus maenas* mean; + 7 *Carcinus maenas* mean; ○ 2 *Dardanus arrosor* mean; ◐ 7 *Uca pugilator* mean.

run into a dark box in which they have previously been given food, although they usually prefer bright surroundings (Fig. 17, curve 2; also Fig. 20). In these examples, a new characteristic was added to the sign stimuli in the releasing mechanism, which can itself initiate the consummatory act. Another example of associative learning may be cited in the gill-wetting behavior of *Ocypode quadrata* which can be conditioned. This beach crab from time to time runs into the surf, sits down and allows a wave to wash over it, thus rewetting the gills. A specimen learned to climb on a piece of wood lying on the sand and to dip itself into a little cup of water. After a few days of learning, typical gill-wetting behavior occurred on a piece of wood even without the little cup.[24]

New characteristics may be added not only to a reward-stimulus complex but also to a punishment-stimulus complex, where the unconditioned stimulus evokes a turning away or flight. In isopods, a

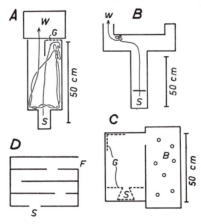

Fig. 18. Mazes used in experiments with: A, *Orconectes limosus*[114]; B, *Pacifastacus trowbridgii*[41]; C, *Uca pugilator*[85]; D, *Carcinus maenas*.[48] S, start; W, water; F, food; B, burrows; G, glass partitions. Running curves are shown in A and B. See text for details.

punitive electrical stimulus which causes fright and turning away could be associated with the tactile stimulus "corrugated substratum," so that after successful training, the tactile stimulus alone elicited the avoidance behavior.[12]

In the acquisition of new sign stimuli, new movement sequences may appear as motor learning, which is the "establishment of an association between a 'voluntary' motor act . . . and the normal reward."[96] To begin with, linkages between a reward (or a newly learned reward characteristic) and a new sequence of movements may be established by training. In simple mazes (Fig. 18), movement sequences leading to the reward are linked with the releasing mechanism for feeding (*Carcinus maenas*[100,113] and *Pagurus longicarpus*[88]), for seeking water (*Pacifastacus trowbridgii*[41] and *Orconectes limosus*[114]), or for seeking shelter (*Uca pugilator*[85]).

Second, in training to reject errors in behavior (e.g. in a maze) withdrawal movements may be associated with a punishment. In a T-maze experiment with *Porcellio scaber* and *Asellus aquaticus* training was established with punitive stimuli inflicted on specimens when they took the wrong direction. After training, isopods also exhibit fright and withdrawal movements as soon as they turn in the wrong direction.[12] Thus the withdrawal behavior originally inherent only in the punitive stimulus had been associatively linked with certain proprioceptive stimuli. In many other maze experiments, training may proceed in a similar way. Thus in *Pacifastacus trowbridgii*[41] and *Orconectes limosus*[114] which have mastered a maze, even turning in the

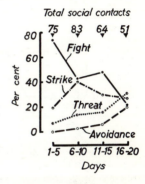

Fig. 19. Percentage of social contacts spent in fight, strike, threat, and avoidance activities of a group of four *Cambarellus shufeldtii* from the first to the twentieth day of communal life. The total social contact figures at the top refer to the respective periods of days over which they are placed (data from Lowe[61]).

wrong direction caused withdrawal. In such a case, the pattern of stimulation encountered during an unsuccessful venture into a blind alley may be considered the punishment. In complex mazes (Fig. 18D), the first stimulus patterns and motor complexes to be associated are those lying nearest the reward, and the maze is mastered progressively from back to front.[100]

The formation of a rank order in a social group of crustaceans (Fig. 19) may be considered a training process (page 479). The loser in fights between individuals comes to associate the distinguishing traits of its opponent with a punishment which comprises the over-all stimulus pattern of a lost fight. From then on, these "personal" distinguishing traits suffice to elicit motor complexes of evasion and avoidance which previously belonged only to the punishment. The personal recognition involved in an established rank order is not influenced even by gross changes of form (e.g. removal of the claws) and is not cancelled even after isolation for several days (page 479).

A single experience may suffice for the formation of an association. *Homarus*[6] and *Carcinus*[100] avoid a trap in which they have been caught once.

The precision and persistence of associative learning can be tested in experiments where training is changed. For example, an *Orconectes limosus*[114] exposed to a Y-maze in which the previously open right exit was closed and the left was opened, ran to and fro in the right branch for about 15 min, mostly along the right wall (Fig. 18A). Earlier, the same individual went through the maze in 48 seconds.

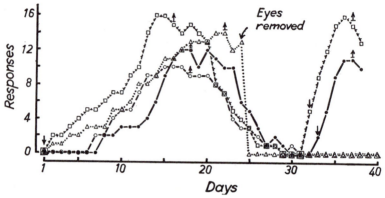

FIG. 20. Feeding training in a colored cylinder plotted as number of conditioned responses which were contacts with the empty hook presented along with the training color (red for curves 1 and 3, green for 2 and 4). From the point ↓ to ↑ there were 5 training experiments per day in which food was offered on the hook; from the next ↑ to ↓ there were no feeding training runs (data from Mikhailoff[66]).

KEY: ● *Dardanus arrosor* (red); ○ *Dardanus arrosor* (green); □ *Palaemon serratus* (red); △ *Palaemon serratus* (green).

During training, learning usually proceeds rapidly at first, then more and more slowly so that the curves are reminiscent of logarithmic functions; this generalization holds for habituation processes (Fig. 17, curve 1) as well as for the mastery of mazes and other types of training (Fig. 17, curves 2–6). The effectiveness of learning depends not only on the duration of training but also on the frequency of training programs. While the proportion of errors decreases from test to test in *Carcinus* during a day's training it is always somewhat higher in the first test of the following day (Fig. 17, curve 4). In three specimens each of *Uca*[85] and of *Cambarus*,[114] the number of errors rose from 7% to 20% in the former and 10% to 26% in the latter during 10–14 training-free days. Similarly, associations in rank order behavior must be solidified again after a long separation of the individuals concerned (page 479). In *Dardanus arrosor* and species of *Palaemon*, the decrease in the effectiveness of training ("forgetting") after training has ceased, corresponds roughly to the increase during the learning period (Fig. 20, curves 1, 2, and 3). A second course of training, however, progresses faster than the first (Fig. 20, curves 1 and 3).

The significance of orienting mechanisms in learning is demonstrated by the following experiments (Fig. 21). After removal of both eyes, the error curve rises abruptly. The error curve of animals which are blind from the start generally lies higher than that of individuals with normal vision. Crustaceans which can see are able to correct their course more readily as they run than blind ones. Thus 76% of seeing

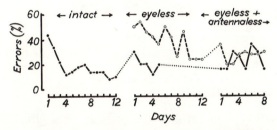

Fig. 21. Errors made by crayfish (*Pacifastacus trowbridgii*) which were 1) intact, 2) eyeless, and 3) both eyeless and antennaless (compiled from Gilhousen[41]). Symbols: Open circles, 8 specimens; filled circles, 11 specimens.

animals which had run along the "wrong" wall nonetheless reached the correct exit, but only 45% of blinded animals achieved the same goal.[41] Tactile orientation is necessary in a maze for recognizing the spot where a turn has to be made, but the turning motion itself is motor-conditioned. Five out of six animals which had mastered a maze attempted to turn off prematurely after their antennae were cut off (Fig. 18B, running trail). A rank order is formed among a group of *Procambarus alleni* which are without either antennae or eyes, but not if they lack both pairs of receptors.[14]

A complex pattern of appetitive behavior, releasing mechanisms, and learned elements is present in the behavior of the hermit crab *Clibanarius misanthropus* toward the shells of the gastropods *Trochus* and *Cerithium*. The former of these are smooth, and endowed with few distinguishing characteristics which would attract attention, while the latter are highly sculptured and therefore present many features of steric interest. In test series, examination times decrease for either type of shell upon repeated presentation of specimens in which the opening is blocked (Fig. 22). If after a test series with *Cerithium*, a *Trochus* is presented, the examination time decreases rapidly (Fig. 22, curve 1). On the other hand a *Cerithium* presented after a series of

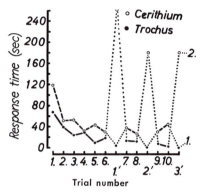

FIG. 22. Mean duration of the examination of snail shells by five *Clibanarius misanthropus*. At 1′, 2′, and 3′, animals previously presented with *Cerithium* shells (curve 1) were given *Trochus* shells; those earlier given *Trochus* (curve 2) then had *Cerithium* (data from Hertz[48]).

Trochus is examined for an unusually long time (Fig. 22, curve 2). (See also page 501.)

C. BEHAVIOR AND EVOLUTION

In the study of evolutionary relationships the comparative study of the behavioral components of Recent forms provides a means of establishing a phylogeny based on ethology. Alterations in behavior are frequently correlated with morphological changes, like the form and function of the raptorial claws of *Squilla*, or the grasping antennae of copepods. The morphological and ethological investigation of twelve species of fiddler crabs led to the conclusion that "related species had fundamental similarities of display in common, and series of species showing progressive specialization of structure in general showed similar progressions in display."[25]

Behavior patterns, therefore, may be just as significant guides for crustacean systematics as morphological characteristics. Thus all decapods (except the Penaeidea) are characterized by egg care beneath the abdomen of the female. Species of *Uca* and many related forms are characterized by beckoning movements of the claws. This behavioral similarity of forms morphologically close to *Uca* has been discovered only quite recently.[3]

There are no obvious structural reasons for some differences in the behavior of related species. In *Uca* the structural elements and movement possibilities are similar yet the display behavior can be classified in two types involving vertical and lateral waving respectively, as described above (Section II,B,3).

Closely related, morphologically very similar, species of *Uca* can often be distinguished by species-specific beckoning behavior.[25] The subspecies *U. beebei* and *U. stenodactyla* differ from each other in the mating behavior. The male of the former turns around in front of the female, while the male of the latter runs to and fro between beckoning phases of the courtship; he also pursues the female, encloses her within his large claw, and runs about with her. *Uca pugnax* males carry out one or more bows in front of a female in a frenzy of excitement, but those of *Uca rapax* do not.

Such observations suggest that "in evolution a change in behavior may precede a change in structure."[25] The beckoning pattern of various species of *Uca* is considered as phylogenetically older than the special form of the claw.[3,80] A primitive beckoning behavior carried out with the two large claws, roughly equal in size, has been discovered in many relatives of *Uca* (*Ilyoplax delsmani*, *Sesarma* sp., *Ocypode ceratophthalma*).[3,98] In *Dotilla myctiroides* and *D. blanfordi*, for example, the two chelipeds are raised laterally upward in front of the body and then swing downward, although the extending movements of the claw, which are so conspicuous in many species of *Uca* (see page 480 and Fig. 7), are barely intimated.[3,3a] The beckoning* seems to be derived from movements in which the bent claws are elevated only slightly in front of the body. Because of this, there are difficulties in tracing the fiddlers' beckoning movement back to ordinary threatening movements of brachyurans (as Hediger, following Crane,[25] attempts to do), in which the claws are fully extended and raised. Conceivably the beckoning is derived only from the preliminary gestures of the threat or of a sort of threat in which the chelipeds are not extended. Perhaps the ritual feeding of male *U. maracoani* during the preliminary phase of courtship has been developed from displacement feeding.

In the vertebrates the development of certain intention movements into social releasers is already known.[60,97] Presumably the inviting bow of the male *Uca annulipes* leading its mate to the burrow, which was interpreted above as an intention movement (page 481), also represents

---

* Beckoning with both claws and a sort of displacement feeding are also shown by courting male *Goniopsis* (Schöne, 1959, unpublished).

a social releaser, perhaps one in the process of formation. The development of such releasers and that of the corresponding inborn releasing mechanism must proceed synchronously. In this case the innate releasing mechanism of female *Uca* must always be adjusted to the eliciting behavior of the males.

The evolutionary development of such processes might be proposed as follows. Since female *Uca* are attracted by the beckoning behavior of the males,[25] those with particularly conspicuous beckoning behavior must, on the average, obtain a female earlier than others. Thus, the development both of the special claw and of the beckoning behavior are selected for. Therefore the behavior may be considered a selective factor which promotes speciation, as already stated in Darwin's theory of sexual selection.

As in other groups of animals with highly developed vision, the fiddler crabs show a phylogenetic trend toward increased conspicuousness of display like that known in spiders, fishes, reptiles, and birds. The large claws become bigger, the movements become more exaggerated and faster while the body is raised during display. This idea is supported by a comparison of the vertical waving type of display shown by the more primitive narrow-fronted species of *Uca* with the lateral waving display of the morphologically more highly developed broad-fronted forms.[28a]

A teleological interpretation is valuable in understanding the phylogenetic implications of functional relationships, however little value it may have in a causal analysis. The biological use of a function indeed has primary selective value and is, therefore, a causal factor in evolution.[97] For example, battles which lead to the damage or even destruction of the partner are inexpedient for the species; therefore the numerous social disputes of gregarious forms are often carried out as harmless ritual fights (page 477). Also a rigid rank order may develop so that dangerous collisions are largely avoided (Fig. 19). Species which do not have frequent social contacts or which are particularly well protected lack such restraint. For example, two *Pagurus longicarpus* without snail shells fight until one of them is dead.[1]

IV. *CONCLUSIONS*

Data already available demonstrate that crustaceans provide numerous cases where many ethological-physiological problems may be profitably studied. As we have seen above, these range all the way from the question of an internal clock to the mechanisms of learning.

The application to behavior of the principle of automatic regulation including feedback brings us closer to an analytical understanding of some biological phenomena. The appropriateness and apparent purposiveness of many behavior patterns can be explained by the action of a sort of control mechanism. Thus the seeming goal-seeking and goal-finding in many chains of behavior result from the functioning of a complex of searching and releasing mechanisms (appetence and releasing mechanism). If an appropriate stimulus situation (made up of sign stimuli) occurs during the searching behavior, the releasing mechanism reacts selectively by eliciting the consummatory act. Many orienting mechanisms direct a movement sequence so that a particular quantitative level in a regulated process is maintained by continuous measurement and correction of deviations from a reference value. Some behavior complexes may be considered as parts of a regulatory system of higher physiological order. For example, the quantities of metabolic fuels and raw materials are maintained in the body at certain definite values by means of patterns of feeding behavior.

For further progress in our understanding of crustacean behavior and its elements, it is particularly desirable to broaden and strengthen the application of experimental methods to the analysis of the higher functions of their central nervous system.

REFERENCES

1. Allee, W. C., and Douglis, M. B. 1945. A dominance order in the hermit crab, *Pagurus longicarpus* Say. *Ecology* 26:411–412.
2. Altevogt, R. 1956. Zur Biologie indischer Winkerkrabben. *Wiss. Film Inst. wiss. Film, Göttingen.*
3. Altevogt, R. 1957a. Untersuchungen zur Biologie und Physiologie indischer Winkerkrabben. *Z. Morphol. Ökol. Tiere* 46:1–110.
3a. Altevogt, R. 1957b. Beiträge zur Biologie und Ethologie von *Dotilla blanfordi* Alcock und *Dotilla myctiroides* (Milne-Edwards) (Crustacea Decapoda). *Z. Morphol. Ökol. Tiere* 46:369–388.
4. Alverdes, F. 1928. Lichtsinn, Gleichgewichtssinn, Tastsinn und ihre Interferenzen bei Garneelen. *Z. wiss Zoöl.* 132:135–170.
5. Andrews, E. A. 1910. Conjugation in the crayfish *Cambarus affinis. J. Exptl. Zool.* 9:236–263.
6. Appellöf, A. 1909. Untersuchungen über den Hummer. *Bergens Museums Skrifter* [N.S.] 1:2–78.
7. Baerends, G. P. 1956. Aufbau des tierischen Verhaltens. *In:* "Handbuch der Zoologie" (W. Kükenthal, ed.), Bd. 8, pp. 1–32. de Gruyter, Berlin.
8. Balss, H. 1955–56. Decapoda. Ökologie. *In:* "Bronn's Tierreich," Bd. 5, Abt. 1, Bch. 7, pp. 1285–1476. Akademische Verlagsges., Leipzig.
9. Barnes, H., Crisp, D. J., and Powell, H. T. 1951. Observations on the orientation of some species of barnacles. *J. Animal Ecol.* 20:227–241.
10. Bethe, A. 1897. Das Nervensystem von *Carcinus maenas*, I, II. *Arch. mikroscop. Anat. u. Entwicklungsmech.* 50:462–544; 590–639.

11. Bethe, A. 1930. Studien über die Plastizität des Nervensystems. Arachnoideen und Crustaceen. *Arch. ges. Physiol. Pflüger's* 224:787–820.

12. Bock, A. 1942. Über das Lernvermögen bei Asseln. *Z. vergleich. Physiol.* 29: 595–637.

13. Bovbjerg, R. V. 1953. Dominance order in the crayfish *Orconectes virilis* (Hagen). *Physiol. Zoöl.* 26:173–178.

14. Bovbjerg, R. V. 1956. Some factors affecting aggressive behavior in crayfish. *Physiol. Zoöl.* 29:127–136.

15. Brightwell, L. R. 1952. Further notes on the hermit crab, *Eupagurus bernhardus* and associated animals. *Proc. Zool. Soc. London* 123:61–64.

16. Brock, F. 1927. Das Verhalten von *Pagurus arrosor* während des Aufsuchens, Ablösens und Aufpflanzens von *Sagartia parasitica*. *Wilhelm Roux' Arch. Entwickungsmech. Organ.* 112:204–238.

17. Broekhuysen, G. J. 1937. Some notes on sex recognition in *Carcinus maenas* (L.). *Arch. néerl. zool.* 3:156–164.

18. Brown, F. A., Jr., Brown, R. A., Webb, H. M., Bennett, M. F., and Shriner, J. 1956. A persistent tidal rhythm of locomotor activity in *Uca pugnax*. *Anat. Record* 125:613.

19. Burkenroad, M. D. 1947a. Reproductive activities of decapod Crustacea. *Am. Naturalist* 81:392–398.

20. Burkenroad, M. D. 1947b. Production of sound by *Uca pugilator* Bosc with the remarks on its nocturnal and mating behavior. *Ecology* 28:458–462.

21. Charniaux-Cotton, H. 1957. Croissance, régénération et déterminisme endocrinien des caractères sexuels d'*Orchestia gammarella* (Pallas). *Ann. sci. nat. Zool. et biol. animale* 19:411–559.

22. Chidester, F. E. 1911. The mating habits of four species of the Brachyura. *Biol. Bull.* 21:235–248.

23. Clarke, G. L. 1930. Change of phototropic and geotropic signs in *Daphnia* induced by change of light intensity. *J. Exptl. Biol.* 7:109–131.

23a. Clarke, W. D. 1955. A new species of the Genus *Heteromysis* (Crustacea, Mysidacea) from the Bahama Islands, commensal with a sea-anemone. *Am. Museum Novitates No.* 1716:1–13.

24. Cowles, R. P. 1908. Habits, reactions and associations in *Ocypoda arenaria*. *Papers Tortugas Lab. Carnegie Inst. Washington* 2:1–41.

25. Crane, J. 1941a. Crabs of the Genus *Uca* from the West Coast of Central America. *Zoologica* 26:145–208.

26. Crane, J. 1941b. On the growth and ecology of brachyuran crabs of the Genus *Ocypode*. *Zoologica* 26:297–310.

27. Crane, J. 1943. Display breeding and relationships of fiddler crabs (Genus *Uca*) in the Northeastern United States. *Zoologica* 28:217–223.

28. Crane, J. 1947. Intertidal brachygnathous crabs from the West Coast of Tropical America with special reference to ecology. *Zoologica* 32:69–94.

28a. Crane, J. 1957. Basic patterns of display in fiddler crabs (Ocypodidae, Genus *Uca*). *Zoologica* 42:69–82.

28b. Crane, J. 1958. Aspects of social behavior in fiddler crabs, with special reference to *Uca maracoani* (Latreille). *Zoologica* 43:113–130.

29. Crisp, D. J., and Knight-Jones, E. W. 1953. The mechanism of aggregation in barnacle populations. *J. Animal Ecol.* 22:360–362.

29a. Crisp, D. J., and Stubbings, H. G. 1957. The orientation of barnacles to water currents. *J. Animal Ecol.* **26**:179–196.

30. Cushing, D. H. 1951. The vertical migration of planktonic Crustacea. *Biol. Revs. Cambridge Phil. Soc.* **26**:158–192.

31. Dembowska, W. S. 1926. Study on the habits of the crab *Dromia vulgaris* M.E. *Biol. Bull.* **50**:162–178.

32. Dembowski, J. B. 1925. On the "speech" of the fiddler crab *Uca pugilator. Prace Inst. Nenckiego* **3**:1–20.

33. Dembowski, J. B. 1926. Notes on the behavior of the fiddler crab. *Biol. Bull.* **50**:179–201.

34. Dietrich, W. 1931. Die lokomotorischen Reaktionen der Landasseln auf Licht und Dunkelheit. *Z. wiss. Zoöl.* **138**:187–232.

35. Doflein, F. 1910. Lebensgewohnheiten und Anpassungen bei dekapoden Krebsen. "Festschrift zum 60 Geburtstag Richard Hertwigs," Vol. 3, pp. 215–292. Fischer, Jena.

36. Fenizia, G. 1935. La *Dromia vulgaris* (M. Edw.) e le sue abitudini. *Archivio zoologiae* **21**:509–539.

37. Fenizia, G. 1937. Sull'istinto di mascheramento dell' *Ethusa mascarone* Herbst. *Bull. inst. océanog. No.* **732**:1–15.

38. Fink, H. K. 1940. Deconditioning of the "fright reflex" in the hermit crab, *Pagurus longicarpus. J. Comp. Psychol.* **32**:33–39.

39. Gibson-Hill, C. A. 1947. Field note on the terrestrial crabs. *Bull. Raffles Museum* **18**:43–52.

40. Giesbrecht, W. 1910. Stomatopoden. *Fauna u. Flora Golfes Neapel, Monogr.* **33**:1–239.

41. Gilhousen, H. C. 1927. The use of vision and of the antennae in the learning of crayfish. *Univ. Calif. (Berkeley) Publs. Physiol.* **7**:73–89.

42. Goodhard, C. B. 1939. Notes on the bionomics of the tube-building amphipod, *Leptocheirus pilosus* Zaddach. *J. Marine Biol. Assoc. United Kingdom* **23**:311–324.

43. Gordon, H. R. S. 1955. Displacement activities in fiddler crabs. *Nature* **176**:356–357.

44. Harms, J. W. 1932. Die Realisation von Genen und die consecutive Adaption. II. *Birgus latro* L. als Landkrebs und seine Beziehungen zu den Coenobiten. *Z. wiss. Zoöl.* **140**:167–290.

45. Harms, J. W. 1937. Lebensablauf und Stammesgeschichte des *Birgus latro* L. von der Weihnachtsinsel. *Jena. Z. Naturw.* **71**:1–34.

46. Havinga, B. 1929. Krebse und Weichtiere. *In:* "Handbuch der Seefischerei Nordeuropas" (H. Lubberts and E. Ehrenbaum, eds.), pp. 1–75. Schweizerbart, Stuttgart.

47. Heinze, K. 1932. Fortpflanzung und Brutpflege bei *Gammarus pulex* L. und *Carcinogammarus roeselii* Gerv. *Zool. Jahrb. Abt. Allgem. Zool. Physiol. Tiere* **51**:397–440.

48. Hertz, M. 1932. Verhalten des Einsiedlerkrebses *Clibanarius misanthropicus* gegenüber verschiedenen Gehäuseformen. *Z. vergleich. Physiol.* **18**:597–621.

49. Hiatt, R. W. 1948. The biology of the lined shore crab *Pachygrapsus crassipes* Randall. *Pacific Sci.* **2**:135–213.

50. Höglund, H. 1943. On the biology and larval development of *Leander squilla* (L.) forma typica de Man. *Svenska Hydrograf.-Biol. Komm. Skrifter* **2**:3–44.

51. Johnson, I. S. 1952. The demonstration of the "host-factor" in commensal crabs. *Trans. Kansas Acad. Sci.* 55:458–464.

52. Jordan, H. 1910. Die Leistungen des Gehirnganglions bei den krebsartigen Tieren. *Arch. ges. Physiol. Pflüger's* 131:317–386.

53. Kinne, O. 1954a. *Gammarus duebeni.* VIII. Die Bedeutung der Kopulation für Eiablage und Häutungsfrequenz. *Biol. Zentr.* 73:190–202.

54. Kinne, O. 1954b. Zur Biologie und Physiologie von *Gammarus duebeni* Lillj. I. *Z. wiss. Zoöl.* 157:427–491.

55. Kinne, O. 1955. *Neomysis vulgaris* Thompson, eine autökologisch biologische Studie. *Biol. Zentr.* 74:160–202.

56. Kühl, H. 1933. Die Fortbewegung der Schwimmkrabben mit Bezug auf die Plastizität des Nervensystems. *Z. vergleich. Physiol.* 19:489–521.

57. Langenbuch, R. 1928. Über die Statocysten einiger Crustaceen. *Zool. Jahrb. Abt. Allgem. Zool. Physiol. Tiere* 44:6–10.

58. Lebour, M. V. 1926. 1. The rearing of crabs in captivity, with a description of the larval stages of *Inachus dorsettensis, Macropodia longirostris* and *Maia squinado. J. Marine Biol. Assoc. United Kingdom* 14:795–820.

59. Lindberg, R. G. 1955. Growth, population dynamics and field behavior in the spiny lobster, *Panulirus interruptus* (Randall). *Univ. Calif. (Berkeley) Publs. Zoöl.* 59:157–248.

60. Lorenz, K. 1953. Die Entwicklung der vergleichenden Verhaltensforschung in den letzten 12 Jahren. *Zool. Anz. Suppl.* 17:37–58.

61. Lowe, M. E. 1956. Dominance-subordinance relationships in *Cambarellus shufeldtii. Tulane Studies Zool.* 4:139–170.

62. Luther, W. 1930. Versuche über die Chemorezeptoren der Brachyuren. *Z. vergleich. Physiol.* 12:177–205.

62a. Luther, W. 1958. Symbiose von Fischen (Gobiidae) mit einem Krebs (*Alpheus djiboutensis*) im Roten Meer. *Z. Tierpsychol.* 15:175–177.

63. MacGinitie, G. E. 1930. The natural history of the mud shrimp *Upogebia pugettensis* (Dana). *Ann. Mag. Nat. Hist.* 10(6):36–44.

64. MacGinitie, G. E. 1937. Notes on the natural history of several marine Crustacea. *Am. Midland Naturalist* 18:1031–1036.

65. Marshall, S. M., and Orr, A. P. 1954. Hatching in *Calanus finmarchicus* and some other copepods. *J. Marine Biol. Assoc. United Kingdom* 33:393–401.

66. Mikhailoff, S. 1923. Expériences réflexologiques. *Bull. inst. océanog.* No. 422: 1–16.

67. Minkiewicz, R. 1907. Analyse expérimentale de l'instinct de déguisement chez les Brachyures Oxyrhynches. *Arch. zool. exptl. et gén.* 7:37–67.

68. Mittelstaedt, H. 1954. Regelung in der Biologie. *Regelungstech.* 2:177–182.

69. Mittelstaedt, H., and von Holst, E. 1953. Reafferenzprinzip und Optomotorik. *Zool. Anz.* 151:253–259.

70. Nouvel, H. 1937. Observation de l'accouplement chez une espèce de mysid *Praunus flexuosus. Compt. rend.* 205:1184–1186.

71. Nouvel, H., and Nouvel, L. 1937. Recherches sur l'accouplement et la ponte chez les Crustacés Décapodes Natantia. *Bull. soc. zool. France* 62:208–221.

72. Ortmann, W. 1906. The crayfishes of the State of Pennsylvania. *Ann. Carnegie Museum* 2:387–406.

73. Palombi, A. 1939. Note biologiche sui Peneidi. *Boll. zool. agrar. e bachicolt. Univ. studi Milano* 10:223–227.

74. Pardi, L. 1954. Über die Orientierung von *Tylos latreillii* Aud. et Sav. (Isopoda terrestria). *Z. Tierpsychol.* 11:175–181.

75. Pardi, L., and Grassi, M. 1955. Experimental modification of direction-finding in *Talitrus saltator* (Montagu) and *Talorchestia deshaysei* (Aud.) (Crustacea-Amphipoda). *Experientia* 11:202–203.

76. Pardi, L., and Papi, F. 1953. Ricerche sull'orientamento di *Talitrus saltator* (Montagu) (Crustacea-Amphipoda). I, II. *Z. vergleich. Physiol.* 35:459–489; 490–518.

77. Pearse, A. S. 1912. The habits of fiddler crabs. *Philippine J. Sci.* 7, Sect. D: 113–132.

78. Peters, N., and Panning, A. 1933. Die chinesische Wollhandkrabbe (*Eriocheir sinensis* H. Milne-Edwards) in Deutschland. *Zool. Anz.* 104, Erganz. Bd.: 1–180.

79. Pieplow, U. 1938. Fischereiwissenschaftliche Monographie von *Cambarus affinis* Say. *Z. Fischerei Hilfswiss.* 36:350–437.

79a. Randall, J. E. 1958. A review of the labrid fish Genus *Labroides*, with descriptions of two new species and notes on ecology. *Pacific Sci.* 12:327–347.

80. Schäfer, W. 1954. Form und Funktion der Brachyurenschere. *Abhandl. senckenberg. naturforsch. Ges.* 489:1–66.

81. Schellenberg, A. 1928. Crustacea. *In:* "Tierwelt Deutschlands" (F. Dahl, ed.), pp. 1–146. Fischer, Jena.

82. Schöne, H. 1952. Zur optischen Lageorientierung ("Lichtrückenorientierung") von dekapoden Krebsen. *Naturwissenschaften* 39:552–553.

83. Schöne, H. 1954. Statocystenfunktion und statische Lageorientierung bei dekapoden Krebsen. *Z. vergleich. Physiol.* 36:241–260.

84. Schöne, H. 1957. Kurssteuerung mittels der Statocysten (Messungen an Krebsen). *Z. vergleich. Physiol.* 39:235–240.

84a. Schöne, H. 1959. Die Lageorientierung mit Statolithenorganen und Augen. *Ergeb. Biol.* 21:161–209.

85. Schwartz, B., and Safir, S. R. 1915. Habit formation in the fiddler crab. *J. Animal Behavior* 5:226–239.

86. Segaar, J. 1929. Über die Funktion der nervösen Zentren bei Crustaceen. *Z. vergleich. Physiol.* 10:120–226.

87. Smallwood, M. E. 1903. The beach flea *Talorchestia longicornis*. *Cold Spring Harbor Monogr.* 1:3–27.

88. Spaulding, E. G. 1904. An establishment of association in the hermit crab, *Eupagurus longicarpus*. *J. Comp. Neurol.* 14:49–61.

89. Stephensen, K. 1940. Amphipoda. *In:* "Die Tierwelt der Nord- und Ostsee" (G. Grimpe and E. Wagler, eds.), pp. 1–183. Akademische Verlagsges., Leipzig.

90. Sutcliffe, W. H., Jr. 1951. Breeding and migration of the Bermuda spiny lobster, *Panulirus argus*. *Proc. Gulf and Caribbean Fisheries Inst.* 4:64–69.

91. Tack, P. I. 1941. The life history of the crayfish *Cambarus immunis* Hagen. *Am. Midland Naturalist* 25:420–444.

92. Templeman, W. 1934. Mating in the American lobster. *Contribs. Can. Biol. and Fisheries* [N.S.] 8:423–458.

93. Templeman, W. 1938. Egg-laying and hatching postures and habits of the American lobster (*Homarus americanus*). *J. Biol. Board, Canada* 3:339–342.

94. ten Cate, J. 1930. Zur Physiologie des ZNS der Einsiedlerkrebse. *Arch. néerl. physiol.* 15:242–252.

95. ten Cate-Kazejewa, B. 1934. Quelques observations sur *Pagurus arrosor*. *Arch. néerl. physiol.*, *Sér. 3c* **19**:502–508.
96. Thorpe, W. H. 1956. "Learning and Instinct in Animals," 493 pp. Methuen, London.
97. Tinbergen, N. 1951. "The Study of Instinct," 228 pp. Oxford Univ. Press, London and New York.
98. Tweedie, M. W. F. 1950. Notes on grapsoid crabs from the Raffles Museum. *Bull. Raffles Museum* **23**:310–324.
99. Ubrig, H. 1952. Der Einfluss von Sauerstoff und Kohlendioxyd auf die taktischen Bewegungen einiger Wassertiere. *Z. vergleich. Physiol.* **34**:479–507.
100. van der Heyde, A. 1920. Über die Lernfähigkeit der Strandkrabbe *Carcinus maenas*. *Biol. Zentr.* **40**:142–155.
100a. Verrill, A. E. 1908. Decapod Crustacea of Bermuda. I. Brachyura and Anomura. *Trans. Conn. Acad. Arts Sci.* **23**:299–424.
101. Verwey, J. 1930. Einiges über die Biologie Ostindischer Mangrovekrabben. *Treubia* **12**:167–261.
102. Volz, P. 1938. Studien über das Knallen der Alpheiden, nach Untersuchungen an *Alpheus dentipes* Guérin und *Synalpheus laevimanus* (Heller). *Z. Morphol. Ökol. Tiere* **34**:272–316.
103. von Buddenbrock, W. 1952. Sinnesphysiologie. *In:* "Vergleichende Physiologie," Bd. 1, 504 pp. Birkhäuser, Basel.
104. von Buddenbrock, W. 1953. Nervenphysiologie. *In:* "Vergleichende Physiologie," Bd. 2, 396 pp. Birkhäuser, Basel.
105. von Eibl-Eibesfeldt, I., and Kramer, S. 1958. Ethology, the comparative study of animal behavior. *Quart. Rev. Biol.* **33**:181–211.
106. von Holst, E. 1939. Die relative Koordination als Phänomen und als Methode zentralnervöser Funktionsanalyse. *Ergeb. Physiol. biol. Chem. u. exptl. Pharmakol.* **42**:228–306.
107. von Holst, E. 1954. Relations between the central nervous system and the peripheral organs. *J. Animal Behavior* **2**:89–94.
108. von Holst, E., and Mittelstaedt, H. 1950. Das Reafferenzprinzip. *Naturwissenschaften* **37**:464–476.
109. Williamson, D. I. 1954. On the mating and breeding of some semiterrestrial amphipods. *Dove Marine Lab. Repts. Ser.* **3**(12):49–65.
110. Wilson, D. P. 1949. Notes from the Plymouth Aquarium. *J. Marine Biol. Assoc. United Kingdom* **29**:345–351.
111. Wolf, E. 1905. Die Fortpflanzungsverhältnisse unserer einheimischen Copepoden. *Zool. Jahrb. Abt. Syst.* **22**:101–280.
112. Wolter, H. 1936. Beitrag zum Lichtsinn von *Carcinus maenas. Zool. Jahrb. Abt. Allgem. Zool. Physiol. Tiere* **58**:581–610.
113. Yerkes, R. 1902. Habit-formation in the green crab, *Carcinus granulatus. Biol. Bull.* **3**:241–244.
114. Yerkes, R. M., and Huggins, G. E. 1903. Habit formation in the crayfish *Cambarus affinis. Harvard Psychol. Studies* **1**:565–577.
115. Zimmer, C. 1927. Isopoda. *In:* "Handbuch der Zoologie" (W. Kükenthal, ed.), Vol. III, pp. 697–766. de Gruyter, Berlin.
116. Zimmer, C., and Gruner, H. E. 1956. Euphausiacea. *In:* "Bronn's Tierreich," Bd. 5, Abt. 1, Bch. 6, pp. 1–281. Akademische Verlagsges., Leipzig.

CHAPTER 14

TALBOT H. WATERMAN

COMPARATIVE PHYSIOLOGY

I. *INTRODUCTION*

Since science is more than a random accumulation of facts, its advancement depends both on empirical data and on their systematization. Hence progress can be obtained either by assimilating fresh facts into old systems of thought or by devising original ways to arrange data so that, in turn, new generalizations and hypotheses may be produced. In each preceding chapter these principles have been used to a considerable extent but only within the restricted range appropriate to a primary emphasis on one or a few functions.

Here an attempt is made to summarize and assess our present knowledge of crustacean physiology by assembling the components into a more unified whole. To do so the nature of comparative physiology is first considered in general terms and then related more specifically to the data for Crustacea. This approach is intended to provide a review of our two volumes which is more than a reiteration of chapter summaries and is at the same time a challenge for biologists and biochemists who are attracted to comparative physiology without being clear about its methodology or goal. This kind of physiology has already been given a heuristic definition in the Preface to Volume I, but for present purposes a more analytical approach is appropriate.

Comparative physiology, like the rest of physiology, obtains its data by measuring the effects of changes in an independent variable, controlled by the experimenter, on dependent functional parameters of organelles, organs, individual organisms, or other biological units. However, comparative physiology is distinguished by the biological nature of the independent variables which it uses. Physical and chemical parameters, like temperature or pH, are the independent variables of general physiology, but in the comparative field biological parameters usually controlled or selected by the physiologist are required for this coordinate. Note that biological units or parameters may be easily distinguished from physical or chemical ones when the level of organization is cellular or higher. However, at lower levels there is a transition range of complexity, probably near the biochemical level of protein or nucleoprotein molecules, below which the term biological has relatively little significance. Simpler units than this are not different from those types which occur ordinarily in nature quite independently of living things.

Sometimes both the independent and dependent variables are continuous quantitative parameters, as when the strength of a crayfish muscle's response to a standard motor volley is measured as a function of simultaneous stimulation of its inhibitory nerve supply (Chapter 6, Vol. II). More frequently the independent variable is a series of discrete complex entities, like species, whose quantitative relationship is not known. Species, classes, or phyla are most often compared in this way, but profitable comparisons may also be made at many other levels. Thus mitochondrial energy transfers may be compared with those in microsomes, liver cell phosphorylation with muscle cell phosphorylation, endocrine regulation with neural regulation, and so on through different developmental stages, individuals, clones, populations, and faunas. Rarely, the independent variable may be continuous and the dependent parameter discrete; this is so where increasing strengths of the same sensory input produce a succession of different kinds of behavioral response like a crab's series of reactions to an intruder: fleeing, fighting, and autotomizing. Finally, both parameters being correlated may be complex discontinuous biological units, as when retinal image formation in a compound eye and in a camera eye are being compared (Chapter 1, Vol. II).

In addition to the difference between the kinds of variables correlated in the general and comparative aspects of physiology, a parallel distinction appears to be valid for the types of causal mechanism,* or explanation,† hypothesized. In the general field physical and chemical causes are used to explain the relationships observed, whereas in com-

---

* Causal relations are usually defined in terms of invariant sequence or necessary connection.[142]

† Causal explanations are here considered to be the only kind satisfactory to the physiologist. Teleological and mnemic explanations[24] appear to be either inductive generalizations or to be nonscientific, as discussed below (Section IV,C).

parative physiology, biological causes, like adaptation or evolution, are employed.

Such considerations show that comparative and general physiology do not differ basically in the functions or organisms studied. Nor does there seem to be any fundamental distinction in their relative emphasis on the differences and similarities which appear in the data. Instead they are distinguishable by the particular attention given to the biological, as contrasted with the physical and chemical, factors affecting an organism's activities. In terms of cartesian coordinates both ordinate and abscissa of comparative physiological functions are biological dimensions, while in general physiology this is true only of the ordinate. Such a difference in emphasis does not indicate incompatibility between the two fields; the physical and chemical explanations of the general physiologist are part of the comparative physiologist's stock in trade, too. However, his additional requirement for biological ways of systematizing and explaining data does introduce new methodological problems for comparative physiology. These are discussed in the next section.

In brief, comparative physiology may be defined as that kind of physiology in which dependent biological variables are systematized in relation to independent biological variables and in which the causal explanations proposed for these relations rest on biological hypotheses. Parallel considerations appear valid for comparative biochemistry and comparative biophysics as branches of biology.

II. *THE COMPARATIVE PROCESS*

The basic methodological problems of comparative physiology are not different in kind from those of obtaining useful knowledge in general.[142] But even those biological variables which appear simple are often parts of highly integrated, self-regulating, steady state systems. Furthermore the dependence of comparative physiology on the correlation of two or more biological parameters increases the chances that at least one dimension under study consists of exceedingly complex units which make precise treatment still more difficult.

Suppose for example, that one wishes to compare the rate of oxygen uptake by a mitochondrion from a crab's claw muscle and a mitochondrion from the same animal's hepatopancreas. Highly precise manometric or spectrophotometric techniques would readily provide quantitative data on the physiological activity itself, which in this instance seems to be a relatively simple, unambiguously definable parameter even though it is only one step of a highly complex process. Yet the independent variable in this comparison, the subcellular particles of two types of cell, is operationally quite different in two important respects.

First, the biological unit concerned is an elaborate complex of many enzyme systems presumably arranged in precise molecular patterns on a characteristic framework. Second, such a unit is not readily amenable to rigorous definition, partly because many of its essential properties may still be unknown. Under such conditions the possibility of identifying the same element and distinguishing it from other rather similar subcellular units may be far from easy or unequivocal. Similar fundamental difficulties appear when any other complex biological entities, like regulatory mechanisms, behavioral patterns, or species of animal are components of functional comparisons. Yet in general the self-identity and recognizability of a thing are essential for its incorporation into any systematic arrangement or logical analysis of data.[142]

Although the philosophical ramifications of this state of affairs are beyond the scope of the present chapter, some practical solution of the dilemma must be sought if, in fact, the methods and goals of comparative physiology are to be demonstrated herein. Probably the initial step in finding such a way out is to examine and evaluate the methods already used by comparative biologists who are aware of these difficulties and who have been, at least in part, successful in minimizing or avoiding them. Such progress has so far been mainly in comparative morphology but is not entirely restricted to that field. There have been a few promising frontal attacks on the problem, but more generally the solution has been sought indirectly by careful choice of the complex units to be compared and by the use of deliberately tempered estimates of the range over which particular comparisons may be judiciously made.

The most satisfactory solutions to the problems under discussion have come from cases where continuous, quantitatively definable biological variables have been compared. The fact that the variables are continuous and measurable indicates that the worst difficulties have either been overcome or were here unimportant in the first place. Perhaps the best example is the correlation of metabolic rate with size, which has been extensively studied in crustaceans as well as other animals of many kinds (Chapter 2, Vol. I). Formally similar techniques have been extended to multidimensional analysis in morphology.[97] Statistical methods of correlation which permit quantitative multifactorial study of relative growth (Chapter 16, Vol. I), of evolutionary integration,[143] and of taxonomic affinity[33, 177, 183, 184] provide well-developed cases in point. Thus the application of biometric techniques to dimensional analysis of eight genera of terrestrial isopods permits them to be analyzed into one closely similar cluster of five, a single neighboring genus, and three more remote forms grouped together.[132] The further development and application of such quantitative multivariate analysis to appropriate comparative physiological problems should be rewarding, particularly where the parameters in the statistical model may be identified with particular biological variables.

When continuous quantitative biological parameters are not available, an indirect approach to the problem of self-identity and recognizability is required. Probably the most instructive effort in this direction has been made by Remane,[154] who has carefully analyzed the methodology of morphological comparisons and their use in constructing phylogenies. In so doing, criteria for the effective comparison of complex qualitative biological variables have been worked out in detail. While quantitative methods like those described above may eventually be extended to deal more generally with such matters, Remane's approach would appear to be particularly useful for present purposes because it is an explicit statement and systematization of processes commonly carried out intuitively by evolutionists and taxonomists. It also clearly distinguishes between descriptive and explanatory comparisons.

Unfortunately, the real issues here have often been obscured by the distraction of attention into arguments or ambiguities arising from terminology. Even though such semantic matters are secondary to the main intention of this review, some resolution of the issues involved is required. The central point is the meaning of the term "homology."*

"Homologue" was first used by Richard Owen in 1843 to mean "the same organ in different animals under every variety of form and function." This definition seems to have been purely descriptive and marked an important advance in the history of comparative anatomy. In later publications Owen referred to his first definition as "special homology" and recognized two additional types of similarity, "serial homology" relating to segmentally repeated structural elements like the pleopods of a lobster and "general homology" relating to similarities of an animal's structure to an archetypal body plan like those hypothesized by natural philosophers and typologists.†[86]

---

* Historical aspects of this subject have been reviewed in detail elsewhere (e.g. Naef,[140] Remane,[154] Simpson[172]).

† Comparative physiology has been given a typological definition in which it is described as the study of physiotypes,[30] which are the functional equivalent of morphotypes or structural archetypes.[208]

Strongly expressed opinions of evolutionists that serial homology is of secondary interest and that general homology (based on typological morphology[144, 208, 209]) may be a metaphysical rather than a scientific concept have tended to obscure the significant content of Owen's special homology as well. This is in large part also due to Darwin's use of homology as an explanatory term for which descent from a common ancestor is assumed to be a major cause of similarities between organisms. On this basis homologs are organs or parts which are similar because the animals bearing them have evolved from the same ancestor. Many evolutionists, including "neo-Darwinians" and "new-systematists"[172] as well as some other biologists,[5] use the word homology predominantly in this phylogenetic explanatory sense.

Nevertheless two factors other than predominant usage by this group of biologists should be considered. First, a number of rather specific but different definitions of homology are in respectable use in various other fields. Thus geneticists recognize homologous chromosomes as those which pair at metaphase, or which have been replicated in autopolyploids, and homologous loci as corresponding sites in homologous chromosomes. Some biologists have defined homologous structures as those with the same genetic basis.[60] In comparative serology the similarity of an antibody to the antigen which induces it is described as homologous.[46, 70] Embryologists commonly refer to structures which differentiate from the same anlage as homologs.[100, 166, 203] In organic chemistry hydrocarbons in homologous series have basically similar structures but differ by one carbon atom and two hydrogen atoms from their nearest neighbors. All these usages of the word (general, phylogenetic, genetic, serological, embryological, and chemical) have one important thing in common: the units homologized have basic similarity of a kind judged significant for the particular field in question.

Second, a number of scientists, in addition to Remane, recognize the primary need in all areas of biology to establish adequate descriptive relations before attempts are made at explanations of such relations.[205] For example, taxonomic affinity must first be established on a descriptive basis of over-all similarities and differences before hypothesizing the phylogenetic relations* ultimately desired in the classification.[33, 131, 135] Similarly, this prior need for organized description of

---

* Although taxonomic characters are usually thought of as diagnostic features whose significance lies in their convenience or phylogenetic implications, Manton has been demonstrating that, for a variety of arthropods at least, many of them are adaptively important.[129]

basic similarities has been explicitly cited for genetic,[119, 198] subcellular,[80] paleontological,[143, 197] and ethological[5, 62, 134, 186] comparisons.*

These various considerations suggest that for purposes of comparative physiology discrimination between descriptive and explanatory comparisons is crucial and also that the first steps toward explanation should consist of establishing basic descriptive similarities and differences. As a guide to this initial procedure, Remane's criteria for morphological comparisons will be used. To avoid semantic confusion, basic similarities are labeled below as homologies only when this word is coupled with appropriate limiting adjectives like descriptive, phylogenetic, and so on.

Descriptive homology (this is the classic pre-Darwinian special homology of Owen) can be recognized, according to Remane,[154] by the degree to which three main criteria may be satisfied. 1) Components being compared show serial similarity of position within the complex structure or species in which they occur. This means that their number and relative linkages are the same. The certainty with which this criterion can be applied decreases if new components or linkages appear or drop out or if linkages change from form to form. 2) Individual components being compared possess special qualities which allow identification even when position and linkages differ considerably. The feather of a bird or chromatophore of a cephalopod may be cited as examples. Here again certainty in applying this criterion will vary with the degree of idiosyncrasy of the component concerned. 3) Large differences in serial position or special qualities between components being compared can be linked together by a continuous series of intermediate stages which may be either purely morphological or ontogenetic within the array of forms under study.

To supplement these main criteria for establishing basic similarities, three auxiliary ones may also be of help.[154] 1) Occurrence of simple structures in a series of otherwise closely related forms. 2) Parallel distribution of other similar characters with the one in question. 3) Lack of scattered occurrence of the component under study in otherwise unrelated forms. Obviously the degree of probability with which basic similarity can be claimed will vary greatly with the completeness of the data and the divergence between the forms being compared.

Although the criteria above have been derived for comparative morphology, they are quite general in nature and should be applicable to

---

* Oliver[142] points out that, in general, causal relations do not become important until a fairly detailed continuous factual "topography" has been mapped out.

physiological comparisons with little change. No evidence exists that the genetics, development, ecology, and evolution of physiological and biochemical characters differ fundamentally from those of morphological ones. Therefore a methodology for comparative physiology may be derived from the above discussion. Attention will be directed first to the initial descriptive analysis. To begin with, the position and relation of the functional element to be compared must be known in detail. Then any of its own peculiar characteristics need to be recognized. Finally an extensive enough series of species (or other complex biological units) must be investigated to demonstrate intermediate stages or discontinuities in the states of the component in question. Such considerations prove the necessity of extensive and coherent information for comparative physiology, a requirement that should restrain the too exuberant use of scattered and isolated data.

Clearly this kind of descriptive comparison of functional systems may be made on many different levels of biological organization. These are reviewed in Section III. The possibilities of explanatory comparisons in comparative physiology are considered in Section IV which deals with causal hypotheses.

III. *DESCRIPTIVE COMPARISONS*

As indicated above, the lower limit for the simplest kind of biological units which may be fruitfully compared in comparative physiology is not a sharply defined boundary. If the transition zone is chosen at the level of a single protein or nucleoprotein molecule, a large and important field, perhaps more properly considered organic chemistry, would be included in biology. To avoid this, the range for the lower limit of biological units could be assumed to lie somewhat higher, at the level of subcellular components like minute masses of protoplasm or organelles such as ribosomes or nematocysts. In tentatively choosing this lower boundary for comparative physiology, note that such a limitation restricts only the experimentally independent variable; the dependent variables, as mentioned above, may be ions, many kinds of molecules, a wide variety of physical parameters or complex biological units or variables.

A. WITHIN INDIVIDUALS

1. *Subcellular.* At this level the functional specialization of various cell components is relevant. Motility of cilia, localization of Krebs cycle and electron transfer enzymes in mitochondria, electrical polar-

ization and other properties of cell membranes, DNA synthesis in chromosomes, shortening of banded fibrillar protein complexes in striated muscle, and operation of mitotic spindles are pertinent examples. However such data are more amenable to a general rather than a comparative physiological analysis. In any case, relatively little is known on this level for crustaceans. Some apposite information relates to ionic transport mechanisms of cell membranes (Chapters 5, 9, 10, Vol. I; Chapter 8, Vol. II) and to the cytology of neurosecretion (Chapter 15, Vol. I; Chapter 8, Vol. II), but its comparative interest emerges mainly on higher levels of comparison.

Functional localization in neurons apparently is a quite general phenomenon.[17, 28, 81] Some crustacean stretch receptor cells discovered by Alexandrowicz (Chapter 2, Vol. II) have provided unusually favorable material for studying such complex specialization within single cells; dendrites, soma, and axon are able to contribute independently to the over-all activity of the neuron.[64, 65] Similar effects apparently occur in decapod cardiac ganglion cells (Chapter 5, Vol. I) and in mechanoreceptor cells of the statocyst (Chapter 2, Vol. II; Schöne[164]).

2. *Cellular*. In acellular or single-celled organisms, comparisons between individuals (Section III,B below) must be at the subcellular or cellular level. Thus comparative physiological interest centers around the specialization of subcellular systems and cyclical changes involved in the differentiation of cells between mitoses.[92]

The division of labor within a multicellular organism is more or less strongly reflected in the functional specialization of its component cells. Comparisons between these units may be made with many dependent variables such as amounts present of different ions, enzymes, metabolites, or structural proteins, as responses to stimulation or temperature change, and as measurements of respiratory rate, work output, and so on. Clearly some of these measurements, such as the amount of K^+ inside a crayfish axon, achieve a comparative functional significance, as opposed to a mere "chemical morphology," only when considered in terms of a larger context such as excitability or membrane transport. Similar considerations apply to the data on the distribution of many kinds of substances in Crustacea.

For instance, actin and myosin are restricted to muscle, hemocyanins to hemolymph (Chapter 3, Vol. I), retinene to photoreceptors (Chapter 1, Vol. II), acetylcholine mainly to the nervous system (Chapter 8, Vol. II), vitamin A in pelagic euphausiids to the eyestalks (Chapter 7, Vol. I), luciferin to light organs (Chapter 5, Vol. II), certain neurosecretory substances to the X-organ-sinus gland complex

(Chapter 15, Vol. I; Chapter 8, Vol. II), and so on. Likewise synthesis, storage, and utilization of such metabolites may occur in quite different cells as in the case of hormones. But without more relational information or more extensive intercellular series to compare, basic similarities and differences, in the sense of descriptive homologies, are not likely to be found on the cellular level.

3. *Tissues, organs, and systems.* In metazoan animals with a high degree of organization the division of labor inherent in the differentiation of various kinds of cells is extended to the development of tissues, organs, and systems with more or less clearly specialized functions. Functional parameters may in such cases be compared between epithelial and connective tissue, between compound and naupliar eyes, or between digestive and nervous systems, and so on, within the same organism. The differences and similarities observed are determined in part by the developmental differentiation of the tissues, organs, or systems, and in part by homeostatic and integrating mechanisms which regulate from moment to moment the levels of activity in the body's many components.

For example, the functional properties of the neuromuscular system in a crayfish claw are determined in the first instance by its particular structural organization and metabolic specialization which arise from its developmental history. But the level of its activity and indeed its total contribution to the individual's welfare are dictated primarily by motor impulses arriving via its efferent innervation. In another sphere, the gonad primordia or the chromatophores in malacostracans fulfill their normal functions only when they are appropriately controlled by hormones.

Such inherent differences in various parts of an individual and their patterns of control comprise another level of comparative physiology more complex than those considered above. A morphological counterpart of this level may be seen in serial homologies where different segments of the body and their appendages or other components are considered from the point of view of their basic similarity. The question of whether the stalked eyes of eucaridans are serial homologs of the jointed appendages of other segments is a classic example. A quantitative, broadly applicable but nonspecific kind of physiological comparison at this level may be made from metabolic rate or respiratory quotient measurements (Chapter 2, Vol. I). But such data for crustaceans are so scattered that few generalizations can be made except that variations of the order of ten times may occur in the metabolic rate of different tissues.

Indirect evidence for the differential distribution of metabolic rates may be inferred from the blood supply of various structures. As in other animals, the relative development of this system seems in crustaceans to reflect the local requirements of the areas it serves (Chapter 5, Vol. I). In the crayfish for instance, capillary networks are most highly developed on the cerebral ganglion, less well developed on the ventral ganglia and parts of the antennal gland, and still less elsewhere. If an assumption of close adaptive correlation between structure and function is valid, these structural data may be interpreted physiologically. A somewhat similar situation prevails in both the efferent and afferent innervation of various structures whose functional significance relative to the rest of the body may be roughly gauged by the size and make-up of its nerve supply (Chapter 7, Vol. II).

Another kind of comparison can be made by contrasting a given tissue or organ as it recurs in different parts of an individual. Thus in crustacean skeletal muscle all the contractile tissue is cross-striated. but apparently the faster a particular muscle is able to shorten, the closer together are its striations (Chapter 9, Vol. II). The most comprehensive data in this general field are the detailed functional comparisons made by Wiersma and his co-workers on peripheral neuromuscular systems and central neurons in particular species of decapod crustaceans, especially crayfish (Chapters 6 and 7, Vol. II).

Both efferent innervation and responses to a given impulse pattern in the motor neurons differ markedly in each of the seven or eight muscles in each pereiopod. In addition the chelipeds and the other thoracic legs may behave differently. Finally each of the several efferent fibers to a single muscle produces its characteristic effect; hence practically every nerve fiber of each muscle in the five pairs of thoracic appendages evokes its own particular response pattern. Four motor fibers are the maximum supplying one muscle, while one shared by two muscles is the minimum. Besides this motor innervation the efferent supply includes peripheral inhibitory fibers, one, or in some cases two, to a muscle. Like the motor axons these give rise to electrical changes in the effector which may facilitate, summate, or produce maintained potentials; their ultimate action diminishes or eliminates the shortening due to motor excitation. The presence of so few efferent fibers supplying these crustacean neuromuscular systems must mean that each muscle fiber has several types of neuromuscular mechanism.

Single muscle fibers may have one to four motor neurons supplying them plus the inhibitory innervation. The endings of each neuron on a muscle fiber are polyterminal, and in some cases there may be two kinds of terminals on a single axon. Typically the innervation is localized on one side of the muscle fiber, and the electrophysiological properties of the innervated side are different from those of the non-innervated one (Chapter 6, Vol. II). The neuromuscular junction is not easily accessible either histologically or pharmacologically, but presumably neurohumors are the transmitter agents at these junctions, and they could conceivably correspond in number with the functional types of junction (Chapter 6, Vol. II).

The many kinds of correlation here possible have been studied in sufficient detail, mainly by Wiersma and his colleagues, to provide an unsurpassed body of comparative data. The various neuromuscular systems show an almost endless series of localized responses, abortive spikes, conducted action potentials, and long-lasting changes in resting potential with the ultimate mechanical responses ranging from a rapid powerful twitch evoked by a single motor spike to a slow and feeble sustained contraction requiring a long train of motor impulses. Despite each great variation, enough is known about these systems so that many fruitful comparisons can be made within individuals, as well as between various decapods and other animal groups as discussed below.

Crustacean peripheral neuromuscular systems may also be compared effectively with other organs or systems in the same individual sharing certain basic properties. Recent work on decapod stretch receptors, statocysts, and cardiac ganglia provide appropriate data (Chapter 5, Vol. I; Chapter 2, Vol. II). Even though these organs have quite distinct functional roles, a number of striking similarities are apparent. Thus in Macrura the levels of excitability at the neuromuscular junction, in the abdominal stretch receptors, and in the cardiac ganglion cells are all correlated with the membrane conductance of the cell concerned.

Neurohumors presumably induce the generator potential at the neuromuscular junction and alter this potential in controlling spontaneous activity in the cardiac ganglion. Comparable conductance changes are induced mechanically by stretch 1) in statocyst hairs (Chapter 2, Vol. II; Schöne[164]), 2) in the sensory cell of the abdominal stretch receptor,[111] and even 3) in the dendrites of cardiac ganglion cells, which thus comprise a single neuron reflex arc (Chapter 5, Vol. I). Similarly the inhibitory fibers of the peripheral neuromuscular junction, the abdominal stretch receptor,[110] and the cardiac ganglion cell all seem to act by producing a neurohumor which returns the membrane conductance to its resting level. Although the specific transmitters concerned are unknown, some suggestive data are available. Thus the influence of acetylcholine on the active transport of NaCl by the gills of *Eriocheir* (Chapter 9, Vol. I) implies a mechanism involving alterations of membrane conductance (Chapter 8, Vol. II).

Changes in membrane conductance are likewise assumed for the physiological action of γ-aminobutyric acid on crustacean stretch receptors[110] and cardiac ganglion (Chapter 5, Vol. I); 5-hydroxytryptamine and adrenaline may act through similar ionic permeability alterations.[121, 206, 207] The specific details of membrane permeability changes and their ultimate effects on the movement of metal ions are not yet well enough known to permit more than tentative basic comparisons.

A combination of functional versatility with cellular parsimony is characteristic not only of the neuromuscular system of decapods, but also their central nervous system.* Our understanding of the comparative physiology of the interneurons concerned is again due primarily to the work of Wiersma and his colleagues on the crayfish (Chapter 7, Vol. II).

In general the CNS contains remarkably few fibers, and with the exception of primary sensory fibers these do not form tracts. In fact each interneuron would appear rather to be the equivalent of a fiber tract in vertebrates. Despite this cellular frugality crustaceans have a large variety of reflexes. Hence each central neuron, like the peripheral motor neurons, must have a complex role in integration. The means of achieving this are suggested by the intercellular relations of single neurons. These are commonly both sensory and motor; also one cell may be a first-order neuron in one reflex and second order in another.

Synaptic connections are not limited to the ends of the neurons but may be dendritic, somatic axonal, and complex branching. There seem even to be ephaptic connections between one lateral giant fiber and another. Such giant interneurons concerned with rapid evasive action are present in the CNS of a number of crustacean groups, where their rapid conduction and numerous efferent connections to major propulsive muscles reflect this special function. Some exceptional sensory cells have their cell bodies located in the CNS although they are typically peripheral (Chapter 7, Vol. II).

The sensory fields of single interneurons are widespread as are their motor connections, but these fields overlap strongly in different

---

* The same combination of attributes occurs in the relatively simple fused compound eye of cladocerans (Chapter 1, Vol. II).

nerve cells. While these various means of obtaining complex patterns of integration with few cells have been discovered (Chapter 7, Vol. II), the comparative physiology of interneurons has not proceeded as far as knowledge of the peripheral systems. However, a considerable catalogue of the functional properties of individual cells of this kind is being accumulated for the crayfish (Chapter 7, Vol. II).

Important relevant data for comparison with these central neurons are available from the Alexandrowicz stretch receptors and the cardiac ganglion discussed above. These organs provide more accessible and much simpler systems which nevertheless share certain CNS properties, particularly in regard to multiple complex intercellular relations and functions of single cells.[28] In addition peripheral inhibition in decapods may provide insight into central inhibition, which also must be important in Crustacea (Chapter 7, Vol. II).

Somewhat similar examples of neuronal coordination could be drawn from data on CNS control of sensory thresholds (Chapter 2, Vol. II), regulation of oriented movements (Chapter 10, Vol. II), and complex behavior (Chapter 13, Vol. II), but the foregoing should illustrate the point.

A number of further comparisons within individuals can be made between their sense organs. For example, the eyes and statocysts of decapods show a closely linked series of similarities and differences.[164] They are similar in that there is yet no direct evidence for spikes in the primary receptor cells although generator potentials certainly arise there. Both types of organ maintain muscle tonus of various parts of the body and are critical for spatial orientation. Both receptors also provide information on direction as well as intensity of the stimuli perceived.

But in the statocyst several stimuli add vectorially before affecting the sensory epithelium, whereas the retina can record the directions of many stimuli simultaneously and independently. Although discrete peripherally, visual information from several light sources apparently adds vectorially in the CNS; the dorsal light reflex (Chapter 10, Vol. II) is in fact comparable to the gravity reflex. However, in Natantia the way these two sensory modalities sum centrally in jointly regulating the particular position assumed is quantitatively affected by the direction of the force of gravity.[164]

In both cases the sensory information from the receptors on the right and left sides is summed centrally, but in the case of eyes, complex vector addition occurs rather than simple arithmetic summation as in gravity receptors. If one eye or statocyst is removed, central compensation may develop so that the continuous turning movement initiated by the remaining member of the pair gradually dies away. Removal of the second organ demonstrates this induced central asymmetry by a turning in the opposite direction despite the absence of asymmetrical peripheral sensory stimulation.[164]

An interesting aspect of comparative sensory physiology which has been little exploited in crustaceans is the comparison of the relative acuities, thresholds, and discrimination capabilities of an individual's various sense organs. For instance in *Artemia* certain visual capabilities are maintained when only the naupliar eye is functioning, but these are less than the visual functions of the compound eyes alone.[120] A more general area for possible development would be the comparison of absolute thresholds[2] in the various sensory modalities of crustaceans; another would be the comparative study of scales of sensory discrimination such as have been constructed for man.[182] Some isolated visual data of the kind needed and relating to intensity discrimination are indeed available for cladocerans and barnacles (Chapter 1, Vol. II).

Hormonal coordination in crustaceans is mainly related, as in other animals, to sustained long-term functions. Thus comparisons can be made between molting (Chapter 15, Vol. I) and reproductive (Chapter 13, Vol. I) cycles, retinal and chromatophoral pigment movements (Chapter 4, Vol. II), metabolic regulation (Chapters 2, 3, 4, 8, and 15, Vol. I; Chapter 8, Vol. II) as well as cardioregulation (Chapter 5, Vol. I), and limb regeneration (Chapter 17, Vol. I). The known sources of hormones concerned are mainly neurosecretory systems: the X-organ-sinus gland complex, the postcommissural organs, the pericardial organs, and perhaps the system of dorsal trunks and median connectives in stomatopods, as well as neurosecretory cells in the central nervous system (Chapter 8, Vol. II). Neurons in general should be added to complete the list of neuroendocrine structures since neurohumors are believed to occur widely in decapods although their number and nature are not yet certain.

Only three endocrine glands, as distinct from neurohormone sources, are known in crustaceans. These are 1) the ovaries, which promote the development of secondary sex characters in female amphipods and isopods (Chapter 13, Vol. I), 2) the androgenic glands, which control male sex differentiation in malacostracans (Chapter 13, Vol. I), and 3) the Y-organs, which initiate proecdysis in the same subclass (Chapter 15, Vol. I). There seems to be no good evidence that the sinus gland has any intrinsic hormonal activity apart from neurosecretory storage and release.

The number and nature of the compounds concerned in chemical coordination are uncertain and to some extent controversial. Five or more neurosecretory substances (Chapter 8, Vol. II) and two or more other hormones (Chapters 13 and 15, Vol. I) are likely, while the neurohumors would seem to number at least two (Chapters 7 and 8, Vol. II). The decapod molting hormone, ecdysone from the Y-organ, shows some similarities to insect ecdysones (Chapter 15, Vol. I), and preliminary separations and histochemical characterizations of neurohumors have been made (Chapter 15, Vol. I; Chapters 4 and 8, Vol. II). Nevertheless, such information is probably more profitably compared at present on the level of differences between species or higher taxa because the interesting comparisons within individuals must be largely based on future detailed biochemical knowledge about synthesis, release, and target tissue action of the substances concerned.

In comparisons within individuals the most complex integrative levels would probably include the general fields of homeostasis and cybernetics. Nervous, hormonal, and other adaptive changes, such as branchiopod hemoglobin synthesis at low oxygen partial pressures (Chapter 12, Vol. I), are known to be involved in crustacean homeostasis, but they have been little studied from a regulative, or cybernetic, point of view. Respiratory (Chapter 2, Vol. I), ionic, osmotic (Chapter 9, Vol. I), metabolic (Chapter 8, Vol. I), allometric (Chapter 16, Vol. I), and behavioral (Chapters 10 and 13, Vol. II) systems have been shown to be under complex regulatory control. Except for the nervous and chemical mechanisms discussed above, there is little that can be said at this level, although some further analysis of these matters on other levels appears below. Feedback loops in crustaceans have mainly been considered in the nervous system (Chapter 13, Vol. II; Schöne[164]) but undoubtedly also occur in chemical coordination (Chapter 13, Vol. I), and in systems where chemical, nervous, and other links are involved together.

B. BETWEEN INDIVIDUALS OF A SPECIES

Individuals of the same species differ from one another in many ways, both physiological and morphological.[200] Since most of the normal differences concerned are mainly quantitative and continuous, the determination of descriptive homologies is usually easier here than at many other comparative levels. For the same reason many data in the present category can be adequately treated by statistical and other quantitative techniques. For instance, the sizes of parts of the body (y) are quite generally related in populations of crustaceans to the magnitude of some reference dimension (x) as follows (Chapter 16, Vol. I):

$$y = bx^a$$

where a is the equilibrium constant and b is the initial growth index.

Similarly oxygen uptake (O_2) per unit weight and body weight (W) are related to each other as follows (Chapter 2, Vol. I):

$$O_2/W = aW^{b-1}$$

where b is usually between 0.67 and 1.0 and a is a constant representing unit metabolic rate. Likewise, heartbeat frequency (F) is related to body weight (W) as follows (Chapter 5, Vol. I):

$$F = kW^{-c}$$

If F is beats per minute and W is grams, then k is 160/min and c is 0.12 for a wide range of crustaceans from cladocerans to stomatopods.

In addition to size, which is the independent variable in the three functions just cited, age, stage of development, or sex (Chapter 13, Vol. I) could be used. Similarly the abscissa could be the phase of various cycles: molting (Chapter 15, Vol. I), reproductive (Chapter 13, Vol. I), diurnal, lunar (Chapter 11, Vol. II), or seasonal, which affect many physiological characters in systematic ways. Also relevant here is the animal's previous history, whether nutritional (Chapter 8, Vol. I), respiratory (Chapter 2, Vol. I), osmotic (Chapter 9, Vol. I), or other, as well as its relation to genetic and geographic races (Chapters 2 and 16, Vol. I). The differences involved may range from alterations in blood calcium levels during various stages of the molt cycle (Chapter 15, Vol. I) to behavioral changes correlated with puberty or phase of sexual cycles (Chapter 13, Vol. I; Chapter 13, Vol. II). Many of these differences, occurring independently in individuals of a species, may be found in successive developmental or adaptive periods of one animal's life span. Usually the same formal analysis will hold for either case just as it does for allometry of size and allometry of growth (Chapter 16, Vol. I).

C. BETWEEN CRUSTACEANS

It is a striking fact that many physiological characteristics of crustaceans seem either to be universal or scattered through the class in a way that shows little obvious correlation with other known elements. Both of these conditions could be apparent rather than real since in many cases the facts are not adequately known or their relations are not understood. Consequently many instances could be cited where certain close similarities in functional organization occur in otherwise quite different forms or conversely where basically similar species differ sharply in some physiological traits.

An example of the former situation may be seen in bioluminescence (Chapter 5, Vol. II). This occurs in three of the eight subclasses of Crustacea: Ostracoda, Copepoda, and Malacostraca. In euphausiids, penaeideans, and carideans the light is usually produced within the body in more or less elaborate photophores, but in mysidaceans, ostracods, and presumably copepods (as well as some decapods), a luminous secretion is squeezed out of the glandular light organs into the sea water, where it luminesces. Although this second group does not seem to have any particular coherence, the luminous eucaridans belong to a reasonably uniform type. Yet if the situation is examined within restricted eucaridan groups like the bathypelagic Sergestidae or Oplophoridae, the histology, innervation, and distribution of photophores still show close similarities in quite distinct species and marked differences in otherwise nearly identical ones.[51]

If one considers the crustaceans that swim dorsal side down, the possibility of systematically arranging the known facts seems even smaller than in the case of light production. Thus some anostracans, cladocerans, copepods, copepod larvae, isopods, amphipods, and carideans have this upside-down swimming, but no orderly sequence is apparent among such diverse types. The same may be said for the strongly developed parasitic habits of copepods, cirripeds, and isopods or for the types of feeding in various groups (Chapter 6, Vol. I). Similar examples could be multiplied severalfold from almost any field of crustacean physiology. The difficulty of ordering such information can be resolved only by further data or by new application of explanatory hypotheses consistent with the known facts.

Unlike the spottily distributed features compared so far, some characters are known to occur more coherently in various crustaceans. For example, melanin occurs as the dark pigment of melanophores and of the retina in Brachyura but is absent from Macrura and Anomura where its place is taken by ommochrome (Chapter 7, Vol. I). The distribution of the universally required vitamin, riboflavin, shows maxima which closely parallel the localization of melanin in Reptantia.

Brachyura, the group in which autotomy is best developed, are also characterized by a type of limb regeneration in which the limb bud is twice folded on itself as it grows (Chapter 17, Vol. I). In Natantia and some Macrura the bud is simply extended. Details are lacking for comparisons with entomostracan regeneration, which occurs in many forms.

The functional organization of the peripheral neuromuscular system of Decapoda is also specific to the major groups (Chapter 6, Vol. II). Natantia seem basically similar to Reptantia except that they usually have eight instead of seven muscles in each pereiopod. The motor innervation consists of the same twelve efferent fibers supplying seven muscles in all Reptantia, but the inhibitory neuron pattern differs characteristically in Scyllaridea, Nephropsidea, Anomura, and Brachyura. Pagurids and dromiids have a peculiar but similar antagonistic action of slow and fast neurons supplying a muscle in the carpo-propodite joint. Reptantia and Stomatopoda have neurons with relatively thin myelin sheaths, but the latter are thick in Natantia where the myelin may have periodic interruptions somewhat like nodes of Ranvier. These heavily sheathed fibers, as in other animals, conduct more rapidly than weakly myelinated ones even larger in diameter (Chapter 6, Vol. II).

In decapods the subesophageal ganglion is required for walking, but in stomatopods (and insects) the thoracic ganglia alone are adequate for this (Chapter 7, Vol. II). Giant fibers in the central nervous system show some coherence in distribution, but this seems mainly correlated with the occurrence of a rapid escape mechanism in aquatic forms.[151] Thus such fibers are absent in Brachyura, where the reduced abdomen precludes the typical macruran and natantian backward swimming escape reflex. Giant fibers are present in Natantia, Nephropsidea, Anomura, and Scyllaridea, although they are not highly developed in the last group (Chapter 7, Vol. II). They also occur in some, but not other, ostracods and in copepods.[35]

Smaller-scale comparisons between crustaceans can be seen in such functions as the terrestrial adaptations of oniscoidean isopods and the variations in the courting behavior of fiddler crab species discussed below (Section IV).

Parasitic castration, which involves the feminization of a male crustacean host by a crustacean parasite, has attracted much attention.[152] For a long time it was the main means of studying crustacean sexual differentiation. The explanation of this alteration in sexuality was controversial for many years, but recent knowledge of the hormonal control of malacostracan sexual differentiation indicates that parasitic castration must result from inactivation of the androgenic gland or its hormone (Chapter 13, Vol. I). The mechanism remains to be determined although some evidence implicates CNS neurosecretory cells.[133] Obviously the whole field of crustacean parasitology is in a rather elementary state in spite of the interesting range of problems it offers, from biochemical specificities to the subtle balance of host-parasite competition.

D. BETWEEN CRUSTACEA AND OTHER TAXA

The term comparative physiology is commonly limited to comparisons between different major groups of animals at the class or phylum level. From the present more inclusive viewpoint this level is only one of many which seem fruitful. Indeed comparisons between major taxa may generally be more speculative because of the difficulties in establishing descriptive homology between them (Section II). Applying the criteria for homology becomes increasingly less certain as the differences between animals and the gaps between them become larger. Hence one's natural impulses to broad generalization must be tempered by this fact and by the further gaps due to our present state of knowledge.

Note that here and in Section III,C above, the entities being compared are systematic ones, like species, families, classes, and so on, as set forth in what is judged to be the best current classification (Chapter 1, Vol. I; Systematic Index, Vol. II). The latter is intended in modern systematics to be phylogenetic, but in practice taxonomic procedures usually depend on descriptive comparisons of morphological, zoogeographic, and other evidence which are themselves used as a basis for hypothesizing evolutionary relationships.[33, 135, 183, 184]

1. *Insects.* As arthropods, crustaceans and insects have many detailed similarities. In their way of life, however, they are quite different. The former are mainly marine forms with a considerable number of fresh-water species and relatively few terrestrial examples, while the latter are predominantly terrestrial with fairly extensive fresh-water representation and almost no marine species. Consequently physiological comparisons between the two classes should include a broad spectrum of similarities and differences.

Respiratory gas exchange and transport mechanisms are quite distinct in crustaceans and insects. Air-filled tracheal systems subserve these functions in most insects including the larval, pupal, and adult aquatic stages. Pseudotracheae in a few isopods are an interesting but exceptional and anatomically sharply localized crustacean occurrence of similar structures (Chapter 2, Vol. I). In general, insect blood has no specialized role in respiratory transport. But in many crustaceans the increased respiratory gas capacity of the blood due to hemoglobin or hemocyanin is crucial for survival. Respiratory pigments in insects are restricted to a few cases, like aquatic larvae of chironomid dipterans, in which plasma hemoglobin serves primarily for oxygen storage rather than for its transport.

Several other blood characteristics are also distinctive in the two classes. Crustacean blood seems less specialized than that of insects. The former has a low magnesium index and a high sodium one, whereas in the latter sodium is low and, at least in the higher orders, magnesium high (Chapter 4, Vol. I). Insects have a higher nonprotein amino acid level in their blood than do crustaceans and most other animals. Yet in crustaceans the blood-tissue gradient of these compounds is much steeper. On the other hand, coagulation of the blood in the two classes is closely similar (Chapter 4, Vol. I).

In crustaceans and insects the circulatory systems are alike in having the blood bathing many tissues flow in sinuses rather than in capillaries and in having extensible elastic ligaments supporting the heart (Chapter 5, Vol. I). Also comparable are the tubular heart with its paired ostia sucking up blood from the prominent pericardium, the alary muscles, the often rather restricted arterial system, the occurrence of accessory hearts, and the weakly developed venous return vessels. The neurogenic control of heartbeat shown by copepods, isopods, amphipods, decapods, and stomatopods, as well as ostracods (apparently), is similar to that of many insects, but in branchiopods the evidence suggests a myogenic beat (Chapter 5, Vol. I).

At least in their anatomical sites ionic and osmotic regulation are quite different in crustaceans and insects. Antennal (and presumably also maxillary) glands and gills, both typically absent in insects, are the main sites of ionic and osmotic control in crustaceans. Nevertheless in both groups the fresh-water species can absorb ions actively against a gradient (Chapter 9, Vol. I), and the mechanism of hyposmotic regulation in *Artemia* shows definite parallels with that of *Aedes* larvae living in salt water. A difference between the classes appears in the ability of blood amino acid changes in insects to compensate for osmotic alterations in inorganic ions.[27]

Water conservation both passive and active is highly developed in terrestrial insects but poorly so even in the most terrestrial crustaceans (Armadillidiidae) (Chapter 11, Vol. I). The cuticle provides the most important passive element in this function. In general the integuments of crustaceans and insects have much in common (Chapter 14, Vol. I). Thus the fore-gut epicuticle of decapods appears descriptively homologous to the larval epicuticle of dipterans. Both contain polyphenol oxidase and harden by quinone tanning, probably of lipoprotein. The occurrence of tyrosinase in the blood of crustaceans and insects is consistent with this hypothesis (Chapters 4 and 14, Vol. I). However, the waxy layer which reduces transpiration through most insect cuticle[13] has not been detected in crustaceans. Nor in the realm of active water conservation is the strongly hyperosmotic urine common in insects known to be present in any terrestrial crustaceans although the latter appear to have made an alternative compromise by reducing over-all nitrogen metabolism (Chapter 11, Vol. I).

Uric acid is not a primary excretory product in crustaceans, whose main nitrogenous waste is ammonia (Chapter 10, Vol. I); insects, however, are characteristically uricotelic although their fresh-water forms are ammonotelic and prodigal of water. The Malpighian tubules of insects have no descriptive homolog in crustaceans, which apparently eliminate the end products of nitrogen metabolism not through the antennal or maxillary glands, but through gills or storage excretory organs (Chapter 10, Vol. I).

The control of both primary and secondary sexual differentiation in crustaceans is quite distinct from that in insects since hormones appear not to be involved in the latter (Chapter 13, Vol. I; Charniaux-Cotton[36]). But molt-cycle regulation, which depends on endocrine and neurosecretory factors, differs only in detail between the two classes (Chapter 15, Vol. I). Close similarity exists between the functions of the X-organ-sinus gland complex and Y-organ in decapods and the protocerebral neurosecretory cell corpus cardiacum system and prothoracic gland of insects. In addition both crustacean and insect ecdysones are effective in the *Calliphora* bioassay and are probably closely related chemically.[32] The correspondence of the two over-all molt control mechanisms is so detailed as to suggest that a homolog of the insect corpus allatum remains to be discovered in Crustacea (Chapter 15, Vol. I).

A close parallel to the type of parasitism shown by *Sacculina* and other rhizocephalans occurs in certain species of strepsipteran insects which parasitize other insects. Here the females are immobile, highly modified endoparasites partly protruding from the body of the host. The insect hosts tend to show modified sexual and other characters due to the parasite's presence. This stylopization, therefore, parallels in a number of ways decapod parasitic castration.

Because of their periodic ecdyses, growth of external dimensions in both crustaceans and insects as in other arthropods is a discontinuous step function. Nevertheless, with the addition of Brooks' rule for the relative size increase per molt, the same allometric techniques which are valid for continuous growth may be used for these animals (Chapter 16, Vol. I). True autotomy occurs only in crustaceans and insects. In the latter, wings (in ants and termites), or limbs (in phasmids), may be cast off at preformed breakage planes; limited regeneration occurs in various groups.[20] This regeneration appears to be under comparable endocrine and neurosecretory control in both crustaceans and insects (Chapter 17, Vol. I).

Both structurally and functionally the sense organs of crustaceans and insects resemble one another closely. This is particularly striking in the compound eyes (Chapter 1, Vol. II). In both groups similar variations in the over-all pattern occur with apposition, superposition, and double eyes being well represented. Also there are many resemblances in detail. For example, many kinds of crustaceans and orders of insects have seven or eight retinular cells per ommatidium. Long rodlike rhabdoms and short fusiform ones occur, respectively, in apposition and superposition eyes in the two classes. The rhabdom microstructure in both is the same and the photosensitive mechanism as in other animal groups depends on a retinene-protein complex.

In contrast to such widespread resemblances in compound eyes, retinal screening pigment control differs in the two classes since it is nervous in insects and hormonal in crustaceans (Chapter 4, Vol. II).

A number of functional comparisons may be made between crustacean and insect vision (Chapter 1, Vol. II). In both, the visual fields of each ommatidium are considerably greater than the angles of axial separation of these units. Nevertheless minimum visible acuity and minimum detectable movement are definitely better than would be expected from these angles.[31] So far there are relatively few measurements of crustacean electroretinograms to compare with the extensive work in insects.[3, 54, 84] But neither in crustaceans nor insects have spikes been detected in the primary receptor cells (this is also true in *Limulus* and vertebrate eyes). Nerve action potentials have been recorded in crustaceans and insects more centrally, but in neither case has any effect of polarized light been found. Similarly optomotor tests have failed in both classes to demonstrate discrimination of the plane of polarization. *Daphnia* and *Apis* have comparable spectral sensitivities excluding the red but extending into the ultraviolet. But in *Artemia*, as in a number of insects, sensitivity extends into the red also. Color vision is present in both classes, as are shifts in wavelength sensitivity associated with adaptation to different intensities.

Among mechanoreceptors the abdominal stretch receptors of crustaceans and insects are strikingly similar (Chapter 2, Vol. II; Table 1); the complex organs of saturniids are especially like those of the crayfish.[66] Myochordotonal organs of decapods resemble the chordotonal receptors of insects, but two important types of mechanoreceptor seem to be absent from one or the other of the two classes; organs of hearing, widespread in insects, are not known in crustaceans, while statocysts do not occur in insects except for organs, in certain dipterous larvae and in water bugs, which work like statocysts in reverse with

TABLE 1

COMPARISON OF STRETCH RECEPTORS

Groups	Afferent neurons		Efferent neurons			Other components
	Tonic	Phasic	Inhibitory	Slow motor	Fast motor	
Crustacea	✓	✓	✓	✓	✓	Two receptor muscles[a]
Odonata, Dictyoptera, Hymenoptera	✓	0	0	0	0	Connective tissue strand
Orthoptera	✓	0	0	0	0	Strand lies on main muscle
Lepidoptera	✓	0	0	✓	0	Receptor muscle, giant nucleus
Amphibia	✓	✓	0	✓	✓	Intrafusal muscle[a]
Mammalia	✓	✓	0	✓	0	Intrafusal muscle, nuclear bag, separate innervation

[a] Share motor innervation with main muscle.

air bubbles pressing upward against a sensory epithelium.[164] Nevertheless insects in general have well-developed gravity and acceleration responses which must be initiated via sense organs unlike the statocysts of crustaceans, mollusks, and vertebrates. Special dynamic mechanoreceptors for spatial orientation have been described in certain flying insects,[137,149] but gravity receptors are just beginning to be known. Thus in the honeybee, sense organs between head and thorax as well as others between thorax and abdomen are responsible for the insect's sense of the vertical.[118] Joint receptors in the legs may assist in this function as has been suggested for Sherrington's fiber in the crayfish (Chapter 7, Vol. II).

From the relatively sparse data on crustacean chemoreceptors a few comparisons may be made. In *Balanus*, as in several insects, the stimulating effect of various inorganic acids is largely dependent on pH, while the responses to chemicals of *Daphnia*, a copepod, and *Balanus* are also similar to those of insects which have thresholds for aliphatic alcohols systematically related to chain length (Chapter 3, Vol. II). However, *Balanus* seems to have five taste modalities, whereas insects have only two. A possible parallel in thermoreceptors may be seen in the transient stimulating effect of cooling on the CNS of the crayfish and cockroach, but similar effects occur in vertebrates too.[103] However, nothing like the exteroceptor heat sensitive areas of Orthoptera[173] have been found in Crustacea (Chapter 3, Vol. II).

Color changes in crustaceans and insects are similar in that both show slow alterations in amount of pigment present as well as faster chromatophoral metachrosis. Chromatophore dispersing hormone is found in extracts of decapod sinus gland and of insect corpora cardiaca as well as in brain cells of some species. Yet the evidence presently available indicates that crustacean and insect chromatophorotropins are chemically and physiologically distinct (Chapter 4, Vol. II; Butenandt[32]). The difference in the control of retinal screening pigments in the two groups is cited above.

There is some evidence that both peripheral and central nervous systems of insects share important properties with those of crustaceans, but the small size of insects makes studies comparable to those of Wiersma on decapods difficult or impossible. Nevertheless insect nervous systems, like those of crustaceans, probably function with relatively few neurons. Fast and slow motor fibers are known to control the leg muscles of both, but peripheral inhibition, although reported in some insects, is absent in the well-studied orthopterans and dictyopterans. It is, in fact, adequately documented only in decapod crustaceans among all animals (Chapter 6, Vol. II). Pharmacological evidence implies that peripheral neuromuscular transmission in both classes may be cholinergic (Chapter 8, Vol. II). This is supported by the presence in insects and crustaceans of acetylcholine, specific choline esterase, and of choline acetylase (Chapters 8 and 9, Vol. II).

However, the marked blood differences in Mg^{++}, K^+, and Na^+ found in the two classes might be expected to have corresponding influences on neuromuscular transmission. Yet this process obviously must be effective in all animals in spite of such ionic differences. The fact that prolonged action potentials are not required for muscle contraction has been suggested to account for the tolerance observed in these arthropods.[95] In the crustaceans themselves the usual effect of Mg^{++} ions or calcium-magnesium ratios on general tonus and excitability are undoubtedly involved in the apparent correlation of blood magnesium index and general sluggishness in various species of anomurans, brachyurans, and stomatopods (Chapter 9, Vol. I). A somewhat similar correlation, with a more obvious adaptive significance, may be seen in phytophagous insects. Here alterations in blood K⁺ would seem to increase general activity at the onset of food deprivation and to decrease spontaneous activity on satiation.[95]

The fact that insect locomotor patterns show adaptive plasticity similar to those in *Astacus* after loss of limbs is another argument in favor of parallel functional organization of the CNS in the two groups (Chapter 9, Vol. II). Normal locomotor patterns also show fundamental similarities although a much greater variety of walking patterns is present in crustaceans.[127] Some dynamic properties of portunid swimming paddles seem to be like those of insect wings.

Sensory and reflex mechanisms for spatial orientation are quite similar in crustaceans and insects whether mediated by eyes, statocysts, or other sense organs.[164] In both cases, for example, the strongest turning movement in the dorsal light reflex is induced by laterally incident light. Also light compass reactions and astronomical orientation seem to be essentially the same (Chapter 10, Vol. II).

In general the behavior of crustaceans is simpler than that of many insects (Chapter 13, Vol. II). Displacement activities are known in *Uca*, mantids, and *Drosophila* while these forms also have well-developed species-specific display patterns.[42,179] But the crab and fruit fly displays are simple stereotypes compared with the elaborate ones of mantids.

2. *Vertebrates*. Despite the many fundamental distinctions between crustaceans and vertebrates, a number of interesting functional similarities may be cited. There are in fact several physiological traits which seem more closely alike in crustaceans and vertebrates than in crustaceans and insects. The respiratory function of blood and the control of sexual differentiation are examples. Less extreme are a number of similarities in the metabolic regulation of the two groups. Thus thermal adaptation in crustaceans has its counterpart in fishes but is absent in several terrestrial mammals tested (Chapter 2, Vol. I). Low partial pressures of oxygen may induce cytochrome synthesis in cladocerans and mammals; they may also stimulate hemoglobin formation in branchiopods as well as fishes and man (Chapter 12, Vol. I). The hemoglobin in crustaceans, however, has a molecular weight about six times that of mammals (Chapter 3, Vol. I).

The efficiency of crustaceans in extracting oxygen for respiration from the surrounding medium is less than that of fish, gastropods, and cephalopods, more than that of various sessile filter feeders like tunicates, and about the same as annelids and echinoderms (Chapter 2, Vol. I). Sluggish benthic crustaceans such as *Libinia* have a smaller gill area per unit weight than fast active species like portunids, a difference which is paralleled by the relation between inactive bottom-living fishes and fast-swimming pelagic ones.[76]

The ionic content of crustacean blood resembles that of vertebrates in its high sodium index and low magnesium titer. In this respect both differ from marine invertebrates in general, from the higher insect orders and, indeed, sea water (Chapter 4, Vol. I). Arthropod and vertebrate blood coagulation are quite distinct, with the plasmatic type of coagulation in crustaceans being a single-phase phenomenon. Nevertheless thrombin will clot crayfish blood, and Ca^{++} is required for blood coagulation in both classes. Blood vessels of crustaceans are similar to those of vertebrates in being functionally more independent of the organs they supply than the nervous system, for example; the blood supply appears to have a more ad hoc relation to local requirements than does innervation (Chapter 5, Vol. I). The structure of the crustacean heart, its relation to the venous return, and the mechanism of its beat control, in malacostracans at least, are also quite distinct from those in vertebrates. Despite these differences, crustacean cardiac output and general circulatory efficiency appear to compare favorably with those of a number of vertebrates. Detailed comparison demonstrates in more ways than one that lobster and fish circulatory systems seem closer to each other than do those of fish and mammals (Chapter 5, Vol. I).

Feeding of crustaceans and vertebrates shows a comparable variety of types, but the several pairs of head, and often thoracic, appendages which form parts of the crustacean feeding mechanism make some details quite different (Chapter 6, Vol. I). Thus filter feeding in ammocoetes larvae, sharks, teleosts, and baleen whales depends on oral or branchial filters, whereas the filtering mechanisms are always appendicular in the many kinds of crustaceans which feed in this manner.

The digestive system of crustaceans seems to lack the enzymatic programming typical of vertebrates and also of insects since the hepatopancreas is the main or only source of digestive enzymes (Chapter 8, Vol. I). These enzymes nevertheless show some type resemblances to their vertebrate counterparts. Thus crustacean amylase is like that of vertebrate saliva and pancreas in requiring chloride ions for activation. Protein digestion, as investigated in the crab, *Maja,* is comparable to that in vertebrates although, like other invertebrates, the crab lacks a pepsin-like enzyme. In crayfish and other decapods fat absorption is aided by the emulsifying action of surface active substances with some properties like the conjugated bile acids of vertebrates (Chapter 8, Vol. I).

Carideans and grapsoid crabs are the only marine invertebrates with hyposmotic regulation in sea water, but this regulatory ability is slight compared with teleosts (Chapter 9, Vol. I). The mechanism involved is not known in these decapods, but *Artemia* regulates hyposmotically in brine by swallowing water and excreting ions in a manner comparable to marine teleosts and some marine birds.[165] In fresh-water crustaceans, as well as many brackish and some marine species, active ion absorption occurs as it does in fresh-water teleosts, amphibians, insects, mollusks, and annelids (Chapter 9, Vol. I). The crabs are exceptional for fresh-water animals since they secrete isosmotic urine; the Astacidae are the only crustaceans known to produce hyposmotic urine although the fresh-water teleosts, amphibians, gastropods, and lamellibranchs do so.

Vertebrates have a far greater range of major nitrogenous end products than the essentially ammonotelic crustaceans. Despite this limitation in crustacean excretion, these arthropods appear to have a more complete battery of enzymes for the catabolism of nucleotides since these are degraded to ammonia, whereas in vertebrates they are broken down only to uric acid or allantoin (Chapter 8, Vol. I).

Although the crustacean mechanism of urine formation is in doubt (Chapter 10, Vol. I), the structure of antennal or maxillary glands with an end-sac and excretory tubule might suggest the gross plan of a single vertebrate nephron with Bowman's capsule and the convoluted tubule. However, available evidence has rather led to the comparison of crustacean excretory organs with aglomerular fish kidneys.[29] The reasonableness of noting such similarities between crustacean and vertebrate excretory organs is increased by the correspondence between the glucose resorbing mechanism in *Homarus* antennal glands and that in many vertebrate kidneys. Normally lobster urine is free of glucose, but when the "tubular maximum" is exceeded, as it is with blood levels of 100 mg %, sugar begins to appear. This crustacean glucose resorptive mechanism, like the vertebrate one, is completely blocked by phlorizin (Chapter 10, Vol. I). The over-all excretory pattern of the lobster is also essentially similar to that of higher mollusks. Thus ionic regulation in both decapod crustaceans and cephalopod mollusks comprises the same sort of selective excretion by renal organs and controlled uptake by permeable surfaces even though the resulting ionic indexes are quite different (Chapter 9, Vol. I; Martin[130]).

Sex determination in crustaceans and vertebrates is basically genetic, whereas their sexual differentiation is hormonally controlled (Chapter 13, Vol. I). With regard to the regulation of sexual differentiation, vertebrates are more uniform than the arthropods, and insects seem to resemble crustaceans less than the latter do vertebrates. Crustacea are also similar to Vertebrata in having the ovaries hormonally prepare the mother for incubation and in having the eyestalk neurosecretory system somehow regulate sex cycles and possibly the secretion of gonadal hormones as does the vertebrate pituitary. The production in malacostracans of male hormone by an anatomically isolated androgenic gland is noteworthy since the hormone with comparable function originates in vertebrates from interstitial cells within the gonad itself (Chapter 13, Vol. I). This is reminiscent of the case in certain teleosts where the islets of Langerhans, usually incorporated within the pancreas in other vertebrates, are isolated from it as an anatomically separate structure.

The presence of an exoskeleton in arthropods makes profound differences in their physiology compared with vertebrates. While the pituitary regulates growth somewhat as the decapod eyestalk does, growth cycles when present in vertebrates are either localized in reproductive elements or are relatively simple periodic functions imposed by nutritional state, light, or, in poikilotherms, temperature. On the other hand, crustacean molt cycles involve everything from simple ionic movements to complex alterations in behavior related to ecdysis (Chapter 15, Vol. I). Their growth in size, obviously, and growth in cell number, apparently, occur only in restricted phases of the whole cycle; where and when cytoplasmic growth takes place is unknown.

While true autotomy does not occur in vertebrates, comparable casting off of certain body parts normally occurs in lizards as well as in starfish, holothurians, gastropods, cephalopods, and in insects (Section III,D,1; Chapter 17, Vol. I). Crustacean limb regeneration, although quite distinctive in detail, shows certain similarities to the same process in vertebrates, where it is much more sharply restricted to particular groups and occurs among tetrapods only in urodele amphibians. For example, innervation of the blastema is required in the regenerating limb stump by both, but in *Asellus* at least, innervation is required throughout the process, whereas in amphibians it is needed only during a certain period (Chapter 17, Vol. I).

Eyes of crustaceans and vertebrates show close similarities in some of their microstructural details and in their photochemical mechanisms (Chapter 1, Vol. II; Miller,[136] Wolken[204]). However, their histological structure and physiological optics differ markedly whether one is comparing naupliar eyes with median photosensitive areas of the verte-brate midbrain or lateral compound eyes with camera eyes. Neurally well developed compound eyes and camera eyes are similar in having second, third, or higher order neurons closely approximated to the primary neurosensory cells of the retina. They may also be alike in having functional units made up of clusters of about seven retinal cells if the reported retinal image size for point source stimulation in the human eye is considered (Chapter 1, Vol. II). However, handling of the resultant primary data differs considerably in the two classes since the convergence of retinal neurosensory cells on secondary neurons is about 7 to 1 in decapods but averages nearer 100 to 1 in man.

It is commonly stated that vertebrate eyes are primarily image-forming structures while compound eyes are mainly movement re-ceptors. Whether true or not, the documentation for such a statement is poor except that far fewer sensory cells and neurons are involved in the compound eye than in the vertebrate eye. In respect to such cellular parsimony, the crustacean eye, peripheral neuromuscular sys-tem, and CNS are similar as pointed out above. The best reported in-tensity discrimination for crustaceans is about the same as for man, but the known ranges for crustacean dark adaptation and the known visual acuities are considerably less than in the best vertebrate sys-tems. Various branchiopods have eye tremors which are suggestive of those in vertebrates and perhaps important in form vision or image fixation (Chapter 1, Vol. II).

Daphnia phototactic intensity discrimination resembles the dark adaptation curves of vertebrates with duplex retinas since the wavelength of maximum sensitivity shifts with adaptation. Although further data are needed, the spectral absorption curve of the visual pigment in pelagic eucaridans seems to be nearer the blue than in neritic or benthic forms (Chapter 1, Vol. II); this parallels the situation found in open-water and deep-sea fishes.

In general crustacean proprioceptors resemble those of vertebrates (Chapter 2, Vol. II; Section IV below). Similarities are particularly striking between the decapod dorsal abdominal stretch receptors of Alexandrowicz and the vertebrate muscle spindle.

The decapod stretch receptor is the only such organ known with a peripheral inhibitory innervation (Table 1). The neuron concerned synapses with the corresponding sensory neuron's dendrites and is one of the few examples of peripheral neuron-to-neuron interaction.[121] The inhibitory mechanism of this abdominal stretch receptor is similar to those involved in vagus action on the pacemakers in frog and tortoise sinus venosus.[111] In both crustaceans and vertebrates the responses of tonic and phasic receptor elements to a constant stimulus is correlated directly with the rate of decay of the generator potential in the sensory endings. Thus the crayfish dorsal fast stretch receptor, one kind of frog skin stretch receptor, and the vertebrate Pacinian corpuscle all show rapid decay of their generator potentials and yield corresponding phasic responses. In contrast, the crayfish dorsal slow stretch receptor, the frog touch receptor, and the frog muscle spindle maintain the generator potential as well as their tonic sustained responses for a relatively long time. The explanations proposed for these different rates of adaptation have been the same for crustaceans and vertebrates.[64, 65, 122]

As in the mechanoreceptors just cited, there are a number of remarkable similarities between the statocyts of malacostracans and the nonacoustic labyrinth of the vertebrates (Chapter 2, Vol. II). In both, the shear created by gravity or other forces acting on a movable statolith or cupula stimulates the underlying epithelium by inducing a generator potential. Electrophysiological evidence, as well as removal of one statocyst or labyrinth, shows that both organs are normally spontaneously active.[164] In *Homarus* the resting position of the statocyst produces a moderate tonic discharge; tilting the organ in one direction increases the spike frequency; tilting in the reverse direction decreases it. Similar results have been obtained in sharks, rays, teleosts, and cats.[164] In lobsters and mammals the receptors stimulated by tilting around the transverse axis are different from those activated by displacement about the longitudinal axis, but in sharks the same fibers respond to both kinds of positional displacement. Not only are the static positional receptors similar in function in the two groups, but so also are those which respond to linear and angular acceleration. The lobster receptors appear to be more sensitive than those of vertebrates in determining angular position, and individual elements apparently have a more discriminating position sense. On the other hand, the semicircular canals of vertebrates show finer discrimination than the rotation receptors of *Homarus* (Chapter 2, Vol. II). Two interesting comparative points may be made here: on the one hand, the lobster is more like a mammal than an elasmobranch in some details of its position receptor function; on the other hand, crustaceans and vertebrates are more closely related in their position and acceleration sense organs, as on several other counts, than either of them is to insects, which have no functionally similar statocysts at all.

Chromatophore control in vertebrates is a far more variable mechanism than the apparently uniform hormonal control mediated by the eyestalk neurosecretory system in decapods (Chapter 4, Vol. II). Thus in cyclostomes, elasmobranchs, and amphibians, intermedin from the intermediate lobe of the pituitary is the main chromatophore regulator; in teleosts, the pigment cells are usually controlled by a double, dispersing and concentrating innervation. Even among reptiles a broad range of control is found since the lizard *Anolis* has an endocrine mechanism regulating color, the horned "toad" *Phrynosoma* has both endocrine and nervous factors involved, and the African chameleon has just nervous control. No chromatophores are present in Crustacea outside the Malacostraca or in Vertebrata above the reptiles. In all these cases two types of color-control factors are present as alternatives or together in the same animal. In one, the classic hormone type, large relatively long-lasting molecules, like polypeptides, act at a distance from their release point. In the other, relatively small, short-lived molecules like acetylcholine or adrenaline are released close to their point of action.[105]

The peripheral neuromuscular system of crustaceans, as discussed above, is quite different from that of vertebrates (Chapter 6, Vol. II). The major comparative distinctions of the crustacean mechanism are the few motor fibers involved, the universal polyneuronal innervation, the absence of classic motor units, the relative unimportance of propagated spikes in the muscles, the high significance in most cases of peripheral facilitation, and the only well-documented instance of peripheral skeletal muscle inhibition. However, the slow muscle fibers of the striated muscles of anomurans may show more comparable neuromuscular relations with vertebrate smooth muscle since in both cases contraction occurs without conducted spikes; also polyneuronal innervation and multiple endings may both be present in this kind of vertebrate neuromuscular system.

The same cholinergic neurohumoral transmission as in vertebrate skeletal muscle is assumed for crustaceans (Chapter 8, Vol. II). Acetylcholine, choline esterase, choline acetylase, and γ-aminobutyric acid are present in the crustacean nervous system as they are in that of vertebrates. However, direct evidence is lacking that Ach is the excitatory transmitter and that GABA is the inhibitory one, although there are grounds for such opinions. Nor is proof available on the degree to which the ultimate influence of each efferent fiber is the result of a specific transmitter substance of its own.

The crustacean CNS, like their peripheral nervous system, differs sharply from that of vertebrates especially in its many fewer neurons, lack of interneuron tracts, preponderance of combined motor and sensory interneurons, and complex synaptic relations (Chapter 7, Vol. II). Slow spontaneous CNS potentials like those common in vertebrates are lacking in crustaceans and many other invertebrates. From a neurological point of view crustacean interneurons resemble those of the vertebrate reticular system in their several kinds of synaptic connections (Chapter 7, Vol. II).

The interaction of response to light and gravity is closely similar in crustaceans and fish.[164] This depends not only on the physiological resemblances of the sensory and reflex mechanisms already discussed, but also on complex activities of the CNS. Thus the turning tendencies which originate in fish utriculi and in the statocysts of *Palaemon, Crangon,* and *Carcinus* summate centrally by the simple addition of the input on the two sides. Similarly in both groups oblique swimming positions or directions are established by maintaining a constant output pattern from the sense organs, as centrifuge experiments prove.[164]

Mechanically fixing a fish's eyes or a natantian's eyestalks results in corresponding cybernetic compensations in the body position independent of any resulting proprioceptor stimulation.[164] This indicates comparable use of reference values in the dorsal light reflex and other visual orientations. In crustaceans, fishes, and mammals central compensation occurs in response to experimentally induced unbalanced equilibrium or visual stimuli. This response gradually builds up to counteract the peripheral asymmetry following unilateral statocyst or utriculus removal. Spontaneous retinal as well as statocyst activity in the absence of external stimuli is present in both crustaceans and fishes. This is apparently concerned with the maintenance of tonus and maximum sensitivity to change although no definitive explanation is available.

Though crustacean migrations (Chapter 12, Vol. II) are not usually thought to be extensive in comparison with those of fishes and birds, one interesting case should be mentioned. This relates to *Eriocheir sinensis,* a catadromous crab which may live more than 600 km from the sea where it was spawned and to which it must return to breed. Relatively little is known about the sensory and behavioral components of this life history although the animal's osmotic and excretory adaptations have been studied (Chapters 9 and 10, Vol. I). It would be interesting to learn whether or not endocrine factors are involved in both the osmotic and the behavioral changes in migratory *Eriocheir* as they are in fishes.[68, 90, 91]

Crustacean behavior includes both rigid and plastic components, but learning seems to make only a restricted contribution (Chapter 13, Vol. II). As cited above, the plasticity exemplified by the appearance of new walking gaits directly and without trial-and-error improvement after limb loss (Chapter 9, Vol. II; von Holst[191]) seems to depend on the pre-existence of alternative pathways in the CNS and the marked overlap of interneuron fields (Chapter 7, Vol. II). Such immediate unlearned adaptive adjustment occurs little, if at all, in vertebrates,[178] a distinction which may depend on the quite different CNS organization in the two classes. Locomotor patterns generally appear to be stereotyped, but the mechanism of limb coordination is various in different forms. Typically in arthropods such coordination is largely determined peripherally by leg joint proprioceptor (crustaceans and most other arthropods) or exteroceptor reflexes (some millipeds like *Geophilus*[191]). In teleosts and amphibians, locomotor coordination is mainly determined centrally by automatic rhythmic centers although the toad requires at least some nonspecific dorsal root input for walking to occur.[77] The steering component in the appetitive activities of crustaceans and vertebrates is determined mainly by exteroceptive stimuli. Yet the resulting kineses and taxes are rarely simple reflexes because the "mood of the CNS, or feedback from it, also participates in modulating even such relatively uncomplicated behavior.[99,164]

Another central integrative influence on behavior in both crustaceans and vertebrates arises from hormonal coordination (Chapters 13 and 15, Vol. I; Chapter 8, Vol. II). For example, the typical sexual behavior of a male *Orchestia gammarellus* is induced by the androgenic gland hormone. This resembles the situation in male vertebrates, which require gonadal hormones for the development of normal mating behavior.[12,147] However, sexual behavior can be quite different in its development and control in various kinds of animal; the external and internal factors involved may not be the same even in males and females of the same species.

IV. *EXPLANATORY COMPARISONS*

Although a strong case can be made that careful descriptive comparisons must always be made first, there is little doubt that explanatory comparisons,* which hypothesize the causal factors under-

---

* The fact that empirical data and straightforward generalizations based thereon provide some intellectual satisfaction suggests that descriptive comparisons in them-

lying the relationships observed, are the comparative physiologist's ultimate objective. While descriptive comparisons may involve only spatial elements, causal relations, as usually defined, contain a temporal sequence.[142] Such deductive or predictive comparisons depend on the formulations of one or more kinds of causal hypotheses which may be primarily 1) genetic, 2) developmental, 3) adaptive, or 4) evolutionary.

The same data might well be considered from all these various points of view, which are mutually exclusive only in certain limited areas. However, rather different time scales are typically involved in the various types of explanation. Adaptive explanations in the physiological sense described below have relatively short temporal extent, usually involving a small fraction of one organism's lifetime; developmental explanations involve a major part or all of a lifetime; evolutionary ones subtend more than one generation and frequently hundreds or thousands; various kinds of genetic explanations span quite different time periods depending on their concern with mechanisms of gene action or matters like long-range genotypic alterations.[192] If these facts are overlooked, confusion may result from attempting to correlate the four kinds of explanation.

Although the arrangement of descriptive data is a first step in making comparisons, note that the same information ordinarily can be arranged in many patterns, some of which will be found particularly suitable for, or suggestive of, a specific kind of explanation. Consequently, examining the fruitfulness of various possible ways of ordering data will be an important methodological step in comparative physiology. Where strong causal relations can be clearly established for a large body of empirical data or for a considerable number of subsidiary hypotheses, the resulting explanation may be considered to be a natural law.[24]

A. GENETIC

Most phenotypic characters of organisms are under the primary control of genetic mechanisms even though nongenetic factors may modulate their expression to a marked degree. Consequently, genetic

---

selves have a certain amount of explanatory content. But this is at the lowest level in the hierarchy of hypotheses and deductions which constitute a well-developed science. Really satisfying explanations require the demonstration of strong causation based on natural laws which have been derived from cause and effect events connected by a continuous temporal chain of intermediate events.[24]

homologies are of basic significance. In fact an animal's genotype will implicitly or explicitly underlie all explanatory comparisons including developmental, adaptive, and phylogenetic ones. For this reason descriptive and explanatory comparisons in general must at least be consistent with the genetic mechanisms known, or inferred, to be involved.

Thus phenotypic similarities may be due to mimic nonhomologous genes[139] or convergent homologous gene mutations.[85] The probability of these occurring is inversely related to the number of genes controlling the function in question. This in turn is often roughly parallel to the complexity of the system considered.[80] On this basis the possibility that any observed pattern of similarities or differences is the result of random genetic variation is high if one or a few genes control the units in question. Pari passu, the likelihood of the pattern's explanation being in some physiologically more interesting area increases with the number of genes concerned in its control.

Direct classic evidence for genetic homology must be obtained from crossbreeding, which is usually possible only in comparisons of individual organisms not more remote than neighboring genera. As a result, interspecific homology of genes must frequently be recognized by the application of criteria quite similar to those of Remane[154] for morphological data: 1) the genes show similar linkage relations, 2) they have comparable pleiotropic effects, 3) the genes occur in similar multiple allelic series, and 4) the structures they control have comparable development and function.[119] The degree to which such criteria can be adequately applied determines the probability of establishing gene homologies.[79]

An alternative biochemical approach to genetic comparisons through a detailed knowledge of the genotypes' nucleoproteins is being actively explored[113] but is still quite speculative. Many other proteins also show high degrees of tissue, individual, and species specificity.[58, 112] Accordingly the opinion has been expressed* that every phenotype ideally could be described in terms of the amino acid sequences and other structural characters of its hierarchy of proteins.[1,113] This suggestion is in line with evidence for the highly precise structure, in-

---

* This notion has the advantage for comparative study of side-stepping unsolved problems concerning the nature of genes and their particular mechanism of action. It does, however, require the fundamental, but probably not unreasonable, assumption that an organism's total complement of proteins exhibits a detailed, if somewhat blurred, image of its genotype. Since quantitative methods of protein analysis are now beginning to be available, this may be an important approach.[1, 188]

cluding amino acid sequences, of the proteins so far studied, and for the one gene-one amino acid correlation implied by the case of sickle cell anemia hemoglobin and that of the species specificity of mammalian insulins.[71,188]

However, some immunological data imply that a whole antigen may be controlled by one or more genes[98] although the chemical nature of the proteins' determinant groups is not yet known.* Furthermore, single gene changes in other cases can lead to elimination, or duplication in new positions, of highly complex integrated systems like complete appendages[74] or body regions.[82] Such genetically controlled molecular or anatomical changes apparently originate through gene action on biosynthetic enzymes[32] and hence on the animal's over-all metabolism.

The data on crustacean genetics are meager although some interesting information is available. Sex chromosomes are known in a number of groups with genetic sex determination (Chapter 13, Vol. I). In branchiopods, ostracods, and decapods male heterogamety is present, while female heterogamety occurs in some copepods and isopods. Races which show polyploid parthenogenesis exist in certain species of branchiopods, ostracods, and isopods. The tetraploid bisexual race of *Artemia* is an exception to the general rule that polyploids are ordinarily parthenogenetic or hermaphroditic.[8] Sexual differentiation in malacostracans is indirectly controlled by genetic factors which determine sex hormone production (Chapter 13, Vol. I).

Mutations have been observed in *Artemia salina*[8] and extensively so in *Gammarus chevreuxi*.[167] Genetic variation of pigmentation has provided favorable study material in the copepods *Tisbe reticulata*,[18] *Porcellidium fimbriatum, P. sarsi, P. lecanioides*,[9] *Tigriopus fulvus*,[23] and in many isopods,[49] including *Armadillidium vulgare*, whose normal black or gray pigmentation may be red under the allelic influence of two other genes effecting synthesis of red melanoid pigment.[94] In natural populations of certain copepods[10] and in the isopod *Jaera marina*[19] a condition of balanced polymorphism exists. The genotypic plasticity implied by this condition may be an important feature in the adaptedness of these crustaceans (Section III,C below; Birch[16]). However, in the isopods *Porcellio* and *Tracheoniscus* no environmental influence occurs in the fluctuating occurrence of a marbled coloration pattern, apparently because the color determining gene is also influential

---

* Serological data on Crustacea are discussed below (Section IV,E) in connection with phylogenic explanations.

in sex determination which has a stronger selective effect.[50] In *Jaera* multifactorial autosomal systems control the allometric growth constants in the different forms concerned (Chapter 16, Vol. I).

B. DEVELOPMENTAL

Many functional differences and similarities between individual animals can be explained in terms of their stage of development. Thus the feeding method (Chapter 6, Vol. I), locomotion (Chapter 9, Vol. II), and visual physiology (Chapter 1, Vol. II) of the nauplius of a penaeid shrimp are quite different from these same functions in the adult animal. The comparative physiologist differs from the developmental biologist in being satisfied in this connection to demonstrate that functional comparisons can be causally related to ontogenetic changes which occur between the stages in question. In contrast, the embryologist requires an explanation relating to physical, chemical, and biological factors which cause an individual to develop from one stage to another or which cause different organs, individuals, or species to develop differently.

Developmental explanatory homologies are derived from descriptive generalizations obtained by tracing the continuity of some part or system through an adequate series of intermediate steps as in Remane's third criterion for homology. Such ontogenetic comparisons obviously cannot be extended over too wide an ontogenetic scale since everything in the individual could ultimately be traced back to the zygote stage, which would not ordinarily provide a useful developmental explanation. Furthermore, the data of experimental embryology indicate that developmental comparisons must be made with great care if phenomena like induction are to be allowed for.[7,100]

In various animal groups the data on physiological ontogeny is extensive. It ranges from descriptions of the appearance or alteration of particular important molecules like antibodies,[45,57,58] enzymes,[102,146] or various metabolites,[44,195,196] to the gradual assembly of complex metabolic cycles,[25,37] regulatory mechanisms,[202] and behavior patterns.[59,93,186] However, the relevant data for crustaceans are few, and it is particularly difficult to make functional ontogenetic comparisons for early stages of development.

With relation to crustacean metabolic ontogeny, oxygen uptake in unfertilized eggs and in diapausing resistant eggs of branchiopods must be extremely low. While fertilization or hatching are followed in general by exponential increases in metabolism with growth (Chapter 2, Vol. I), such activities as cell division, protoplasmic synthesis, tissue or organ differentiation, and metamorphosis must override such regular relations at various times during ontogeny. The influence of such processes, where they have morphometric effects, can be seen in relative growth curves, which show changes in slope and discontinuities at critical stages in development (Chapter 16, Vol. I). Undoubtedly alterations of this kind mark shifts in the metabolic steady state of the animal and are effected by endocrine and other long-term integrating factors.

Growth phenomena have been particularly studied in Crustacea with regard to differentiation of secondary sex characters, like the male gnathopod of amphipods, female abdomen of brachyurans, or male claw of fiddler crabs (Chapters 13 and 16, Vol. I). Such structures develop under continuing hormonal control, but because of ecdyses, their appearance is usually quite abrupt and associated with one or more prepubertal and pubertal molts (Chapter 15, Vol. I). Limb regeneration takes place in a rather similar fashion in the period after leg loss (Chapter 17, Vol. I). In a complex case of sexual maturation like that of the protandrous hermaphrodite isopod *Anilocra* male prepuberty, male puberty, female prepuberty, and female puberty succeed each other respectively at molts 3, 5, 7, and 9 (Chapter 16, Vol. I).

The mechanism of primary and secondary sex differentiation in malacostracans and the endocrine processes involved have been clarified by experimental extirpation or implantation of androgenic glands, ovaries, or testes, especially in *Orchestia* by Charniaux-Cotton (Chapter 13, Vol. I). But the factors which regulate larval molting and metamorphosis are uncertain although possibly X- and Y-organs may begin to function in molt during the later stages of larval development (Chapter 15, Vol. I). In crabs like *Maja, Callinectes,* and *Cancer,* molting ceases at puberty as in most insects; this anecdysis is mainly effected by Y-organ degeneration in some species or by heightened X-organ activity in others.

Striking functional changes may be expected when a particular system differentiates or degenerates. Thus, in the zoeal stage of a penaeid, compound eyes are present in addition to the naupliar eye already functional in earlier stages. On the other hand the lateral eyes of the cyprid larva of barnacles become vestigial and internal at metamorphosis. The development of the naupliar eye in branchiopods like *Triops* is a complicated process involving in part a proliferation zone also important in compound eye and optic tract differentiation.[47] This complex derivation may well be reflected in functional properties of this system as in the lateral eye of the insect *Notonecta*, where the retinal area formed embryonically is color sensitive and that formed postembryonically is color blind.[158]

Behavioral, as well as purely sensory, changes accompany not only such obvious structural alterations, but also more subtle ontogenetic modifications. For instance, the nauplii of Anostraca, the nauplii and cyprid larvae of cirripedia as well as *Homarus* larvae all tend to be positively phototactic at early stages, then become less so, or negative, later (Chapter 10, Vol. II). Also vertical distribution and extent of diurnal vertical migration may vary with development. For example, metanauplii of *Euphausia superba* and *Bosmina coregoni* occur in deep water. Later larval stages migrate diurnally, and the adolescents remain permanently near the surface (Chapter 12, Vol. I).

Obviously, alterations in activity relating to mating behavior (Chapter 13, Vol. I), courtship displays (Chapter 13, Vol. II), maternal care, and other reproductive functions appear at puberty. They are often cyclic thereafter. Other ethological, as well as structural, changes are most striking in development when successive stages have quite different ecological relations, like benthic in contrast to pelagic, free-swimming as opposed to sessile, or free-living compared with parasitic.

C. Adaptive

Living things exist only when a large number of factors are present together both within the organism and in its surroundings. From the physiologist's point of view, biological survival is caused by, in the sense of being an invariable consequence of, the presence of a highly specific multivariate physical and chemical complex. Any of its numerous components which are essential for survival may be said to be adaptive. Deviations of any factor which lead to the system's displacement from an optimal biological state (operationally defined for particular cases in terms of some measurement like growth rate, metabolic rate, reproductive rate, species survival and so on) are maladaptive or negatively adaptive; changes which result in the system approaching or reaching an optimal state are positively adaptive.

Clearly, changes which result in a life or death alternative are at one extreme of those possible; those which have no detectable effect on survival are at the other extreme. As defined here adaptations and adaptive alterations can only be recognized by experiments; these must prove or measure each relevant factor's influence on survival on the appropriate time scale.[192] In this sense physiology is the study of the functional relations of organisms in the light of the myriad factors which cause them to be alive.

Several important categories of adaptive explanation exist. Most obvious is the Darwinian type of adaptedness, in which organismal factors can be related to environmental factors in a moderately simple way. The correlation usually found between desert habitat and water-conserving mechanisms is an example.[39, 162] Less obvious but equally important adaptive characters are the internal elements concerned with metabolic systems and their regulation (Florkin;[67] Chapter 12, Vol. I). For example, factors like molting hormones or resting potentials, while important in growth and response mechanisms, are themselves involved in the animal's environmental interactions only in indirect complex ways.*

Nevertheless, environmental changes may induce such displacements in these internal factors that the position of the optimal biological state is shifted to a new adaptive range. In essence this property of living systems is reminiscent of Le Chatelier's principle which states the tendency of physical and chemical systems in equilibrium to react to change by adjustments which tend to minimize the effects of the change.[73] Internal biological responses of this kind may be phenotypic acclimations to such environmental alterations as decreased or increased temperatures (Chapters 2 and 12, Vol. I; references[1, 106, 150, 187]); if they involve natural selection of genotypes they are more appropriately considered under genetic or phylogenetic explanations.[16, 117] Homeostatic mechanisms are, however, one of the important characteristic features of the physiological domain.

Self-regulating systems of this kind have sometimes been considered to require a noncausal teleological explanation perhaps expressed in nonintentional, but yet goal-directed, terms.[24, 109] However, the statement that over a considerable range of external and internal conditions a lobster maintains a specific level of blood Mg^{++} is just an empirical datum, or more correctly an inductive generalization based on many observations (Chapter 9, Vol. I). For a physiologist to "explain" the Mg^{++} exchange in the antennal glands and gills by saying that they are directed toward the goal of regulating the ion at some specific

---

* Another proposed way of discriminating adaptations is to classify as exogenous those, like epidermal callosities, which appear directly related to an external stimulus, and as endogenous those, like sweat glands, which do not have such a direct correlation with the environment.[192]

blood level in milligrams per milliliter would seem quite unscientific and provide little, if any, intellectual satisfaction. This would be obtained only when the observations are given a causal explanation.*

Many of the predominantly internal aspects of crustacean physiology could be examined from the point of view of their adaptive explanation. For example, the circulation of crustaceans and other arthropods, as mentioned above in Section III,D,1 is a so-called open system and differs as a whole from that in mollusks, annelids, and vertebrates. This distinctive arthropod organization may be functionally related to the special problem of maintaining effective blood supply to the tissues during ecdysis (Chapters 5 and 15, Vol. I). In turn the "cryptic" neuromuscular junction of crustaceans has been explained as an adaptation to polyneuronal neurohumoral transmission with an open circulatory system (Chapter 8, Vol. II).

On the environmental side, complex systems of interrelations concerned with survival may be seen in a number of important characteristics of ecological niches. Thus competition, predation, productivity, and organism or population growth are not simply related to any elementary physiological functions. Nevertheless in population studies over-all adaptive relations may be quantitatively studied as functions of genotype and survival.[117a,192]

In addition, there are a host of adaptive functions which depend on the nature of the universe and of matter and energy. These are not often explicitly considered but clearly have a strongly restrictive effect both on the types of environment available,[88] and on the structures and functions possible for living things.[11,80,128,145,160,172,186] As L. J. Henderson elegantly demonstrated nearly fifty years ago, the fitness of the environment is complementary to the fitness of the organism.[88] Thus life depends on the existence of a strictly limited selection of specific elements and molecules as well as on the quantal, thermodynamic, and kinetic properties of matter in general. Physiological optics is fundamentally like camera optics, and retinal photochemistry is basically related to photons, as is any inorganic photochemical system. Hence there may be few or essentially no alternative solutions to specific problems of physiological adaptation. Clearly, recognition of such fundamental restrictions cannot be based on lack of knowledge or the concept will give rise only to specious explanations.

---

* The notion that learning and heredity also require peculiar noncausal ("mnemic" in their case) explanations[24] seems equally unsatisfactory from a physiological point of view.

While the danger of using lack of knowledge as evidence is a serious one, a number of crustacean systems may be mentioned where few or no alternative physiological solutions seem to be available for solving particular problems. Thus a close similarity in basic energy-producing mechanisms is evident in Crustacea as in all living things (Chapters 2, 3, and 8, Vol. I; Krebs[108, 109]). Glycolysis, the Krebs cycle, and the electron transfer system through the cytochromes seem fundamentally the same in plants, animals, and most microorganisms. However, alternative pathways are well known in parts of the reaction chain and specific components may differ markedly in detail even within a single cell or between forward and backward reactions. Further study will undoubtedly prove that adaptive and evolutionary differences in detail occur, but present knowledge of crustacean energy metabolism is far less satisfactory than for insects,[157] cephalopods,[72] and vertebrates.

More specific, systematically widely distributed components present in Crustacea may also come into the present category where few if any physiological alternatives are known. For example, the quantitative amino acid composition of crustacean muscle is sufficiently like that of various fishes, amphibians, reptiles, birds, and mammals to suggest a uniform pattern for all animal muscle protein (Chapter 8, Vol. I). This is consonant with the apparent correlation of any considerable amount of mechanical work in animals with the contractile protein, actomyosin, and the close similarity of the pattern of exogenous amino acids required in the diets of all animal species (from protozoans to man) which have been carefully studied.[104]

Evidence is accumulating that the functional centers of proteins which endow them with the properties of antigens, enzymes, and hormones in various animals often appear as a common essential core within total molecules which otherwise vary in ways not yet known to be functionally significant.[1, 46, 71, 107, 188]

Conjugated proteins also may show widespread or universal dependence on a specific prosthetic group which does not vary while the protein moiety may vary much or little. For instance, the same iron porphyrin is the prosthetic group of hemoglobin, cytochrome c, catalase, and peroxidase. Between these different types of molecules the proteins differ markedly, but within any one type small differences distinguish the particular protein part of the molecule as it occurs in various situations.

This is true of the hemoglobins which occur widely as respiratory pigments in entomostracans as well as many other organisms (Chapters

2, 3, and 12, Vol. I). Protoheme is the prosthetic group in all hemo-globins, and the pigment's peculiar properties in various species and developmental stages depend on relatively small structural differences in the globin moiety. In crustaceans the apparent molecular weight of their hemoglobins is twice that of insect hemoglobins and six times that of mammals, although in crustaceans it is much smaller than in annelids.

Hemoglobins are not the only plasma proteins that may increase the respiratory capacity of crustacean blood. The hemocyanins of decapods and stomatopods (Chapters 2 and 3, Vol. I) are an alterna-tive. Rather similar copper-containing respiratory chromoproteins also occur in the plasma of gastropods, cephalopods, xiphosurans, and arachnids. Although only entomostracan crustaceans may contain hemoglobins, and only malacostracans, hemocyanins, many members of both groups contain neither, and some in both groups may have their respiratory pigment present only under certain conditions or periodically. Explanations of these facts require further experimental and biochemical work especially in the case of hemocyanins because molecular weight, amino acid composition, copper and nitrogen content are known to vary considerably in this type of molecule.

Another example may be taken from carotenoid protein complexes. All biochemically known visual responses are mediated by vitamin A aldehyde attached to different specific protein opsins (Chapter 7, Vol. I; Chapter 1, Vol. II). The latter presumably determine the charac-teristic features of the absorption spectra, and hence the detailed spec-tral sensitivity of the various species.[44, 75, 138] These generalities hold at least for two decapods, possibly a euphausiid, the honeybee, a dipteran, a squid, and all vertebrates. The comparative biochemistry of this sys-tem in crustaceans has been so little studied that bare statements of its occurrence are about all that can be made. But in insects apparently and in vertebrates, more than one such photosensitive conjugated protein may be present in the same retina. Changes during development may occur[196] and in closely related forms different specific pigments may be present, all conforming to the general type.[48]

Most of these differences are due to the specific opsins concerned, but two different classes of teleost photopigments were shown by Wald[193] to depend on a slight difference in the saturation of their carotenoid prosthetic groups. Surveys of the distribution of these two pigment types indicate that retinene$_1$ (vitamin A$_1$ aldehyde) is the carotenoid moiety of the visual pigments of crustaceans and all other invertebrates studied, as well as of most marine and terrestrial vertebrates; retinene$_2$ (which has one more conjugated double bond than retinene$_1$) occurs in most fresh-water teleosts and amphibians.[194]

Wald has interpreted this distribution pattern in vertebrates from an evolutionary point of view.[194, 196] However, the genetic basis of such stability at so simple a biochemical level is uncertain unless the character has adaptive significance and hence is maintained precisely by natural selection. However, no adaptive significance has been proved for the two retinenes in spite of a strong correlation of retinene$_2$ with fresh-water habitat and mixtures of the two retinenes with euryhaline vertebrates.[138, 194] Furthermore, new data apparently inconsistent with interpretations of the older information suggest that present explanations may be premature.[49, 195]

Adaptive significance has, on the other hand, been suggested for the position of the absorption maximum of photochemical systems of crustaceans living in deeper water where daylight intensities are strongly attenuated. Vitamin A is ordinarily present in large amounts in pelagic, and especially deeper water pelagic, crustaceans. Mesopelagic or bathypelagic euphausiids have the highest concentrations, and 90% of it is localized in the eyestalks. In contrast to pelagic species, benthic or littoral amphipods, mysidaceans, euphausiids, and decapods have little or no detectable vitamin A in their tissues (Chapter 7, Vol. I). Furthermore, two pelagic species studied apparently do have the wavelength of maximum absorption of their visual pigments displaced to 460–465 mμ, which is near the wavelength of maximum transmittance for clear oceanic water (Chapter 1, Vol. II). This could be of adaptive significance since transmittance of sea water is such that a shift of this sort would increase the perceived daylight intensity at a given depth and considerably augment the maximum depth for vision. A comparable displacement in the wavelength sensitivity curves of deep-water fishes has been explained in the same way.[52, 138]

Where more than one adaptive alternative is available, different functional systems may be present to solve similar problems. Biological elements which fulfill the same adaptive requirement were called analogous by Owen whether or not they are also homologous in his sense of the word. Other definitions of analogy[141, 154, 159, 172] have also been used. Most frequently, alternative definitions of analogy have made it antithetical to homology, so that analogous structures could not be homologs. Thus in Owen's sense the pectoral fin of a whale and the wing-flipper of a penguin would be at the same time descriptively homologous and functionally analogous. For the principal alternative kind of analogy these vertebrate pectoral appendages could not be analogs because they are homologs. Analogy in this sense would be found only in cases where different structures, which are not descriptively homologous, do the same thing, like the wing of a cicada and the wing of a sea gull.

In the present discussion Owen's definition will be used for analogy, and other shades of meaning indicated by modifiers. Methodologically the careful determination of basic functional similarities, following the Remane model, is particularly important since the mere presence of a given recognizable unit like hemoglobin,[163] prolactin,[78] or melanophore-stimulating hormone[71] does not directly identify the functional system to which it belongs. It may in fact do different things in different places.

Not only may a variety of functional means be used by different animals in adapting to some special ecological situation,[154] but also a given configuration of physiological characters may tolerate or adjust to a wide range of ecological conditions. The means of achieving a limited degree of terrestrialness in isopods, anomurans, and brachyurans exemplifies the former situation, while the adaptations of various euryhaline or eurythermal crustaceans could be cited for the second. As a result of such complex interrelations, the actual distributions of animals are affected by so many factors that even species with rather special requirements vary from being sharply endemic (like *Thermosbaena*) to nearly cosmopolitan (like *Triops*).[123, 124] Nevertheless certain cases of geographical distribution can be largely accounted for in terms of the interaction of one environmental parameter with a relatively simple element in the biological system. Thus the distributions of different species of the isopod *Limnoria* correspond quite well with their optimal temperatures for reproduction.[14]

Perhaps the broadest and most coherent range of ecological adaptive correlations in crustaceans may be found in the general area of water balance and ionic regulation (Chapters 9 and 10, Vol. I). Most crustaceans are aquatic; the marine forms are mainly isosmotic with the environment and have relatively unspecialized excretory abilities. Yet ionic regulation is universal and extends to every ion. Such an efficient regulatory system is probably required by crustaceans in general to re-establish normal ionic balance after ecdysis (Chapters 4 and 15, Vol. I). If so, this regulatory ability might then permit forms to adjust for living in brackish water,[155] fresh water, and brine.

Adaptation to fresh water is present in many crustacean groups; most branchiopods, many copepods and ostracods, as well as some anaspidaceans, thermosbaenaceans, isopods, amphipods, mysids, macrurans, and brachyurans live in fresh water. Of the few forms studied physiologically, crayfishes seem best adapted since they can conserve ions by producing hypotonic urine. However, the apparent low rate of urine flow in crayfishes is difficult to reconcile with the other data. Since the excretory organs of *Gammarus pulex* and *Asellus aquaticus* resemble those of crayfish in being large and in containing an extra segment, hyposmotic urine production has been suggested for these two forms also (Chapter 10, Vol. I).

A second group of crustaceans seems less well adapted to fresh water; this includes the crabs *Potamon* and *Eriocheir*, the caridean *Palaemonetes antennarius*, as well as the branchiopods *Triops*, *Branchipus*, and *Chirocephalus*. None of these survive for long in distilled water. The decapods have blood hyposmotic to sea water, which reduces the metabolic work needed to remove water absorbed osmotically, but they produce isosmotic urine. This is exceptional in fresh-water animals and must entail considerable losses of ions particularly if the urine flow rate is high as it is in *Palaemonetes antennarius*. The elimination of larval development in crayfish and in *Potamon*, as well as the long seaward migration of *Eriocheir* to breed, may be correlated with fresh-water adaptation. However, branchiopods in fresh water regularly hatch as nauplii which gradually develop into adults through a series of molts (Chapter 9, Vol. I).

In brackish-water crustaceans there is little evidence of functional adaptation although some of them maintain hyperosmotic blood and increase the rate of urine flow in dilute media. The facts suggest that the brine-living forms, *Artemia* and the copepod *Canthocamptus*, most resemble fresh-water relatives although the saline species maintain blood hyposmotic to the environment. Euryhaline crabs, like *Carcinus* and *Potamon*, have greater amounts of intracellular nonprotein amino acids when adapted to sea water than they do when adapted to a less saline environment. This might be a significant factor in their osmotic acclimation, but the question has not yet been studied (Chapter 12, Vol. I). Euryhalinity in crabs, as in fishes, is associated with greater amounts of riboflavin (Chapter 7, Vol. I), but the adaptive significance of this fact is not known.

Since crustacean bioluminescence is limited to marine forms, some adaptive correlation might be expected between these two factors. But cirripeds, nebaliaceans, tanaidaceans, and stomatopods are exclusively marine groups, yet have no luminous species, while ostracods and copepods have numerous fresh-water representatives. However, the luminous mysidaceans, euphausiids, and natantians occur not only in groups that are predominantly or exclusively marine, but also in groups which are mainly pelagic and bathypelagic in habit. No clear adaptive pattern can be seen for bioluminescence in crustaceans; this is also true for the animal kingdom as a whole.[83]

Crustacean adaptedness to terrestrial environments is modest (Chapter 11, Vol. I). Lack of an impermeable integument (Chapter 14, Vol. I) and absence of any adjustment of major end products of nitrogen metabolism to availability of water (Chapter 10, Vol. I) mean that even in the most terrestrial species water conservation is inefficient. Some sparing of water is effected apparently by reducing the amount of nitrogen metabolism (Chapters 10 and 11, Vol. I); the latter may be regulated in certain semiterrestrial isopods and amphipods in accordance with the current availability of water.

In *Birgus* a degree of adjustment of internal osmotic pressure is known to be effected by selective drinking of fresh or salt water, and in semiterrestrial crabs hyposmotic regulation occurs (Chapter 10, Vol. I). However, terrestrial crustaceans in general seem to be osmotically tolerant rather than osmotically independent (Chapter 11, Vol. I). All except oniscoideans have larval stages which must live in water, and the adult itself must be in a number of cases return to the sea more or less frequently. But even the most terrestrial crustaceans spend a large proportion of their time in air saturated or nearly saturated with water; they succeed as land animals essentially by being cryptozoic.

Some other crustacean adaptive variations are well enough known to permit comparisons. For example, resistance to low partial pressures of oxygen in four species of amphipod, in *Asellus*, and in several crayfishes varies with the likelihood of there being inadequate amounts of oxygen present in the normal environment (Chapter 2, Vol. I). Likewise in a series of isopods and amphipods the ability to regulate ventilation apparently is related to the same factor. A somewhat similar adaptation to low partial pressures of oxygen is seen in the branchiopods which, as cited above (Section III,D,2), can synthesize hemoglobin and cytochrome under respiratory stress (Chapter 12, Vol. I). The amounts of riboflavin present in various isopods are inversely related to ambient oxygen partial pressures (Chapter 7, Vol. I). In a number of crabs greater terrestrialness involves an increased rate of oxygen uptake and a concomitant reduction in relative gill area per gram which could be related to water conservation or the increased accessibility of oxygen in air (Chapter 2, Vol. I).

Evidence from cave crustaceans suggests that in forms not usually subjected to environmental stress, thermal and osmotic changes have proportionately larger metabolic effects than they do in species regularly exposed to a more variable environment (Chapter 12, Vol. I). Homeostatic mechanisms thus seem better developed where they are ordinarily required. This is compatible with the reduction or absence of eyes, loss of pigmentation, and lowered metabolic rate that are also common in cave species.

The situation in the deep sea must be rather different because eyes may be relatively enormous and pigmentation unusually intense in habitats where daylight intensities are low or negligible. The most likely factor responsible for such differences is the widespread presence in the mesopelagic and bathypelagic zones of well-developed light organs not only in crustaceans, but also in cephalopods and fishes (Chapter 5, Vol. II; Harvey[83]). Photometric measurements demonstrate the considerable contribution made by bioluminescence to underwater illumination near the limits of the photic zone and below it.[38, 101]

However, certain conditions in the abyssopelagic and hadopelagic zones may be more like those in caves, since light organs, eyes, and pigmentation are often, but not always, reduced or absent in these extreme deep-sea regions as they often are in caves.[26] No decapods have been caught below 6000 m (where the pressure is about 600 atmospheres), suggesting that high hydrostatic pressures may effect some metabolic limitation. But other crustaceans are found at 6000 m and greater depths, including isopods and amphipods from the Philippine Trench (10,210 m), as well as pelagic or benthic ostracods, copepods, cirripeds, tanaidaceans, cumaceans, and mysidaceans between 6500 and 7500 m.[26] Some species appear to be stenobathic, others eurybathic; hence physiological adaptations related to pressure will be quite directly involved in range determination, as are those for temperature and salinity.

Ecological and physiological interactions in crustacean symbioses constitute another field of great potential interest. Commensalism and parasitism are widespread in the class (Chapter 1, Vol. I), but relatively little is known about the comparative physiology of these states. A large number of coherent series can be recognized with different degrees of interdependence between symbiote and host. The latter are often also crustaceans because all the Epicaridea and most of the Rhizocephala attack members of their own class. Crustaceans live commensally with a wide variety of sessile animals ranging from sponges to tunicates and often show related complex behavioral adaptations (Chapter 13, Vol. II).

Among the parasitic forms, series of increasing degrees of specialization occur with feeding habits (Chapter 6, Vol. I), dependent either on the piercing, biting, or sucking mouth parts common in epiparasitic copepods and isopods, or on the rootlike absorptive organs, perhaps derived from the peduncle, in parasitic cirripeds.[34] Either kind of series may reach its furthest specialization with internal parasites of greatly simplified structure like entoniscid isopods or rhizocephalan cirripeds. In view of the marked structural alterations commonly present in symbiotic forms, equally drastic functional specialization may be expected.

Respiratory adaptations may well occur, for example, in the copepods which live in echinoderm and tunicate digestive tracts. Parasites are known to have metabolic effects on crustacean hosts (Chapter 12, Vol. I), but there are relatively few data available. Microorganisms in the digestive tract of *Oniscus asellus* are reported to provide thiamine to the isopod (Chapter 7, Vol. I), while bacteria in *Porcellio scaber* supply chitinase and cellulase. This latter relation is an exception to the general rule that the intestinal microflora and microfauna of crustaceans do not seem to contribute to their host's digestive capacities (Chapter 8, Vol. I).

Reproductive adaptations of parasitic crustaceans commonly involve hermaphroditism, sometimes including self-fertilization. Dwarf parasitic males may be present, and both gnathiidean and epicaridean isopods have special larvae generally absent in peracaridans which are ordinarily epimorphic (Chapter 1, Vol. I). Such elaboration of post-embryonic development is consistent with the complex life histories of many parasitic crustaceans (Chapter 15, Vol. I) in which there may be more than one host, as in parasitic protozoans and worms. Sex determination in some parasitic copepods, as well as bopyrid and entoniscid isopods, depends on whether or not the larvae settle on a host or on a female of their own species. In the former case they become female, in the latter male. This type of phenotypic sex determination resembles that in the echiuroid *Bonellia* (Chapter 13, Vol. I).

D. EVOLUTIONARY

Hypotheses explaining similarities and differences between biological units in terms of evolution may be formulated from descriptive homologies if the assumption is made that basic similarity is a direct reflection of relationship. In that case the number and closeness of the structural and functional descriptive homologies which can be established between the two entities being compared, determine the closeness of their relation in an evolutionary sense. Such relationships may be quantified and used as a basis for establishing phylogenies by several different techniques. The method of homology bridges[154] is a simple example. In this procedure graphic inclusion of species or types each sharing one of a series of important homologous characters within a common perimeter is used to demonstrate the distribution of known similarities and differences. Counting the bridges so formed provides a semiquantitative estimate of relationship.

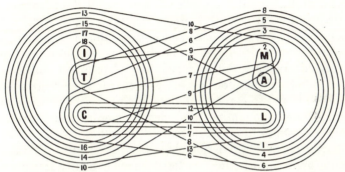

Fig. 1. Relationships between six orders of the Superorder Peracarida demonstrated by the method of homology bridges. Groups sharing any of the 18 descriptive homologies studied are enclosed within a perimeter. The bridges so formed clearly indicate that there are two groups of three orders which form two major divisions of the superorder. A, Amphipoda; C, Cumacea; I, Isopoda; L, Lophogastrida; M, Mysida; T, Tanaidacea; 1, pyloric funnel; 2, all limbs present at hatching; 3, dorsal anterior ceca; 4, pyloric bristle sieve; 5, completely functional antennal glands; 6, frontal organ; 7, primary gills; 8, paired segmental arteries; 9, accessory gills; 10, embryo flexed dorsally in egg; 11, esophageal flap valve; 12, tripartite ventral part of cardiac stomach; 13, maxillary glands; 14, syncytial mid-gut; 15, dorsal hook plate in gastric mill; 16, last thoracic appendages absent at hatching; 17, stage without oöstegites after each brood; 18, secondary gills. (Redrawn from Siewing.[168])

This procedure has been applied by Siewing[168,169] in comparative morphological studies of interrelationships within the Peracarida (Fig. 1) and the Malacostraca. In an analysis of the occurrence of 18 predominantly morphological features in four orders and two suborders of peracaridans, homology bridges demonstrate that two major subgroups are present, consisting on the one hand of Lophogastrida, Mysida, and Amphipoda, and on the other of Cumacea, Tanaidacea, and Isopoda (Chapter 1, Vol. I).

More quantitative methods of estimating taxonomic affinity have been cited above (Section II). One problem in applying all such techniques is the weighting assigned to each character. If only a few parameters are used, this may cause serious difficulties, but if many (of the order of 100) are used, weighting may have little or no importance, presumably because the characters chosen are then a random sample of all those which constitute the organism.[177]

The reduction of multidimensional comparative data by such procedures to a single coordinate representing degree of evolutionary relationship is subject to a serious obstacle arising from the need to assume constant and equal rates of evolution for all the parameters used (the basic assumption usually is that resemblance and relationship are proportional). The common occurrence of parallel, convergent, and regressive evolution as well as quite different evolutionary rates for various characters or animals make this assumption liable to gross error if no other information is used in constructing phylogenies.

Actually all possible relevant data including paleontological, zoogeographic, genetic, adaptive, and developmental must be carefully considered in establishing phylogenetic hypotheses even when these rest primarily on descriptive homologies.[55, 125, 154, 161, 171, 209] Where available, stratigraphic information on fossil forms is highly important since it is usually the least indirect way of establishing chronological relationships or even just direction of evolutionary change.[15] When all possible information has been assembled and organized, evolutionary deductions or predictions can be made. These may be either on a restricted scale where evidence for convergent or parallel evolution of some element, like loss of free-swimming larvae or the number of propulsive limbs used in locomotion,[129] is weighed. A crustacean example may be seen in the studies of chromosomal and taxonomic evolution within the superspecies *Jaera marina* and related isopods.[181]

On the other hand, the study may be on a large scale ranging more or less widely through animal groups and evolutionary time. In this latter case, a phylogenetic tree is often used to summarize the complex interrelations inferred. Thus Vandel[189, 190] has developed a phylogeny for terrestrial isopods based on zoogeographic, paleontological, genetic, and morphological information. Many similar hypotheses have been proposed for other small groups (e.g. Siewing[168]) as well as the larger taxa;[153, 169, 170, 174] a modification of the tree for crustaceans is presented below (Fig. 3). Clearly the validity of any such two- or three-dimensional phylogenetic diagram depends on the success with which the multivariate taxonomic parameters can be reduced to so few coordinates.

In establishing evolutionary causal relations to explain comparative physiological data there are two extreme approaches. On the one hand, the functional data may be assigned to the appropriate taxonomic position in a phylogenetic system which has already been substantially worked out on the basis of other evidence. If the distribution of the physiological characters shows congruence with at least some major branchings of the phylogenetic tree, the conclusion is then drawn that the elements being compared are homologs in the Darwinian evolutionary sense and that their similarities and differences can be explained thereby.

This procedure has the advantage of being relatively easy if taxonomists and evolutionists provide a ready-made phylogeny. It also permits phylogenetic "explanations" of a sort to be made on the basis of little new data. However, this approach contributes nothing new to knowledge about evolution unless the basic similarities and differences have been worked out with care and in detail comparable to those already used in deducing the phylogeny in the first place, or in other words, if a descriptive procedure like that spelled out by Remane[154] has not been followed. Consequently, such an approach may easily lead to over-optimistic estimates of our understanding; when more adequate analysis is made, serious re-evaluation may be required, as with the supposed embryonic recapitulation in the chick of the evolution of vertebrate nitrogen excretion[56] and the evolution of phosphagens in the animal kingdom.[61]

On the other hand, the functional data itself may first be used to establish a detailed and orderly pattern of relationships. If this is done adequately, a self-contained phylogeny or fragment thereof may be derived primarily on the basis of physiological data. Then this physiological phylogeny can be compared point by point with the pattern of evolutionary development hypothesized on the basis of all previously available evidence. In cases where this alternative has been carefully followed, the physiological family tree hypothesized has been closely similar to the one independently derived from other data, as would be expected if methods of establishing phylogeny in general are valid.[33, 89, 154, 209] Usually some details are different in the two resulting phylogenies, and these suggest points where all the evidence needs reconsideration or extension to resolve the dilemma.

Obviously this second approach to the evolutionary explanation of comparative physiological data is much to be preferred. It makes a definite contribution to evolution in its own right and is demonstrably more likely to lead to significant hypotheses and predictions. The reason this method is not always used doubtless arises from the infrequency with which adequate data are applied to the task and to some extent from imperfect appreciation of the methodology by biochemists and physiologists.

The rest of this section is an attempt to apply these general principles to crustacean physiological data.

To examine possible correlations of crustacean comparative physiology with their phylogeny, the fairly extensive data on osmotic relations and terrestrialness, discussed above in Section IV,C, may be reconsidered. To begin with, Recent species of those malacostracan groups which on paleontological and comparative morphological evidence[169] seem most primitive (Chapter 1, Vol. I) are all marine. On this basis we may tentatively conclude that malacostracans in other habitats have evolved from marine forms.* Unfortunately, ionic and osmotic relations have not been studied in any of the crucial primitive groups although known crustacean excretory patterns imply a central position for the marine forms (Chapter 10, Vol. I).

Tentative acceptance of this point permits us to formulate certain hypotheses about the routes followed and the phylogenetic homologies of the adaptive changes concerned. The semiterrestrial and terrestrial series of crustaceans originates in neritic forms and moves onto the land through the littoral zone of rocks, beach, or marsh (Chapter 11, Vol. I). This must have happened at least four times independently since the amphipod beach fleas, oniscoideans, anomurans, and brachyurans with terrestrial tendencies are far less closely related to one another in other ways than they are to fully aquatic marine forms in their own systematic groups.

In most cases these evolutionary transitions are made within the scope of single genera or families. However, a continuous and probably phylogenetically homologous series showing increasing terrestrialness can be cited from the oniscoidean isopods (Chapter 11, Vol. I). In this group terrestrialness of habitat, ability to survive in dry air, and structural specialization can all be arranged roughly in the same order of families, starting with the least developed and ranging successively to the most highly adapted: Ligiidae, Trichoniscidae, Oniscidae, Porcellionidae, and Armadillidiidae. Such a series derived from physiological-ecological data is the same as the one hypothesized on the basis of extensive morphological and chromosomal evidence.[190]

The presence in primitive insects (Entotrophi and Thysanura), as

---

* Note, however, that the question of fresh-water or marine origin even of vertebrates, much better documented both paleontologically and physiologically than the crustacean case, can still be seriously argued both ways.[156]

well as in the related myriapod Symphyla, of extensive internal aerial respiratory organs and a definitely waterproof integument is in marked contrast to even the most terrestrial oniscoidean. Other physiological deficiencies for further evolution of terrestrialness in crustaceans have been cited above (Section IV,C). The several postulated sequences of semiterrestrial and terrestrial crustacean evolution, while not supported directly by paleontological data, are at least consistent with the evidence that the groups in which landward movements occurred are among the most advanced peracaridans and reptantians.

The fresh-water malacostracans suggest an evolutionary history derived from marine forms through brackish water.* Again there must have been a number of independent series of fresh-water invasions since isopods, amphipods, carideans, macrurans, and brachyurans seem to have independently evolved in the same direction. As in their terrestrial evolution, so in their physiological adaptations to fresh water, crustaceans have clearly been quite limited. Nevertheless two levels of fresh-water evolution have been reached. In the first the urine is isosmotic with blood, and the animals soon die in distilled water; in the second the urine is hyposmotic and the excretory organs are larger and specialized accordingly. As mentioned above, the crabs and one of the carideans have reached only the first level while the crayfishes and possibly two peracaridans have reached the second. Presumably the crabs and crayfishes each represent independent parallel series of adaptations, but even these are sharply restricted by the scope of available data since the two phylogenetic levels are not represented together in a single series.

Evolution of brine-living forms has occurred from fresh-water species in anostracans and in copepods independently. *Artemia* has evolved the ability to hyporegulate its blood osmotic pressure for living in brine; palaemonids have done so (relative to sea water) as an adaptation to fresh water while certain crabs have as well for a semiterrestrial existence (Chapter 10, Vol. I). The physiological result is therefore convergent, but the ecological significance is different for each and a separate phylogeny must be involved in the three instances.

The case already cited (Section III,D,1 and 2; Table 1) of proprioceptors in a wide variety of animals also illustrates striking con-

---

* The reverse direction has been followed in the evolution of seaward migrations in salmonids, which has been well documented by Hoar[90, 91] from osmotic and behavioral evidence. The physiological data for these teleosts are supported by independent anatomical, ecological, and zoogeographical facts.

vergence and parallelism in their evolution. In general these mechanoreceptors show marked similarities in crustaceans, insects, *Limulus*
and other chelicerates, as well as vertebrates. Stretch receptors of arthropods and vertebrates are particularly interesting.

In crustaceans and two classes of vertebrates, a special receptor
muscle is present to regulate sensitivity by controlling the tension
acting on the sense organ. This allows for central adjustment of receptor sensitivity to current conditions in the system. In decapods and
amphibians this slip of muscle shares its innervation with the main
contractile element and a double, slow and fast, motor innervation is
present. Thus amphibians are more like crustaceans in these respects
than they are like mammals. In the last group the spindle muscle has
its own innervation. This presumably allows for finer control but
requires more complex CNS integration.[63]

The lepidopteran organ parallels in several aspects of its detailed
structure the vertebrate spindle.[66] But within the Class Insecta itself
there are three types of increasing complexity which roughly follow
the generally accepted notions of insect evolutionary advance through
the various orders. This series suggests that the complex decapod abdominal stretch receptor must be convergent with the type in Lepidoptera. The same conclusion for a case of close evolutionary convergence
is even more certain in comparing the arthropod organs with vertebrate
muscle spindles.

Probably the best cases for physiological phylogenies in crustaceans,
as in other animals, can be found in comparative biochemistry and
ethology. Within short taxonomic ranges, biochemical systematics may
be quite effectively worked out with various kinds of molecules, as it
has been for various pigments in butterflies[69] and in *Drosophila*.[96] However, the comparative biochemistry of proteins undoubtedly provides
the ultimate and most decisive data short of nucleoproteins or genes
themselves. The potential strength of such information depends on the
fact discussed above (Section IV,A) that the total protein hierarchy
of an animal shows a high degree of specificity which for certain
components extends down to each individual genotype or even tissue
type.[58] Hence a classification based on similarities and differences in
such protein components potentially is a powerful tool for establishing
phylogenetic relationships. Note, however, that protein specificity may
be low or zero for other components.[1]

Until recently the precise structure of proteins could not be
determined. Even now only a beginning has been made in this important study. Hence less direct methods have been required for com-

parative protein biochemistry. The most useful of these depends on the immunological reactions certain proteins evoke in vertebrates, particularly mammals.[46, 112] In response to antigenic proteins of this sort, antibodies are synthesized; these in turn react strongly with the corresponding (homologous) antigen. Antigens from closely related species or tissues may also react with such an antibody (heterologous reaction), but those from remotely related forms do not react or react weakly. Since the number of chemical groups determining immunological specificity in a large protein like hemocyanin probably reach several hundred,[46] and since the genetic control mechanism seems to consist of many genes,[98] it is not unexpected that a considerable series of heterologous reactions may be obtained with antibodies induced by various animals and tested with various antigens.[22]

The intensity of these heterologous reactions has been assumed to indicate the degree of similarity between the antigens and antibodies concerned; in turn these protein similarities have been interpreted to represent the degree of relationship between the species possessing them. While considerable skepticism has been expressed for some of the techniques used and for unwarranted interpretations of the findings, adequate methods and proper use of data provide generalizations which may be useful in evolutionary explanations.[21, 53, 70, 210]

However, the problem of interpretation is complex. The differences and similarities between proteins are multidimensional and the relationships between antigenic groups which are only parts of the molecules, indicate little or nothing about the rest of its structure. Even so, the assumed correlation between protein molecular structure and evolutionary relationships is subject to the same difficulties of convergence, parallelism, and rates of evolution that are encountered in gross morphology. This is emphasized by the fact already mentioned that in comparing different organisms their protein specificities range from strong to zero. Furthermore the antigenic properties of different proteins also vary from high to negligible.

Despite such problems there are some interesting relevant data. Serum proteins of animals conveniently enough show a high degree of immunological specificity so that they have been extensively studied since the pioneer work of Nuttall on a variety of different animals.[21, 112] In Crustacea, hemocyanin appears to be the main antigenic serum protein[115] so that serological phylogeny has so far been restricted to forms containing this respiratory pigment. No cross reactions have been found between antigens and antisera in the three Phyla Arthropoda, Annelida, and Mollusca.[116] Within the arthropods however, crustacean sera show some relation to that of *Limulus,* but the latter gives stronger heterologous reactions with arachnids, especially scorpions.

Cross reactions have been studied with rabbit antisera prepared against 17 species of decapods from seven systematic groups.[115] As is usually the case, the heterologous reactions of various antigens yield different strengths of interaction with various antisera.[22] Thus the interaction of anticrab serum with all the various antigens establishes a linear array which has the same order but differs quantitatively from that obtained, for example, with antilobster serum and the same antigens. Hence a multidimensional set of relations results from a series of such comparisons. Although the interrelations by no means match exactly, data of this sort can be reduced to three-dimensional models.

Thus in the series of crustacean species studied the four groups of Brachyura involved are closer to one another than to any of the Macrura and Anomura tested (Fig. 2). But, judged on this basis, Scyllaridea and Paguridea are more remote from the Brachyura than are the Nephropsidea. In general the relationships determined serologically for decapods agree with those hypothesized on the basis of morphological and paleontological evidence. This is so even though immunological tests have been run on only a very small fraction of the known species of the various taxa concerned. One may conclude that such comparative studies of proteins, if carried out with adequate techniques, provide a potentially important quantitative series of relationships which may be explained in evolutionary terms and may be weighed with other available evidence of many sorts in establishing phylogenies.

Ethology provides a second good example of a phylogenetic homology in Crustacea even though this is taxonomically quite localized to a single genus of crabs. In showing species-specific behavior whose relationships may be traced through an extensive series, crustaceans seem similar to a number of other animal groups (Chapter 13, Vol. II; references[4, 114, 134, 161]).

In fact the pioneers in the field of ethology were specifically studying behavior patterns for evidence of taxonomic relationships when they made their original contributions to the field.[87, 199] More recently physiological phylogenies based on behavior have been deduced for insects,[6, 41, 62, 126, 161, 179] spiders,[40] fishes,[90, 201] and birds.[134, 186] This considerable body of data and the explanations thereof show that the problems of determining behavioral descriptive homologies and of discovering their probable evolutionary pathways from primitive to advanced

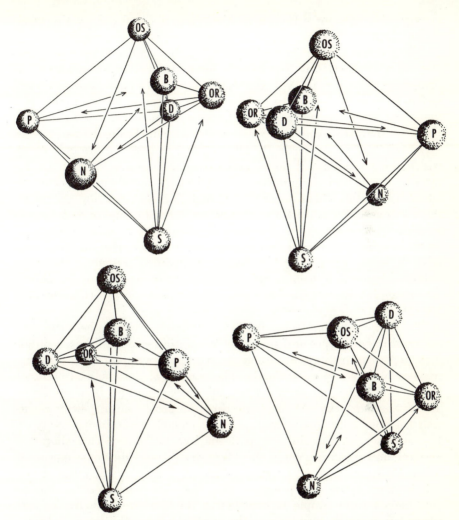

Fɪɢ. 2. Relationships between seven groups of reptantian decapods shown as a three-dimensional model drawn from four directions. The spheres represent the groups; the shortness of the connecting rods, their degree of serological similarity. The fact that all the rods do not fit indicates that the actual relationships are multidimensional, and reducing them to three dimensions causes some inconsistencies. In a phylogenetic series, S would probably be most primitive, with N and P being successively derived from this ancestral stock, and with the four crab groups, B, D, OR, and OS, being the most highly evolved types. B, Brachyrhyncha; D, Dromiacea; N, Nephropsidea; OR, Oxyrhyncha; OS, Oxystomata; P, Paguridea; S, Scyllaridea. (Redrawn from Leone.[115])

to regressive are not different in kind from those faced by the morphologist.[4, 62, 114, 134, 161, 180]

For crustaceans, Crane's continuing studies on the behavior of fiddler crabs in the Genus *Uca* provide the best data for evolutionary explanations (Chapter 13, Vol. II). About 50 species have been analyzed so far. Most of the evidence is for courtship displays by the males, but there are some species-specific fighting movements, too.[43] Two main types of male courting are present: 1) in which the large claw is waved up and down vertically and copulation is above ground; 2) in which the large claw is flexed and extended laterally moving the tip more or less in a circle and the male entices the female into his burrow where copulation takes place.[42] Although Type 1 courting occurs in those species of *Uca* which have a narrow-fronted carapace and Type 2 in those with broad fronts, there are no obvious morphological features which specifically restrict the display movements to two different patterns in these groups. It has been repeatedly observed in different animal groups that behavioral differences may be present in sibling species which cannot be differentiated morphologically (Chapter 13, Vol. II; Baerends,[6] Mayr[134]).

Parallel evolution from simple to complex courting behavior has occurred in both types of display. As in mantids, spiders, fishes, reptiles, and birds with display, the trend in *Uca* appears to be toward increasing conspicuousness of the male. The waving of the cheliped becomes higher and wider; in certain cases this beckoning also becomes faster and somewhat jerky. At the same time the accompanying body elevation becomes both higher and more prolonged. In both display types the species with the simplest patterns live along protected shores of streams and estuaries while the most conspicuous displays appear in forms living on exposed seaward beaches.[42] Two kinds of internal evidence support the interpretation that the evolutionary series has in fact moved from simple to complex in the cases studied. In the first place low-intensity displays of the species having the most elaborate courtship resemble the full display in those with the simpler patterns. Second, a number of the species having the most complex courtship show displacement behavior in conflict situations between display and flight.

This information may suggest that the simple end of the species-specific series of behavior patterns is the primitive one, but as is usually the case, highly convincing conclusions about such things require paleontological evidence, which naturally is sharply restricted in ethology.[161] Stronger conclusions may become possible when the ethological data are compared with all other available information which has a bearing on ocypodid crab evolution.

In retrospect, crustacean comparative physiology appears to offer a promising source of generalizations which are capable of evolutionary explanation. The available data, however, can do little more than imply such potentialities since they are mainly on a small scale and scattered through the class in a way little related to probable phylogeny. In comparison with the morphological and other information routinely used in establishing taxonomic relations most physiological and biochemical evidence is weak even for animals better known in these respects than crustaceans.

Consequently, good progress in this area can be expected only when more extensive data are deliberately taken with the possibility of phylogenetic homologies in mind and when the particular species and systems studied have been chosen for their relevance to the problem. To do this, other evidence for relationship should be used in designing new experiments. More specifically the physiology of apparently primitive, advanced, regressive, or ancestral species should be compared for evidence supporting or in conflict with present interpretations. Within the Crustacea an effective sample needs to be taken both from closely similar forms and from quite disparate ones. As a stimulus to this kind of programming, a possible phylogeny of Crustacea based on evidence from a variety of fields is presented in Fig. 3. On a broader scale, a similar approach is required, for example, to determine what contributions physiology can make to the vexing problems of arthropod origins, as well as those involved in the relations between crustaceans and other major groups in the phylum.

For comparative physiology to make significant contributions to such problems a well-planned, carefully executed series of measurements is needed for the reasons just mentioned. Furthermore, even extensive comparative morphological, embryological, paleontological, and zoogeographical evidence, all used together, is scarcely adequate at present to determine, for instance, whether arthropods are a monophyletic array or not. The evidence on this point has been read in opposite directions by careful well-informed workers.[175, 176, 185] Thus Tiegs and Manton[185] have challenged the widely held opinion that the presence in crustaceans and insects of mandibles, compound eyes, and closely similar thoracic walking legs are signs of common ancestry rather than of convergent evolution. In view of the scarcity and spottiness of critical functional data and also of the frequent occurrence of convergent evolution in known physiological systems, such major

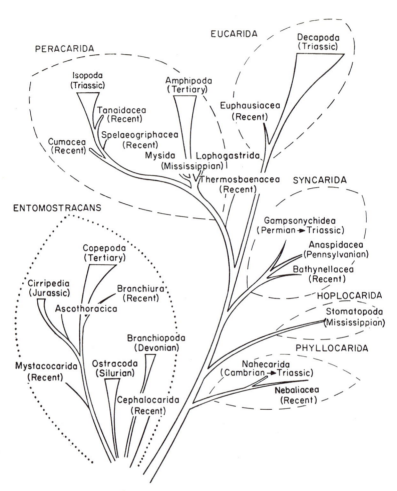

Fig. 3. Possible phylogeny of the Class Crustacea. The main branch at the right represents the Malacostraca comprising six superorders if the Thermosbaenacea are placed in the Pancarida as proposed by Siewing.[170] The period of the earliest known fossil forms is indicated under the various groups; for extinct groups the latest fossil record is also indicated. Note that the frequently cited Paleozoic occurrence (Chapter 1, Vol. I) of Cirripedia now seems dubious. A rough indication of the number of species among Recent forms is given by the breadth of the branch they terminate. (Derived mainly from Siewing,[169] Remane,[153] and Piveteau.[148])

phylogenetic uncertainties prove that much remains to be done before comparative physiology and evolution can be brought to the degree of correlation that seems highly desirable.

V. CONCLUSIONS

This chapter was originally conceived as a summary of the preceding 30 chapters on the physiology of Crustacea and as a conclusion to our whole work. To avoid a bare repetition of salient points already well made by the other contributors, the device of constructing the summary as an analysis of the nature of comparative physiology has been adopted. By this means the facts and patterns previously presented from one viewpoint could be viewed in other contexts which might aid in their more thorough understanding. At the same time an analysis of comparative methodology and the kinds of results that can be obtained therewith might direct attention to several aspects of the subject which, at least in the physiological field, have ordinarily been overlooked.

In discussing these matters a number of points have emerged which have more than parochial interest. For example, comparative physiology has been given a considerably broader definition than has been usual. This emphasizes the large number of different levels from the subcellular to the supraorganismic which fall within its province. The whole question of how biological comparisons may be effectively made is considered from a general point of view before its particular application to physiology is discussed. From this arises an appreciation of the importance of establishing adequate descriptive comparisons and generalizations before explanatory comparisons and hypotheses are made. While terminology has not been a primary concern, confusion arising from various usages of the terms homology and analogy has been avoided by explicit definitions.

However, descriptive comparisons are seen only as the first major step in developing a comparative physiology. Explanations are recognized as required for further progress. These appear to fall into four major categories: 1) genetic, 2) developmental, 3) adaptive, and 4) evolutionary. While these obviously overlap in extenso, they have the operational advantage of roughly coinciding with major traditional approaches to biology.

A quite general outcome of the discussion relates to the crucial need for interdisciplinary understanding and cooperation in advancing comparative physiology. On the one hand it is important that the physiologist and biochemist be more than superficially aware of the outlook and results of the systematists and morphologists. Conversely it is also important that the systematist and morphologist understand the methodology and conclusions of the experimental biologist. Structure and function surely cannot be separated except to the detriment of properly understanding the biological significance of either. Cytochemistry of mitochondria, the behavior of a termite colony, and the topology of enzyme systems seem analytically little different from the structural problems classically dealt with by the anatomist and the systematist. All are describable in terms of patterns of organization which may be arranged in orderly ways. All have basically similar relations to genetics, development, adaptation, and evolution.

A method of approach which recognizes this natural community should strengthen and unify the whole field. While this cannot be done with the Crustacea alone, perhaps their study along such lines will stimulate discussion and new research which in turn can induce further developments of greater depth and breadth.

References

1. Anfinsen, C. B. 1959. "The Molecular Basis of Evolution," 228 pp. Wiley, New York; Chapman and Hall, London.

2. Autrum, H. 1948. Über Energie- und Zeitgrenzender Sinnesempfindungen. *Naturwiss.* 35:361–369.

3. Autrum, H., and Hoffman, E. 1957. Die Wirkung von Pikrotoxin und Nikotin auf das Retinogramm von Insekten. *Z. Naturforsch.* 12b:752–757.

4. Baerends, G. P. 1957. Behavior: the ethological analysis of fish behavior. *In:* "The Physiology of Fishes" (M. E. Brown, ed.), Vol. II, pp. 229–269. Academic Press, New York.

5. Baerends, G. P. 1958. Comparative methods and the concept of homology in the study of behaviour. *Arch. néerl. zool.* 13, Suppl. 1: 401–417.

6. Baerends, G. P. 1959. Ethological studies of insect behavior. *Ann. Rev. Entomol.* 4:207–234.

7. Baltzer, F. 1950. Entwicklungsphysiologische Betrachtungen über Probleme der Homologie und Evolution. *Rev. suisse zool.* 57:451–477.

8. Barigozzi, C. 1957. Différenciation des génotypes et distribution géographique d'*Artemia salina* Leach: Données et problèmes. *Année biol.* 33:241–250.

9. Battaglia, B. 1957. Ecological differentiation and incipient intraspecific isolation in marine copepods. *Année biol.* 33:259–268.

10. Battaglia, B. 1958. Balanced polymorphism in *Tisbe reticulata*, a marine copepod. *Evolution* 12:358–364.

11. Bautzmann, H. 1954. Analoge histofunktionelle Strukturen bei invertebraten und vertebraten Formen von extremstem systematischen Abstand (Spongiaria-Aves, Homo). *Anat. Anz.* 101:9–16.

12. Beach, F. A. 1958. Evolutionary aspects of psychoendocrinology. *In:* "Behavior and Evolution" (A. Roe and G. G. Simpson, eds.), pp. 81–102. Yale Univ. Press, New Haven, Connecticut.

13. Beament, J. W. L. 1958. The effect of temperature on the waterproofing mechanism of an insect. *J. Exptl. Biol.* **35**:494–519.

14. Beckman, C., and Menzies, R. 1960. The relationship of reproductive temperature and the geographical range of the marine woodborer *Limnoria tripunctata*. *Biol. Bull.* **118**:9–16.

15. Bigelow, R. S. 1958. Classification and phylogeny. *Systematic Zool.* **7**:49–59.

16. Birch, L. C. 1960. The genetic factor in population ecology. *Am. Naturalist* **94**:5–24.

17. Bishop, G. H. 1956. Natural history of the nerve impulse. *Physiol. Revs.* **36**:376–399.

18. Bocquet, C. 1951. Recherches sur *Tisbe* (= *Idyaea*) *reticulata*, n. sp. *Arch. zool. exptl. et gén.* **87**:335–416.

19. Bocquet, C. 1953. Recherches sur le polymorphisme naturel des *Jaera marina* (Fabr.) (Isopodes Asellotes). Essai de systématique évolutive. *Arch. zool. exptl. et gén.* **90**:187–450.

20. Bodenstein, D. 1953. Regeneration. *In:* "Insect Physiology" (K. D. Roeder, ed.), pp. 866–878. Wiley, New York.

21. Boyden, A. 1953. Fifty years of systematic serology. *Systematic Zool.* **2**:19–30.

22. Boyden, A. 1959. Serology as an aid to systematics. *XV Intern. Congr. Zool. London, 1958, Proc.*, pp. 120–122.

23. Božić, B. 1957. Recherches taxonomiques sur les formes du genre *Tigriopus* Norman. *Année biol.* **33**:269–273.

24. Braithwaite, R. B. 1953. "Scientific Explanation," 376 pp. Cambridge Univ. Press, London and New York.

25. Brown, G. W., and Cohen, P. P. 1958. Biosynthesis of urea in metamorphosing tadpoles. *In:* "The Chemical Basis of Development" (W. D. McElroy and B. Glass, eds.), pp. 495–513. Johns Hopkins Press, Baltimore, Maryland.

26. Bruun, A. F. 1957. Deep sea and abyssal depths. *Geol. Soc. Am. Mem. No.* **67**, Vol. 1: 641–672.

27. Buck, J. B. 1953. The internal environment in regulation and metamorphosis. *In:* "Insect Physiology" (K. D. Roeder, ed.), pp. 191–217. Wiley, New York.

28. Bullock, T. H. 1959. Neuron doctrine and electrophysiology. *Science* **129**:997–1002.

29. Burger, J. W. 1957. The general form of excretion in the lobster, *Homarus. Biol. Bull.* **113**:207–223.

30. Burkhardt, D. 1960. Die Eigenschaften und Funktionstypen der Sinnesorgane. *Ergeb. Biol.* **22**:226–267.

31. Burtt, E. T., and Catton, W. T. 1954. Visual perception of movement in the locust. *J. Physiol. (London)* **125**:566–580.

32. Butenandt, A. 1959. Wirkstoffe des Insektenreiches. *Naturwiss.* **46**:461–470.

33. Cain, A. J., and Harrison, G. A. 1958. An analysis of the taxonomist's judgment of affinity. *Proc. Zool. Soc. London* **131**:85–98.

34. Calman, W. T. 1909. Crustacea. *In:* "A Treatise on Zoology" (R. Lankester, ed.), Vol. 7, Part 3, pp. 1–346. Black, London.

35. Cannon, H. G. 1940. On the anatomy of *Gigantocypris mülleri. Discovery Repts.* **19**:185–244.

36. Charniaux-Cotton, H. 1958. Contrôle hormonal de la différenciation du sexe et de la reproduction chez les Crustacés supérieurs. *Bull. soc. zool. France* **83**:314–336.

37. Clark, H. 1953. Metabolism of the black snake embryo. *J. Exptl. Biol.* **30**:492–505.

38. Clarke, G. L., and Hubbard, C. J. 1959. Quantitative records of the luminescent flashing of oceanic animals in great depths. *Limnol. and Oceanog.* **4**:163–180.

39. Cloudsley-Thompson, J. L. (ed.) 1954. "Biology of Deserts," 223 pp. Institute of Biology, London.

40. Crane, J. 1949. Comparative biology of salticid spiders at Rancho Grande, Venezuela. Part IV: An analysis of display. *Zoologica* **34**:159–214.

41. Crane, J. 1952. A comparative study of innate defensive behavior in Trinidad mantids (Orthoptera, Mantoidea). *Zoologica* **37**:259–293.

42. Crane, J. 1957. Basic patterns of display in fiddler crabs (Ocypodidae, Genus *Uca*). *Zoologica* **42**:69–82.

43. Crane, J. 1958. Aspects of social behavior in fiddler crabs, with special reference to *Uca maracoani* (Latreille). *Zoologica* **43**:113–130.

44. Crescitelli, F. 1958. The natural history of visual pigments. *Ann. N. Y. Acad. Sci.* **74**:230–255.

45. Croisille, Y. 1958. Les méthodes immunochimiques appliquées à l'étude du développement embryonnaire. *Année biol.* **34**:331–349.

46. Cushing, J. E., and Campbell, D. H. 1957. "Principles of Immunology," 344 pp. McGraw-Hill, New York.

47. Dahl, E. 1959. The ontogeny and comparative anatomy of some protocerebral sense organs in notostracan phyllopods. *Quart. J. Microscop. Sci.* **100**:445–462.

48. Dartnall, H. J. A. 1957. "The Visual Pigments," 216 pp. Methuen, London; Wiley, New York.

49. de Lattin, G. 1939. Untersuchungen über die Farbvariabilität der Isopoden. I. Über genotypische und modifikative Pigmentreduktion. *Zool. Anz.* **125**:309–324.

50. de Lattin, G. 1954. Zur Populationsgenetik geschlechtsbeeinflussender Farbfaktoren bei Porcellioniden (Crust. Isop.). *Caryologia* **6**, Suppl.: 883–888.

51. Dennell, R. 1940. On the structure of the photophores of some decapod Crustacea. *Discovery Repts.* **20**:307–382.

52. Denton, E. J., and Warren, F. J. 1957. The photosensitive pigments in the retinae of deep-sea fishes. *J. Marine Biol. Assoc. United Kingdom* **36**:651–662.

53. Dessauer, H. C., and Fox, W. 1956. Characteristic electrophoretic patterns of plasma proteins of orders of Amphibia and Reptilia. *Science* **124**:225–226.

54. Dethier, V. G. 1953. Vision. *In:* "Insect Physiology" (K. D. Roeder, ed.), pp. 488–522. Wiley, New York.

55. Dobzhansky, T. 1951. "Genetics and the Origin of Species," 3rd ed., 364 pp. Columbia Univ. Press, New York.

56. Eakin, R. E., and Fisher, J. R. 1958. Patterns of nitrogen excretion in developing chick embryos. *In:* "The Chemical Basis of Development" (W. D. McElroy and B. Glass, eds.), pp. 514–525. Johns Hopkins Press, Baltimore, Maryland.

57. Ebert, J. D. 1958. Immunochemical analysis of development. *In:* "The Chemical Basis of Development" (W. D. McElroy and B. Glass, eds.), pp. 526–545. Johns Hopkins Press, Baltimore, Maryland.

58. Ebert, J. D. 1959. The acquisition of biological specificity. *In:* "The Cell" (J. Brachet and A. E. Mirsky, eds.), Vol. I, pp. 619–693. Academic Press, New York.

59. Eibl-Eibesfeldt, I., and Kramer, S. 1958. Ethology, the comparative study of animal behavior. *Quart. Rev. Biol.* **33**:181–211.

60. Emerson, A. E. 1949. Adaptation. *In:* "Principles of Animal Ecology" (W. C. Allee, ed.), pp. 630–640. Saunders, Philadelphia.

61. Ennor, A. H., and Morrison, J. F. 1958. Biochemistry of the phosphagens and related guanidines. *Physiol. Revs.* **38**:631–674.

62. Evans, H. E. 1957. "Studies on the Comparative Ethology of Digger Wasps of the Genus *Bembix*," 248 pp. Comstock, Ithaca, New York.

63. Eyzaguirre, C. 1957. Functional organization of neuromuscular spindle in toad. *J. Neurophysiol.* **20**:523–542.

64. Eyzaguirre, C., and Kuffler, S. W. 1955a. Processes of excitation in the dendrites and in the soma of isolated sensory nerve cells of the lobster and crayfish. *J. Gen. Physiol.* **39**:87–119.

65. Eyzaguirre, C., and Kuffler, S. W. 1955b. Further study of soma, dendrite, and axon excitation in single neurons. *J. Gen. Physiol.* **39**:121–153.

66. Finlayson, L. H., and Lowenstein, O. 1958. The structure and function of abdominal stretch receptors in insects. *Proc. Roy. Soc.* **B148**:433–449.

67. Florkin, M. 1952. Comparative biochemistry. *Ann. Rev. Biochem.* **21**:459–472.

68. Fontaine, M. 1954. Du déterminisme physiologique des migrations. *Biol. Revs. Cambridge Phil. Soc.* **29**:390–418.

69. Ford, E. B. 1944. Studies on the chemistry of pigments in the Lepidoptera, with special reference to their bearing on systematics. 3. The red pigments of the Papilionidae. *Proc. Roy. Entomol. Soc. London* **A19**:92–106.

70. Gell, P. G. H., Hawkes, J. C., and Wright, S. T. C. 1960. The application of immunological methods to the taxonomy of species within the Genus *Solanum*. *Proc. Roy. Soc.* **B151**:364–383.

71. Geschwind, I. I. 1959. Species variation in protein and polypeptide hormones. *In:* "Comparative Endocrinology" (A. Gorbman, ed.), pp. 421–443. Wiley, New York.

72. Ghiretti-Magaldi, A., Giuditta, A., and Ghiretti, F. 1958. Pathways of terminal respiration in marine invertebrates. I. The respiratory system in cephalopods. *J. Cellular Comp. Physiol.* **52**:389–429.

73. Glasstone, S. 1946. "Elements of Physical Chemistry," 695 pp. Van Nostrand, New York.

74. Goldschmidt, R. B. 1952. Homoeotic mutants and evolution. *Acta Biotheoretica* **10**:87–104.

75. Goldsmith, T. H. 1958. On the visual system of the bee (*Apis mellifera*). *Ann. N. Y. Acad. Sci.* **74**:223–229.

76. Gray, I. E. 1957. A comparative study of the gill area of crabs. *Biol. Bull.* **112**:34–42.

77. Gray, J. 1950. The role of peripheral sense organs during locomotion in the vertebrates. *Symposia Soc. Exptl. Biol. No.* **4**:112–126.

78. Green, J. D., and Maxwell, D. S. 1959. Comparative anatomy of the hypophysis and observations on the mechanism of neurosecretion. *In:* "Comparative Endocrinology" (A. Gorbman, ed.), pp. 368–392. Wiley, New York.

79. Green, M. M. 1955. Homologous eye color mutants in the honeybee and *Drosophila*. *Evolution* **9**:215–216.

80. Grimstone, A. V. 1959. Cytology, homology and phylogeny—a note on "organic design." *Am. Naturalist* **93**:273–282.

81. Grundfest, H. 1959. Evolution of conduction in the nervous system. *In:* "Evolution of Nervous Control" (A. D. Bass, ed.), pp. 43–86. American Association for the Advancement of Science, Washington, D.C.
82. Grüneberg, H. 1953. Genetical studies on the skeleton of the mouse. VI. Danforth's short-tail. *J. Genet.* **51**:317–326.
83. Harvey, E. N. 1952. "Bioluminescence," 649 pp. Academic Press, New York.
84. Hassenstein, B. 1957. Über Belichtungspotentiale in den Augen der Fliegen *Sarcophaga* und *Eristalis*. *J. Insect Physiol.* **1**:124–130.
85. Heberer, G. 1953. Begriff und Bedeutung der parallelen Evolution. *Zool. Anz. Suppl.* **17**:435–442.
86. Heberer, G. 1957. Theorie der additiven Typogenese. *In:* "Die Evolution der Organismen" (G. Heberer, ed.), 2nd ed., pp. 857–914. Fischer, Stuttgart.
87. Heinroth, O. 1911. Beiträge zur Biologie, namentlich Ethologie und Psychologie der Anatiden. *Verhandl. V Intern. Ornithol. Kongr. Berlin, 1911*, pp. 589–702.
88. Henderson, L. J. 1913. "The Fitness of the Environment," 317 pp. Macmillan, New York.
89. Hennig, W. 1950. "Grundzüge einer Theorie der Phylogenetischen Systematik," 370 pp. Deutscher Zentralverlag, Berlin.
90. Hoar, W. S. 1958. The evolution of migratory behaviour among juvenile salmon of the Genus *Oncorhynchus*. *J. Fisheries Research Board Can.* **15**:391–428.
91. Hoar, W. S. 1959. Endocrine factors in the ecological adaptation of fishes. *In:* "Comparative Endocrinology" (A. Gorbman, ed.), pp. 1–23. Wiley, New York.
92. Holz, G. G., Jr. 1960. Structural and functional changes in a generation of *Tetrahymena*. *Biol. Bull.* **118**:84–95.
93. Hooker, D. 1952. "The Prenatal Origin of Behavior," 143 pp. Univ. of Kansas Press, Lawrence.
94. Howard, H. W. 1953. The genetics of *Armadillidium vulgare* Latr. III. Dominant and recessive genes for red body colour. *J. Genet.* **51**:259–269.
95. Hoyle, G. 1957. "Comparative Physiology of the Nervous Control of Muscular Contraction," 147 pp. Cambridge Univ. Press, London and New York.
96. Hubby, J. L., and Throckmorton, L. H. 1960. Evolution and pteridine metabolism in the Genus *Drosophila*. *Proc. Natl. Acad. Sci. U. S.* **46**:65–78.
97. Imbrie, J. 1956. Biometrical methods in the study of invertebrate fossils. *Bull. Am. Museum Nat. Hist.* **108**:215–252.
98. Irwin, M. R. 1955. On interrelationships of the cellular antigens of several species of *Streptopelia*. *Evolution* **9**:261–279.
99. Jander, R. 1959. Spontaneous changes in the angular orientation of animals. *Anat. Record* **134**:587.
100. Källén, B. 1959. Embryological aspects of the concept of homology. *Arkiv Zool.* **12**:137–142.
101. Kampa, E. M., and Boden, B. P. 1954. Sonic scattering layer studies—an interim report. Bermuda Biological Station, Nonr 1135(01), Report I, 28 pp.
102. Kennan, A. L., and Cohen, P. P. 1959. Biochemical studies of the developing mammalian fetus. 1. Urea cycle enzymes. *Developmental Biol.* **1**:511–525.
103. Kerkut, G. A., and Taylor, B. J. R. 1958. The effect of temperature changes on the activity of poikilotherms. *Behaviour* **13**:259–279.
104. Kidder, G. W. 1953. The nutrition of invertebrate animals. *In:* "Biochemistry and Physiology of Nutrition" (G. H. Bourne and G. W. Kidder, eds.), Vol. II, pp. 162–196. Academic Press, New York.

105. Knowles, F. G. W. 1959. The control of pigmentary effectors. *In:* "Comparative Endocrinology" (A. Gorbman, ed.), pp. 223–232. Wiley, New York.

106. Knox, W. E., Auerbach, V. H., and Lin, E. C. C. 1956. Enzymatic and metabolic adaptations in animals. *Physiol. Revs.* **36:**164–254.

107. Koshland, D. E., Jr., Ray, W. J., Jr., and Erwin, M. J. 1958. Protein structure and enzyme action. *Federation Proc.* **17:**1145–1157.

108. Krebs, H. A. 1954a. Some aspects of the metabolism of adenosine phosphates. *Bull. Johns Hopkins Hosp.* **95:**34–44.

109. Krebs, H. A. 1954b. Excursion into the borderland of biochemistry and philosophy. *Bull. Johns Hopkins Hosp.* **95:**45–51.

110. Kuffler, S. W., and Edwards, C. 1958. Mechanism of gamma aminobutyric acid (GABA) action and its relation to synaptic inhibition. *J. Neurophysiol.* **21:**589–610.

111. Kuffler, S. W., and Eyzaguirre, C. 1955. Synaptic inhibition in an isolated nerve cell. *J. Gen. Physiol.* **39:**155–184.

112. Landsteiner, K. 1947. "The Specificity of Serological Reactions," 310 pp. Harvard Univ. Press, Cambridge, Massachusetts.

113. Lederberg, J. 1960. A view of genetics. *Science* **131:**269–276.

114. Lehrman, D. S. 1956. Comparative physiology (Behavior). *Ann. Rev. Physiol.* **18:**527–542.

115. Leone, C. A. 1954a. Further serological data on the relationships of some decapod Crustacea. *Evolution* **8:**192–205.

116. Leone, C. A. 1954b. Serological studies of some arachnids, other arthropods, and mollusks. *Physiol. Zoöl.* **27:**317–325.

117. Lewontin, R. C. 1957. The adaptations of populations to varying environments. *Cold Spring Harbor Symposia Quant. Biol.* **22:**395–408.

117a. Lewontin, R. C., and White, M. J. D. 1960. Interaction between inversion polymorphisms of two chromosome pairs in the grasshopper, *Moraba scurra. Evolution* **14:**116–129.

118. Lindauer, M., and Nedel, J. O. 1959. Ein Schweresinnesorgan der Honigbiene. *Z. vergleich. Physiol.* **42:**334–364.

119. Little, C. C. 1958. Coat color genes in rodents and carnivores. *Quart. Rev. Biol.* **33:**103–137.

120. Lochhead, J. H., and Resner, R. 1959. Functions of the eyes and neurosecretion in Crustacea Anostraca. *XV Intern. Congr. Zool. London, 1958, Proc.*, pp. 397–399.

121. Loewenstein, W. R. 1956a. Modulation of cutaneous mechanoreceptors by sympathetic stimulation. *J. Physiol. (London)* **132:**40–60.

122. Loewenstein, W. R. 1956b. Excitation and changes in adaptation by stretch of mechanoreceptors. *J. Physiol. (London)* **133:**588–602.

123. Longhurst, A. R. 1955. Evolution in the Notostraca. *Evolution* **9:**84–86.

124. Longhurst, A. R. 1958. Abnormal variation in Notostraca. *Systematic Zool.* **7:**84–88.

125. Lüers, H., and Ulrich, H. 1954. Genetik und Evolutionsforschung bei Tieren. *In:* "Die Evolution der Organismen" (G. Heberer, ed.), 2nd ed., pp. 552–661. Fischer, Stuttgart.

126. Manning, A. 1959. The sexual behaviour of two sibling *Drosophila* species. *Behaviour* **15:**123–145.

127. Manton, S. M. 1953. Locomotory habits and the evolution of the larger arthropodan groups. *Symposia Soc. Exptl. Biol. No.* **7**:339–376.
128. Manton, S. M. 1954. The evolution of arthropodan locomotory mechanisms. Part 4. The structure, habits and evolution of the Diplopoda. *J. Linnean Soc. London, Zool.* **42**:299–368.
129. Manton, S. M. 1958. Habits of life and evolution of body design in Arthropoda. *J. Linnean Soc. London, Zool.* **44**:58–72.
130. Martin, A. W. 1958. Comparative physiology (Excretion). *Ann. Rev. Physiol.* **20**:225–242.
131. Maslin, T. P. 1952. Morphological criteria of phyletic relationships. *Systematic Zool.* **1**:49–70.
132. Matsakis, J. 1957. Sur la classification et les affinités de quelques Isopodes terrestres. Arguments biométriques. *Compt. rend.* **245**:584–586.
133. Matsumoto, K. 1954. Neurosecretion in the thoracic ganglion of the crab, *Eriocheir japonicus. Biol. Bull.* **106**:60–88.
134. Mayr, E. 1958. Behavior and systematics. *In:* "Behavior and Evolution" (A. Roe and G. G. Simpson, eds.), pp. 341–362. Yale Univ. Press, New Haven, Connecticut.
135. Michener, C. D., and Sokal, R. R. 1957. A quantitative approach to a problem in classification. *Evolution* **11**:130–162.
136. Miller, W. H. 1958. Fine structures of some invertebrate photoreceptors. *Ann. N. Y. Acad. Sci.* **74**:204–209.
137. Mittelstaedt, H. 1950. Physiologie des Gleichgewichtsinnes bei fliegenden Libellen. *Z. vergleich. Physiol.* **32**:422–463.
138. Munz, F. W. 1958. The photosensitive retinal pigments of fishes from relatively turbid coastal waters. *J. Gen. Physiol.* **42**:445–459.
139. Nachtsheim, H. 1959. Probleme vergleichender Genetik bei Säugern. *Naturwiss.* **46**:565–573.
140. Naef, A. 1931. Allgemeine Morphologie. I. Die Gestalt als Begriff und Idee. *In:* "Handbuch der Vergleichenden Anatomie der Wirbeltiere" (L. Bolk, ed.), Vol. I, pp. 77–118. Urban and Schwarzenberg, Berlin.
141. Novikoff, M. M. 1953. Regularity of form in organisms. *Systematic Zool.* **2**:57–62.
142. Oliver, W. D. 1951. "Theory of Order," 345 pp. Antioch Press, Yellow Springs, Ohio.
143. Olson, E. C., and Miller, R. L. 1958. "Morphological Integration," 317 pp. Univ. of Chicago Press.
144. Orton, G. L. 1953. The systematics of vertebrate larvae. *Systematic Zool.* **2**:63–75.
145. Pantin, C. F. A. 1951. Organic design. *Advancement of Sci.* **8**:138–150.
146. Pasteels, J. J. 1958. Comparative cytochemistry of the fertilized egg. *In:* "The Chemical Basis of Development" (W. D. McElroy and B. Glass, eds.), pp. 381–403. Johns Hopkins Press, Baltimore, Maryland.
147. Pickford, G. E., and Atz, J. W. 1957. "The Physiology of the Pituitary Gland of Fishes," 613 pp. New York Zoological Society.
148. Piveteau, J. (ed.). 1953. "Traité de Paléontologie," Vol. 3, 1063 pp. Masson, Paris.
149. Pringle, J. W. S. 1948. The gyroscopic mechanism of the halteres of Diptera. *Trans. Roy. Soc. London* **B233**:347–384.

150. Prosser, C. L. (ed.). 1958. "Physiological Adaptation," 185 pp. American Physiological Society, Washington, D.C.

151. Prosser, C. L. 1959. Comparative neurophysiology. *In:* "Evolution of Nervous Control" (A. D. Bass, ed.), pp. 31–42. American Association for the Advancement of Science, Washington, D.C.

152. Reinhard, E. G. 1956. Parasitic castration of Crustacea. *Exptl. Parasitol.* **5:**79–107.

153. Remane, A. 1954. Die Geschichte der Tiere. *In:* "Die Evolution der Organismen" (G. Heberer, ed.), 2nd ed., pp. 340–422. Fischer, Stuttgart.

154. Remane, A. 1956. "Die Grundlagen des Natürlichen Systems der Vergleichenden Anatomie und der Phylogenetik," 2nd ed., 364 pp. Akademische Verlagsges., Leipzig.

155. Remane, A., and Schlieper, C. 1958. "Die Biologie des Brackwassers," 348 pp. Schweizerbart, Stuttgart.

156. Robertson, J. D. 1957. The habitat of early vertebrates. *Biol. Revs. Cambridge Phil. Soc.* **32:**156–187.

157. Rockstein, M. 1957. Some aspects of intermediary metabolism of carbohydrates in insects. *Ann. Rev. Entomol.* **2:**19–36.

158. Rokohl, R. 1942. Über die regionale Verschiedenheit der Farbentüchtigkeit im zusammengesetzten Auge von *Notonecta glauca. Z. vergleich. Physiol.* **29:**638–676.

159. Scharrer, E. 1956. The concept of analogy. *Pubbl. staz. zool. Napoli* **28:**204–213.

160. Scharrer, E. 1959. General and phylogenetic interpretations of neuroendocrine interrelations. *In:* "Comparative Endocrinology" (A. Gorbman, ed.), pp. 233–249. Wiley, New York.

161. Schmidt, R. S. 1955. The evolution of nest-building behavior in *Apicotermes* (Isoptera). *Evolution* **9:**157–181.

162. Schmidt-Nielsen, B. 1954. Water conservation in small desert rodents. *In:* "Biology of Deserts" (J. L. Cloudsley-Thompson, ed.), pp. 173–181. Institute of Biology, London.

163. Scholander, P. F. 1960. Oxygen transport through hemoglobin solutions. *Science* **131:**585–590.

164. Schöne, H. 1959. Die Lageorientierung mit Statolithenorganen und Augen. *Ergeb. Biol.* **21:**11–209.

165. Scothorne, R. J. 1958. Histochemical study of the nasal (supra-orbital) gland of the duck. *Nature* **182:**732.

166. Segal, S. J. 1959. Comparative aspects of gonadal morphology, physiology, and antigenicity. *In:* "Comparative Endocrinology" (A. Gorbman, ed.), pp. 553–567. Wiley, New York.

167. Sexton, E. W., and Clark, A. R. 1936. A summary of the work on the amphipod *Gammarus chevreuxi* Sexton carried out at the Plymouth Laboratory (1912–1936). *J. Marine Biol. Assoc. United Kingdom* **21:**357–414.

168. Siewing, R. 1953. Morphologische Untersuchungen an Tanaidaceen und Lophogastriden. *Z. wiss. Zoöl.* **157:**333–426.

169. Siewing, R. 1956. Untersuchungen zur Morphologie der Malacostraca (Crustacea). *Zool. Jahrb. Abt. Anat. u. Ontog. Tiere* **75:**39–176.

170. Siewing, R. 1957. Anatomie und Histologie von *Thermosbaena mirabilis. Abhandl. math. naturw. Kl. Akad. Wiss. (Mainz)* **7:**3–270.

171. Simpson, G. G. 1953. "The Major Features of Evolution," 434 pp. Columbia Univ. Press, New York.

172. Simpson, G. G. 1959. Anatomy and morphology: classification and evolution: 1859 and 1959. *Proc. Am. Phil. Soc.* **103**:286–306.

173. Slifer, E. H. 1957. The specialized heat-sensitive areas of the Moroccan locust, *Dociostaurus maroccanus* (Thunberg), and of several closely-related species. *Ann. Entomol. Soc. Am.* **50**:496–499.

174. Snodgrass, R. E. 1938. Evolution of the Annelida, Onychophora and Arthropoda. *Smithsonian Inst. Publ. Misc. Collections* **97** (6):1–159.

175. Snodgrass, R. E. 1951. "Comparative Studies on the Head of Mandibulate Arthropods," 181 pp. Comstock, Ithaca, New York.

176. Snodgrass, R. E. 1956. Crustacean metamorphoses. *Smithsonian Inst. Publ. Misc. Collections* **131** (10):1–78.

177. Sokal, R. R., and Michener, C. D. 1958. A statistical method of evaluating systematic relationships. *Univ. Kansas Sci. Bull.* **38**:1409–1438.

178. Sperry, R. W. 1958. Physiological plasticity and brain circuit theory. *In:* "Biological and Biochemical Bases of Behavior" (H. F. Harlow and C. N. Woolsey, eds.), pp. 401–424. Univ. of Wisconsin Press, Madison.

179. Spieth, H. T. 1952. Mating behavior within the Genus *Drosophila* (Diptera). *Bull. Am. Museum Nat. Hist.* **99**:401–474.

180. Spurway, H. 1955. The causes of domestication: an attempt to integrate some ideas of Konrad Lorenz with evolution theory. *J. Genet.* **53**:325–362.

181. Staiger, H., and Bocquet, C. 1956. Les chromosomes de la super-espèce *Jaera marina* (F.) et de quelques autres Janiridae (Isopodes Asellotes). *Bull. biol. France et Belg.* **90**:1–32.

182. Stevens, S. S. 1959. The quantification of sensation. *Daedalus* **88**:606–621.

183. Stroud, C. P. 1953. An application of factor analysis to the systematics of *Kalotermes*. *Systematic Zool.* **2**:76–92.

184. Sturtevant, A. H. 1942. The classification of the Genus *Drosophila* with nine new classifications. *Texas Univ. Publ. No.* **4213**:1–51.

185. Tiegs, O. W., and Manton, S. M. 1958. The evolution of the Arthropoda. *Biol. Revs. Cambridge Phil. Soc.* **33**:255–337.

186. Tinbergen, N. 1959. Comparative studies of the behavior of gulls (Laridae): a progress report. *Behaviour* **15**:1–70.

187. Todd, M.-E., and Dehnel, P. A. 1960. Effect of temperature and salinity on heat tolerance in two grapsoid crabs, *Hemigrapsus nudus* and *Hemigrapsus oregonensis*. *Biol. Bull.* **118**:150–172.

188. Tuppy, H. 1959. Aminosäure-Sequenzen in Proteinen. *Naturwiss.* **46**:35–43.

189. Vandel, A. 1945. La répartition géographique des Oniscoidea (Crustacés Isopodes terrestres). *Bull. biol. France et Belg.* **79**:221–272.

190. Vandel, A. 1947. Recherches sur la génétique et la sexualité des Isopodes terrestres. X. Étude des garnitures chromosomiques de quelques espèces d'Isopodes marins, dulçaquicoles et terrestres. *Bull. biol. France et Belg.* **81**:154–176.

191. von Holst, E. 1935. Die Koordination der Bewegung bei den Arthropoden. *Biol. Revs. Cambridge Phil. Soc.* **10**:234–261.

192. Waddington, C. H. 1957. "The Strategy of the Genes," 262 pp. Allen and Unwin, London.

193. Wald, G. 1937. Visual purple system in fresh-water fishes. *Nature* **139**:1017–1018.

194. Wald, G. 1952. Biochemical evolution. *In:* "Modern Trends in Physiology and Biochemistry" (E. S. G. Barron, ed.), pp. 337–376. Academic Press, New York.
195. Wald, G. 1956. The metamorphosis of visual systems in the sea lamprey. *J. Gen. Physiol.* **40**:901–914.
196. Wald, G. 1958. The significance of vertebrate metamorphosis. *Science* **128**:1481–1490.
197. Watson, D. M. S. 1951. "Paleontology and Modern Biology," 216 pp. Yale Univ. Press, New Haven, Connecticut.
198. White, M. J. D. 1957. Cytogenetics and systematic entomology. *Ann. Rev. Entomol.* **2**:71–90.
199. Whitman, C. O. 1898. Animal behavior. Biological Lectures, Marine Biological Laboratories, Woods Hole, Massachusetts. 1898, pp. 285–338.
200. Williams, R. J. 1956. "Biochemical Individuality," 214 pp. Wiley, New York.
201. Winn, H. E. 1958. Comparative reproductive behavior and ecology of fourteen species of darters (Pisces-Percidae). *Ecol. Monographs* **28**:155–191.
202. Witschi, E. 1959. Endocrine basis for reproductive adaptations in birds. *In:* "Comparative Endocrinology" (A. Gorbman, ed.), pp. 517–523. Wiley, New York.
203. Witschi, E., and Chang, C. Y. 1959. Amphibian ovulation and spermiation. *In:* "Comparative Endocrinology" (A. Gorbman, ed.), pp. 149–160. Wiley, New York.
204. Wolken, J. J. 1958. Studies of photoreceptor structures. *Ann. N. Y. Acad. Sci.* **74**:164–181.
205. Woodger, J. H. 1945. On biological transformations. *In:* "Essays on Growth and Form Presented to D'Arcy Wentworth Thompson" (W. E. LeGros Clark and P. B. Medawar, eds.), pp. 95–120. Clarendon Press, Oxford.
206. Woolley, D. W. 1957. Probable evolutionary relationship of serotonin and indoleacetic acid, and some practical consequences therefrom. *Nature* **180**:630–633.
207. Woolley, D. W. 1958. A probable mechanism of action of serotonin. *Proc. Natl. Acad. Sci. U. S.* **44**:197–201.
208. Zangerl, R. 1948. The methods of comparative anatomy and its contribution to the study of evolution. *Evolution* **2**:351–374.
209. Zimmermann, W. 1954. Methoden der Phylogenetik. *In:* "Die Evolution der Organismen" (G. Heberer, ed.), 2nd ed., pp. 25–102. Fischer, Stuttgart.
210. Zweig, G., and Crenshaw, J. W. 1957. Differentiation of species by paper electrophoresis of serum proteins of *Pseudemys* turtles. *Science* **126**:1065–1067.

Reference numbers in parentheses are citations for which the author's name does not appear in the text. Boldface page numbers indicate the location of actual bibliographic entries.

A

Abbott, C. H., 113(1), 122(1), **128**, 371(1), 372(1), **393**

Abramowitz, A. A., 136(1, 2), 138(3), 143(6), 144(5), 145(2, 5, 6), 146(6), 147(4, 6), **163**, 297(1, 2), **305**, 403(1), **426**

Abramowitz, R. K., 143(6), 145(6), 146(6), 147(6), **163**

Achundow, J., 159(89), **168**

Adams, R. T., 223, 227, **239**

Adelman, W. J., 195(82, 83), **240**

Alexandrowicz, J. S., 69(1, 2, 3), 70, 74(4, 5), **104**, 196, 220(1), **236**, 244(2), 253(1), **276**, 290(6), 291, 295(3, 4), 296(5, 6), **305**, 529, 534, 550

Allee, W. C., 127(2), **128**, 387(2, 3, 4), **393**, 476(1), 478(1), **515**

Allen, E. D., 244, 246(3), 247(3), 251, **276**

Alles, G. A., 289(92), **309**

Allison, J. B., 118(19, 20), 119(19, 20), 121(18, 19), 124(18, 19, 20), **129**

Altevogt, R., 466, 467(3), 469, 470(3), 475, 477(2, 3, 3a), 478, 480(3), 481(2, 3), 482(2, 3), 502(3), 512(3), 513(3, 3a), **515**

Alverdes, F., 16(1), **53**, 376(5), 377(5, 6), **393**, 491(4), **515**

Amar, R., 1(2), **53**

Anderson, J., **173**

Anderson, R. S., 179(2), 180, **187**

Anderson, W. W., 447(1, 166), **455**, **463**

Andrews, C. W., 331(1), 332(1), **356**

Andrews, E. A., 479(5), 482(5), **515**

Anfinsen, C. B., 556(1), 561(1), 563(1), 576(1), **584**

Appellöf, A., 468(6), 485(6), 505(6), 510(6), **515**

Apstein, C., 439(2), **455**

Arden, G. B., 35(3), **53**

Arthur, D. R., 452(3), **455**

Atkins, D., 332(2), **356**

Atz, J. W., 554(147), **590**

Atzler, M., 160(7), **164**

Auerbach, V. H., 561(106), **589**

Augustinsson, K. B., 282(8), 284(7), **305**

Autrum, H., 27(5), 34(4), 36, 37, 40(5), 45(7), 49(9), 51, 52, **53**, 535(2), 543(3), **584**

B

Bacq, Z. M., 286(9, 10), **305**

Baerends, G. P., 487(7), 501(7), 503(7), **515**, 526(5), 527(5), 578(4, 6), 580, **584**

Bainbridge, R., 49(10, 11), 50, 52(11), **53**, 338, **359**, 382(7), **393**, 439(5, 70), 440, 441, 442(69, 70), 443(4, 6), 444(70), 446(6), 447(7, 70), 448(7, 70), **455**, **458**

Baldi, E., 317(3), 320(4), 322(4), 323(4), 327(4), 328, 331(4), **356**

Balss, H., 9(13), 14(12), 15(13), 16(13), 17(13), 18(12), 19(12), 21(12), 25(13), 29(13), 39(12), **53**, 78(7), 102(6), **104**, 111(4), 113(3), **128**, 176(3), **187**, 242, **277**, 332(5), 333(7), 340(6), 350(6), **356**, 466(8), 470(8), 472(8), 473(8), 475(8), 482(8), 485(8), 486(8), 487(8), **515**

Baltzer, F., 558(7), **584**

Barber, S. B., 32, 38, 39, 41, 51, 122(5, 6), 124(5, 6), **128**

Barigozzi, C., 557(8), **584**

Barlow, H. B., 20(14), **53**

Barnes, H., 470(9), **515**
Barnes, T. C., 68(8), **104**, 113(7, 8), 122(7, 8), **128**, 253(5), **277**, 380(8, 9), **393**
Barth, G., 74(9), 76, 77, **104**
Bartley, S. H., 32(15), 35(15), 38(15), **53**
Battaglia, B., 557(9, 10), **584**
Bauer, V., 100(10), **104**, 350(8), **356**
Bauers, C., 371(10), 375(10), **393**
Bautzmann, H., 562(1), **584**
Baylor, E. R., 7(17), 8(17), 31(17), 46(17), 48(17), 49(15b, 16), 51, 52(15a), **53**, **54**, **61**, 127(9), **128**, 287(11), **305**, 321(9), 348(9), 350 (9), **357**, 382(11), **393**, 442(8), 443 (8), 448(8), **455**
Bazemore, A., 290(12), **305**
Beach, F. A., 554(12), **585**
Beament, J. W. L., 542(13), **585**
Beckman, C., 566(14), **585**
Beer, T., 100(11), **104**
Bekker, J. M., 287(13), **306**
Bell, J. C., 118(10), **128**
Bellisai, I., 373(12), **393**
Bennett, M. F., 403(67), 410(2, 10), 412(9, 20), 413(8), 415(19), 417 (68), 421(70), 422(18), 423, 424(7, 20), **427**, **428**, **430**, 502(18), **516**
Bennitt, R., 152, 153(9), 155(8), **164**, 405(3), 406(3), **427**
Bergren, W. R., 222(3), **236**
Berisina, M., 195(4), **236**
Berkeley, A. A., 315(10), **357**
Bernard, F., 13, 14(18), 15(18), 16(18), 20(18), 21(18), 29(18), **54**
Bernhard, C. G., 27(19), **54**
Bernhards, H., 13, **54**
Bethe, A., 40(21), **54**, 68(13), 78(12), 81(13), 85(13), 91(13), 99(13), **104**, 244, 246, 254, 255(6), 256(6), 258, **277**, 318(11, 12), 319(11, 12), 320 (13), 322(12, 13), 327(11), 328, 330 12), 331(12), 332(11, 12), 340(11), 342(11), 343(11), **357**, 382(13), 385 (13), **393**, 466(10), 467(10), 473 (10), 474(10), 482(10), 486(10), 493(10, 11), 494, 496, 498, 499(11), **515**, **516**

Biedermann, W., 192, 202, 209, **236**
Bigelow, H. B., 434(9), 435(9), 438(9), 439(9), **455**
Bigelow, R. S., 572(15), **585**
Billet, A., 171(20), **188**
Birch, L. C., 557, 561(16), **585**
Birge, E. A., 122(11), 127(11), **129**, 434 (85), **459**
Birukow, G., 37(22), **54**, 377(14), 379 (14), 392(14), **393**
Bishop, G. H., 529(17), **585**
Bliss, A. F., 43(23), 44(23), **54**
Bliss, D. E., 139(11, 12), 140(11), 154 (11), **164**, 293(14, 15), 294(14, 15), 295(15), 296(15), 300(15), **306**
Blum, H. F., 345(15), 346(14), 351(14), **357**, 372(15), **393**
Bock, A., 508(12), 509(12), **516**
Bocquet, C., 557(18, 19), 572(181), **585**, **592**
Boden, B. P., 569(101), **588**
Bodenstein, D., 159, **164**, 543(20), **585**
Boettiger, E. G., 74, 75, 77
Bogorov, B. G., 434(10), 435(10), 439 (10), **455**
Bohn, G., 314(16), **357**, 372(16), **393**
Boistel, J., 235(6a), **236**
Bonnet, V., 254(8), **277**, 287(16), **306**
Boot, L. M., 284, **310**
Böttger, G., 147(14), **164**
Bovbjerg, R. V., 479(13, 14), 505(14), 511(14), **516**
Bowman, T. E., 139(15), **164**, 171
Boyden, A., 577(21, 22), 578(22), **585**
Božić, B., 557(23), **585**
Brady, G. S., 435(11), **455**
Braithwaite, R. B., 522(24), 555(24), 561(24), 565(24), **585**
Brenner, H., 220(7), **236**, 316(17), **357**
Brigham, E. H., 183(12), **188**
Brightwell, L. R., 470(15), **516**
Broad, C., 447(12), **455**
Brock, F., 67(14), 68(15), **104**, **105**, 385(17), 386, 388(18), **394**, 470(16), 471, 501, **516**
Bröcker, H., 14(24), 36(24), 37(24), 39(24), 40(24), **54**
Broekhuysen, G. J., 480(17), **516**
Bronk, D. W., 222(8), **236**

Brooks, J. L., 122(12), **129**, 375(19), 385(19), **394**

Brooks, W. K., 68, **105**, 542

Brown, F. A., Jr., 31(159), 35(159), 51 (173), **60**, **61**, 134(17, 23, 33), 135 (18, 19), 136(21, 26, 27, 30), 138 (18, 19), 139(16, 20, 21), 140(21, 22), 141(24), 142(31), 143(31), 155 (109), 156(28), 161(29), **164**, **165**, **169**, 295(17, 19), 297(18), **306**, 402, 403(5, 67), 404(13, 69), 406(69), 407(11, 22, 69), 408(22), 410(10), 411, 412(9, 20), 413(8), 414(80), 415(16, 19), 416, 417(17, 71), 418 (17), 419(12, 17), 420(14, 15, 17), 421(13, 70, 71), 422(6a, 17, 18), 423, 424(7, 20, 21), **427**, **428**, **430**, 502(18), **516**

Brown, G. G., 101(17), **105**

Brown, G. W., 558(25), **585**

Brown, R. A., 410(2, 10), 413(8), 421(70), **427**, **430**, 502(18), **516**

Brundin, T. M., 372(20), 376(20), **394**

Bruun, A. F., 569(26), **585**

Bryant, S. H., 194(54), **239**

Buck, J. B., 541(27), **585**

Buehl, C. C., 259(28), **278**

Bullock, T. H., 101(24), **105**, 125(14), 126(13), **129**, 259(9), 260(10), **277**, 287(20), **306**, 529(28), 534(28), **585**

Bumpus, H. C., 452(13), **455**

Burger, J. W., 548(29), **585**

Burke, W., 74(18), 75, 77(18), 101(18), **105**, 194(9), **236**

Burkenroad, M. D., 176, **187**, 447(14, 15, 16), **455**, **456**, 479(19), 480(19), 482(20), 485(19), **516**

Burkhardt, D., 524(30), **585**

Burtt, E. T., 7(25), 21(25), 25(26a), 27(25), 30(26b), 51, **54**, 543(31), **585**

Butenandt, A., 542(32), 545, 557(32), **585**

C

Cain, A. J., 524(33), 526(33), 540(33), 573(33), **585**

Caldwell, P. S., 221(10), **237**

Calman, W. T., 570(34), **585**

Camien, M. N., 221(11), **237**

Campbell, D. H., 526(46), 563(46), 577(46), **586**

Cannon, H. G., 333(19, 21, 23), 334(21), 336(20, 23), 339, 340(20, 23), 342(20, 22), 344, 350(18), **357**, 539(35), **585**

Capenos, J., 14(233), 27(233), **64**

Carlisle, D. B., 134(34, 80), 139(35, 79), 140(80), 141(79, 80), 144(80, 81), 145, 161(80), **165**, **167**, 290(22), 291(23), 293(24, 60), 294(21, 60), 295(60), 298(61), 299(62), **305**, **306**, **308**

Carlson, S. P., 138(36, 37), 142, 143(37), **165**, 297(25), **306**, 403(23, 24), **428**

Carstam, S. P., 136(38), 138(38), 144(38a), **165**, 298(26), **306**

Caselli, A., 272(11), **277**

Caspers, H., 402, **428**

Castle, E. S., 49(27), **54**, 152, **165**

Catton, W. T., 7(25), 21(25), 25(26a), 27(25), 30(26b), 51, **54**, 543(31), **585**

Chace, F. A., Jr., 14(225), 22(225, 226), 31(217), **63**, **64**, 186, **187**, **190**, 414 (78), **430**, 433(163), 435(163, 165), 436(163), **463**

Chadwick, L. E., 116(24), 117(24), 118(24), 121(24), **129**, 341(24), 350(24), **357**

Chang, C. Y., 526(203), **593**

Chang, J. J., 184(6), **187**

Chapman, G. B., 142(60a), **166**, 300(56), 302(122), **308**, **311**

Charniaux-Cotton, H., 505(21), **516**, 542, 559, **586**

Chase, A. M., 177(38a), 180(8), 181(7, 59), 182(59), 183(9, 10, 12, 45, 52), 184(11, 62), **187**, **188**, **189**, **190**

Chefurka, W., 282(27), **306**

Chidester, F. E., 482(22), **516**

Christensen, E., 67(86), **108**, 259(49), 268(49), 270, 271, **279**

Chun, C., 4(28), 14(28), 15(28), 16(28), 17(28), 19(28), 21(28), 25(28), **54**, 175(13), **188**, 443(17), **456**

Clark, A. R., 557(167), **591**

Clark, G. P., 81(19), 85(19), 105
Clark, H., 558(37), 586
Clark, L. B., 39(29), 40(29), 54
Clarke, G. L., 31(30, 217), 54, 63, 370(21), 373(21), 394, 433(163), 434(20, 21, 22), 435(20, 21, 163), 436(163), 441(18, 19, 21), 442(19), 444(21), 448(19), 456, 463, 504 (23), 516, 569(38), 586
Clarke, W. D., 472(23a), 516
Claus, C., 79, 105
Cloudsley-Thompson, J. L., 112(15), 113(15), 122(15), 129, 371(24), 372(22, 23), 384(22), 394, 452(3, 23), 455, 456, 561(39), 586
Coblentz, W. W., 177(14), 178, 188
Cochran, D. M., 315(25), 357
Cohen, M. J., 79(22), 80, 85, 86(23), 87, 88, 89, 90, 97, 101(22, 24), 105
Cohen, P. P., 558(25, 102), 585, 588
Coker, R. E., 434(62), 458
Cole, L. C., 452(24), 456
Cole, W. H., 118(19, 20), 119(19, 20), 124(16, 17, 18, 19, 20), 129, 374(25), 394
Coleman, P. D., 195(84), 240
Collinge, W. E., 451(25, 26), 456
Colman, J. S., 434(132), 461
Congdon, E. D., 152(40), 165
Cooke, I. M., 290(105), 310
Cornsweet, J. C., 23(153), 60
Cornsweet, T. N., 23(153), 60
Correale, P., 290(28), 306
Corteggiani, E., 283(29), 306
Cowles, R. P., 469(24), 473(24), 508(24), 516
Craig, L. C., 299
Crane, J., 102(25), 105, 468(28), 469(25), 470(25, 28b), 473(25, 28), 475(28, 28b), 476(25, 28b), 477(25, 28b), 480(25), 481(25, 27, 28a, 28b), 482(25), 499(25), 500(25), 503(28a), 505(25, 26), 506(25), 512(25), 513, 514(25, 28a), 516, 546(42), 578(40, 41), 580(42, 43), 586
Crawford, D. R., 449(27), 452(27), 456
Creaser, E. P., 450(28), 456
Crenshaw, J. W., 577(210), 593

Crescitelli, F., 558(44), 564(44), 586
Crisp, D. J., 19(38), 25(38), 26(38), 33(38), 34(38), 39(38), 55, 151(43), 165, 336(115), 343(115), 361, 387(26), 394, 470(9, 29), 505(29a), 515, 516, 517
Croisille, Y., 558(45), 586
Cronin, L. E., 451(29), 456
Crozier, W. J., 34(33), 36(33, 34), 37 (32, 33, 34), 49(31), 54, 390(57), 395
Cunningham, J. T., 175(60), 176, 184, 190
Cushing, D. H., 352(26), 357, 375(27), 389(27), 394, 432, 433(30), 437, 438(30), 439(30), 442(30), 444, 456, 504(30), 517
Cushing, J. E., 526(46), 563(46), 577(46), 586
Cuvier, G., 434(31), 456

D

Dahl, E., 6(35), 55, 293(30), 306, 559(47), 586
Dahlgren, U., 175, 188
Dakin, W. J., 435(32), 456
D'Ancona, U., 198(12), 237
Daniel, R. J., 315(27), 357
Dartnall, H. J. A., 564(48), 586
Daumer, K., 43(36), 44(36), 46(36), 55
Davenport, D., 286(31), 287(32), 306
Dawson, C. E., 449(33), 450, 456
Day, M. F., 161(41), 165
Debaisieux, P., 9(37), 13(37), 14(37), 55, 148, 165
de Bruin, G. H. P., 19(38), 25(38), 26(38), 33(38), 34(38), 39(38), 55, 151(43), 165
de Harven, E., 286(39), 307
Dehnel, P. A., 561(187), 592
Delage, Y., 78, 105
de Lattin, G., 5(39), 37(39), 55, 557(49), 558(50), 565(49), 586
del Cañizo, J., 29(40), 55
del Castillo, J., 289(33), 306
del Portillo, J., 15(41), 55
Dembowska, W. S., 471(31), 499, 517

Dembowski, J. B., 330(28), 335(28), 357, 468(33), 469(33), 474(32), 488, 501(32), 517

Demoll, R., 6(43), 42(42), 55, 69(27), 97(28), 105, 349, 357

Dennell, R., 176, 186, 188, 314(31), 335(30), 339(30), 340(30), 343(30), 344(30), 345(30), 350(30), 357, 538(51), 586

Denton, E. J., 29(144), 31(44a), 33(144), 44(44, 44a), 55, 60, 565(52), 586

de Riville, G., 172

DeRobertis, E., 20(45, 46), 55

de Smidt, W. J. J., 449(27), 452(27), 456

Dessauer, H. C., 577(53), 586

Dethier, F., 296(34), 306

Dethier, V. G., 7(47), 15(48), 18, 37(48), 55, 109(23), 116(24), 117(24), 118(24), 120(21, 23), 121(21, 22, 23, 24), 125(23), 129, 543(54), 586

de Vries, H., 21(49), 23(49), 55

Dice, L. R., 434(34), 443(34), 444(34), 456

Diecke, F. P. J., 125(14), 129

Dietrich, W., 38(50), 55, 338(32), 357, 376(28), 377(28), 394, 492(34), 517

Dijkgraaf, S., 41(51, 52), 55, 68(33), 69(33), 79(35), 85, 91, 93, 94, 95, 96, 97, 99(29), 100(30, 31), 101(31), 104(33, 34), 105, 382(29, 30), 383 (30), 394

Dixon, A. Y., 334(33), 358

Dobkiewicz, L. V., 16(53), 55

Dobzhansky, T., 572(55), 586

Dodt, E., 37(54), 55

Doflein, F., 15(55), 16(55), 40(56), 55, 67(36), 105, 319(34), 320(34), 343(34), 344(34), 345(34), 358, 385(31), 394, 467(35), 474(35), 506(35), 517

Doochin, H. D., 7(57), 56

Douglis, M. B., 476(1), 478(1), 515

Drach, P., 321(35), 358

Drzewina, A., 380(32), 394, 415(26), 428

Dubuisson, M., 194(47), 238

Duchâteau, G., 221(11), 237

Dupont-Raabe, M., 134(80), 140(80), 141(80), 144(80, 81), 145, 159(44), 161(44, 45, 46, 47, 48, 80), 165, 167, 298(61), 299(62), 308

Durand, J. B., 139(11), 140(11), 154(11), 164, 293(14, 35), 294(14, 35), 295(35), 296(35), 306, 307

E

Eakin, R. E., 573(56), 586

Easton, D. M., 283(36), 284(36), 285(36), 307

Ebert, J. D., 556(58), 558(57, 58), 576(58), 586

Eccles, J. C., 210(13), 237

Eckert, B., 49(58), 50, 56, 382(33), 394

Eckert, F., 347(36), 358

Ederstrom, H. E., 134(23), 141(24), 164, 295(17), 306

Edman, P., 298(37), 299(37), 307

Edney, E. B., 452(35), 453, 456, 457

Edwards, C., 290(38), 307, 532(110), 533(110), 589

Edwards, G. A., 147(49), 165, 286(39), 307, 321(158), 363, 410(27), 412 (27), 428

Egelhaaf, A., 45(187), 62

Eibl-Eibesfeldt, I., 487(105), 502(105), 503(105), 506(105), 520, 558(59), 587

Ekman, S., 434(37), 457

Elliott, K. A. C., 290(12, 40), 305, 307

Ellis, C. H., 228(70), 229(70), 230, 231(14), 233(14), 237, 239, 286(41), 307

Ellis, R. A., 10, 21, 25

Elmhirst, R., 448(38, 39), 453(40), 457

Emerson, A. E., 526(60), 587

Enami, M., 139(50), 165, 294(42), 295(42), 307, 402(28), 404(28), 428

Ennor, A. H., 573(61), 587

Enzmann, M., 374(58), 395

Eriksson, S., 314(37), 332(37), 333(37), 334(37), 335(37), 336(37), 342(37), 343(37), 358

Erwin, M. J., 563(107), 589

Esterly, C. O., 414, **428**, 434(42, 43, 47), 435(41, 43, 44), 444(43, 46), 445 (42), **457**

Evans, H. E., 527(62), 578(62), 580(62), **587**

Everest, F. A., 101(46), **106**

Ewald, W. F., 348(38), **358**, 370(34), 372(34), 373(34), 374(34), 376(35), **394**, 442(48), **457**

Exner S., 10, 14, 18, 19(59), 21(59), 22, 23(59), 24, 25, 26, 39, **56**, 80

Eyden, D., 439(49), **457**

Eymers, G., 177(17), **188**

Eyzaguirre, C., 70(37, 38), 72(38), 73, **105**, **106**, 529(64, 65), 532(111), 551(64, 65, 111), 576(63), **587**, **589**

F

Fabricius, O., 172

Fage, L., 171(18), **188**

Fänge, R., 142(96), 143(96), 144(96), 145, 146, 147(96), **168**, 298(37, 72), 299(37), **307**, **308**

Farran, G. P., 434(50, 51), 435(50, 51), 444(51), **457**

Farre, A., 66(39), **106**

Fatt, P., 206, 207(14a, 15), 208(16), 211(17), 212, 213(17), 233(14a, 15), 234, 235(6a), **236**, **237**

Feldberg, W., 285(43), **307**

Feng, T. P., 195(4), **236**

Fenizia, G., 471(36), 472(37), 473(37), 504(36), **517**

Filteau, G., 435(52), **457**

Fingerman, M., 51(173), **61**, 134(52), 135(51), 136(51), 144(51a, 51c), 155(25, 28), 156(28, 51b), **164**, **166**, 402(33), 403, 404(13, 32, 33), 405(34, 35), 407(11), 410(32), 413(31), 414(36), 419(12), 421(13), **427**, **428**

Fink, H. K., 507, **517**

Finlayson, L. H., 544(66), 576(66), **587**

Fischbach, E., 372(36), 385(36), 388(36), **394**

Fisher, J. R., 573(56), **586**

Fisher, L. R., 43(59a), 44(59a), **56**

Florey, E., 69(40, 85), 72(40), 74(85), **106**, **108**, 147(53), **166**, 231(18), 232(19, 20), **237**, 283(44), 287(50), 288(48, 120), 289(46, 50), 290(12, 45, 46, 50), **305**, **307**, **311**

Florey, Elisabeth, 69(40), 72(40), **106**, 232(20), **237**, 287(50), 289(50), 290 (50), **307**

Florkin, M., 221(11), **237**, 561, **587**

Flückiger, E., 319(39), **358**

Fontaine, M., 553(68), **587**

Ford, E. B., 576(69), **587**

Forsman, B., 333(40), **358**

Fox, H. Munro, 23(60), **56**, 321(42), 336(41), 343(41), 351(41), 352(42), **358**

Fox, W., 577(53), **586**

Foxon, G. E. H., 313(43), 334(44), 336(43), 340(43), 345(43), 346(43), 351(43), 354(43), **358**, 448(53), **457**

Fraenkel, G. S., 103(41), **106**, 113(25), 126(25), **129**, 365(38), 372(38), 373(38), 376(37, 38, 39), 377(37, 38), 387(38), 388(39), **394**, **395**, 453(54), **457**

Franz, V., 374(40), **395**

Fraser, F. C., 435(55), 438(55), **457**

Fricke, H., 5(61), 14(61), 22(61), **56**

Friedl, F., 144(113), **169**, 298(100), **310**

Friedrich, H., 7(62), 15(193), 29(193), 41(193), 48(193), **56**, 62, 81(83), 91(83), **108**, 376(41), 382(122), **395**, **398**

Frizzi, G., 159(55), **166**

Fröhlich, A., 81(42), 85(42), 99(42), **106**

Fryer, G., 351(45), **358**

Furshpan, E. J., 69(85), 74(85), **108**, 208(22), 209, 215(21), **237**, 262(12), **277**, 288(120), **311**

Furusawa, K., 195(23), **237**

G

Gabe, M., 296(51, 52), **307**

Gaffron, M., 41(63), **56**

Gallagher, J. C., 39

Gallwitz, U., 27(5), 37(5), 40(5), **53**

Gamble, F. W., 402(43), 410(43), **428, 429**

Gardiner, A. C., 433(143), 434(57, 143, 144), 435,(56, 57, 142, 143, 144), 438(56), 439(56), 446(142, 144), **457, 458, 462**

Gauld, D. T., 445(58), **458**

Gebler, K., 319(46), **358**

Gell, P. G. H., 526(70), 577(70), **587**

George, C. J., 315(47), 354(47), **358**

Gerard, R. W., 193(24), **237**

Gerstaecker, A., 67(43), 78(43), 102(43), 106

Geschwind, I. I., 557(71), 563(71), 566(71), **587**

Ghiretti, F., 563(72), **587**

Ghiretti-Magaldi, A., 563(72), **587**

Giard, A., 171(19, 20), **188**

Gibson-Hill, C. A., 466(39), 467(39), 486(39), 503(39), **517**

Giersberg, H., 160, **166**

Giesbrecht, W., 173, 175, 187, **188**, 446 (40), 467(40), 485(40), **517**

Gilchrist, J. D. F., 449(59), **458**

Gilhousen, H. C., 508(41), 509(41), 511, **517**

Ginet, R., 334(48), **358**

Ginsborg, B. L., 207(14a), 233(14a), **237**

Gislén, T., 314(49), **358**

Giuditta, A., 563(72), **587**

Glasstone, S., 561(73), **587**

Goldie, E. H., 43(59a), 44(59a), **56**

Goldschmidt, R. B., 557(74), **587**

Goldsmith, T. H., 14(64), 27(64), 51(64), **56**, 564(75), **587**

Gomori, G., 296, **307**

Gompel, M., 411, **428**

Goodhard, C. B., 469(42), 487(42), **517**

Gordon, H. R. S., 503(43), **517**

Gordon, H. T., 233(64), **239**, 286(116), **310**

Goto, T., 182(53a), **190**

Gottsche, C. M., 23(65), **56**

Graham, C. H., 28(82), **57**

Graham, J., 193(24), **237**

Graham, M., 450, **458**

Grahn, M., 282(8), **305**

Gran, H. H., 435(61), **458**

Granit, R., 36(67), 37(67), 46(66), **56**

Grassi, M., 379(82), 380(82), **396**, 453 (118), **460**, 504(75), **519**

Graves, R. C., 417(68), **430**

Gravier, C., 330(50), 332(50), **358**

Gray, I. E., 547(76), **587**

Gray, J., 554(77), **587**

Green, J., 335(51), **358**

Green, J. D., 566(78), **587**

Green, J. P., 144(113a), **169**

Green, M. M., 556(79), **587**

Greene, C. W., 186, **188**

Greene, H. H., 186, **188**

Grimstone, A. V., 527(80), 556(80), 562 (80), **587**

Grobben, K., 79, **105**

Groom, T. T., 370(42), **395**

Gross, F., 254(39), **278**

Grover, W. W., 434(62), **458**

Grundfest, H., 261(18), **277**, 529(81), **588**

Grüneberg, H., 557(82), **588**

Gruner, H.-E., 5(236), 14(236), 16(236), 19(236), 23(236), 24, 25(236), 29 (236), **64**, 475(116), **520**

Grüsser, O.-J., 27(68), **56**

Gunn, D. L., 103(41), **106**, 113(25, 26), 126(25), **129**, 366(44), 376(39), 383(43), 388(39), **395**, 453(54, 63), **457, 458**

Gunther, E. R., 433(71), 434(71), 435 (71), 436(71), 438(71), 439(71), 442(71), 445(71), 447(71), **458**

Gurney, R., 345(52), **358**

Guttman, B., 144(113), **169**, 298(100), **310**

Guyselman, J. B., 136(27), **164**, 409(39), 410(39), **428**

H

Hadley, P. B., 387(45), **395**

Hadorn, E., 45(188), **62**, 159(55), **166**

Hagins, W. A., 274(37), **278**, 289(101), **310**

Haidinger, W., 49, **56**

Halme, E., 434(64), **458**

Hanaoka, T., 14(72), 26(70), 27(70), 28(72), 33(70, 71), 43(72), **56**

Haneda, Y., 171(25), 172, 178(27), 184
(26), 187(26), **188**
Hanko, B., 333(53), **358**
Hansen, K. V., 434(65), 435(65), 444
(65), **458**
Hanson, H. J., 177(28), **188**
Hanström, B., 14(75), 29(74, 76), 46
(73), **56**, 110, 111, **129**, 138(56),
139(58), 142(56), 147(57), 159, 161
(59), **166**, 291(55), 292(54, 55),
293(54, 55), **307**
Harding, J. P., 314(54), 333(54), **358**
Hardy, A. C., 338, 352(55), **359**, 433
(71), 434(71), 435(71), 436(71),
438(71), 439(70, 71), 440, 441(72),
442(69, 70, 72), 444(70), 445(66, 67,
68, 71), 446, 447(70, 71), 448(70),
458
Hardy, W. B., 258, **277**
Harms, J. W., 1(77), **57**, 100(44), 102
(44), **106**, 319(56), **359**, 466(44,
45), 467(44, 45), 486(44), 487(44,
45), 503(44), **517**
Harris, J. E., 1(78), 49(79), **57**, 347,
348(57, 58, 59), **359**, 373(46), 374
(46), 389(46), **395**, 439(74), 441,
442, 446, 448(74), **458**
Harris, S. J., 409(59), **429**
Harrison, G. A., 524(33), 526(33), 540
(33), 573(33), **585**
Hart, T. J., 332(60), 334(60), 345(60),
359
Hartline, H. K., 26(81), 27(84), 28, 33,
34(83), 52(84), **57**
Hartridge, H., 46(86), **57**
Harvey, E. N., 171(36), 174(29), 177
(38a), 178(27, 32, 35, 36), 179(31,
34, 37, 37a), 180(30, 33, 39, 59),
181, 182(59), 185(35), 186(36), **188**,
189, **190**, 568(83), 569, **588**
Haskin, H. H., 289(117), **311**
Hassenstein, B., 25(88), 34(88), 39(88),
40(87, 88), 41(88), **57**, 543(84), **588**
Hastings, J. W., 179(40, 46), **189**
Haswell, W. A., 353(117), **361**
Havinga, B., 468(46), 470(46), 504(46),
517
Hawkes, J. C., 526(70), 577(70), **587**
Hay, W. P., 451(75), 452(75), **458**

Heberdey, R. F., 5(91), 16(91), 22(91),
31, 35(90), 38(91), 43(90), 44(90),
46(89, 90, 91), 47(91), **57**
Heberer, G., 525(86), 556(85), **588**
Hecht, S., 32(93), 39(92, 94), **57**
Hediger, H., 513
Heegaard, P., 334(61), 352(61), **359**
Heinroth, O., 578(87), **588**
Heinze, K., 479(47), 484(47), 486(47),
517
Helfer, R. G., 230(71), **240**
Hempel, G., 335(62), **359**
Henderson, L. J., 562(88), **588**
Henke, K., 15(95), **57**, 372(47), 375(47),
376(47), 377(47), **395**
Hennig, W., 573(89), **588**
Hensel, H., 125(28), 126(28), **129**
Hensen, V., 78(45), 79(45), 97(45),
100(45), **106**
Henwood, W., 150(72), **167**
Herrick, F. H., 68, **105**, 340(64), 345
(64), 353(63), 354(63), **359**, 450
(76), **458**
Hersey, J. B., 438(77), **458**
Herter, K., 1(96), 16(96), **57**, 126(29),
127(29, 30), **129**, 257, 258(14), **277**,
318(66), 322(66), 327, 330(66), 331
(66), 336(65), 339(65), **359**, 371
(48), 372(48), 373(49), 375(49),
395
Hertz, M., 40(97), 41(98), 47(99), **57**,
58, 470(48), 501(48), 508(48), 512,
517
Hess, C., 7(100), 34(100), 43(100), 46,
58
Hess, W. N., 2(101), **58**
Hesse, R., 13(102), 20(102), 21(102), **58**
Hiatt, R. W., 466(49), 468(49), 473(49),
474(49), 476(49), 477(49), 482(49),
486(49), 488(49), 499(49), **517**
Hichar, J. K., 288, 290
Hickling, C. F., 435(78), 439(78), **458**
Hill, A. V., 195(25), **237**
Hines, M. N., 136(27), 155(25, 28),
156(28), **164**, 405(40), 407(11),
419(12), 420(14), **427**, **428**
Hirata, Y., 182(53a), **190**
Hitchcock, H. B., 136(60), **166**
Hjort, J., 435(110), **460**

Hoar, W. S., 553(90, 91), 575, 578(90), 588
Hocking, B., 341(67), 342(67), 359
Hodge, M. H., 142(60a), 166, 300(56), 308
Hodgkin, A. L., 194(26, 28), 195(27), 233(28), 237
Hodgson, E. S., 109(34, 34a), 114(34, 34a), 115, 116, 117(32), 118(32), 121(31), 124(34), 126(33, 35), 129, 130
Hoffmann, E., 37(6), 53, 543(3), 584
Hoffmann, P., 192, 202, 237
Hogben, L., 134, 166
Höglund, H., 467(50), 479(50), 480(50), 482(50), 485(50), 486(50), 517
Holmes, S. J., 113(36), 130, 317(68), 333(68), 342(68), 344(68), 345(68), 350(68), 359, 373(50), 395
Holmes, W., 193(30), 194(30), 238, 245, 277
Holt, E. W. L., 345(79), 459
Holz, G. G., Jr., 529(92), 588
Homann, H., 19(103), 58
Homuth, E. S., 113(36), 130
Hooker, D., 558(93), 588
Hosoi, T., 139(62), 166
Howard, H. W., 557(94), 588
Hoÿle, G., 7(104), 58, 193(32, 33, 34), 202, 209(32, 34), 210, 211, 213, 214, 215(31), 219(34), 223(32), 224(32), 230(33), 238, 545(95), 546(95), 588
Hubbard, C. J., 569(38), 586
Hubbard, R., 20(105, 207), 28(207), 43(207), 44(207), 45, 58, 63
Hubby, J. L., 576(96), 588
Huggins, G. E., 508(114), 520
Hughes, C. W., 177(14), 178, 188
Hughes, G. M., 327(69), 359
Humm, H. J., 334(118), 336(118), 361
Huntsman, A. G., 445(80), 459
Hutchins, H., 10
Hutchinson, G. E., 347(70), 359
Hyman, O. W., 340(71), 359

I

Idyll, C. P., 449(33), 450, 456
Ikari, C., 14(72), 28(72), 43(72), 56

Illig, G., 175(42), 189
Imbrie, J., 524(97), 588
Irwin, M. R., 557(98), 577(98), 588
Israel, H. R., 447(81), 459
Issel, R., 389(51), 395

J

Jahn, T. L., 13(157), 33(157), 37, 60, 117(37), 130, 157(107), 169
Jander, R., 52, 554(99), 588
Jasper, H. H., 220(35), 238
Johnson, G. E., 245, 277
Johnson, I. S., 124(38), 130, 504(51), 518
Johnson, M. W., 101(46), 106, 451(82), 459
Jolly, V. H., 434(83), 459
Jordan, H., 257(17), 277, 493(52), 518
Juday, C., 434(84), 435(84, 85), 459
Judd, D. B., 8(106), 58
Julien, A., 283(57), 308

K

Källén, B., 526(100), 558(100), 588
Kalmus, H., 143(63), 166, 402(41), 403(41), 408, 409(42), 429
Kamada, T., 194(36), 238
Kampa, E. M., 43(107), 44(107), 58, 569(101), 588
Kao, C. Y., 261(18), 277
Kato, K., 175(51), 189
Kato, M., 22(161), 60
Katsuki, Y., 101(24), 105
Katz, B., 194(9), 206, 207(15), 208(16), 210(41), 211(17), 212, 213(17), 230(41), 233(15), 234, 236, 237, 238, 286(58), 289(33), 306, 308
Keeble, F. W., 402(43), 410(43), 428, 429
Keighley, G., 222(37), 238
Keim, W., 243, 277
Kemp, S., 177, 189
Kennan, A. L., 558(102), 588
Kennedy, D., 3(108), 44(109), 49(15b), 54, 58
Kennedy, J. S., 366(44), 395
Kerkut, G. A., 545(103), 588

Kerz, M., 49(110), **58**
Kesling, R. V., 314(72), 323(73), 329(72), 336(72), 344(72), 350(72), **359**
Ketterer, B., 162(86), **168**
Kidder, G. W., 563(104), **588**
Kikuchi, K., 372(52), **395**, 432, 433(86), 434(86, 87), 435(86, 87), 438(87), **459**
King, J. E., 447(1), **455**
Kinne, O., 465(53), 479(54), 483, 484(53), 502(54), **518**
Kinosita, H., 194(36), **238**
Kinzig, H., 66(47), 78(47), 80, 97(47), **106**
Kleinholz, L. H., 22(111), **58**, 135(66), 136(66, 74), 137(67), 150(71, 71b, 72), 153(64, 65), 154(71a), 155(67, 73), 156(65), 157(65, 68, 69, 70), 158(68), **166**, **167**, 402(46, 50), 403(46), 406(47, 48), 407(44, 45) **429**
Kleitman, N., 402(51), **429**
Klie, W., 329(74), 332(74), **359**
Knight-Jones, E. W., 442(88), **459**, 470(29), **516**
Knowles, F. G. W., 134(80), 136(75, 76, 78), 137, 139(79), 140(80), 141(77, 79, 80), 144(80, 81), 145, 155(73, 77, 78), 157(77, 78), 158(77), 161(80), **167**, 291(23), 293(60), 294(60), 295(59, 60), 298(61), 299(62), **306**, **308**, 552(105), **589**
Knox, W. E., 561(106), **589**
Koch, H. J., 289(63), **308**
Koehler, O., 46(112), **58**, 365(54), 367(54), 372(53), 390(53), 392(55), **395**
Koepke, H. W., 330(75), 332(75), **359**
Koepke, M., 330(75), 332(75), **359**
Koller, G., 48(114), **58**, 135(83), 136, 137(84), 138, **167**
Konishi, J., 26(115), 33(116), **58**
Korringa, P., 402, **429**
Koshland, D. E., Jr., 563(107), **589**
Kramer, S., 487(105), **520**, 558(59), **587**
Krebs, H. A., 528, 561(109), 563, **589**
Kreidl, A., 78, 80, 91(48), **106**
Krieger, K. R., 248(20), **277**

Krijgsman, B. J., 115(39), 116(55), **130**, 286(64), 287(13), **306**, **308**, 385(56), **395**
Krijgsman, N. E., 115(39), **130**, 385(56), **395**
Kropp, B., 138(85), **168**, 374(58), 390(57), **395**
Krüger, P., 373(59), **395**
Krumbach, T., 67(52), 78(52), **106**, 111(40), **130**, 332(80), 333(80), 335(80), 336(80), 339(80), 340(80), 342(80), 345(80), **360**
Kruyt, W., 41(177), **61**
Kubo, I., 390(60), **395**
Kuffler, S., 26(117), 38(117), **58**, 69(49), 70(37, 38, 49), 71, 72(38, 50), 73, 74(49), **105**, **106**, 192(39), 210(40, 41), 220(38), 230(41), **238**, 290(38), **307**, 529(64, 65), 532(110, 111), 551(64, 65, 111), **587**, **589**
Kühl, H., 314(78), 316(77), 319(76, 78), 320(78), 323(78), 327(79), 330(78), 331(78), 333(78), 336(78), 339(78), 340, 341(78), 343(78), 344(78), 350(78), 351(78), 352(78), **359**, **360**, 493(56), 499(56), **518**
Kühn, A., 45(187), 46(118), **58**, **62**, 68(51), 79, 81(51), 84(51), **105**, **106**, 365(61), 366(61), 367(61, 62), 369, 377, **396**
Kuiper, J. W., 19, 25
Kükenthal, W., 67(52), 78(52), **106**, 111(40), **130**, 332(80), 333(80), 335(80), 336(80), 339(80), 340(80), 342(80), 345(80), **360**
Kunkel, B. W., 335(81), 342(81), **360**
Kupelwieser, H., 46, **62**, 347(163), **363**, 372(125), **398**
Kupka, E., 5(91), 16(91), 22(91), 31, 38(91), 46(91), 47(91), **57**
Kuwabara, M., 33(134), 34(134), **59**

L

Lago, A. D., 414(36), **428**
Landgrebe, F. W., 162(86, 117), **168**, **169**
Landsteiner, K., 556(112), 577(112), **589**
Lang, D., 85(53), **106**

Langenbuch, R., 78(54), 106, 389(63), 396, 488(57), 518
Langer, H., 45(7), 53
Langford, R. R., 434(89), 435(89), 459
Latarche, M., 435(32), 456
Lebour, M. V., 435(90), 446(91), 459, 498(58), 518
Lederberg, J., 556(113), 589
Lee, T. H., 162(87, 88), 168
Lehrman, D. S., 578(114), 580(114), 589
Leone, C. A., 577(115, 116), 578(115), 579, 589
Lerner, A. B., 162(87, 88), 168
Levin, A., 195(42), 238
Lewis, P. R., 221(43), 238
Lewis, S. E., 282(65), 284(65), 308
Lewontin, R. C., 561(117), 562(117a), 589
Leydig, F., 434(92), 459
Lin, E. C. C., 561(106), 589
Lindauer, M., 544(118), 589
Lindberg, R. G., 100(55), 101(55), 106, 329(82), 331(82), 332(82), 353(82), 354(82), 360, 466(59), 470(59), 474(59), 475(59), 477(59), 485(59), 518
Linder, F., 343(83), 360
Lindner, M. J., 447(1, 166), 455, 463
List, T., 314(84), 315(84), 322(84), 323(84), 327(84), 328, 329(84), 331(84), 360
Little, C. C., 527(119), 556(119), 589
Lloyd, A. J., 127(41), 130
Lochhead, J. H., 1(119), 7(119), 43(119), 58, 323(86), 327(86), 336(86, 89), 339(86), 340(86), 342(86), 343(85, 86), 344(86), 345(86, 89), 347(87, 89), 348(86), 349(86, 87, 88, 89), 350(86, 89), 360, 535(120), 589
Loeb, J., 121(42), 130, 365(65), 370(42), 372(64, 65), 376(67), 388, 391(66), 395, 396, 440, 443, 459
Loewenstein, W. R., 533(121), 550(121), 551(122), 589
Lohmann, K., 222(46), 238
Longhurst, A. R., 566(123, 124), 589
Lorenz, K., 487(60), 513(60), 518

Lowe, M. E., 144(51a), 156(51b), 166, 479(61), 509, 518
Lowenstein, O., 99(57, 58), 106, 544(66), 576(66), 587
Lowndes, A. G., 335(90), 336(90, 91), 338(91), 339, 340(90, 91), 342(91), 344(91), 347(92), 351(90, 91), 352(90, 91), 353(90), 360
Lozéron, H., 434(95), 435(95), 459
Lucas, C. E., 443(96), 445(97, 98), 459
Lucas, K., 192, 238
Luce, R. H., 42, 43(189), 62, 373(116), 398
Lüdtke, H., 22(120), 58
Lüers, H., 572(125), 589
Lundblad, O., 332(93), 333(93), 360
Luntz, A., 321(94), 360
Luther, W., 68(59), 107, 111, 115(43), 116(43), 124(43), 130, 385(68), 396, 472(62a), 507(62), 518
Lyon, E. P., 81(60), 85(60), 91(60), 99(60), 107

M

McDonald, P. R., 34(83), 57
McElroy, W. D., 177(38a), 179(46), 183, 189
Macey, E. J., 424(21), 428
MacGinitie, G. E., 331(97), 334(96), 335(95, 96), 360, 451(100), 453(100), 460, 469(63), 483(64), 486(63), 518
McGinnis, M. O., 127(44), 130, 374(69), 396
Machado, A. L., 285(70), 308
Machne, X., 194(9), 236
MacKay, D. C. G., 336(98), 338(98), 352(98), 360
Mackintosh, N. A., 433(101), 434(101, 102), 435(101, 102), 438(101), 460
MacNichol, E. F., Jr., 27(84), 52(84), 57
Maloney, M. T., 434(103), 435(103), 438(103), 443(103), 460
Mangelsdorf, A. F., 36(31), 49(31), 54
Mann, T., 285(43), 307
Manning, A., 578(126), 589

Manton, S. M., 313(103), 314(103), 322
    (101), 324(101, 103), 325(101), 326
    (101), 327(100), 328, 329(101), 332
    (101, 102), 333(23), 336(100), 342
    (99), 343(100), 352(100), 353(100),
    357, 360, 361, 526(129), 546(127),
    562(128), 572(129), 581, 590, 592
Marchand, J. M., 436(160), 449(160),
    462
Margalef, R., 318(104), 343(104), 352
    (104), 361
Marmont, G., 196(45), 210(45), 230(45),
    238
Marnay, A., 283(66), 308
Marsh, C. D., 127(45), 130
Marshall, S. M., 127(46), 130, 432,
    437(104), 439(104), 460, 486(65),
    518
Martin, A. W., 548, 590
Martin, M. F., 5(121), 59
Martini, E., 159(89), 168
Maslin, T. P., 526(131), 590
Mason, H. S., 181, 189
Mason, P., 1(78), 57, 347(58), 348(58),
    359
Mast, S. O., 7(122), 43(122), 59
Mathes, I., 385(69), 396
Mathias, P., 345(105), 361
Matsakis, J., 525(132), 590
Matsumoto, K., 294(67, 68), 295(68),
    308, 539(133), 590
Matthews, A., 453(136), 461
Matula, J., 318(106, 107), 361
Mauchline, J., 9(123), 59
Maxwell, D. S., 566(78), 587
Maxwell, S. S., 391(66), 396
Maynard, D. M., 287(69), 296(69a), 302
    (69a), 308
Maynard, E., 302
Mayr, E., 527(134), 578(134), 580, 590
Mayrat, A., 5(124), 6(124), 13, 14(124),
    20(124), 28(124), 59
Mead, H. T., 336(108), 361
Médioni, J., 2(162a), 43(162a), 48
    (162a), 61
Meek, A., 434(105), 450(106), 451(105),
    452(105), 460
Meglitsch, A., 161(29), 164
Megušar, F., 138(90), 168, 403(54), 429

Mendelson, M., 231(58b), 239
Menke, H., 402(55), 410(55), 417(55),
    429
Menner, E., 318(109), 336(109), 344
    (109), 350(109), 361
Menzies, R., 566(14), 585
Merker, E., 2(125), 6(125), 59
Merrick, A. D., 152(10), 164
Meyer, G. F., 30(126), 59
Meyerhof, O., 222(46), 238
Michener, C. D., 524(177), 526(135),
    540(135), 572(177), 590, 592
Mikhailoff, S., 510, 518
Milkman, R. D., 44(109), 58
Miller, R. L., 524(143), 527(143), 590
Miller, W. H., 14(127, 128), 59, 549,
    590
Minkiewicz, R., 496(67), 518
Mintz, E. V., 39(92), 57
Mitchell, Y., 321(42), 352(42), 358
Mittelstaedt, H., 39(201), 41, 42(129),
    59, 62, 367(71), 368(71, 127), 396,
    398, 487(108), 490(107, 108), 492
    (69), 518, 520, 544(137), 590
Moller-Racke, I., 7(194), 41(195), 62,
    382(123), 398
Monnier, A. M., 194(47), 238
Monod, T., 1(130), 59, 352(110), 361
Moore, A. R., 274(37), 278, 289(101),
    310
Moore, B., 415(56), 429, 443(107), 460
Moore, G. M., 323(111), 333(111), 361
Moore, H. B., 387(72), 396, 434(108),
    435(108), 438(77), 458, 460
Morgan, T. H., 255(21), 277, 445(109),
    460
Morrison, J. F., 573(61), 587
Moulton, J. W., 101(61), 107
Müller, A., 372(73), 376(73), 377(73),
    396
Müller, G. W., 333(112), 361
Müller, J., 17, 21(131), 59
Müller, R. T., 319(113), 321(113), 336
    (113), 349(113), 350(113), 351
    (113), 361, 373(74), 374(74), 390
    (74), 396
Munz, F. W., 564(138), 565(138), 590
Murray, J., 179, 435(110), 460
Muthe, P. T., 315(47), 354(47), 358

N

Nachmansohn, D., 284(66), 285(70), 287 (20), **306, 308**
Nachtsheim, H., 556(139), **590**
Naef, A., 525, **590**
Nagahama, H., 202(48), **238**
Nagano, T., 22(132), 43(133), **59,** 135 (92), 147(94), 150(92), 153(91), 156(91), 157(91, 95), 158(93), **168,** 406(57), **429**
Nagel, W. A., 391(75), **396**
Nageotte, J., 193(49), **238**
Naka, K., 33(134), 34(134), **59**
Nakazawa, K., 435(111), **460**
Nedel, J. O., 544(118), **589**
Needham, A. E., 315(114), **361**
Newcombe, C. L., 451(112), **460**
Nicholls, A. G., 432, 435(113), **460**
Nichols, E. L., 178, **189**
Nicol, J. A. C., 184(48, 49), **189**
Nikitine, B., 444(114), **460**
Norris, E., 336(115), 343(115), **361**
Northrop, J. H., 376(67), **396**
Nouvel, H., 479(70, 71), 482(71), 485 (71), **518**
Nouvel, L., 479(71), 482(71), 485(71), **518**
Novikoff (Nowikoff), M. M., 13(136), 16(137), 20(135, 136), **59,** 565(141), **590**
Novitski, E., 267(48), **279,** 286(121), **311**
Nowikoff, M. M. (*see* Novikoff, M. M.)
Nunnemacher, R. F., 25, 31(217), **63,** 414(78), **430,** 433(163), 435(163, 165), 436(163), **463**
Nuttall, G. H. F., 577

O

O'Brien, B., 18(138), **59**
Okada, Y. K., 174(50), 175(51), **189**
Oliver, W. D., 522(142), 523(142), 524 (142), 527, 555(142), **590**
Olson, E. C., 524(143), 527(143), **590**
Orr, A. P., 127(46), **130,** 432, 437(104), 439(104), **460,** 486(65), **518**

Ortmann, A. E., 67(43), 78(43), 102 (43), **106**
Ortmann, W., 468(72), 487(72), **518**
Orton, G. L., 526(144), **590**
Osborne, A. W., 183(52), **189**
Östlund, E., 142(96), 143(96), 144(96), 145, 146, 147(96), **168,** 289(71), 298(37, 72), 299(37), **307, 308**
Ostwald, W., 439(115), **460**
Otterstrom, A., 435(116), **460**
Owen, R., 525, 526, 527, 565, 566

P

Palombi, A., 482(73), 483, **518**
Panning, A., 331(121), 332(121), 336 (121), 338(121), **361,** 466(78), 473 (78), 474(78), 480(78), 482(78), **519**
Panouse, J. B., 141(97), 155(97), **168**
Pantin, C. F. A., 562(145), **590**
Papi, F., 7(139), 51, **59,** 368(78), 379(77, 79, 83, 84), 380(76), 382(84), 388 (79), 392(78), **396, 397,** 451(119), **460,** 492(76), **519**
Parameswaran, R., 294(73), **308**
Pardi, L., 51, 379(79, 80, 81, 82, 83, 84), 380(82), 382(84), 388(79), **396, 397,** 451(119), 453(118), **460,** 492 (74, 76), 504(74, 75), **519**
Park, O., 402, 409(59), **429**
Parker, G. H., 4(140), 14(140), 20(141), **59,** 117(48), 118(48), 127(47), 130, 148, 152(98), 161(99), 162, **168,** 336 (116), 338(116), 351(116), **361,** 436 (120), 442, **460**
Parker, T. J., 353(117), **361**
Passano, L. M., 139(35, 101, 102), 140 (101, 102), 154(101, 102), 165, **168,** 291(75), 293(24, 74, 75), 300(76), **306, 308, 309**
Pasteels, J. J., 558(146), **590**
Paton, W. N., 441(72), 442(72), **458**
Peabody, E. B., 6(142), 22(142), **60,** 149, **168**
Pearsall, W. H., 443(121), **460**
Pearse, A. S., 334(118), 336(118), **361,** 468, 469(77), 476(77), 477(77), 482 (77), **519**

Pearson, J. C., 336(119), 340(119), 343 (119), 350(119), **361**

Pennak, R. W., 122(49), 127(49), **130,** 323(120), 332(120), **361,** 434(122, 124), 435(122, 124), **461**

Percival, E., 448(123), **461**

Pérez-González, M. D., 142(103a), 144 (103a), **168,** 298(77), 302, **309**

Perkins, E. B., 136, 138(85, 105), 142 (105), 153(104), **168, 169,** 297(78, 79), **309**

Pesta, O., 176

Peters, E., 2(143), **60**

Peters, H. M., 102(62), **107**

Peters, N., 331(121), 332(121), 336 (121), 338(121), **361,** 466(78), 473 (78), 474(78), 480(78), 482(78), **519**

Pezard, A., 220(35), **238**

Philpott, D. E., 14(64), 27(64), 51(64), **56**

Phipps, C. F., 372(85), **397**

Pickford, G. E., 554(147), **590**

Pielou, D. P., 366(44), **395**

Pieplow, U., 467(79), 474(79), 482(79), 485(79), 487(79), **519**

Pierantoni, U., 175, **190**

Piéron, H., 402(60), 410(60), **429**

Pirenne, M. H., 29(144), 33(144), **60**

Piveteau, J., 582, **590**

Plate, L., 371(86), 372(86), **397**

Plew, W. F., 434(124), **461**

Polyak, S., 26(145), **60**

Potter, D. D., 262(12), **277,** 293(81), 294(80, 81), 295(81), 300(80, 81), 302, **309**

Powell, H. T., 470(9), **515**

Pravda, O., 319(122), **361**

Precht, H., 365(87), **397**

Prentiss, C. W., 66(63), 78(63), 79(63), 81(63), 97(63), 100(63), **107**

Priebatsch, I., 160(106), **169**

Pringle, J. W. S., 77(64, 66, 67), 103 (65), **107,** 544(149), **590**

Prosser, C. L., 2(146), 3(146), **60,** 67 (68), 69(68), **107,** 125(50), 126 (50), **130,** 244(23), 258, 259(25, 26, 27, 28), 267(26), 268(23, 24), 274 (26), **277, 278,** 284, 287(83, 84),

288(83), 289(83), **309,** 317(124), 318(124), 319(123), **362,** 539(151), 561(150), **591**

Pumphrey, R. J., 100(69), **107,** 193(30), 194(30), **238**

Pyle, R. W., 293(86), 296(86), **309**

Q

Qasim, S. Z., 442(88), **459**

R

Rabaud, E., 41(147), **60,** 389(88), **397**

Rádl, E., 15(148), 40(148), **60,** 347(125), **362**

Ralph, C. I., 424(7), **427**

Ramadan, M. M., 14(149), 17(149), **60**

Randall, J. E., 472(79a), **519**

Rasquin, P., 6(150), **60**

Rathbun, M. J., 451(125), **461**

Ratliff, F., 23(153), 28(85), **57, 60**

Ray, W. J., Jr., 563(107), **589**

Rehm, M., 297(86a), **309**

Reid, D. M., 334(126), **362**

Reinhard, E. G., 539(152), **591**

Remane, A., 323(127), **362,** 525, 526, 527, 556, 565(154), 566(154, 155), 571(154), 572(153, 154), 573, 582, **591**

Resner, R., 1(119), 7(119), 43(119), **58,** 535(120), **589**

Retzius, G., 244, **278**

Reuben, N., 315(47), 354(47), **358**

Ricardo, C. K., 433(170), 434(170), 435 (170), 438(170), **463**

Richards, A. G., 13(151), **60**

Richet, C., 192(50), **238**

Riedel, A. H., 33(152), **60**

Riggs, L. A., 23(153), **60**

Ripley, S. H., 67(86), **108,** 202(72), 203, 205, 228(73), **240,** 259(49), 268 (49), 270, 271, **279**

Robbins, J., 232(50a), **238,** 290(105), **310**

Robert, P., 2(162a), 43(162a), 48(162a), **61**

Roberts, T. D. M., 99(57), **106**

Roberts, T. W., 409(59, 61), 410(61), 429

Robertson, L. D., 574(156), 591

Robertson, J. David, 249, 250(30), 251, 262, 278

Rockstein, M., 563(157), 591

Roeder, K. D., 126(35), 130, 288(87, 102, 103), 309, 310

Roeder, S., 288(87), 309

Rokohl, R., 560(158), 591

Rose, M., 6(154), 60, 127(51), 130, 370(89), 372(89), 373(89), 374 (89), 387(89), 391(90), 397, 440, 443(126), 461

Rosenbloom, L., 6(150), 60

Rosenstadt, B., 14(155), 60

Rothenberg, M. A., 287(20), 306

Ruck, P., 7(156), 13(157), 33(157), 37, 60, 157(107), 169

Runnström, S., 372(91), 397

Ruska, H., 286(39), 307

Russell, F. S., 432, 433(128), 434(127, 130, 132), 435(127, 128), 437(128), 438(127, 130), 440(129), 446(131), 461

Rustad, D., 438(134), 446(133), 461

Ruttner-Kolisko, A., 391(92), 397

S

Safir, S. R., 507, 508(85), 509(85), 510 (85), 519

Sánchez y Sánchez, D., 47(158), 60

Sand, A., 99(58), 106

Sandeen, M. I., 31(159), 35(159), 60, 136(26, 30), 139(108), 140, 141 (108), 144(51c), 155(32, 109), 164, 165, 166, 169, 403, 404(13), 407(22), 408(22), 412(20), 415(19), 417(71), 421(13, 71), 424(20), 427, 428, 430

Sander, W., 35(160), 60

Sankey, J. H. P., 452(3), 455

Santschi, F., 377, 397

Sarlet, H., 221(11), 237

Sars, G. O., 323(129), 336(128), 342 (128), 362

Sato, S., 22(161), 60

Savage, R. E., 434(134), 435(134), 444 (134), 461

Sawaya, P., 135(110), 169, 286(88), 309

Ščerbakov, A. P., 380(94), 397

Schäfer, W., 313(130), 314(130), 315, 319(130), 329(130), 330(130), 331 (130), 333(130), 334(130), 335 (130), 336(130), 339(130), 341 (130), 342(130), 362, 466(80), 467 (80), 472(80), 473(80), 474(80), 477, 500, 513(80), 519

Schäferna, K., 344(131), 362

Schallek, W., 273(31, 50), 274(31, 51), 278, 279, 283(89), 285(89), 288 (90), 289(91, 92), 309, 318(132), 362, 373(95), 374(96), 397, 409 (62), 429, 444(135), 461

Schaller, F., 42(162), 60, 103(70), 107, 382(97, 123), 397, 398

Scharrer, B., 282(93, 94), 291(93), 304, 309

Scharrer, E., 282(93, 94), 291(93), 309, 562(160), 565(159), 591

Scheer, B. T., 222, 238

Scheer, M. A. R., 222, 238

Scheffer, D., 2(162a), 43(162a), 48 (162a), 61

Scheibel, A. B., 275(32), 278

Scheibel, M. E., 275(32), 278

Schellenberg, A., 334(133), 342(133), 362, 483, 519

Scheuring, L., 14(163), 61

Schlechtendal, A., 48(164), 61

Schlick, W., 335(134), 362

Schlieper, C., 48(165), 61, 566(155), 591

Schmid, H., 45(188), 62

Schmidt, B., 127(52), 130

Schmidt, R. S., 572(161), 578(161), 580 (161), 591

Schmidt-Nielsen, B., 561(162), 591

Schneider, G., 35(166), 61

Scholander, P. F., 566(163), 591

Schöne, H., 79(72), 81, 82(73), 83, 85(72), 91(72), 103(73a), 107, 365 (99, 100, 101), 368(98, 99, 100, 101), 389(100, 101), 390, 392(100, 101), 397, 467, 474, 476, 488(82, 83, 84a), 489(84, 84a), 490, 491, 492, 493(83), 497, 503, 506, 513, 519, 529, 532, 534(164), 535(164), 536, 544(164),

546(164), 551(164), 553(164), 554 (164), 591
Schreiber, E., 332(135), 333(135), 336 (135), 344(135), 350(135), 362
Schröder, R., 389(102), 397
Schultze, M., 14, 28(167), 61
Schulz, E., 33(196), 35(196), 62
Schulz, H., 2(168), 6(168), 7(168), 61, 369(103), 374(103), 397
Schuster-Dieterichs, O., 314(136), 330 (136), 333(136), 362
Schwartz, B., 507, 508(85), 509(85), 510 (85), 519
Scothorne, R. J., 548(165), 591
Scourfield, D. J., 335(138), 345(138), 347(138), 351(137), 362
Scudamore, H. H., 141(24), 142(31), 143(31), 164, 165, 297(18), 306, 414(63), 429
Segaar, J., 258(33), 278, 493(86), 519
Segal, S. J., 526(166), 591
Seifert, R., 15(169), 33(170), 61, 112 (53), 122(53), 130, 344(139), 349 (139), 362, 370(105), 371(105), 372(105), 374(104), 397
Sesar, M., 78(74), 107
Sexton, E. W., 453(136), 461, 557(167), 591
Shaw, J., 221, 239
Sheard, K., 435(137), 449(137), 461
Sherrington, C., 68, 107, 272, 544
Shimomura, O., 182(53a), 190
Shriner, J., 410(2, 10), 413(8), 421(71), 427, 430, 502(18), 516
Siewing, R., 571, 572(169, 170), 574(169), 582, 591
Silber, R. H., 221(53), 239
Simpson, G. G., 525, 526(172), 562(172), 565(172), 572(171), 592
Sjögren, S., 138(111), 169
Skogsberg, T., 346(140), 350(140), 362
Slifer, E. H., 545(173), 592
Slome, D., 134(61), 166
Sloper, J. C., 297(95, 96), 310
Smallman, B. N., 282(27, 65), 284(65, 123), 285(97), 306, 308, 310, 311
Smallwood, M. E., 313(141), 332(142), 334(141), 335(141), 362, 451(138), 461, 479(87), 519

Smith, F. E., 7(17), 8(17), 31(17), 46 (17), 48(17), 49(16), 51, 54, 61, 127 (9), 128, 321(9), 348(9), 350(9), 357, 382(11), 393, 442(8), 443(8), 448(8), 455
Smith, F. G. W., 435(139), 449(139, 140), 461
Smith, R. I., 153(112), 155(112), 169, 283(98), 287(99), 310, 420(64), 430
Snodgrass, R. E., 76(76), 107, 313(144), 335(143), 336(143), 340(143), 362, 572(174), 581(175, 176), 592
Snook, T., 138(105), 142(105), 169, 297 (79), 309
Sokal, R. R., 524(177), 526(135), 540 (135), 572(177), 590, 592
Sollmann, T., 319(145), 363
Sømme, J. D., 434(141), 435(141), 461
Southern, R., 433(143), 434(143, 144), 435(142, 143, 144), 446(142, 144), 462
Spandl, H., 323(146), 363
Spaulding, E. G., 507, 508(88), 519
Spaulding, M. H., 447(145), 462
Sperry, R. W., 39(172), 61, 320(147), 363, 554(178), 592
Spiegel, A., 113(54), 118(54), 130
Spieth, H. T., 546(179), 578(179), 592
Spooner, G. M., 369(106), 370, 398
Spurway, H., 580(180), 592
Staiger, H., 572(181), 592
Stålberg, G., 343(148), 363, 373(107), 398
Stehr, W. C., 373(108), 398
Stephens, G. C., 51(173), 61, 144(113, 113a), 169, 298(100), 310, 417(65, 68), 420(15), 427, 430
Stephensen, K., 435(146), 462, 469(89), 472(89), 519
Steuer, A., 434(147), 435(147), 462
Stevens, S. S., 535(182), 592
Stöcker, M., 36, 37, 53
Stockhammer, K., 13(174), 18(174), 49 (174a), 51(174, 174a), 61
Storch, O., 315(149), 323(149), 336(150, 151), 338, 340(150, 151), 342(149), 344(151), 350(151), 351(151), 353 (151), 363
Störmer, L., 435(148), 462

Strauss, E., 5(175), 16(175), 61
Strehler, B. L., 179(54), 190
Stroud, C. P., 524(183), 540(183), 592
Strouhal, H., 385(69), 396
Stubbings, H. G., 505(29a), 517
Stumpf, H., 49(9), 52, 53
Sturtevant, A. H., 524(184), 540(184), 592
Suganuma, Y., 14(72), 28(72), 43(72), 56
Sundararaj, B. I., 144(51c), 156(51b), 166
Suneson, S., 135(114), 136(114), 169
Sutcliffe, W. H., Jr., 449(149, 150, 151), 450, 453(152), 454, 462, 485(90), 504(90), 519

T

Tack, P. I., 467(91), 485(91), 486(91), 500(91), 519
Tait, J., 315(153), 316(153), 322(152), 323(153), 331(152), 332(152), 333(155), 353(153, 154), 363
Takagi, S., 174(55), 179(55), 190
Tashiro, S., 387(4), 393
Tattersall, O. S., 16(176), 61, 333(156), 334(156), 345(156), 351(156), 353(156), 363, 446(153), 462
Tattersall, W. M., 16(176), 61, 333(156), 334(156), 345(156), 351(156), 353(156), 363, 435(79), 446(153), 459, 462
Taylor, B. J. R., 545(103), 588
Templeman, W., 332(135), 363, 450(154, 155, 156), 452(154), 462, 480(92), 484(92), 485(93), 486(93), 519
ten Cate, J., 258(34), 278, 493(94), 496(94), 499(94), 519
ten Cate-Kazejewa, B., 507, 520
Terao, A., 177, 185(56), 190
Ter-Poghossian, A., 434(157), 435(157), 462
Thienemann, A., 434(158), 435(158), 462
Thienes, C. H., 231(14), 233(14), 237, 286(41), 307
Thomsen, M., 161(115), 169

Thorpe, W. H., 487(96), 506(96), 508(96), 520
Throckmorton, L. H., 576(96), 588
Tiegs, O. W., 581, 592
Tinbergen, N., 41(177), 61, 487(97), 504(97), 506, 513(97), 520, 527(186), 558(186), 562(186), 578(186), 592
Tobias, J. M., 194(54), 239
Todd, M.-E., 561(187), 592
Tonner, F., 13(178), 47(178), 61, 74(77), 107, 253, 278
Toriumi, M., 22(161), 60
Travis, D., 450(28), 456
Tressler, W. L., 434(103), 435(103), 438(103), 443(103), 460
Trojan, E., 175, 179(57), 190
Tsuji, F. I., 180(39, 59), 181, 182, 184(62), 189, 190
Tuppy, H., 556(188), 557(188), 563(188), 592
Turano, A., 14(233), 27(233), 64
Turner, C. H., 380(109), 398
Turner, R. S., 194(55), 239, 255(36), 260(36, 52), 264(52), 274(37), 278, 279, 289(101), 310
Twarog, B. M., 288(102, 103), 310
Tweedie, M. W. F., 466(98), 469, 474(98), 477, 513(98), 520

U

Ubrig, H., 385(110), 398, 504(99), 520
Ullyott, P., 435(159), 443(121), 460, 462
Ulrich, H., 572(125), 589
Umbach, W., 22(179), 61

V

Vaissière, R., 6(154), 7(179a), 60, 61
Valente, D., 321(158), 363
Vallentin, R., 175(60), 176, 184, 190
Vandel, A., 572(190), 574(190), 592
van der Heyde, A., 507, 508(100), 509(100), 510(100), 520
van der Kloot, W. G., 232(50a), 238, 290(105), 305(104), 310
van Essen, J., 22(180), 61

van Harreveld, A., 197, 198, 199, 201, 203(61), 214(58), 218(77), 219, 226, 229(61), 231(58a, 58b), **239**, **240**, 285

Van Heerdt, P. F., 116(55), **130**

Van Schouwenburg, K. L., 177(17), **188**

van Tets, G. F., 380(111), 388(111), **398**

Veil, C., 315(159), 318(159), **363**

Verkhovskaya, I. N., 49, **62**, 380(112), **398**

Verrier, M.-L., 16(182), 41(147), **60**, **62**

Verrill, A. E., 482(100a), **520**

Verwey, J., 334(160), **363**, 467(101), 469(101), 481(101), **520**

Viallanes, M. H., 28(183), **62**

Viaud, G., 1, 2(184), 3, 43(184), 46(184), 47(184), **62**, 365(113, 114, 115), 369 (113), 370(114), 373(113), 374 (113, 114), **398**

Vincent, D., 283(57), **308**

Viscontini, M., 45(187, 188), **62**

Visscher, J. P., 42, 43(189), **62**, 373 (116), **398**

Voelkel, H., 323(161), 327, 328, 329, 353 (161), **363**

Volz, P., 101(78), **107**, 474(102), 477 (102), 479(102), 506(102), **520**

von Bonde, C., 436(160), 449(160), **462**

von Buddenbrock, W., 7(190, 194), 15 (193), 21(191), 22(192), 29(193), 32, 33(196), 35(196), 41(193, 195), 48(193), 51(192), **62**, 81(82, 83), 84(81), 91(83), 103(79, 80), **107**, **108**, 109(56, 57), 112(56, 57), 113 (56, 57), 116(56), 117(56, 57), 118 (56, 57), 120, 124, **131**, 222, **239**, 241, **278**, 349, **363**, 365(117, 120), 372(118), 377(119, 121), 378(121), 379(121), 382(121, 122, 123), 389 (117, 121), **398**, 492(103), 496 (104), 497(104), 504(103), **520**

von Freidenfelt, T., 434(161), **463**

von Frisch, K., 46, 49, **62**, 152, **169**, 347 (163), **363**, 372(125), 392(124), **398**

von Fritsche, H., 451(162), **463**

von Gavel, L., 38(199), **62**

von Helmholtz, H., 39(200), 49(200), **62**

von Hess, C. (*see* Hess, C.)

von Holst, E., 39(201), 41, **62**, 320(164, 165), **363**, 368(126, 127), 392(126), **398**, 487(108), 490(107, 108), 492 (69), 502, **518**, **520**, 554, **592**

von Kaulbersz, G., 371(128), **399**

von Schiller, P., 39(202), **62**

von Uxkühl, J., 254(39), **278**

Vowles, D. M., 51(204), 52, **63**

W

Waddington, C. H., 555(192), 561(192), 562(192), **592**

Wagler, E., 346(166), **364**, 387(129), **399**

Wagner, H. G., 27(84), 28(85), 52(84), **57**

Wald, G., 20(207), 28(207), 31(205), 32 (93), 43(207), 44(206, 207), 45, **57**, **63**, 558(195, 196), 564(196), 565(194, 195, 196), **592**, **593**

Waldes, V., 275(40), **278**

Waloff, N., 113(58), 122(58), **131**, 372 (130), 383(130), 384, 388(130), **399**

Walop, J. N., 283(106), 284, 285(106, 107), **310**

Waring, H., 162(86, 117), **168**, **169**

Warren, F. J., 31(44a), 44(44a), **55**, 565(52), **586**

Watanabe, H., 174(61), **190**

Waterman, T. H., 2(208), 3, 7(211), 21 (212), 25, 27(219), 30, 31(217, 218), 32, 38, 39, 41, 48(214, 215, 218), 49 (10, 11, 216c), 50, 51(209, 210, 213, 216, 216b), 52(11, 210, 216a, 216b, 216c, 219), **53**, **63**, 157(118), **169**, 234(63), **239**, 286(109), **310**, 382(7, 131), **393**, **399**, 433(163), 435(163), 436(163), 447(7), 448(7), **455**, **463**, 472

Watkin, E. E., 334(167, 168), 343(167), 345(168), 350(168), **364**

Watson, D. M. S., 527(197), **593**

Wautier, J., 352(169), **364**

Weale, R. A., 35(3), **53**

Webb, H. M., 155(32), **165**, 403(67), 404 (13, 69), 406(69), 407(22, 69), 408 (22), 410(10), 412(9, 20), 413(8),

415(16, 19), 416, 417(17, 68, 71), 418(17), 419, 420(17), 421(13, 70, 71), 422(17, 18), 423, 424(20, 21), **427, 428**, 430, 502(18), **516**

Webb, W., 319(145), **363**

Weber, H., 23, **63**

Weir, J. H., 184(62), **190**

Weis-Fogh, T., 341(170), 342(170), **364**

Weismann, A., 434(164), 445(164), **463**

Wellington, W. G., 7(221), 51(222), **63**

Wells, P. H., 1(223), **63**

Welsh, J. H., 2(224), 3(224), 14(225), 22(225, 226), **64**, 135(119, 121), 136(74), 139(11, 12), 140(11), 152 (120), 153(120, 121, 122), 154(11), 157(121), **164, 167, 169,** 186(63, 64), **190,** 233(64), **239,** 282(114), 283(110), 286(110, 111, 112, 116), 289(115, 117), 290(113, 115), 293 (14, 15), 294(14, 15), 295(15), 296 (69a), 300(15), 302(69a), **306, 308, 310, 311,** 321(171), 352(171), **364,** 374(132), **399,** 402, 405(74), 406 (72, 73, 74, 77), 407(76), 410(72, 75), 414(78), 415(77), 415(77), **429, 430,** 435(165), **463**

Wenke, W., 4(227), 15(227), **64**

Werringloer, A., 17(228), **64**

Wertheim, G. K., 31(30), **54**

Wesenberg-Lund, C., 336(172), 346 (172), 350(172), **364**

Westell, W. E., 31(218), 48(218), **63,** 382(131), **399**

Wetzel, A., 1(229), 35(229), 40(229), 48(229), **64,** 74(84), 108, 333(173), 342(173), **364,** 376(133), **399**

Weymouth, F. W., 447(166), **463**

Wharton, G. W., 334(118), 336(118), **361**

Wheeler, F. J. G., 414(79, 80), **430**

White, G. M., 43(230), **64**

White, M. J. D., 527(198), 562(117a), **589, 593**

Whitear, M., 74(5), **104,** 244(2), **276**

Whitman, C. O., 578(199), **593**

Whitsell, J. S., 134(52), **166**

Wiersma, C. A. G., 27(219), 30, 51, 52(219), **63,** 67(86), 69(85), 74(85), 75, 77, **108,** 157(118), **169,** 193(32,

33, 34, 65), 194(66), 196(45), 197, 199, 201, 202(32, 72), 203(61), 205, 208(22), 209(32, 34, 68, 78), 210 (45), 211, 213, 214, 218(77), 219, 222(3, 37), 223(32), 224(32, 67), 225, 226, 227, 228(65, 70, 73), 229 (61, 70), 230(71), 233(14), 235(79), **236, 237, 238, 239, 240,** 245(41), 248, 249(43, 46), 254, 259(49), 260 (41, 52), 261(41), 262, 263(42), 264 (44, 52), 265, 266(43), 267(48), 268 (49), 269(47), 270, 271, 272(45, 47), 273(31, 50), 274(31, 44, 51), **278, 279,** 286(41, 121), 288(90, 118, 119, 120), 289(91, 92), **307, 309, 311,** 531, 532, 533, 545

Wigglesworth, V. B., 18, **64,** 366, **399**

Willey, R. B., 302(122), **311**

Williams, R. J., 536(200), **593**

Williamson, D. I., 379(136), 383(135), **399,** 484(109), **520**

Williamson, H. C., 448(167), **463**

Wilson, C. B., 345(175), 351(174), **364**

Wilson, D. P., 467(110), **520**

Winn, H. E., 578(201), **593**

With, C., 435(168), **463**

Witschi, E., 526(203), 558(202), **593**

Wojtusiak, R. J., 376(137), **399**

Wolf, E., 483, 484(111), **520**

Wolf, Ernst, 34(33), 36(33, 34), 37(32, 33, 34, 232), 39(94), **54, 57, 64**

Wolfe, L. S., 284(123), **311**

Wolfe, U. K., 49(79), **57,** 348(59), **359,** 373(46), 374(46), 389(46), **395,** 439(74), 441, 442, 448(74), **458**

Wolken, J. J., 14(233), 27(233), **64,** 549, **593**

Wolter, H., 378, 379(138), 382(138), **399,** 492(112), 493(112), **520**

Woltereck, R., 171(65), **190,** 336(176), 338(176), 346(176, 177), 347, 348, 351(176), **364**

Wood, F. D., 254(53), **279**

Wood, H. E., 254(53), **279**

Woodger, J. H., 526(205), **593**

Woolley, D. W., 533(206, 207), **593**

Worcester, D. C., 353(178), **364**

Worthington, E. B., 433(170), 434(169, 170), 435(170), 438(169, 170), 445 (169), **463**

Wright, E. B., 194(81), 195(82, 83, 84), 209(78), 232(80), **240**

Wright, S. T. C., 526(70), 577(70), **587**

Wulff, V. J., 117(37), **130**, 134(33), **165**, 295(19), **306**

Y

Yasaki, Y., 173, **190**

Yasumi, Y., 14(72), 28(72), 43(72), **56**

Yatsu, N., 174, **190**

Yerkes, R. M., 127(59), **131**, 374(139), 375(139), **399**, 507, 508(113, 114), 509(114), 510(114), **520**

Yonge, C. M., 85(53), **106**, 127(41), **130**, 354(179), **364**

Young, J. Z., 193(30), 194(30, 85), **238, 240**

Young, R. W., 101(46), **106**

Z

Zangerl, R., 525(208), 526(208), **593**

Zawadzki, B., 235(79), **240**

Zerrahn-Wolf, G., 36(34), 37(34), **54**

Ziegler-Günder, I., 45(234), **64**

Zimmer, C., 1(235), 5(236), 14(236), 16(235, 236), 19(236), 23(236), 24, 25(236), 29(236), **64**, 323(180), 335 (181), 340(181), 342(181), **364**, 387 (140), **399**, 469(115), 475(116), 487 (115), **520**

Zimmermann, W., 526(209), 572(209), 573(209), **593**

Zweig, G., 577(210), **593**

The classification of Recent Crustacea employed in this book is given here as an aid in using the Systematic Index.* At the present time such a classification cannot claim to be definitive. Approximate counts of known species are shown in parentheses and examples of well-known genera are given after each terminal group to assist in recognition.

Class Crustacea (26,000+)
    Subclass Cephalocarida (2): *Hutchinsoniella*
    Subclass Branchiopoda (800+)
        Order Anostraca (175+): *Artemia*
        Order Notostraca (15): *Lepidurus*
        Order Diplostraca (605+)
            Suborder Conchostraca (180+): *Eulimnadia*
            Suborder Cladocera (425+): *Daphnia*
    Subclass Ostracoda (2000+)
        Order Myodocopa (300+): *Cypridina*
        Order Cladocopa (30+): *Polycope*
        Order Podocopa (1600+): *Cypris*
        Order Platycopa (30+): *Cytherella*
    Subclass Mystacocarida (3): *Derocheilocaris*
    Subclass Copepoda (4500+)
        Order Calanoida (1200+): *Calanus*
        Order Harpacticoida (1200+): *Canthocamptus*
        Order Cyclopoida (1000+): *Cyclops*
        Order Notodelphyoida (300+): *Doropygus*
        Order Monstrilloida (35): *Monstrilla*
        Order Caligoida (400+): *Penella*
        Order Lernaeopodoida (300+): *Salmincola*
    Subclass Branchiura (75): *Argulus*
    Subclass Cirripedia (800+)
        Order Thoracica (550+)
            Suborder Lepadomorpha (300+): *Lepas*
            Suborder Verrucomorpha (50+): *Verruca*
            Suborder Balanomorpha (200+): *Balanus*
        Order Acrothoracica (12+): *Trypetesa*
        Order Ascothoracica (25+): *Synagoga*
        Order Apoda (1): *Proteolepas*
        Order Rhizocephala (200+): *Sacculina*
    Subclass Malacostraca (18,000+)
      Series Leptostraca (7)

---

* This synopsis, extracted from Chapter 1, Vol. I, has been prepared by Dr. Fenner A. Chace, Jr., of the U. S. National Museum.

Superorder Phyllocarida (7)
  Order Nebaliacea (7): *Nebalia*
Series Eumalacostraca (18,000+)
  Superorder Syncarida (6)
    Order Anaspidacea (6): *Anaspides*
  Superorder Peracarida (9000+)
    Order Thermosbaenacea* (4): *Thermosbaena*
    Order Spelaeogriphacea (1): *Spelaeogriphus*
    Order Mysidacea (450+)
      Suborder Lophogastrida (30): *Gnathophausia*
      Suborder Mysida (420+): *Mysis*
    Order Cumacea (425+): *Diastylis*
    Order Tanaidacea (250+): *Apseudes*
    Order Isopoda (4000+)
      Suborder Gnathiidea (75+): *Gnathia*
      Suborder Anthuridea (100+): *Anthura*
      Suborder Flabellifera (1400+): *Limnoria*
      Suborder Valvifera (600+): *Idotea*
      Suborder Asellota (500+): *Asellus*
      Suborder Phreatoicidea (50+): *Phreatoicus*
      Suborder Epicaridea (350+): *Bopyrus*
      Suborder Oniscoidea (900+): *Ligia*
    Order Amphipoda (3600+)
      Suborder Gammaridea (3000+): *Gammarus*
      Suborder Hyperiidea (300+): *Phronima*
      Suborder Caprellidea (250+): *Caprella*
      Suborder Ingolfiellidea (4): *Ingolfiella*
  Superorder Eucarida (8600+)
    Order Euphausiacea (90+): *Euphausia*
    Order Decapoda (8321+)
      Suborder Natantia (1930)
        Section Penaeidea (318): *Sergestes*
        Section Caridea (1590)
          Superfamily Oplophoroida (208): *Acanthephyra*
          Superfamily Stylodactyloida (7): *Stylodactylus*
          Superfamily Pasiphaeoida (60): *Leptochela*
          Superfamily Bresilioida (13): *Bresilia*
          Superfamily Palaemonoida (399): *Palaemon*
          Superfamily Psalidopodoida (3): *Psalidopus*
          Superfamily Alpheoida (614): *Alpheus*
          Superfamily Pandaloida (115): *Pandalus*
          Superfamily Crangonoida (171): *Crangon*
        Section Stenopodidea (22): *Stenopus*
      Suborder Reptantia (6391+)
        Section Macrura (693)
          Superfamily Eryonidea (39): *Polycheles*

---

* Presence of a dorsal marsupium instead of a ventral one comprised of oöstegites indicates that these are not proper peracarids and may require a new superorder.

Superfamily Scyllaridea (84): *Palinurus*
Superfamily Nephropsidea (313): *Homarus*
Superfamily Thalassinidea (257): *Callianassa*
Section Anomura (1270)
Superfamily Galatheidea (572): *Galathea*
Superfamily Paguridea (642): *Pagurus*
Superfamily Hippidea (56): *Emerita*
Section Brachyura (4428+)
Subsection Gymnopleura (30): *Ranina*
Subsection Dromiacea (200)
Superfamily Dromiidea (175): *Dromia*
Superfamily Thelxiopeidea (25): *Thelxiope*
Subsection Oxystomata (480): *Calappa*
Subsection Brachygnatha (3718+)
Superfamily Brachyrhyncha (2842+): *Cancer*
Superfamily Oxyrhyncha (876+): *Maja*
Superorder Hoplocarida (180+)
Order Stomatopoda (180+): *Squilla*

NOTE: Names which have been superseded are given within brackets. The synonymies are by no means complete, but merely indicate those names incorrectly given in the citations from the literature in this volume. Page numbers in italics indicate illustrations.

A

Acanthephyra [*Acanthophyra*], Oplophoroida, 319, 343, 616
A. *eximia* S. I. Smith, 16
A. *purpurea* A. Milne-Edwards, 433, 435
Acanthomysis longicornis (H. Milne Edwards) [*Dasymysis longicornis*], Mysida, 435
[*Acanthophyra*] see *Acanthephyra*
Acartia, Calanoida, 373, 414, 442, 444
A. *clausi* Giesbrecht, 371, 434, 438, 440
A. *longiremis* (Lilljeborg), 434, 438
A. *spinata* Esterly, 434
A. *tonsa* Dana, 374, 434
[*Achialus agilis*] see *Anchialina agilis*
Acrothoracica, 5, 615
Adamsia palliata (Bohadsch), Anthozoa, 470
Aedes, Insecta, 541
Aega, Flabellifera, 376

[*Alcippe*] see *Trypetesa*
Algae, 333, 443, 472, 485
Alona, Cladocera, 323, 371
[*Alphaeus*] see *Alpheus*
Alpheoida, 29, 616
Alpheus [*Alphaeus*], Alpheoida, 101, 616
A. *armillatus* H. Milne Edwards [*Crangon armillatus*], 2
A. *dentipes* Guérin, 470, 474, 477, 479, 506
A. *djiboutensis* De Man, 471
Ammocoetes, Cyclostomata, 547
Ampeliscidae, Gammaridea, 5, 16
Amphibia, 134, 162, 544, 548, 549, 552, 554, 563, 565, 576
Amphipoda, 1, 2, 5, 14, 16, 22, 34, 41, 43, 48, 51, 78, 111, 152, 155, 171, 313, 317, 332–335, 339, 342–345, 350, 351, 355, 371, 372, 376, 379, *380*, 383, 389, 391, 435, 436, 447, 451, 469, 472, 479, 487, 492, 535, 538, 541, 559,

565, 566, 568, 569, *571*, 574, 575,
  582, 616
[*Amphitoe*] see *Ampithoe*
Ampithoe [*Amphitoe*], Gammaridea, 317,
  333, 344, 345, 350, 371
Anagasta [*Ephestia*], Insecta, 161
A. kuhniella (Zeller), 45
Anaspidacea, 5, 78, 111, 353, 566, *582*,
  616
Anaspides, Anaspidacea, 327, 343, 484,
  616
Anchialina agilis (G. O. Sars) [*Achialus
  agilis*], Mysida, 435, 446
Anchistioides antiguensis (Schmitt),
  Palaemonoida, 158, 405, 406, 414
Anemones, see Sea anemones
Anilocra, Flabellifera, 559
Annelida, 184, 304, 313, 314, 547, 548,
  562, 564, 577
Anolis, Reptilia, 162, 552
[*Anamalocera*] see *Anomalocera*
Anomalocera [*Anamalocera*], Calanoida,
  4, 336
A. patersoni (Templeton), 434, 438
Anomura, 29, 69, 74, 101, 111, 204, *205*,
  219, 229, 252, 260, 289, 292, 319, 329,
  334, 387, 538, 539, 545, 552, 566, 574,
  578, 617
Anostraca, 4, 6, 122, 127, 319, 321, 339,
  340, 342–344, 346, 349–351, 371–
  374, 538, 560, 575, 615
Antarctomysis, Mysida, 435
Anthura, Anthuridea, 616
Anthuridea, 616
Ants, 17, 52, 543
Apherusa clevei G. O. Sars, Gammaridea,
  435
Apis, Insecta, 21, 32, 37, 39, 47, 543
Apoda, 5, 615
Apseudes, Tanaidacea, 616
[*Apus*] see *Triops*
[*A. cancriformis*] see *Triops cancriformis*
Arachnida, 23, 77, 392, 514, 564, 578, 580
Argis, Crangonoida, 336
Argulus, Branchiura, 6, 16, 331, 339, 350,
  375, 484, 615
A. foliaceus (Linnaeus), 1, 127, 373, 390
Aristaeinae, Penaeidea, 447
Aristeus, Penaeidea, 173

Armadillidiidae, Oniscoidea, 541, 574
Armadillidium [*Armidillidium*], Oniscoidea, 15, 372, 375, 376
A. cinereum Arcangeli, 372, 375
A. vulgare (Latreille), 113, 122, 452, 557
[*Armidillidium*] see *Armadillidium*
Artemia, Anostraca, 1, 4, 6, *7*, 15, 16, 23,
  218, 344, 346, 349, 350, 370, 372, 373,
  535, 541, 543, 548, 557, 567, 575, 615
A. salina (Linnaeus), 33, 43, 46, 371, 557
Arthropoda, 2, 8, 13, 14, 17–21, 26–28, 38,
  44, 46, 49, 51, 65, 122, 126, 191, 276,
  286, 304, 313, 322, 325, 327, 328, 354,
  355, 496, 526, 540, 542, 545, 547–549,
  554, 562, 576, 577, 581
Ascothoracica, 5, *582*, 615
Asellota, 616
Asellus, Asellota, 36, 37, 387, 492, 549,
  616
A. aquaticus Linnaeus, 388, 509, 567
A. communis Say, 37, 373, 387
Astacidae, Nephropsidea, 548
Astacilla, Valvifera, 333, 345, 472
[*Astacura*] see Nephropsidea
Astacus [*Potamobius*], Nephropsidea, 14,
  84, 85, 91, 97, 112, 143, 318, 320,
  322, 323, 327, 328, *329*, 331, 353, 371,
  391, 402, 409, 486, 506, 546
A. astacus (Linnaeus) [*A. fluviatilis*, *A.
  potamobius*, *Potamobius astacus*, *P.
  fluviatilis*], *12*, *13*, 45, 68, *81*, 143,
  207, *243*, 283, 409, 503
[*A. fluviatilis*] see *A. astacus*
[*A. gammarus*] see *Homarus gammarus*
[*A. potamobius*] see *A. astacus*
[*A. trowbridgii*] see *Pacifastacus trow-
  bridgii*
Asteroidea, 549
Athanas, Alpheoida, 29
[*A. nistescens*] see *A. nitescens*
A. nitescens (Leach) [*A. nistescens*], 485
[*Atya swammerdamii*] see *Nototropis
  swammerdamii*
Atyidae, Oplophoroida, 173

B

Bacteria, 171, 173, 179, 184, 570
Balanomorpha, 387, 470, 615

Balanus, Balanomorpha, 8, *42,* 121, 343, 352, 373, 374, 440, 442, 443, 544, 545, 615
B. amphitrite Darwin, 43, 373, 387
B. balanoides (Linnaeus), 118
B. improvisus Darwin, 7, *32,* 43, 371, 373, 387
B. improvisus var. *assimilis* Darwin, 387
Barnacles, Thoracica, *7,* 33, 118, 119, 327, 502, 505, 535, 559
Bartholomea annulata (Lesueur), Coelenterata, 472
Bathynellacea, Syncarida, *582*
Bathyporeia, Gammaridea, 334, 343, 350
Bees, 51, 382
Beetles, 40, 116
Bentheuphausia, Euphausiacea, 173
Birds, 431, 466, 473, 514, 527, 548, 553, 563, 578, 580
Birgus, Paguridea, 319, 331–333, 451, 467, 568
B. latro (Linnaeus), 1, 466, 467, 486, 487
Blattids, Insecta, 159
Blepharipoda, Hippidea, 224, 226
B. occidentalis Randall, 219, *226*
Blowflies, Insecta, 285
Bonellia, Echiuroidea, 570
Bopyridae, Epicaridea, 570
Bopyrus, Epicaridea, 616
Boreomysis microps G. O. Sars, Mysida, 435
Bosmina, Cladocera, 46, 348, 437
B. coregoni Baird, 434, 438, 560
B. longirostris (O. F. Müller), 434
Bosminopsis deitersi Richard, Cladocera, 434
Brachygnatha, 617
Brachyrhyncha, *579,* 617
Brachyura, 29, 74, 100, 101, *110,* 111, 116, 134, 135, 138, 153–155, 202, 204, *205,* 219, 229, 260, 283, 284, 291, *292,* 293, *315,* 327, 329, 335, 387, 440, 448, 473, 474, 482, 493, 513, 538, 539, 546, 559, 566, 567, 574, 575, 578, 617
Branchiopoda, 48, 314, 434, 536, 541, 546, 550, 557–559, 566–568, *582,* 615
Branchipus, Anostraca, 318, 344, 373, 567
[*Branchipus serratus*] see *Eubranchipus serratus*

Branchiura, 1, 5, 127, 336, 351, *582,* 615
Bresilia, Bresilioida, 616
Bresilioida, 616
Bryozoa, 472
Bunodeopsis prehensa (Richters), Coelenterata, 473
Butterflies, 576
Bythotrephes longimanus F. Leydig, Cladocera, 434, 438

C

Calanoida, 4, 338, 340, 342–344, 351–353, 434, 435, 615
Calanoides acutus Giesbrecht [*Calanus acutus*], Calanoida, 434, 438
Calanopia americana Dahl, Calanoida, 434
Calanus, Calanoida, *336,* 344, 351, 432, 433, 437–439, 441–445, 615
[*C. acutus*] see *Calanoides acutus*
C. finmarchicus (Gunnerus), *432,* 434, 435, 438–440, 444
[*C. helgolandica*] see *C. helgolandicus*
C. helgolandicus (Claus) [*C. helgolandica*], 376
C. hyperboreus Krøyer, 434
C. propinquus Brady, 433, 434
C. simillimus Giesbrecht, 434
Calappa, Oxystomata, 334, 617
C. flammea (Herbst), 158, 406
Caligoida, 4, 615
Caligus, Caligoida, 334, 352
C. rapax H. Milne Edwards, 442
Calliactis parasitica (Couch) [*Sagartia parasitica*], Coelenterata, 470
Callianassa, Thalassinidea, 253, 255, 260, 274, 334, 335, 617
C. californiensis Dana, 194
C. subterranea (Montagu), 14
Callinectes, Brachyrhyncha, 14, 44, 293–295, 304, 404, 482, 559
[*C. hastatus*] see *C. sapidus*
C. sapidus Rathbun [*C. hastatus*], 43, 283, 341, 404, 450, 452, 482
Calliphora, Insecta, 34, 36, 37, 159, 542
Calocaris, Thalassinidea, 29
Cambarellus, Nephropsidea, 144, 479

C. shufeldtii (Faxon), 413, 479, *509*

Cambarus, Nephropsidea (see also *Procambarus*), 33, 34, 36, 37, 113, 116, 124, 135, 152, 153, 156, 371, 373, 374, 380, 410, 412, 415, 467, 474, 486, 498, 500, 510

[*C. affinis*] see *Orconectes limosus*

C. ayersii Steele, 1

[*C. bartoni*] see *C. bartonii*

C. bartonii (Fabricius) [*C. bartoni*], *36*, 37, 158, 406, 487

C. bartonii sciotensis Rhoades, *114*, 115

[*C. clarkii*] see *Procambarus clarkii*

C. diogenes Girard, 409, 468

[*C. immunis*] see *Orconectes immunis*

[*C. limosus*] see *Orconectes limosus*

[*C. obscurus*] see *Orconectes obscurus*

[*C. pellucidus*] see *Orconectes pellucidus*

[*C. virilis*] see *Orconectes virilis*

Camptocercus rectirostris Schödler, Cladocera, 335

Cancer [*Platycarcinus*], Brachyrhyncha, 152, 173, 214, 451, 474, 493, 559, 617

C. antennarius Stimpson, 223, 229

C. anthonyi Rathbun, 229, *230*

C. irroratus Say, 283, 285, 302

C. magister Dana, 338, 352

C. pagurus Linnaeus, 283, 467, 485

Candacia, Calanoida, 336, 434

Candona, Podocopa, 323

Canthocamptus, Harpacticoida, 333, 567, 615

Caprella, Caprellidea, 40, 333, 342, 616

[*C. dentata*] see *C. liparotensis*

C. liparotensis Haller [*C. dentata*], 35, 48, 472

Caprellidae, Caprellidea, 376

Caprellidea, 42, 616

Carausius [*Dixippus*], Insecta, 34, 160

C. morosus Brunner, 159, *160*

[*Carcinides*] see *Carcinus*

Carcinus [*Carcinides*], Brachyrhyncha, 15, 29, 40, 41, 68, 74, 77, 79, 85, 91, 93, 96, 112, 116, 120, 124, 143, 144, 146, 152, 221, 246, 284, 294, 297, 318–320, 330–332, 371, 376, 377, *378*, 380, 382, 442, 466–468, 473, 474, 486, 492, 499, 500, 502, 507, 510, 553, 567

[*C. granulatus*] see *C. maenas*

C. maenas (Linnaeus) [*C. granulatus*], 48, 68, 74, *75*, 91, *93*, *95*, *97*, 101, *111*, 115, 194, 220, 221, *246*, 283–285, 302, 378, 385, 442, 473, 480, 482, 485, 493–495, *496*, *507*, *508*

[*Cardiosoma*] see *Cardisoma*

Cardisoma [*Cardiosoma*], Brachyrhyncha, 451, 467

C. carnifex (Herbst), 486

Caridea, 14, 25, 30, 100, 135, 138, 405, 447, 472, 538, 548, 567, 575, 616

Carp louse, see *Argulus*

Caterpillars, 332

Cats, 551

Cecropia, Insecta, 305

Centipedes, Myriapoda, 320

Centropages, Calanoida, 442, 484

C. hamatus Lilljeborg, 434

C. typicus Krøyer, 352, 434, 438

Cephalocarida, *582*, 615

Cephalopoda, 4, 28, 44, 194, 206, 207, 233, 242, 527, 546, 548, 549, 563, 564, 569

Ceriodaphnia, Cladocera, 46, 434

Cerithium, Gastropoda, 511, *512*

Chameleons, 162, 552

[*Cheirocephalus*] see *Chirocephalus*

Chelicerata, 122, 576

Chickens, 573

Chiridotea, Valvifera, 333, 334

Chirocephalus [*Cheirocephalus*], Anostraca, 339, 371, 567

Chironomids, Insecta, 541

[*Chirudina streetsii*] see *Chirundina streetsii*

Chirundina streetsii Giesbrecht [*Chirudina streetsii*], Calanoida, 434

Chlorella, Chlorophyta, 443

[*Chthalamus fragilis*] see *Chthamalus fragilis*

Chthamalus fragilis Darwin [*Chthalamus fragilis*], Balanomorpha, 373

Chydorids, Cladocera, 332, 335, 342, 345, 348

Chydorus, Cladocera, 348

Cicadas, 566

Cirolana salvadorensis Schuster, Flabellifera, 333

Cirripedia, 7, 43, 118, 122, 275, 370–374, 376, 436, 538, 560, 567, 569, 570, *582*, 615

Cladocera, 2, 4, 5, 16, 17, 22, 31, 43, 46, 48, 49, 111, 122, 127, 314, 319, 323, 333, 335, 336, *337*, 338, 342, 345, 347–351, 369–374, 376, 380, 387, 434, 436, 438, 444, 502, 533, 535, 537, 538, 546, 615

Cladocopa, 4, 615

Clausocalanus laticeps Farran, Calanoida, 434

Clibanarius misanthropus (Risso), Paguridea, 470, 501, 511, *512*

Cockroaches, 192, 288, 302, 545

Coelenterata, 471, 472

Coenobita, Paguridea, 102

C. cavipes Stimpson, 390

Columba, Aves, 37

Conchoecia, Myodocopa, 172

Conchostraca, 4, 17, 333, 336, 340, 342, 343, 345, 349, 350, 615

Copepoda, 6, 7, 46, 111, 121, 122, 134, 171, 172, *173*, 175, 178–180, 184, 187, 323, 334, 336, *337*, 338, 340, 342–345, 350–353, 356, 369–374, 376, 387, 388, 414, 415, 432–443, 447, 484, 486, 512, 538, 539, 541, 544, 557, 566, 567, 569, 570, 575, *582*, 615

Copilia, Cyclopoida, 4

Corethra, Insecta, 159

Corophium, Gammaridea, 332, 334, 345, 376, 377, 469

Corycaeus [*Coryceus*], Cyclopoida, 4, 172

[*Coryceus*] see *Corycaeus*

Crabs, *10, 11, 13,* 14, 41, 48, 51, 78, 79, 85, 91, 93, 94, 96–99, 102, 103, *110,* 116, 124, 139, 155, 207, *219,* 221, 222, 228, 230, 242, 247, 252, 254–258, 289, 293, 294, 300, 304, 313, 318–321, 323, 329–336, *337,* 338–341, 350–356, 385, 390, *403,* 404, 405, 410–413, 415, 417–425, 451–454, 465–477, *478,* 479–482, 486–488, 492–496, 498, 500–508, 512–514, 522, 523, 546–548, 553, 559, 567, 568, 575, 578, *579,* 580, 581

Crabs, army, 473

Crabs, blue, see *Callinectes*

Crabs, coconut, see *Birgus*

Crabs, fiddler, see *Uca*

Crabs, ghost, see *Ocypode*

Crabs, green, see *Carcinus*

Crabs, hermit, see Paguridea

Crabs, horseshoe, see *Limulus* and Xiphosura

Crabs, land, see under Habitat, terrestrial

Crabs, mangrove, see *Goniopsis*

Crabs, oyster, see *Pinnotheres*

Crabs, pea, 332

Crabs, robber, see *Birgus*

Crabs, rock, see *Grapsus*

Crabs, sand, see *Emerita*

Crabs, spider, 112, 252, 472

[*Crago*] see *Crangon*

Crangon [*Crago*], Crangonoida, 85, 101, 113, 118, 120, 135–138, 141, 147, 161, 295, 297, 318, 389, *390,* 447, 468, 485, *489, 490,* 497, 500, 504, 553, 616

[*C. allmani*] see *C. allmani*

C. allmani Kinahan [*C. allmani*], 293

[*C. armillatus*] see *Alpheus armillatus*

C. crangon (Linnaeus) [*C. vulgaris*], 48, 113, 117, 143, 147, 479, 488

[*C. vulgaris*] see *C. crangon*

Crangonoida, 616

Crayfishes, Nephropsidea, 2, 3, 33, 34, 67–69, 72, 114, 126, 157, 192, 194, 195, 198, 208, 209, 211, 213, 222–224, 228, 230, 232, 233, 242, 244, *245,* 247, 248, 250, 254, 255, 258, 260, 262–264, 266, *267,* 269–274, 276, 287–290, 293, 294, 315–318, 323, 385, 402, 409, 410, 413, 414, 479, 497, *511,* 522, 529–531, 533, 534, 544, 545, 547, 551, 567, 568, 575

Crickets, 37, 101

Cruregens, Anthuridea, 331

Ctenocalanus vanus Giesbrecht, Calanoida, 433

Ctenophora, 179, 184

Culicids, Insecta, 159

Cumacea, 1, 5, 14, 16, 17, 22, 111, 333–335, 342, 371, 435, 569, *571, 582,* 616

Cyathura, Anthuridea, 488

C. carinata (Krøyer), 389

Cyclopidae, Cyclopoida, 391

Cyclopoida, 4, 338, 343, 344, 435, 615

Cyclops, Cyclopoida, 345, 435, 615

C. bicuspidatus Claus, 435, 438

C. brevicornis O. F. Müller, 172

C. hyalinus Rehberg, 435

[*C. leucarti*] see *C. leuckarti*

C. leuckarti Claus [*C. leucarti*], 345, 435

C. oithonoides G. O. Sars, 435

C. strenuus Fischer, 435

Cyclostomata, Agnatha, 162, 552

Cylisticus, Oniscoidea, 376

C. convexus (De Geer), 49, 127

Cyphocaris anonyx Boeck [*Cyphocaryx anonyx*], Gammaridea, 435

[*Cyphocaryx anonyx*] see *Cyphocaris anonyx*

Cypridina, Myodocopa, 172, 174, 175, *178*, 179–183, 187, 615

C. hilgendorfii G. W. Müller, *172*, *174*, 177–179

C. noctiluca Kajiyama, 184

C. norvegica Baird [*C. norwegica*], 179

[*C. norwegica*] see *C. norvegica*

Cypridinidae, Myodocopa, 4, 7, 172

Cypridopsis, Podocopa, 371

C. vidua (O. F. Müller) [*Pionocypris vidua*], 236, 241

Cyprinotus incongruens (Ramdohr) [*Heterocypris incongruens*], Podocopa, 351

Cypris, Podocopa, 371, 615

Cyprois marginata (Strauss), Podocopa, 351

Cytherella, Platycopa, 615

Cyzicus, Conchostraca, 345

D

Dadaya macrops (Daday), Cladocera, 351

Daphnia, Cladocera, 1, 2, *3*, 6–8, 16, 22, *31*, 32, 34, 35, 38, 43, 44, 46, 47, 49, *50*, 51, 53, 121, 286, 319, 321, *336*, 338, 347–351, 369, 372–377, 380, 437–439, 441–443, 446, 448, 504, 543, 544, 550, 615

D. cucullata G. O. Sars, 434

D. longispina O. F. Müller, 127, 352, 434, 435

D. lumholzi G. O. Sars, 434, 438

D. magna Straus, 46, 49, 321, 348, 352, 374, 385, 390, 441

D. pulex (De Geer), 2, 5, 43, 46, 49, 127, 374, 385, 434, 443

Daphniidae, Cladocera, 434

Dardanus arrosor (Herbst) [*Pagurus arrosor, P. striatus*], Paguridea, 385, *386*, 467, 470, *471*, 501, *507*, *510*, 511

Darwinula, Podocopa, 323

[*Dasymysis longicornis*] see *Acanthomysis longicornis*

Decapoda, 1, 2, 5, 6, 9, *10*, *13*, 14, 16, 19, 28, 30, 33, 43, 48, 51, 66, 74, 76–79, *83*, 84, 91, 101, 103, 104, 111–113, 118, 126, 134, 152, 171, 173, 175, 176, *177*, 178, 179, 184, 186, 191–194, 198, 202, *205*, 206, 220, 229, 236, 241, 252, 256–258, 260, 275, 283, 286, 290, 292, 295, 296, 304, 316, 319–322, 351, 371, 374, 376, 382, 385, 389, 435, 436, 442, 446, 447, 450, 467, 472, 473, 476, 484, 486, 491, 497, 499, 500, 502, 512, 529, 531–536, 538, 539, 541, 542, 544, 545, 547–550, 552, 557, 564, 565, 567, 569, 576, 578, *579*, *582*, 616

Derocheilocaris, Mystacocarida, 615

Diaphanosoma, Cladocera, 345

D. brachyurum (Liévin), 434

D. excisum G. O. Sars, 433, 434

Diaptomus, Calanoida, 351, 353, 434, 437, 438, 484

D. banforanus Kiefer, 434, 438

D. birgei Marsh, 434

[*D. galeboides*] see *Thermodiaptomus galeboides*

D. gracilis G. O. Sars, 352, 434, *483*, 484

D. japonicus Burckhardt, 434

D. laciniatus Lilljeborg, 434

D. leptopus Forbes, 434

D. minutus Lilljeborg, 434

D. oregonensis Lilljeborg, 434

D. pacificus Burckhardt, 434

D. shoshone Forbes, 434

Diastylis, Cumacea, 371, 435, 616

Diatoms, Chrysophyta, 443

Dictyoptera, Insecta, 544, 545

Diogenes pugilator (Roux), Paguridea, 470

Diplostraca, 434, 615

Diptera, Insecta, 27, 30, 103, 159, 541, 544, 564

[Dissodactyla melittae] see *Dissodactylus mellitae*
Dissodactylus mellitae (Rathbun) [*Dissodactyla melittae*], Brachyrhyncha, 124, 504
[Dixippus] see *Carausius*
Dorippe, Oxystomata, 330
Dorippidae, Oxystomata, 327
Doropygus, Notodelphyoida, 615
Doryline ants, 17
Dotilla blanfordi Alcock, Brachyrhyncha, 469, 513
[D. mycteriodes] see *D. myctiroides*
D. myctiroides H. Milne Edwards [*D. mycteriodes*], 469, 477, 513
Drepanopus pectinatus Brady, Calanoida, 434
Drepanothrix, Cladocera, 323
Dromia, Dromiidea, 14, 331, 472, 473, 499, 500, 504, 617
D. vulgaris H. Milne Edwards, 470, *499*
Dromiacea, *579*, 617
Dromiidea, 228, 539, 617
Drosophila, Insecta, 32, 546, 576
Dytiscus, Insecta, 159

E

Earthworms, Oligochaeta, 320, 451
Echinodermata, 6, 191, 504, 547, 570
Echiuroidea, 570
Elasmobranchii, 162, 551, 552
Elminius, Balanomorpha, 470
Emerita, Hippidea, 29, 334–336, 340, 451, 452, 466, 617
E. analoga (Stimpson), 451
Entomostracans, 29, 46, 122, 134, 314, 380, 539, 563, 564, *582*
Entoniscidae, Epicaridea, 570
Entotrophi, Insecta, 574
[Ephestia kuhniella] see *Anagasta kuhniella*
Epicaridea, 569, 570, 616
Eriocheir, Brachyrhyncha, 33, 220, 257, 289, 318, 330–332, 338, 466, 473, 474, 480, 485, 507, 533, 553, 567
E. sinensis (H. Milne Edwards), 94, 116, 289, 482, 553
Eriphia spinifrons (Herbst) [*Eriphia spinifrons*], Brachyrhyncha, 385

Eryonidea, 616
[Eryphia spinifrons] see *Eriphia spinifrons*
Ethusa [*Ethusia*], Oxystomata, 472
E. mascarone (Herbst), *472*, 473
[Ethusia] see *Ethusa*
Eubranchipus serratus Forbes [*Branchipus serratus*], Anostraca, 127, 371, 390
Eucalanus, Calanoida, 434
E. elongatus (Dana), 434, 445
Eucarida, 6, 15, 20, 530, 538, 550, *582*, 616
Euchaeta acuta Giesbrecht, Calanoida, 434
[E. gracilis] see *Pareuchaeta gracilis*
[E. tonsa] see *Pareuchaeta tonsa*
Euchirella, Calanoida, 434
E. curticauda Giesbrecht, 434
[E. galatea] see *E. galeata*
E. galeata Giesbrecht [*E. galatea*], 434
Eucopia unguiculata (Willemoes-Suhm), Lophogastrida, 435
Eulimnadia, Conchostraca, 615
Eumalacostraca, 616
[Eupagurus] see *Pagurus*
[E. bernhardus] see *Pagurus bernhardus*
[E. longicarpus] see *Pagurus longicarpus*
[E. prideauxi] see *Pagurus prideauxii*
Euphausia, Euphausiacea, 44, 173, 616
E. brevis Hansen, 435
[E. fridgida] see *E. frigida*
E. frigida Hansen [*E. fridgida*], 433, 435
E. hemigibba Hansen, 435
E. krohnii Brandt [*E. mulleri*], 435
[E. mulleri] see *E. krohnii*
E. pacifica Hansen, 43, 44, 435
E. superba Dana, 435, 438, 475, 560
E. tenera Hansen, 435
E. triacantha Holt and Tattersall [*E. tricantha*], 435
[E. tricantha] see *E. triacantha*
[E. valentini] see *E. vallentini*
E. vallentini Stebbing [*E. valentini*], 435
Euphausiacea, 5, 16, 19, 25, 29, 44, 171, 173, 175, *176*, 177, 178, 184, 336, 342, 352, 435, 436, 438, 439, 446, 447, 484, 529, 538, 564, 565, 567, *582*, 616
Euphausiidae, Euphausiacea, 173

Eurypterida, 6
Eurytemora, Calanoida, 344
E. velox (Lilljeborg), 434
[*Eusicyonia*] see *Sicyonia*
[*E. carinata*] see *Sicyonia carinata*
[*Euterpe acutifrons*] see *Euterpina acutifrons*
Euterpina acutifrons (Dana) [*Euterpe acutifrons*], Harpacticoida, 387
Evadne, Cladocera, 434, 438
[*E. nordmani*] see *E. nordmanni*
E. nordmanni Lovén [*E. nordmani*], 434

F

Fireflies, see *Photuris*
Fishes, 44, 46, 100, 127, 186, 320, 341, 352, 354, 368, 392, 431, 466, 473, 502, 514, 546–548, 550, 553, 563, 565, 567, 569, 578, 580
Fish louse, see *Argulus*
Flabellifera, 616
Flagellates, 443
Flea, beach, 152, 171, 451, 574
Flies, Diptera, 121, 284, 466
Flying fish, 355
Fossils, 572, *582*
Frogs, 192, 284, 550, 551
Fruit flies, see *Drosophila*
Funchalia woodwardi Johnson, Penaeidea, 435

G

Gaetanus unicornis Esterly, Calanoida, 434
Galathea, Galatheidea, 14, 40, 353, 371, 442, 617
Galatheidea, 617
Galleria, Insecta, 159
Gammaridea, 323, 332, 335, 336, 342, 343, 435, 483, 616
Gammarus, Gammaridea, 22, *148*, 151, 173, 371, 372, 387, 391, 443, 453, 502, 616
G. chevreuxi Sexton, 453, 557
G. duebeni Lilljeborg, 465, 479, *483*, 484
G. mucronatus Say, 372
G. pulex (Linnaeus), 479, 484, 486, 567
Gampsonychidea, Syncarida, *582*

Gastropoda, 41, 48, 470, 473, 511, 546, 548, 549, 564
Gastrosaccus, Mysida, 334
G. spinifer (Goës), 333, 334
Gecarcinus, Brachyrhyncha, 294, 296, 300
G. lateralis (Freminville), *300*
[*Gecarcoidea humei*] see *G. lalandei*
[*G. humei natalis*] see *G. lalandei natalis*
G. lalandei H. Milne Edwards [*G. humei, G. lalandii*], Brachyrhyncha, 486
[*G. lalandii*] see *G. lalandei*
G. lalandei natalis (Pocock) [*G. humei natalis*], 467
[*Gelasimus*] see *Uca*
Gennadas elegans (S. I. Smith) [*Gennadus elegans*], Penaeidea, 433, 435
[*Gennadus elegans*] see *Gennadas elegans*
Geophilus, Myriapoda, 554
Geotrupes, Insecta, 392
Geryon affinis A. Milne-Edwards and Bouvier, Brachyrhyncha, *110*
Gigantocypris, Myodocopa, 4
Gnathia, Gnathiidea, 616
Gnathiidea, 352, 570, 616
Gnathophausia, Lophogastrida, 172, 175, 616
Gobiids, Teleostomi, 471
Goneplacidae, Brachyrhyncha, 327
Goniopsis, Brachyrhyncha, *10*, *11*, 32, 38, 39, 41, 51, 492, 503, 513
G. cruentata (Latreille) [*G. cruentatus*], *10*, *11*, 474
[*G. cruentatus*] see *G. cruentata*
Grapsidae, Brachyrhyncha, 252, 466, 548
Grapsus, Brachyrhyncha, 21
G. grapsus (Linnaeus), *10*, *11*, 468
Graptoleberis, Cladocera, 333, 334
Grasshoppers, 101, 192, 335
Gymnopleura, 617

H

Halocypridae, Myodocopa, 172
Haloptilus ocellatus Wolfenden [*Holoptilus ocellatus*], Calanoida, 434
Harpacticoida, 4, 323, 333, 435, 615
Harpacticus superflexus Willey, Harpacticoida, 435

Haustorius, Gammaridea, 335, 339, 340, 343–345, 350

Hemichordates, 6

Hemigrapsus, Brachyrhyncha, 139, 153, 388, 420

H. nudus (Dana), 380

H. oregonensis (Dana), 380

Hemimysis, Mysida, 340, 349

H. lamornae (Couch), 333, 374, 376

Heptacarpus geniculatus (Stimpson) [*Spirontocaris alcimede*], Alpheoida, 406

Heterocarpus, Pandaloida, 173, 178, 179

H. sibogae De Man, 178

[*Heterochaeta*] see *Heterorhabdus*

[*H. papilligera*] see *Heterorhabdus papilliger*

[*Heterocypris incongruens*] see *Cyprinotus incongruens*

Heteromysis actiniae Clarke, Mysida, 472

Heterorhabdus [*Heterochaeta*], Calanoida, 172, 175, 434

H. papilliger (Claus) [*Heterochaeta papilligera*], 187

Hippa, Hippidea, 29, 374

Hippidea, 617

Hippolysmata, Alpheoida, 472

Hippolyte pleuracantha Stimpson, Alpheoida, 158, 406

H. varians Leach, 402, 410

Holopedium, Cladocera, 345

H. gibberum Zaddach, 434

[*Holoptilus ocellatus*] see *Haloptilus ocellatus*

Holothuroidea, 549

Homarus, Nephropsidea, 15, 25, 28, 33, 44, 69, 76, 85, 86, *88, 89, 90,* 98, 99, 101, 103, 152, 198, 226, 247, 284, 294, 318, 332, 333, 345, 353, 354, 372, 470, 484–486, 504, 510, 548, 551, 560, 617

H. americanus H. Milne Edwards, 43, 44, *45, 71,* 85, *86, 87,* 97, 135, 194, 283, 285, 293, 373, 387, 450, 452, 480, 486

H. gammarus (Linnaeus) [*Astacus gammarus, Homarus vulgaris*], 69, *70,* 209, *225,* 284, 448, 479, 485

[*H. vulgaris*] see *H. gammarus*

Honeybees, 37, 43, 49, 52, 544, 564

Hoplocarida, *582,* 617

[*Hoplophorus*] see *Oplophorus*

[*Hoplophorus novaezelandie*] see *Oplophorus novaezeelandiae*

Horned toad, see *Phrynosoma*

Humans, see Man

Hutchinsoniella, Cephalocarida, 615

Hyalella knickerbockeri (Bate), Gammaridea, 373

Hyas, Oxyrhyncha, 112, 333

H. araneus (Linnaeus), 472

Hydroids, Hydrozoa, 333, 472

Hymenodora glacialis (Buchholz), Oplophoroida, 14, 435

H. gracilis S. I. Smith, 187

Hymenopenaeus [*Hymenopeneus*], Penaeidea, 173

[*Hymenopeneus*] see *Hymenopenaeus*

Hymenoptera, Insecta, 544

Hyperiidea, 342, 435, 436, 447, 616

I

Idotea [*Idothea*], Valvifera, 22, *149,* 150, 371, 417, 616

I. balthica (Pallas) [*I. baltica, I. tricuspidata*], 402

[*I. baltica*] see *I. balthica*

[*I. exotica*] see *Ligia exotica*

[*I. tricuspidata*] see *I. balthica*

[*Idothea*] see *Idotea*

Ilyocryptus, Cladocera, 333

Ilyoplax, Brachyrhyncha, 503

I. delsmani De Man, 513

Inachus dorsettensis (Pennant) [*I. scorpio*], Oxyrhyncha, *472,* 498

[*I. scorpio*] see *I. dorsettensis*

Ingolfiella, Ingolfiellidea, 616

Ingolfiellidea, 616

Insecta, 6, 7, 13, 15, 17–19, 21, 23, 25, 27, 29, 30, 33–37, 40, 41, 44, 45, 49, 51, 76, 103, 109, 116, 117, 120, 121, 125, 126, 159–161, 192, 215, 258, 282, 284, 291, 296, 297, 304, 316, 320, 341, 342, 350, 354, 368, 372, *378,* 382, 392, 402, 431, 536, 539–549, 551, 559, 560, 563, 564, 574, 576, 578, 581

Insects, stick, see *Carausius*

Invertebrates, 109, 112, 116, 125, 126, 162, 241, 251, 259, 287, 303, 304, 375, 488, 502, 548, 553, 564

Isopoda, 1, 2, 5, 13, 22, 41, 49, 51, 78, 112, 113, 122, 126, 127, 135, 136, 150, 157, 171, 315, 316, 322, 323, 326, 331–333, 336, 343, 345, 351, 371, 372, 375–377, 379, 383, 385, 389, 391, 402, 436, 451, 453, 466, 468, 469, 472, 487, 488, 492, 508, 509, 525, 535, 538–541, 557, 566, 568–572, 574, 575, 582, 616

J

Jaera, Asellota, 558

J. marina (Fabricius), 557, 572

Jasus lalandei (H. Milne Edwards) [J. lalandii], Scyllaridea, 115, 385, 449

[J. lalandii] see J. lalandei

Jaxea, Thalassinidea, 354

L

Labidocera, Calanoida, 4, 338, 371

L. aestiva Wheeler, 351, 436

Laccophilus, Insecta, 121

L. maculosus (Germar), 116

Lamellibranchiata, 548

Latreutes fucorum (Fabricius), Alpheoida, 158, 406

Laura, Ascothoracica, 5

[Leander] see Palaemon, also footnote on page 297

[L. adspersus] see Palaemon squilla

[L. affinis] see Palaemon northropi

[L. longirostris] see Palaemon longirostris

[L. paucidens] see Palaemon paucidens

[L. serratus] see Palaemon serratus

[L. squilla] see Palaemon squilla

L. tenuicornis (Say), Palaemonoida, 158, 297, 406

[L. treillanus] see Palaemon serratus

Lepadomorpha, 615

Lepas, Lepadomorpha, 376, 615

Lepidoptera, Insecta, 544, 576

Lepidurus, Notostraca, 615

Leptestheriella, Conchostraca, 333, 343, 349

Leptocheirus, Gammaridea, 469

Leptochela, Pasiphaeoida, 173, 616

Leptodora, Cladocera, 338, 348, 373

[L. hyalina] see L. kindtii

L. kindtii (Focke) [L. hyalina], 434

Leptomysis, Mysida, 349

L. gracilis G. O. Sars, 435

Leptostraca, 111, 615

Lernaea, Caligoida, 345

Lernaeopodoida, 4, 615

[Leuckartia] see Lucicutia

[L. flavicornis] see Lucicutia flavicornis

Leucon nasica (Krøyer), Cumacea, 1

Leucophaea maderae (Fabricius), Insecta, 302

Leydigiopsis, Cladocera, 323

Libinia, Oxyrhyncha, 152, 547

[L. caniculata] see L. emarginata

L. emarginata Leach [L. caniculata], 283

Ligia, Oniscoidea, 13, 22, 33, 34, 37, 122, 150, 157, 161, 323, 326, 331, 371, 380, 402, 403, 616

L. baudiniana H. Milne Edwards, 113, 122, 402

L. exotica Roux [Idotea exotica], 402, 404

L. occidentalis Dana [Ligyda occidentalis], 37, 113, 122

L. oceanica (Linnaeus), 332, 452, 466, 468

Ligiidae, Oniscoidea, 574

[Ligyda occidentalis] see Ligia occidentalis

Limnadia, Conchostraca, 4

Limnocalanus grimaldi (De Guerne), Calanoida, 434

L. macrurus G. O. Sars, 434

[L. sinensis] see Sinocalanus sinensis

Limnoria, Flabellifera, 566, 616

L. lignorum (Rathke), 451

Limnosida, Cladocera, 345

Limulus, Xiphosura, 21, 27, 28, 34, 39, 51, 52, 77, 123, 124, 157, 272, 374, 543, 576, 578

L. polyphemus (Linnaeus), 122

[Liocarcinus] see Macropipus

Lizards, 549, 552

Lobsters, Nephropsidea, 44, 71, 79, 86, 97, 99, 101, 103, 192, 194, 195, 208, 209,

224, 244, 246, 247, 251, 255, 284, 315, 345, 385, 450, 454, 465, 468, 477, 485, 502–504, 525, 547, 548, 551, 561

Lobsters, spiny, *10*, 69, 115, 328, 449, *450* (see also *Jasus, Palinurus*, etc.)

Locusta, Insecta, 21, 40, 51, 341

Lophogastrida, 172, *571*, *582*, 616

Lophothrix frontalis Giesbrecht [*Scolecithrix frontalis*], Calanoida, 434

Loxorhynchus, Oxyrhyncha, 252

L. grandis Stimpson, 229

Lucicutia [*Leuckartia*], Calanoida, 172

L. flavicornis (Claus) [*Leuckartia flavicornis*], 187, 434

L. lucida Farran, 434

Lybia tesselata (Latreille), Brachyrhyncha, 473

Lynceus, Conchostraca, 345

Lysiosquilla, Stomatopoda, 466

Lysmata, Alpheoida, 34, 39, 41, 345

M

Macrobrachium, Palaemonoida, 152, 153, 405

M. acanthurus (Wiegmann), 158, 405, 406

M. olfersii (Wiegmann), 158, 405, 406

Macrocheira kaempferi De Haan, Oxyrhyncha, 194, 202

[*Macromysis*] see *Praunus*

[*M. flexuosa*] see *Praunus flexuosus*

[*M. inermis*] see *Praunus inermis*

Macropipus [*Liocarcinus, Portunus*], Brachyrhyncha, 144, 146, *234*, 258, 313, 318, 319, 330, 331, 333, 341, 442, *466*, *473*, *499*, *500*

Macropodia longirostris (Fabricius), Oxyrhyncha, 498

M. rostrata (Linnaeus) [*Stenorhynchus rostratus*], *12*, *13*

Macrosetella, Harpacticoida, 4

Macrura, 2, 14, 29, 74, *80*, 134, 154, 204, 283, 284, 467, 469, 473, 486, 532, 538, 539, 566, 567, 575, 578, 616

[*Maia*] see *Maja*

Maja [*Maia*], Oxyrhyncha, 41, 76, 91, 93, 94, 96, 472, 496, 547, 559, 617

M. squinado (Herbst), 283

M. verrucosa H. Milne Edwards, 85, 91, 385

Malacostraca, 6, 29, 48, 78, 134, 171, 175, 293, 314, 315, 323, 336, 340, 343, 351, 353–355, 435, 474, 530, 535, 538, 539, 547, 549, 551, 552, 557, 559, 564, 571, 574, 575, *582*, 615

Mammals, 46, 109, 117, 120, 121, 232, 275, 290, 303, 320, 402, 544, 546, 547, 551, 553, 557, 563, 564, 576, 577

Man, 13, 23, 30–32, 35, 39, 43, 44, 47, 49, 117, 303, 473, 535, 546, 550, 563

Mantids, Insecta, 546, 580

Matuta, Oxystomata, 102, 319, 339

Medusae, Coelenterata, 320

Megaligia, Oniscoidea, 171

Meganyctiphanes, Euphausiacea, 44, 173, 352, 446, 448

[*M. couchii*] see *Nyctiphanes couchii*

M. norvegica (M. Sars) [*Nyctiphanes norvegica*], 43, 44, *176*, 178, 179, 184, 435, 440

[*Melittae quinquesperforata*] see *Mellita quinquiesperforata*

Mellita quinquiesperforata (Leske) [*Melittae quinquesperforata*], Echinodermata, 124, 504

Meningodora vesca (S. I. Smith) [*Notostomus vescus*], Oplophoroida, 16

Menippe, Brachyrhyncha, 473

Mesocyclops oithonoides (G. O. Sars), Cyclopoida, 435

Mesocypris terrestris Harding, Podocopa, 333

Metazoa, 530

[*Metoponorthus pruinosus*] see *Porcellionides pruinosus*

Metridia, Calanoida, 172

M. gerlachei Giesbrecht, 434

M. longa (Lubbock), 434

M. lucens Boeck, 434

Microcalanus pusillus G. O. Sars, Calanoida, 434

M. pygmaeus G. O. Sars, 434, 438

Microorganisms, 563, 570

Mictyris longicarpus Latreille, Brachyrhyncha, 473, 474, 475

Millipedes, Myriapoda, 112, 554

Miracia, Harpacticoida, 4

Mites, Acarina, 2, 3
Moina, Cladocera, 46
M. brachiata (Jurine), 434
M. dubia De Guerne and Richard, 434
Mollusca, 191, 290, 304, 474, 544, 548, 562, 577
Monstrilla, Monstrilloida, 615
Monstrilloida, 4, 615
Moths, 45, 161
Munida, Galatheidea, 194, 448
[M. bamffia] see M. rugosa
[M. banffica] see M. rugosa
M. rugosa (Fabricius) [M. bamffia, M. banffica], 448
Musca, Insecta, 284
Mussels, 472
Myodocopa, 4, 615
Myriapoda, 355, 575
Mysida, 6, 14, 16, 20, 25, 43, 172, 175, 184, 333, 334, 342, 345, 350, 351, 353, 446, 447, 449, 472, 483, 566, 571, 582, 616
Mysidacea, 5, 16, 78, 100, 171, 172, 175, 340, 342, 371–373, 376, 387, 435–437, 446, 538, 565, 567, 569, 616
Mysidae, Mysida, 474
Mysidium, Mysida, 49
M. gracile (Dana), 49, 50, 380
Mysis, Mysida, 78, 79, 172, 343, 616
M. mixta Lilljeborg, 435
M. relicta Lovén, 435
Mystacocarida, 4, 6, 582, 615

N

Nahecarida, Phyllocarida, 582
Natantia, 2, 68, 69, 136, 193, 203, 204, 260, 292, 293, 435, 436, 447, 467, 482, 484, 486, 534, 538, 539, 553, 567, 616
Nautilocorystes, Brachyrhyncha, 339
Nebalia, Nebaliacea, 16, 333, 616
Nebaliacea, 5, 567, 582, 616
Nebaliella, Nebaliacea, 333, 334
Nekton, 446, 447
Nematobrachion, Euphausiacea, 173
[Nematocelis megalops] see Nematoscelis megalops
Nematoscelis, Euphausiacea, 173, 175

N. megalops G. O. Sars [Nematocelis megalops], 435
Nephrops, Nephropsidea, 345
N. norvegicus (Linnaeus) [N. norvegicus], 44
[N. norwegicus] see N. norvegicus
Nephropsidea [Astacura], 204, 205, 229, 260, 539, 578, 579, 617
[Neptunus] see Portunus, also footnote on page 341
Niphargus, Gammaridea, 334, 371
Notodelphyoida, 4, 615
Notodromas monacha (O. F. Müller), Podocopa, 351
Notonecta, Insecta, 159, 560
[Notostomus vescus] see Meningodora vesca
Notostraca, 4, 323, 327, 332–334, 336, 342, 343, 351, 352, 615
Nototropis swammerdamii (H. Milne Edwards) [Atya swammerdamii], Gammaridea, 34, 43
Nyctiphanes, Euphausiacea, 173, 446
N. couchii Bell [Meganyctiphanes couchii], 435, 438
[N. norwegica] see Meganyctiphanes norvegica
N. simplex Hansen, 435

O

Octopus, Cephalopoda, 473, 474
Ocypode, Brachyrhyncha, 102, 330, 332, 473, 504
[O. albicans] see O. quadrata
[O. arenaria] see O. quadrata
O. ceratophthalma (Pallas), 466, 470, 474, 513
O. cursor (Linnaeus) [O. hippeus], 332
O. gaudichaudii H. Milne Edwards and Lucas, 332, 505
[O. hippeus] see O. cursor
O. occidentalis Stimpson, 330
O. quadrata (Fabricius) [O. arenaria, O. albicans], 469, 508
Ocypodidae, 469, 503, 581
Odonata, Insecta, 544
Oithona frigida Giesbrecht, Cyclopoida, 435, 438

O. nana Giesbrecht, 435, 438
O. similis Claus, 435
Oncaea, Cyclopoida, 172
O. borealis G. O. Sars, 435
O. conifera Giesbrecht, *173*, 187
Oncocypris mulleri (Daday), Podocopa, 351
Oniscidae, Oniscoidea, 574
Oniscoidea, 332, 539, 568, 574, 575, 616
Oniscus, Oniscoidea, 5, 38, 173, 376, 377
O. asellus Linnaeus [*O. murarius*], 112, 113, 122, 126, 127, 372, 373, 375, 376, 383, 384, 570
[*O. murarius*] see *O. asellus*
Ophryoxus, Cladocera, 323
Oplophoridae, Oplophoroida, 538
Oplophoroida, 616
Oplophorus [*Hoplophorus*], Oplophoroida, 173
O. novaezeelandiae De Man [*Hoplophorus novaezelandie*], 177
Orchestia, Gammaridea, 332, 333, 372, 376, 484, 559
[*O. gammarella*] see *O. gammarellus*
O. gammarellus (Pallas) [*O. gammarella*], 505, 554
O. mediterranea Costa, 484
Orconectes, Nephropsidea, 25, 295, 409, 410, 412, 414
O. clypeatus (Hay), 410, 414
O. immunis (Hagen) [*Cambarus immunis*], 486
O. limosus (Rafinesque) [*Cambarus affinis, C. limosus*], 118, 244, *245*, 283, 479, 482, *483*, 485, 486, *508*, 509, 510
O. obscurus (Hagen) [*Cambarus obscurus*], 487
O. pellucidus (Tellkampf) [*Cambarus pellucidus*], 409
O. virilis Hagen [*Cambarus virilis*], 2, 158, *267*, 283, 285, 290, 294, 296, 405, 406, 409, 410, 479
Orithyia, Oxystomata, 339
Orthoptera, Insecta, 159, 544, 545
Ostracoda, 6, 7, 111, 122, 171, 172, *174*, 178–180, 184, 187, 322, 323, 327, 328, 332, 333, 336, 340, 344, 350, 351, 371, 374, 391, 538, 539, 541, 557, 566, 567, 569, *582*, 615

Oxyrhyncha, *579*, 617
Oxystomata, *579*, 617

P

Pachygrapsus, Brachyrhyncha, 153, 215, 223, 224, 226, 228, 229, 473, 474, 486, 499
P. crassipes Randall, 224, 229, 466, 468, 473, 476, 477, 482, 488
Pacifastacus, Nephropsidea, 157
P. trowbridgii (Stimpson) [*Astacus trowbridgii*], 135, *199*, *508*, 509, *511*
Paguridae, Paguridea, 112, 228, 255, 385, 388, 415, 466, 467, 470, 473, 500, 501, 503, *507*, 511
Paguridea, 41, 67, 100, 102, 327, 539, 578, *579*, 617
Pagurus [*Eupagurus*], Paguridea, 36, 39, 40, 48, 49, 76, 91, 112, 120, 201, 212, 371, 376, 484, 496, 506, 617
[*P. arrosor*] see *Dardanus arrosor*
P. bernhardus (Linnaeus) [*Eupagurus bernhardus*], 34, 37, 224, 467, 470, 493, 499
P. longicarpus Say [*Eupagurus longicarpus*], 476, *507*, *508*, 514
P. prideauxii Leach [*Eupagurus prideauxi*], 470, 486
[*Pagurus striatus*] see *Dardanus arrosor*
Palaemon [*Leander*], Palaemonoida, 14, 15, 34, 39, 41, *79*, 80, 91, 113, 141, 143, 144, *145*, *146*, 147, 152, 155, 157, 161, 194, 297–299, 320, 344, 349, 371, 385, 448, 467, 474, 479, 485, 486, 491, 506, 511, 553, 616
[*P. adspersus*] see *P. squilla*
[*P. fabrici*] see *P. squilla*
P. longirostris H. Milne Edwards [*Leander longirostris*], 486
P. northropi (Rankin) [*Leander affinis*], 158, 406, 447
P. paucidens De Haan [*Leander paucidens*], 43, 158, 406
P. serratus (Pennant) [*Leander serratus, L. treillanus*], 19, 33, 34, 113, 134, 144, 158, 194, *245*, 371, 510
P. squilla (Linnaeus) [*Leander adspersus, L. squilla, Palaemon adspersus,*

P. fabrici], 48, *137*, 144, 145, 147, 297, 298, 371, 467, 480, 482, 485

[*P. treillanus*] see *P. serratus*

[*P. varians*] see *Palaemonetes varians*

Palaemonetes, Palaemonoida, 31, 35, 43, 82, 85, 135–139, 141–144, 147, 150– 153, *154*, 155–157, 297, 372, 389, 391, 404, 406, 407, *408*, 466, 467, 479, 480, 485, *489*, *490*, 497, 499, 504, 506

P. antennarius (H. Milne Edwards), 567

P. varians (Leach) [*Palaemon varians*], *82*, 476, 488, 491, *492*

Palaemonidae, Palaemonoida, 575

Palaemonoida, 616

[Palinura] see Scyllaridea

Palinuridae, Scyllaridea, 14, 101, 193

Palinurus, Scyllaridea, 41, 76, 91, 198, 318, 328, 382, 617

P. elephas (Fabricius) [*P. quadricornus*, *P. vulgaris*, *Panulirus vulgaris*], 68, 101, 467

[*P. interruptus*] see *Panulirus interruptus*

[*P. longipes*] see *Panulirus longipes*

[*P. quadricornus*] see *Palinurus elephas*

[*P. vulgaris*] see *Palinurus elephas*

Pancarida, *582*

Pandaloida, 616

Pandalus, Pandaloida, 39, 144, 298, 616

P. borealis Krøyer, 143, 145, *146*, 298

P. montagui Leach, 33, 34

Pandanus, Spermatophyta, 487

Panulirus, Scyllaridea, *10*, *11*, 15, 101, *214*, 223, *227*, 329, 331, 332, 353, 354, 452, 454, 466, 470, 474, 485, 501, 504, 506

[*P. americanus*] see *P. argus*

P. argus (Latreille) [*P. americanus*], 2, *10*, *11*, 24, 25, 101, 449, 453, 485, 503

P. guttatus (Latreille), 2, 449

P. interruptus (Randall) [*Palinurus interruptus*], 101, *197*, *209*, 212, *214*, 215, 223, 224, 229, 435, 449, 470, 474, 475, 477, 485

P. japonicus (von Siebold), 26

P. longipes (A. Milne-Edwards) [*Palinurus longipes*], 435, 449

[*P. vulgaris*] see *Palinurus elephas*

Paracalanus parvus (Claus), Calanoida, 434

[*Paraeuchaeta*] see *Pareuchaeta*

Paragnathia, Gnathiidea, 1

Paranaspides, Anaspidacea, 343, 352

P. lacustris G. Smith, 5, 6

Parapandalus richardi (Coutière) [*Plesionika nana*], Pandaloida, 176, 435

Parapasiphae sulcatifrons S. I. Smith, Pasiphaeoida, 435

Parapronoe crustulum Claus, Hyperiidea, 171

Parasellidae, Asellota, 340, 351

Parathemisto gaudichaudi (Guérin), Hyperiidea, 435

P. gracilipes (Norman) [*P. oblivia*, *Themisto gracilipes*], 435

[*P. oblivia*] see *P. gracilipes*

Paratya [*Xiphocaridina*], Oplophoroida, 147, 153, 156, 157, 173

P. compressa (De Haan), 43, 158, 406

Pareuchaeta [*Paraeuchaeta*], Calanoida, 434

P. antarctica (Giesbrecht), 434

P. gracilis (G. O. Sars) [*Euchaeta gracilis*], 434

P. tonsa (Giesbrecht) [*Euchaeta tonsa*], 434

Parthenope serrata (H. Milne Edwards), Oxyrhyncha, 158, 406

Pasiphaeoida, 616

Penaeidae, Penaeidea, 14

Penaeidea, 317, 336, 482, 484, 512, 538, 558, 559, 616

Penaeinae, Penaeidea, 447

Penaeopsis goodei (S. I. Smith), Penaeidea, 158, 406

Penaeus, Penaeidea, 295, 343

P. duorarum Burkenroad, 24, 447, 449

P. setiferus (Linnaeus), 447, 449

Penella, Caligoida, 615

Penguins, 565

[*Pentacheles*] see *Polycheles*

Peracantha truncata (O. F. Müller), Cladocera, 2

Peracarida, 51, 322, 327, 486, 570, *571*, 575, *582*, 616

Periplaneta, Insecta, 37

P. americana (Linnaeus), 288

Petrolisthes, Galatheidea, 289
Phasmids, Insecta, 159, 161, 543
Phormia, Insecta, 121
Photinus pyralis (Linnaeus), Insecta, *178*
Photuris [*Photurus*], Insecta, 25, 178, 179
[*Photurus*] see *Photuris*
Phreatoicidea, 616
Phreatoicus, Phreatoicidea, 616
Phronima, Hyperiidea, 5, 24, 616
P. sedentaria (Forskål), 487
Phrynosoma, Reptilia, 162, 552
Phycomyces, Fungi, 49
Phyllocarida, *582*, 616
[*Phyllotalestris*] see *Phyllothalestris*
Phyllothalestris [*Phyllotalestris*], Harpacticoida, 377
P. mysis (Claus), 376, 377
Physachaeus ctenurus Alcock, Oxyrhyncha, *110*
Phytoplankton, Algae, 46, 442, 443, 445, 449
Pigeons, see *Columba*
Pinnotheres, Brachyrhyncha, 321, 332, 352, 374
Plankton, 127, 352, *370*, 389, 414, 432, 437, 439–442, 445, 446, 454, 455
Plants, 442, 445, 563
Platyarthrus, Oniscoidea, 385
P. hoffmannseggi (Brandt), 122, 375, 385
[*Platycarcinus*] see *Cancer*
Platycopa, 4, 615
[*Plesionika nana*] see *Parapandalus richardi*
Pleuromamma [*Pleuromanna, Pleuromma*], Calanoida, 172
P. abdominalis (Lubbock), 434
P. gracilis (Claus) [*Pleuromma gracile*], 187, 434
P. robusta (F. Dahl), 434
P. xiphias (Giesbrecht), 434
[*Pleuromanna*] see *Pleuromamma*
[*Pleuromma*] see *Pleuromamma*
[*P. gracile*] see *Pleuromamma gracilis*
[*Podocera*] see *Podocerus*
Podocerus [*Podocera*], Gammaridea, 371
Podocopa, 4, 615
Podon polyphemoides (Leuckart), Cladocera, 434

Polybius, Brachyrhyncha, 331, 339, 344, 352
Polycheles [*Pentacheles*], Eryonidea, 173, 616
Polycope, Cladocopa, 615
Polyphemus, Cladocera, 433
P. pediculus (Linnaeus), 434
Pontella, Calanoida, 172
P. mediterranea (Claus) [*Pontellina mediterranea*], 353
[*Pontellina mediterranea*] see *Pontella mediterranea*
Porcellana, Galatheidea, 351
Porcellidium fimbriatum Claus, Harpacticoida, 557
P. lecanioides Claus, 557
P. sarsi Bocquet, 557
Porcellio, Oniscoidea, 38, 122, 372, 375–377, 557
P. scaber Latreille, 113, 122, 126, 372, 375, 383, *384*, 388, 452, 453, 487, 509, 570
Porcellionidae, Oniscoidea, 574
Porifera, 471, 569
Portunidae, Brachyrhyncha, 293, 320, 323, 330, 336, 339–344, 350–354, 356, 466, 493, 546, 547
Portunus [*Neptunus*], Brachyrhyncha, *336*, 341
[*Portunus*] see *Macropipus,* also footnote on page 341
P. anceps (Saussure), 158, 406
P. depressifrons (Stimpson), 158, 406
[*Potamobius*] see *Astacus*
[*P. astacus*] see *Astacus astacus*
[*P. fluviatilis*] see *Astacus astacus*
Potamon, Brachyrhyncha, 567
Potamonids, Brachyrhyncha, 487
Praunus [*Macromysis*], Mysida, 14, 39, 402, 410
P. flexuosus (O. F. Müller) [*Macromysis flexuosa*], 6, 33, 34, 345, 351, 371, 479, *483*
P. inermis (Rathke) [*Macromysis inermis*], 371
Prawns, 16, 31, 34, 41, 135, 138, 150, 152, 155, 173, 193, 245, 255, 402, 406, 407, 415, 489
Primno macropa Guérin, Hyperiidea, 435

Pristicephalus, Anostraca, 344
Procambarus, Nephropsidea, 14, 27, 224, 226–228, 247, 248, 410, 412, 479
P. alleni (Faxon), 479, 505, 511
P. clarkii (Girard) [*Cambarus clarkii*], 2, 26, 43, 194, *197, 198, 201, 210,* 211, *213,* 215, *223,* 224, 229, *230, 249–251,* 260, *262, 265, 270,* 283, 288, 409
Pronoidae, Hyperiidea, 171
Proteolepas, Apoda, 615
Protozoa, 563, 570
Psalidopodoida, 616
Psalidopus, Psalidopodoida, 616
Pseudeuphausia [*Pseudoeuphausia*], Euphausiacea, 173
Pseudocalanus elongatus (Boeck), Calanoida, 434
[*Pseudoeuphausia*] see *Pseudeuphausia*
Pterygota, Insecta, 17
Pyrocypris, Myodocopa, 172

R

Rabbits, 578
Rana, Amphibia, 37
R. esculenta Linnaeus, 284
Randallia, Oxystomata, 219, 226
R. ornata (Randall), *219*
Ranina, Gymnopleura, 617
Rats, 285
Rays, Elasmobranchii, 551
Reptantia, 136, 193, 194, 202–204, *205,* 292, 435, 436, 538, 539, 575, *579,* 616
Reptilia, 162, 514, 552, 563, 580
Rhincalanus gigas Brady, Calanoida, 434, 438
Rhizocephala, 5, 542, 569, 570, 615

S

Sacculina, Rhizocephala, 542, 615
Sagartia, Anthozoa, 501
[*S. parasitica*] see *Calliactis parasitica*
Salmincola, Lernaeopodoida, 615
Salmonids, Teleostomi, 575
Sand dollars, Echinodermata, 124, 504
Sapphirina, Cyclopoida, 6
Saturniids, Insecta, 544
Scaphocalanus echinatus (Farran) [*Scolecithrix echinata*], Calanoida, 434

S. magnus A. Scott [*Scolecithrix magna*], Calanoida, 434
Scapholeberis [*Scapholebris*], Cladocera, 351, 371
S. mucronata (O. F. Müller), 2
[*Scapholebris*] see *Scapholeberis*
Schistocerca, Insecta, 341
Schistomysis [*Shistomysis*], Mysida, 435
Scolecithricella dentata (Giesbrecht) [*Scolecithrix dentata*], Calanoida, 434
S. minor (Brady), 436
S. ovata (Farran) [*Scolecithrix ovata*], 435
[*Scolecithrix dentata*] see *Scolecithricella dentata*
[*S. echinata*] see *Scaphocalanus echinatus*
[*S. frontalis*] see *Lophothrix frontalis*
[*S. magna*] see *Scaphocalanus magnus*
[*S. ovata*] see *Scolecithricella ovata*
Scorpions, Arachnida, 578
Scyllaridea [Palinura], 204, *205,* 230, 260, 539, 578, *579,* 617
Scypholanceola, Hyperiidea, 171
Sea anemones, Coelenterata, 470, *471,* 472, 473
Sea gulls, 566
Sergestes, Penaeidea, 173, 176, 179, 345, 616
S. arcticus Krøyer, 435
S. atlanticus H. Milne Edwards, 435
S. challengeri Hansen, 177
S. corniculum Krøyer, 435
S. prehensilis Bate, 177, 178, 185, 435
S. regalis Gordon, 176
S. sargassi Ortmann, 435
Sergestidae, Penaeidea, 16, 19, 25, 538
Serolidae, Flabellifera, 343
Serolis, Flabellifera, 333, 334
Sesarma, Brachyrhyncha, 295, 473, 513
S. taeniolata White, 481
Sharks, Elasmobranchii, 547, 551
[*Shistomysis*] see *Schistomysis*
Shrimp, Natantia, 16, 80, 82, 101, 113, 173, 175, *176, 177,* 179, 184–186, 193, 194, *203,* 220, 224, 228, 244, 250, 297, 319, 332, 334, 336, 343, 345, 353, 354, 405, 447, 454, 467, 472, 506, 558
Shrimp, brine, see *Artemia*

Shrimp, ghost, 253
Shrimp, sand, 334
Shrimp, snapping, 101
Sicyonella, Penaeidea, 447
Sicyonia [*Eusicyonia*], Penaeidea, 158, 317, 318, 345, 406
S. carinata (Brünnich), 482, *483*
Sida, Cladocera, 348
Silkworms, Insecta, 305
Simocephalus, Cladocera, 345, 371
Sinocalanus sinensis (Poppe) [*Limnocalanus sinensis*], Calanoida, 435
Snails, Gastropoda, 467, 470, 496, 500–503, 511, *512*, 514
[*Solenocera membranacea*] see *S. membranaceum*
S. membranaceum (Risso) [*S. membranacea, S. siphonocera*], Penaeidea, 435
[*S. siphonocera*] see *S. membranaceum*
Solenocerinae, Penaeidea, 447
Spelaeogriphacea, *582*, 616
Spelaeogriphus, Spelaeogriphacea, 616
Sphaeromidae, Flabellifera, 343, 345
Spiders, see Arachnida
Spiders, crab, Thomisidae, 329
[*Spirontocaris alcimede*] see *Heptacarpus geniculatus*
Sponges, see Porifera
Squids, see Cephalopoda
Squilla, Stomatopoda, 15, 39, 40, 300, 318, 332, 340, 342, 343, 349, 350, 372, 466, 485, *512*, 617
S. mantis Latreille, 42, 69, 295, 328, 467
Starfishes, see Asteroidea
[*Steilocheiron*] see *Stylocheiron*
Stenopodidea, 616
Stenopus, Stenopodidea, 616
S. hispidus (Olivier), *68, 203*, 224
[*Stenorhynchus rostratus*] see *Macropodia rostrata*
Stomatopoda, 5, 6, 15, 18, 19, 42, 46, 69, 193, 194, 203, 258, 343, 382, 535, 537, 539, 541, 546, 564, 567, *582*, 617
Streblocerus, Cladocera, 323
Streetsia, Hyperiidea, 171
Strepsiptera, Insecta, 542
Stylocheiron [*Steilocheiron*], Euphausiacea, 5, 173

S. suhmii G. O. Sars, 435
Stylodactyloida, 616
Stylodactylus, Stylodactyloida, 616
Suberites, Porifera, 471
Symphyla, Myriapoda, 575
Synagoga, Ascothoracica, 615
Syncarida, 327, 336, *582*, 616
Systellaspis, Oplophoroida, 173, 178, 179, 186
S. debilis (A. Milne-Edwards), 178, 185, 187

T

Tachycines, Insecta, 36, 37
Talitridae, Gammaridea, 335, 355
Talitrus, Gammaridea, 379, 382, 453, 492, 504
T. saltator (Montagu), 51, 342, 379, *380*, 388, 451
Talorchestia, Gammaridea, 152, 334, 335, 371, 453
T. longicornis (Say), 313, 451, 479
Tanaidacea, 5, 111, 567, 569, *571, 582*, 616
Tanaidae, Tanaidacea, 342
Tanymastix, Anostraca, 319, 321
T. lacunae (Guérin), 373, 374, 390
Teleosts, 6, 162, 472, 547–549, 551, 552, 554, 564, 565, 575
Temora longicornis (O. F. Müller), Calanoida, 435
Termites, Insecta, 543, 584
Tessarabrachion, Euphausiacea, 173
Tetrapods, Vertebrata, 549
Thalassinidea, 354, 617
Thelxiope, Thelxiopeidea, 617
Thelxiopeidea, 617
[*Themisto gracilipes*] see *Parathemisto gracilipes*
Thermodiaptomus galeboides (G. O. Sars) [*Diaptomus galeboides*], Calanoida, 435
Thermosbaena, Thermosbaenacea, 566, 616
Thermosbaenacea, 5, 566, *582*, 616
Thomisidae, Arachnida, 329
Thoracica, 5, 615
Thysanoessa, Euphausiacea, 173, 435, 446
T. gregaria G. O. Sars, 435

T. inermis Krøyer, 435
T. raschii (M. Sars), 435
Thysanopoda, Euphausiacea, 173
T. acutifrons Holt and Tattersall, 433, 435
T. aequalis Hansen, 435
T. obtusifrons G. O. Sars, 435
Thysanura, Insecta, 574
Tigriopus fulvus (Fischer), Harpacticoida, 557
Tisbe reticulata Bocquet, Harpacticoida, 557
Toads, 506, 552, 554
Tortoises, 550
Tracheoniscus, Oniscoidea, 557
T. rathkei (Brandt), 452
Trachypeneopsis mobilispinis (Rathbun), Penaeidea, 158, 406
Trichoniscidae, Oniscoidea, 574
Trichoniscus, Oniscoidea, 376
Trilobites, 334
Triops [*Apus*], Notostraca, 15, 23, 351, 352, 374, 559, 566, 567
T. cancriformis (Bosc), 112, 318, 343, 391
[*Tripetesa*] see *Trypetesa*
Trochus, Gastropoda, 511, *512*
Trypetesa [*Tripetesa*], Acrothoracica, 373, 615
Tunicata, 487, 546, 547, 569, 570
Turtles, 354
Tylos, Oniscoidea, 382, 492, 504
T. latreillei Audouin and Savigny [*T. latreillii*], 51, 379
[*T. latreillii*] see *T. latreillei*

U

Uca [*Gelasimus*], Brachyrhyncha, 39, 40, 91, 136, 139, *140*, 141–144, 146, 147, 297–299, *302*, 335, 340, 371, 390, 391, 403, 410–412, 415, 418, 421–423, 467, *468*, 469, 470, 473, 476, 477, 479–482, 498, 499, 501, 503, 505, 506, 510, 512–514, 539, 546, 559, 580
U. annulipes (Latreille), 477, *480*, 481, 502, 513
U. beebei Crane [*U. stenodactyla beebei*], 505, 513

U. cumulanta Crane, 503
U. deichmanni Rathbun, 503
U. festae Nobili, 503
U. forcipata (Adams and White), 476
U. inversa (Hoffmann), 503
U. lactea (De Haan), 503
U. leptodactyla Rathbun, 503
U. maracoani (Latreille), 470, 475, 476, 481, 513
U. marionis (Desmarest), *475*, 476, 477, *478*
U. pugilator (Bosc), 136, 138, 143, 144, 298, *302*, 335, 403, 405, 410–412, 424, 451, 468, 474, 481, 482, 485, 486, *488*, 500, *507*, *508*, 509
U. pugnax (S. I. Smith), 138, 302, 373, 390, *403*, 404, 405, 410, *411*, 412, *413*, *416*, 417, *418*, 419–421, *423*, 424, 502, 513
U. rapax (S. I. Smith), 513
U. rhizophorae Tweedie [*U. rizophorae*], 503
[*U. rizophorae*] see *U. rhizophorae*
U. saltitanta Crane, 481
U. speciosa (Ives), 405
U. stenodactyla (H. Milne Edwards and Lucas) [*U. stenodactyla stenodactyla*], 513
[*U. stenodactyla beebei*] see *U. beebei*
[*U. stenodactyla stenodactyla*] see *U. stenodactyla*
U. terpsichores Crane [*U. terpsychore*], 476
[*U. terpsychore*] see *U. terpsichores*
Undeuchaeta major Giesbrecht, Calanoida, 435
U. minor Giesbrecht, 435
Unionicola, Acarina, 2
U. ypsilophorus van Beneden, *3*
Upogebia, Thalassinidea, 335, 470, 486
U. pugettensis (Dana), 469
Urodela, Amphibia, 549
Urothoe, Gammaridea, 334, 345, 350

V

Valvifera, 616
Verruca, Verrucomorpha, 615
Verrucomorpha, 615

Vertebrata, 6, 18, 20, 26–29, 33, 35, 38,
    44, 77, 93, 98, 99, 103, 109, 116,
    117, 120, 125, 126, 150, 151, 161,
    162, 177, 191–196, 206, 210, 235,
    236, 241, 248, 259, 265, 275, 276,
    281, 284–286, 288–291, 296, 297,
    302–304, 315–317, 320, 321, 354,
    355, 488, 492, 502, 513, 533, 543–
    554, 562–565, 573, 574, 576, 577
Vespa, Insecta, 37
Vibilia antarctica Stebbing, Hyperiidea,
    433
V. propinqua Stebbing, 435

W

Wasps, 286
Water bugs, 544
Water fleas, see Cladocera
Whales, 547, 565

Wood lice, Oniscoidea, 171, *384*, 451–453
Worms, see also Annelida, 260, 570

X

Xantho, Brachyrhyncha, 411
[*Xanthodes sternberghii*] see *Xanthodius
    sternberghii*
Xanthodius sternberghii Stimpson [*Xan-
    thodes sternberghii*], Brachyrhyncha,
    475
Xiphosura, see also *Limulus*, 6, 7, 564

Z

Zenobiana [*Zoenobiana*], Valvifera, 469
Z. prismatica Risso, 389
[*Zoenobiana*] see *Zenobiana*
Zooplankton, see Plankton

Page numbers in italics indicate the location of illustrations.

A

Abdomen, 113, 122, 160, 208, 270, 289, 539, 559
  function in: egg carrying, 354
    locomotion, 265, 334–336, 338, 342, 350, 353–355, 452
Abdominal ganglia, see under Ganglia
Abdominal musculature, 115, 220, 288, 315
Abdominal segments, see under Body segments
Abdominal stretch receptors (of Alexandrowicz), see under Muscle receptor organs and Stretch receptors
Abductor muscles, *202*
Abreptor, 335
Absorption spectra, luciferin, 180, 181, *182*
  rhodopsin, 44
  visual pigments, 43, 44, *45*
Acceleration, angular, 80, 91, 94, 96–98, 103, 346
  receptors, 493, 551
Acceleration, linear, 97
  receptors, 551
Acceleration, responses to, 544
Accelerators, cardiac, 266, 267
Acclimation, osmotic, 567
  phenotypic, 561
  thermal, 125
Accommodation, 19, 195
Acetic acid, 122, 124
  as chemical stimulus, 112, 113, 118, 120, 124
Acetone, 285, 297, 298
Acetylcholine (Ach), 216, 231, 274, 281–290, 300, 529, 552
  bound, 285, 286, 300
  destruction by choline esterase, 283
  distribution, 282–284, 304, 552
  effects on: autotomy, 289
    intestine, 231, 273

heart, 231, 273, 283, 286, 287, 290
  melanophores, 146, 147
  membrane conductance, 289, 533
  neuromuscular system, 231, 273, 286, 545
  pigment dispersal, 162
  spontaneous activity, 287
  synaptic transmission, 288, 289
  free, 285
  functions of, 286–289
  hydrolysis, 284, 289
  nicotine-like action, 287
  potentiation by anticholine esterases, 283
  storage problem, 285, 300
  synthesis, 284, 285
Acetylcholine esterase, 284
Acetylcholine system, 282–286, 289
Acetyl coenzyme A, 285
Acetyl-β-methylcholine (Mecholyl), 284
Ach, see Acetylcholine
Acicula, 313
Acids, 120–122, 222, 285, 544
ACTH, see Adrenocorticotrophic hormone
Actin, 221, 529
Action potentials, 196, 208, *209*, 214, 215, *217*, 218, 224, 228, 241, 253, 259–265, 287, 303, 534, 543, 545
  abortive, 207, 208, *209*, *214*, 226, 227, 532
  afferent, 265
  all-or-nothing responses, 208, 209
  in chemoreceptors, *115*, *123*, 124
  conduction rate, 207, 260, 539
  diphasic, 209, *225*, *226*, *262*
  effects of calcium and sodium on, 194, 233
  electrical fields, 260
  facilitation, 199
  fatigue, 199, 231
  frequency, 264
  inhibition, 210, 212, 213, *217*

in median eye nerve, 7
monophasic, 224, 225, *226*
in muscles, *225*, *226*, 231–235
in nerves, 28, 195, 196, 210, 212, 213, *217*, *223*, 231, 232, 259
propagated, 207–210, 225, 226, 232, 233, 235, 532, 552
in receptor cells, 543
rising phase, 233
spatial extent, 194
in statocysts, 85
in thermoreceptors, 126
visual, 27, 28, 30, 36, 40, 51, 157
Action spectra, 42
Actomyosin, 563
Acuity, sensory, 535
visual, see Visual acuity
Adaptation, 367, 368, 526, 562, 574, 575
background, see Background adaptation
behavioral, 453, 499, 506, 569
definition, 560
ecological, 44, 409, 543, 564–570
endogenous, 561
as explanation, 523, 555, 560–570, 583
exogenous, 561
genetic, 557
limitations, 562, 563
locomotor, 313–315, 317, 333, 335, 340, 354, 554
in mechanoreceptors, 69, 70, 74, 76, 89, 91
osmotic, 566, 567, 575
and phylogeny, 572
and physiological rhythms, 415
and physiology, 561
reproductive, 566, 570
respiratory, 343, 387, 401, 568, 570
sensory (see also adaptation in specific receptors or senses), 442, 543, 565
terrestrial, 453, 539, 542, 566, 568
thermal, 125, 128, 415, 546, 566, 568, 569
in thermoreceptors, 126
visual (see also Dark adaptation and Light adaptation), 2, 3, 7, 8, 16, 29, 33–35, 44, *267*
Adaptedness, Darwinian, 561
Hendersonian, 562, 563

Adaptive explanations, 555, 560–570, 583
Adductor muscles, *202*
Adenosine triphosphatase (ATPase), 285
Adenosine triphosphate (ATP), 221, 222, 285
effect on bioluminescence, 179
Adrenaline (epinephrine), 232, 274, 303, 304, 533, 552
effects on: autotomy, 289
bioluminescence, 186
erythrophores, 147
heart, 289
melanophores, 146, 147
pigment concentration, 162
Adrenocorticotrophic hormone (ACTH), 299
Advanced forms, 578, 580, 581
Aesthetascs, 109, *110*, 111
After-images, to movement, 41
After-nystagmus, 93, 94
Age, effects of, 186, 263, 264, 374, 391, 537
Alanine, 124
Alary muscles, 541
Alcohols, 121, 181, 183, 299, 372, 545
Aldehydes, and bioluminescence, 179
Alimentary canal (see also Gut), 176
Aliphatic compounds, 119–121, 545
Alkaloids, 372
Allantoin, 548
Alleles, 556, 557
Allometry (see Relative growth)
All-or-nothing responses, 152, 155, 208, *209*, 275
Alpha-substances, 144, 298
Aluminum oxide, 146, 298
Ameboid movement, 135
Amines, 233, 281, 287, 289, 290, 296, 297, 304, 552
Amino acids (see also entries under names of specific acids), 124, 181, 182, 221, 231, 541, 556, 557, 563, 567, 576
γ-Aminobutyric acid (GABA), 290, 533, 552
Ammonia, 287, 289, 542, 548
Ammonotely, see under Excretion and Nitrogen metabolism

Ampullae, of sensory hairs, 65, *80*
Amylase, 547
Amyltrimethylammonium, 274
Analogies, 103, 117, 565, 566, 583
Androgenic glands, 535, 539, 549, 554
  effects of implantation, 505, 559
  effects of removal, 559
Anecdyses, see Ecdyses
Anemotaxes, 387, 388
Anesthesia, 152, 161
Animal exclusion theory, see Plankton
  exclusion theory
Anions, 121, 122
Anisotrophy, in muscle, 220
Antennae (second antennae), 67, *68*, 101,
  110, 111–114, 254, 255, 268, 272,
  388, 477
  beat frequency, 348, 374
  chemosensory function, 112–114, 116,
    117, 384
  effect of removal, 100, 385, 511
  grasping, 512
  locomotor function, 323, 328, 334, 336,
    338, 340, 344, 347, 350–352, 447
  and phototaxes, 441
  reflex control, 347, 348
  and steering, 350, 351, 448
  temperature sensitivity, 126
Antennal glands, 144, 541, 542, 548, *571*
  function in ionic and osmotic regula-
    tion, 541, 561
  structure, 531, 548
Antennal nerves, *496*
Antennular nerves, *110*, *496*
Antennules (first antennae), *68*, *86*, *92*,
  93, *110*, *115*, 254, 470
  chemosensory function, 111–116, 118,
    124, 385
  locomotor function, 323, 327, 336, 338,
    344, 350
  as osmoreceptors, 385
  rheotactic responses by, 68, 387, 388
Anoxia, see Oxygen deficiency
Antibodies, development of, 558, 577
Anticholine esterases, see under Choline
  esterases
Antigens, 577, 578
  functional centers, 563
  and genes, 557

Antisera, 577, 578
Antizoea larvae, 5
Anus, 272
Apodemes, *75*, 209, 220
Apophyses, 220
Appendage beat, 321, *336*, *337*, 338–344,
  351–353
Appendage rhythms, see Metachronal
  rhythms and Phase differences
Appendages (see also Chelipeds, Pereiopods, etc.), 126, 220, 252, 253, 256,
  258, 266, *270*, *271*, 313, 474, 530
  caudal, in locomotion, 333
  effects of amputation, 320, 322, 493,
    499
  effects of statocysts on position (see
    also under Proprioceptors), *497*,
    498
  evolution, 314
  extension and flexion, 253, 273, 331,
    333
  grasping, 113, 115–117, 332, 333, 498,
    505
  innervation, 202, *203*, 204, 215, 246,
    268, 273, 531, 539, 549
  and locomotion, 313, 314, *315*, 322–
    324, 330, 336–342, 349–356
  propulsive, 323–325, *326*, *329*, 330, 331,
    572
  reflexes, see under Reflexes
  specialization, 314, 329, 335–341, 354–
    356, 469
  structure, 314, 317, 322, 327
  swimming, see under Swimming
  thoracic, see Thoracic appendages
  walking legs, see Pereiopods
Appetitive behavior, see under Behavior
  patterns
Apposition eyes, see under Compound
  eyes
Arginine, 296
Arginine phosphate, 222
Archetypes, 525
Arteries, *249*, 541, *571*
Arthrodial membrane, 314, 315
Arthropod origins (see also under Evolution and Phylogeny), 581, 582
Asphyxiation, see also Oxygen deficiency,
  259

Astigmatism, 17, 42
Astronomical orientation, see under Orientation
A-Substance, 144, 298, 299
Asymmetry, 90, 187, 255
ATP, see Adenosine triphosphate
ATPase, see Adenosine triphosphatase
Atropine, 147, 232, 274, 287, 288
Attractants, see under Stimuli, chemical
Autotomy, 252–255, 319, 467, 474, 538, 543, 549
    action of acetylcholine and drugs on, 289
    effect on melanophores, 405
    muscles, 254
    preformed breakage plane, 543
    reflexes, 289
    threshold, 254, 255
Avoidance responses, see under Behavior patterns
Axolemmal membranes, 250, 251
Axons, 191–196, 202, 206, 215, 216, 233, 244, 247, 250, 253, 255, 258, 259, 268–272
    accelerating, 241
    acetylcholine content, 283
    antagonistic, 228
    asymmetrical, 271, 272
    bilateral, 270
    collaterals, 247
    degeneration, 258
    effect of chemicals on, 286
    effect of cutting, 258
    efferent (see also Inhibitory axons and Motor axons), 191, 196, 202, 216, 244–246
    functional specialization, 529
    giant, see Giant fibers
    heterolateral, 271
    homolateral, 270
    integrating, 276
    inhibitory, see Inhibitory axons
    motor, see Motor axons
    multisegmental, 245, 246
    optic, 10–13, 27, 29, 30, 150, 153, 175
    permeability, 194
    pigmentomotor, 157
    quintuplotomic branching, 197
    recruitment, 224, 225

    reflexes (single axon), 252, 253
    of retinular cells, 12, 13, 28
    sensory, 244, 246, 253
    sinus gland, 294, 295, 300
    triplotomic branching, 197
Axon terminals, 291, 294, 299, 300
Axoplasm, 244, 250, 261, 262, 299

B

Background adaptation, 136, 141, 142, 147
    black, 159, 160, 162
    colors, 48, 135, 136, 138
    illuminated, 135, 136, 137, 156, 162
    white, 141, 159, 160, 162
Bacteria, luminous infection with, 171
Barium, 233
Barometric pressure, and diurnal rhythms, 409
    fluctuations, 401, 413, 424
Basal cells, retinular, see under Retinular cells
Bases, see Basipodites
Basement membranes, photophores, 177
Basilar membranes, optic, 10, 11, 12, 13–15, 21, 148, 149, 150, 151, 154
    function, 26
    structure, 9, 10, 11
Basipodites (bases), 254, 273, 315
Behavior (see also Ethology), 124, 252, 465–520, 522, 524, 546
    analysis (see also under Adaptation), 85, 368, 487–514
    control, 128, 365, 368, 369, 487, 498, 500–506, 515, 536
    development, 498, 502, 504–512, 558, 560, 580
    effects of surgery, 494, 495, 509, 511
    effects of statocysts, see under Statocysts
    and evolution, 512–514, 580
    and habitats, 560
    homologous, 578
    hormonal control, 502, 505, 506
    and migrations (see also under Diurnal vertical migrations and Migrations), 441, 553

plastic, 498, 499, 506, 549, 553, 554, 562

relation to morphology, 505, 506, 512, 513

releasing mechanisms, see Releasing mechanisms

rigid, 498, 499, 553, 554

species-specific, see under Species specificity

Behavioral experiments, 66, 115, 117, 118, 120, 503, 504

maze-running, 503, 507, 508, 509, 510, 511

and migration, 441

mirror, 377, 379, 475, 501

Behavioral and sensory correlations, 85

Behavior patterns (see also Copulation, Defense, Display, Escape, Feeding, Learning, Mating, Sexual), appetitive, 500–503, 511, 515, 554, 581, 582

avoidance, 40, 53, 375, 386, 505, 506, 508–510

beckoning, 477, 480, 481, 498, 501, 502, 506, 512–514, 580

species-specific, 481, 513

body care and cleaning, 467, 468, 484, 495, 498, 503

bowing, 480, 481, 502, 513

camouflage and masking, 470, 471, 472, 473, 496, 498–500

and bioluminescence, 186

materials, 470–472

claw waving, see Behavior patterns, beckoning

clinging, and sign stimulus, 500

conditioning, see under Learning

consummatory acts, 500–503, 507, 515

courtship (see also under Display), 470, 476, 481, 482, 513

dancing, 477, 481, 482

displacement activity, 503, 513, 546, 580

drumming, 477, 481, 486

fighting, 474, 475, 478, 484, 500, 501, 503, 505, 509, 514

methods, 255, 473, 474, 476, 477, 479

species-specific, 580

fright, 118, 505, 507, 508, 509

habituation, see under Learning

individual, 466–472

maternal, 484–487

ritualized, 476, 477, 481, 513, 514

searching, 115, 476, 477, 487, 488, 504, 509, 515

social, 187, 474–479, 511, 514

activity phases, 475–477

and systematics, 512

threat, 255, 473, 474, 476, 477, 493, 505, 513

Bender muscles, 202, 204, 229, 230

Benzene, 181

Benzine, 297

Benzoylcholine, 284

Bile acids, 548

Binocular vision, 42

Bioassays, of acetylcholine, 283

Calliphora test, 542

of hormones, 141–145, 146, 147, 298, 299

Biochemistry, comparative, 576

and genetic comparisons, 556, 557

of muscle fibers, 221, 222

Biology, limits, 528

Bioluminescence, 171–190

adaptiveness, 568

biochemistry, see Luciferin and Luciferase

control, 184–186

hormonal, 175, 186

muscular, 175, 184

and deep-water illumination, 569

description, 175, 177, 178, 184–186

effects of various substances, 179, 180, 186

evolution, 174

occurrence and distribution, 171–174, 538, 567, 568

oxygen requirements, 179–181

related to maturity or season, 186

rhythms, 415

secondary, 171

spectral emission, 175, 177, 178, 180, 185

uses to animal, 186, 187

Biomechanics, 314–316

Birefringence, and polarized light sensitivity, 51

flow, 336

Blastema, 549

Bleaching, visual pigments, 28, 44

Blind forms, 43, 173, 409, 569

Blood (see also Hemolymph), 138, 146, 221, 295, 296, 348, 542
 hyperosmotic, 567
 hyposmotic, 567
 ionic regulation, 561
 respiratory functions, 540, 541, 546
 and urine, 542, 548, 567, 575

Blood cells, granular, 296, 297

Blood coagulation, 541, 547

Blood composition, amino acids, 541
 acetylcholine, 283, 284
 choline esterases, 284
 electrolytes, 221
 hormones, 136, 403
 ionic, 541, 545–548, 561, 562
 magnesium, 547, 561, 562
 and behavior, 545, 546
 sugars, 548

Blood pressures, 575

Blood sinuses, 293–295, 541

Blood supply, compound eyes, 9, *10*, *11*, 153
 effect on chromatophores, 136
 ganglia, 531
 and metabolic rates, 531

Blood vessels (see also specific arteries and veins), 547

Blue, color discrimination, 48

Body axes, major, 322, 323, 345, 350, 351, 356, 367
 position (see also Rotation), 323, 367, 375, 378, 382, 387, *497*

Body care, see under Behavior patterns

Body orientation, 313, 322, 323, 345–349, 441, 470, *492*, 505
 autoregulation, 322
 in swimming, see under Swimming

Body posture, 67, 68, 84, 103

Body segments (see also specific segments), 252, 261, 266, 269, 270
 abdominal, 317, 353
 vestigial, 242

Body weight and size, 273, 321, 524, 537

Bowman's capsule, 548

Brain (see also Ganglia, cerebral and supraesophageal), 242, *243*, 246–248, 255–261, 268, 272, 276, *292*, 293–295, 305
 effects of: extracts, 153, 232
 implantation, 159
 removal, 256
 as hormone source, 545
 inhibitory action, 256, 258, 272, 273, 318
 structure, 248, 249
 vertebrate, 284, 285, 290

Brain waves, 259, 553

Brain-corpora cardiaca-corpora allata system, 291

Branchial cavities, 112, 116, 176, 342

Branchial tufts, 467

Breeding migrations, see under Migrations, mating

Breeding, and swarming, 448, 449

Brightness, 25, 42, 48
 apparent, *36*

Bristle sieve, pyloric, *571*

Brood pouch, 484, 486

Brooks' rule, 542, 543

Bunson-Roscoe law, 7, *32*, 33

Buoyancy, center, 345, 346, 348, 349

Burrowing, see under Locomotion types

Burrows, 451, 466, *468*, 469, 472–477, 479, 485, 500, 513, 580
 construction, *468*, 469, 476, 477, *488*
 functions, 470, 473, 475, 481

C

Caffeine, effects on light responses, 372
 effects on melanophores, 146

Calcium, 221, 233–235, 274, 414
 effects on neuromuscular transmission, 234

Calcium chloride, 122
 effects on melanophores, 146

Calcium deposition, effect of eyestalk removal, 414

Calcium ions, and action potentials, 233
 and blood coagulation, 547
 effect on excitability, 233

Calcium-magnesium ratio, effect on tonus and excitability, 545, 546
Callosities, 561
Calyptopis larvae, 5, 336, 342, 438
Camouflage, see under Behavior patterns
Canals (tubules) of Leydig, 109
Capillaries, 531, 541
Carapace (see also Exoskeleton), 113, 254, 268, 270
Carbon dioxide, as radioactive tracer, 222
  effects on: retinal pigment migration, 161
    light responses, 372, 443
    swimming direction, *489*, 504
Cardiac ganglia, see under Ganglia
Cardiac output, 547
Cardiac stomach, *571*
Carina, 470
Carotenoproteins (see also Rhodopsin), 543, 564, 565
Carpopodites (carpus), *197, 202*, 215, 227, 228, 270, 474
Catalase, 563
Caudal furca, 323, 338
Caudal photoreceptor (6th abdominal ganglion), 2, 3, 259, 268
Causal explanations, 514, 522, 562
Causal relations, 465, 527, 554, 555
  evolutionary, 572, 573
Ceca, dorsal anterior, *571*
Cell division, 529, 558
Cell membranes, polarization, 529
Cells (see also under types, e.g. Neurons), differentiation, 529, 530
Cellulae superiores mediales, 493–495
Cellular parsimony, 53, 533, 545, 550
Cellulase, 570
Central nervous system (CNS) (see also Brain, Ganglia, etc.), 126, 139, 141, 142, 147, 163, 191, 204, 235, 241–279, 291, 303, 368, 546, 554
  and asymmetry, 534, 535, 553
  and behavior, 487, 500–515
  cellular parsimony, 533, 545
  centers for physiological rhythms, 402, 403, 410, 417, 418, *419*, 554
  compensatory action, see Compensation, central
  control of: feeding, 256
    locomotion, 313, 317–321, 353, 355, 488, 489
    orientation, 490, 493–498
    receptor sensitivity, 8, 77, 496, 576
  effects of: cooling, 545
    drugs, 273–275
    light, 6, 267, 268, 550
    surgical interference, 195, 256–258, 376, 493–496, 502
  effects on: kineses, 366, 367, 392, 554
    taxes, 367–369, 392, 554
  giant fibers, see Giant fibers
  hemicenters, 368, 369
  higher centers, 368, 369, 376
  higher functions, 250, 276, 515 ·
  histology, 241–251, 297
  integrating action, 66, 67, 83, 91, 206, 269, 576
  moods, 368, 369, 554
  neuro-endocrines, 155, 281
  neurons, see under Neurons
  neurosecretory cells, see Neurosecretory cells
  peripheral models, 534
  physiology, 260–273, 305
  plasticity, 276, 498, 499
  reference values, 490, 491
  reflexes (see also Compensatory reflexes), 251–258
  releasing mechanisms, see Releasing mechanisms
  spontaneous activity, 258–260, 274
  structure, 242, *243*, 244–250, 272, 275, 276
  synapses, see Synapses
  tracts, 533, 552
  vertebrate visual pathways, 26
  visual responses, 267, 268, 496
Centrifuge experiments, 389, 390, 553
Cephalothorax, *86*, 350, 354
Cerci, 388
Cerebral ganglia, see under Ganglia
cff, see Critical flicker fusion frequency
Chalimus postlarvae, 334
Chelipeds (chelae, claws), 192, 195, 220, 224, 254, 266, 269, *270, 271*, 272, 330–332, 335, 530, 559
  effects of removal, 509
  functions: 467, 468, 474, 501, 505

in chemoreception, 112–115, 124
in fighting, 255, 473, 474, 476, 479
closer muscles, see Closer muscles
opener muscles, see Opener muscles
raptorial, see Raptorial claws
snapping, see Snapping claws
structure, 390, 467, 481
waving, see under Behavior patterns
Chemical gradients, 383, 385
Chemiluminescence, 177, 180
Chemoreception, 109–125, 256, 384, 385, 544
  behavioral evidence, 109, 112, 117, 125
  electrophysiological evidence, 112, 114
Chemoreceptor mechanisms, 109, 112–115, 124, 125
Chemoreceptors, 109–114, 115, 116–122, 123, 124, 259, 544, 545
  comparisons in insects and vertebrates, 117
  discrimination, 122–124
  effect of respiratory currents, 385, 386
  kinetic and tactic effects, 385, 391
  modalities, 116–120
  physiology, 116–125
  structure, 109–112
  temperature sensitivity, 126
  thresholds, see under Thresholds
  types, 112, 119, 120, 384, 385
Chemosensory hairs, 114, 124
Chiasma externa, 10, 11
Chiasma interna, 29
Chitin, 13, 222
Chitinase, 570
Chloretone, 152
Chloride, 235, 547
Chloride ion (Cl-), 221, 547
Chlorobutanol, 146
Chloroform, 297
Choline, 233, 285
  acetylation, 285
Choline acetylase, 282, 285, 545, 552
Choline esterases, 282–285, 289, 305, 545, 552
  effects on melanophores, 147
  occurrence of, 284
  inhibitors of (anticholine esterases), 283, 288, 304

Choline esters, 283, 287, 289
Cholinergic transmission, see under Neuromuscular transmission and Synaptic transmission
Chordotonal organs, 66, 76, 544
Chromaffin granules, 302
Chromatography, 142, 144, 145, 146, 181, 182, 298, 299
Chromatophore control, 136–147, 160, 163
  diurnal rhythms, 136, 416, 417
  effects of light, 135–137, 417
  evolution, 162
  hormonal (see also Chromatophorotropins), 136–147, 159, 160, 162, 163, 186, 303, 404, 535, 545, 551, 552
  hypotheses for mechanism, 136–139
  nervous, 159, 162, 552
  persistent rhythms, 402–405
  vascular, 136
Chromatophore index, 145
Chromatophores (see also Erythrophores, Melanophores, etc.), 1, 133–139, 142–147, 159–162, 292, 419, 527, 530
  innervation, 162
  occurrence and distribution, 133, 134, 552
  responses to background, see Background adaptation
  stages of expansion and contraction, 134, 136, 145, 162, 302, 403, 423
  types, 133, 135, 159
Chromatophorotropic hormones, see Chromatophorotropins
Chromatophorotropins, 136–139, 140, 141–145, 146, 147, 161, 163, 552
  chemical nature, 140, 142–146, 161, 297–299
  chromatophore-concentrating, 137, 138, 162
  chromatophore-dispersing, 137, 138, 159, 162, 545
  comparisons between crustaceans and insects, 545
  and diurnal rhythms, 403
  numbers, 140, 141, 161
  precursors, 144

purification, 144–146, 297–299
secretion and sources, 140–142
specificity, 138, 146, 161
storage, 302
Chromopolypeptides, 181
Chromoproteins, 538, 548, 564
Chromosomes, 526, 529, 557, 572
Chronaxie, 195, 318
Chymotrypsin, 144, 299
Cilia, 354, 528
Cinematography, 322, 336
Circle of confusion, visual, 22
Circulatory systems, (see also under Arteries, Hearts, etc.), 281, 291, 294, 541, 547, 562
Circumesophageal commissures, see under Commissures
Circumesophageal connectives, seè under Connectives
Circus movements (manège movements), 69, 257, 368, 377, 493
Cirri (barnacle pereiopods), 118, 119, 275, 287, 502
Classification (see also Systematics and Taxonomic), 526, 540
Claws, see Chelipeds
Cleaning, see under Behavior patterns
Climbing, see under Locomotion types
Clocks, physiological, 51, 379–380, *381*, 391, 422, 426, 453, 492, 504, 514
Closer muscles, 193, *202*, 204, *214*, 215, 219, 220, *223*, 224, 225, *226*, 230, 316, 317
Closer systems, 195, 225, 226, 229, 230
Closing nets, 432
Closing reflexes, see under Reflexes, appendage
Closing response, of barnacles, 119, 120, 124
CNS, see Central nervous system
Cocaine hydrochloride, 146
Coenzyme A, 282, 285
Color blindness, 560
Color changes, 134, 135, 139, 141, 142, 147, 159–163, 425, 480, 552
control, see under Chromatophore control
in insects and vertebrates, 159–162

rhythms, 402, *403*, 404, 405, 415, 417, 420
types, 545
Color contrast, 46
Color dances, 46
Color matching, 48
Color patterns, external, 22
Color receptors, 46
Color vision, 13, 42, 46–48, 52, 53, 373, 374, 543, 560
importance, 46, 48
methods of demonstration, 46, 48, *510*
occurrence, 48
Commensalism, see Symbioses
Commercial value of crustaceans, 304, 449
Commissural ganglia, see under Ganglia
Commissures, 242, 248, 266, 268, 270, 273
circumesophageal, 255, *262*, *267*
effects of cutting, 256–258
esophageal, 247, 252, 260, 268
effects of cutting, 494, 495, 502
postesophageal, 295
Common chemical sense, 118
Comparative physiology, 77, 99, 103, 117, 354, 521–593
Comparisons, 527, 555, 558
cellular, 529
between crustaceans, 537–540, 571
descriptive, 527–556, 583
within individuals, 528–536
within species, 536, 537
explanatory, 527, 554–583
genetic, 527, 556, 557
with insects, 540–546
methods, 523–528
morphological, 524, 525, 527, 540, 571
subcellular, 527–529
tissues, organs, and systems, 530–536
with vertebrates, 546–554
Compensation, central, 369, 376, 497, 498, 534, 535, 553
Compensatory reflexes (see also Eyestalk reflexes and under Locomotion), 41, 69, 81–86, 91, 99, 103, 104, 493
Competition, 540, 562
Complementary colors, 46

Complex behavior (see also Behavior), 465–520
Compound eyes (see also Basilar membranes, Rhabdoms, etc.), 2, 1–6, 8, 9, *10*, *11*, 12–26, *27*, 28–52, 133, 134, 152, 153, *154*, 160, 161, *292*, 347, 348, 522, 530, 535, 550, 559
　apposition, 9, *10*, *11*, 14, 15, 22, 23, 25, 26, 543
　blood supply, 9, *10*, *11*
　cellular parsimony, 533
　dark adapted (see also Dark adaptation), *148*, 150
　degenerate, 1, 5, 6, 16, 559
　development, 559, 560
　and directional orientation, 378
　diurnal, 22
　double, 16, 24, 543
　effects of removal, 1, 2, 33, 349
　electrical responses (see also Electroretinograms), 36
　evolution, 16, 17, 581, 582
　fast, 34, 36, 37, 40
　form vision, 35–42
　functional effects of retinal pigment migration, 35
　functional units, 8, 26–30, 38, 47, 52
　fused (cyclopean), 4, 5, 17, 347, 348
　glow, 153
　image formation, 8, 17–26, 38, 39
　intensity discrimination, 30–35
　light adapted (see also Light adaptation), *148*, 150
　of *Limulus*, 157
　nocturnal, 23
　optics, 8, 17–19, 23, *24*, 25, 26, 151
　photosensitive site, 20, 26, *27*, 28, 543
　polarized light sensitivity, 13, 48–53
　sessile, 4, 5, 41, 148, 150
　slow, 36, 40
　specialized, 15–17, 29
　stalked, 4, 5, 9, 17, 29, 41, 150, 530
　structure, 8, 9, *10*, *11*, 12–17, 148, 378
　superposition, 9, *10*, *11*, 14–16, 19–23, *24*, 25, 26, 29, 34, 40, 41, 543
　thresholds, 21, 28, 30, 31
　time functions, 35–42
　types, 9
　visual fields, see Visual fields

　wavelength sensitivity, 31, 42–48
Conducted responses, see under Action potentials
Condyle, 315
Cones, crystalline, see Crystalline cones
Cones, vertebrate retinal, 18, 35, 37
Conflict behavior, see under Behavior patterns, displacement activity
Connectives, circumesophageal, 295, 493
　median, 295
Connective tissues, 9, 193, *251*, 253
Contractile mechanisms, 218, 221, 229, 235
　effects of drugs, 231, 232
Contractin, 137
Contractions, muscular, 192, 195, 205, 209, 210, 216, *217*, 218 *225*, 226–229, 231–236, 255, 256, 545
　compared to luminous flashing, 177
　fatigue, 199, 231
　rate, 199, 316, 531
　tonic, see Tonus
　twitch, 200, 207, 219, 224–228, 232, 233, 317, 532
Contrast, visual, 22
Convergence, evolutionary, see under Evolution
　neural, 30
Convoluted tubule, of nephron, 548
Cooling, effect on central nervous system, 545
Coordination, hormonal, see under Regulation
　locomotor, see under Locomotion
　nervous, see under Regulation
Copepodid postlarvae, Stage V, 437
Copepodite, see Copepodid
Copulation, *173*, 257, 465, 480–482, *483*, 484, 496, 498, 500, 505, 580
　effects of central nervous system surgery on, 495
　inhibition of, 256
　precopulation, 481–484
Copper, 564
Cornea, *10–13*, 21, *24*, *27*, 150, *154*, 254
　filtering action, 44
Corneagenous cells, 9, *12*, *13*
Corneal facets, 5, 9, 18, 23
　geometry, 28

noncontiguous, 16
and resolution, 20
size, *12*, *13*, 15
Corneal lenses (see also Lenses), 9, 16, 18, 20, 21, 134
Corpora allata, 291, 542
Corpora cardiaca, 159, 161, 291, 297, 302, 304, 545
Countercurrent separation, 182, 298, 299
Courtship, see under Behavior patterns
Coxae, 315
Coxal proprioceptors, 74
Critical flicker fusion frequency (*cff*), 34, 35, *36*, 37
Crossbreeding, 556
Cross reactions, serological, 577, 578
Crusher claws (see also Chelipeds), 225
Crystalline cone cells, 9, *12*, *13*
Crystalline cones, 9, *10–13*, 14, 16–21, 23, *24*, *27*, 134, *148*, *149*, 150
functions, 21, 26
image formation, 19
refraction by, 18, 19, 25
Crystalline cone stalks, *10*, *11*
waveguide action, 25, 26
Cumarin, 118, 120, 124
Cupula, 93, 551
Curare, 146, 231, 232
Cuticle (see also Exoskeleton and Integument), 111, 159, 314, 541, 542
Cutter claws (see also Chelipeds), *225*, 226
Cybernetics (see also Feedback mechanisms), 490, 491, 536, 553
Cycles (see also Rhythms), behavioral, 504, 505
diurnal, 408–410, 412, 417, 424, 537
endogenous, 422
exogenous, 425
growth, 537, 549
lunar, 404, 409, 410, 413, 424, 426, 537
molting, 535, 537, 542, 549
reproductive, 372, 505, 535, 537, 549
seasonal, 401, 537
solar, 404
tidal, 122, 401, 404, 405, 410, 421, 424, 426, 469

Cypris larvae, 5, 42, 336, 373, 470, 505, 559, 560
Cysteine, 285
Cystine, 297
Cytochrome *c*, 563
Cytochromes, 546, 568
Cytoplasm, 159
Cytoplasmic streaming, 134

D

Dactylopodites (dactyls), 75, *202*, 254, 270, 272
Dark adaptation, 8, *10–13*, 20, 22, 33–35, *148*, *149*, 150–153, 155–158, 161, 348, 550
components, 29, 33, 34
hormonal control, 155, 156, 407, 408
range, 37
rate changes during day, 407
in superposition eyes, 23, 29
Darkness, central nervous system responses to, 267, 268
effects of: *137*, 155–158, 162, 267, 268, 372
on eyes, 348, 494, 495
on locomotion, 442, 444
on persistent rhythms, 400–406, 409, 410, 415, *416*, 418, 426
Darwinian adaptedness, 561
Darwinian homologies, 573
Darwinian sexual selection theory, 514
Day length, relation to persistent rhythms, 412
DDT, see Dichlorodiphenyltrichloroethane
Deceleration, angular, 91, 94, 96, 97, 103
linear, 97
Decussation, 247, 260
Deductions, scientific, 555
Defense, 255, 256, 470, 496, 497
effects of central nervous system surgery on, 495
methods, 186, 473, 474
reflexes, 255, 256, 266, 268, 269
Deep scattering layers, 438, 455
Degeneration, compound eyes, 1, 5, 6, 16, 559
larval eyes, 1

Dehydration (see also Humidity and Hygrokineses), 113
Dehydrogenases, 184
Demarcation currents, 195
Dendrites, 111, 295, 529
  effect of stretch on, 71, 253
Denervation, 138
Deoxyribonucleic acid (DNA), 529
Depolarization, 209–211, *214*
Depth, daytime plankton distribution, 433, 437, 438, 445
  and migrations, 453
  perception, 41, 42, 442
Dermal light sense (see also under Light sensitivity), 1, 2, 43, 52
  and color vision, 47, 48
  and intensity discrimination, 32, 33
Desiccation, 401
Development (see also Differentiation and Growth), complex, 559, 570
  epimorphic, 570
  and horizontal migrations, 448
  and phylogeny, 572
  postembryonic, 127
  stages, 537
Developmental explanations, 555, 558–560, 583
DFP, see Diisopropyl fluorophosphate
Dialysis, 144
Diapause, 305, 558
Dichlorodiphenyltrichloroethane (DDT), 147, 233, 286
Dichroism, 51
Diets, amino acid requirements, 563
Difference spectra, 43, 44, *45*
Differentiation (see also Development and Growth), 529, 530, 559
Digestive enzymes, **547**
Digestive gland, see Hepatopancreas
Digitoxin, 302
Dihydroxyindole, 290
Diisopropyl fluorophosphate (DFP), 274, 289
Dioptric systems, see Physiological optics
Discrimination, sensory, see Sensory discrimination
Displacement, angular, see Rotation and Turning
  linear, 77, 91, 493

Displacement activity, see under Behavior patterns
Display, 477, 481, 503, 513, 514
  courtship, 470, 476, 546, 580
  development and occurrence, 502, 512, 514
Distribution, geographical, 566
Diurnal rhythms (see also under Cycles and Rhythms), 21, 379, 380, 392, 401, *403*, 404, 412
  of chromatophores, see under Chromatophore control
  effects of barometric pressure and temperature, 409, 415, 417
  endogenous, 492
  hormonal control, see under Regulation, hormonal
  and light responses, see under Light responses
  of melanophores, see under Melanophore control
  persistent, 158, 159, 409, 412, 414, *416*, 418–425
  phase shifts, 417–420
  of retinal pigments, see under Retinal pigment migrations
  two-center hypothesis for regulation, *419*
Diurnal vertical migrations, 127, 352, 414, 432–447, 455
  anomalies, 438–440
  bathypelagic, 437
  day depths, 433, 437, 438, 445
  effects of: gravity, 439–441, 444
    hydrostatic pressures, 414, 442
    light, 7, 374, 389, 391, 439, 441
    temperature, 443, 444
  and evolution, 445
  factors controlling, 373, 414, 436, 440–445
  mechanisms of, 439, 440
  occurrence, 434–436, 444
  ontogenetic changes, 436, 444, 560
  patterns, 433, 434, 436, 438–445, 454
  and physiological rhythms, 414, 437, 444
  previous reviews, 432
  sex differences, 437
  significance, 445, 446

spatial extent, 433, 434
speed, 436, 439
terrestrial, 452
DNA, see Deoxyribonucleic acid
Dorsal light reflex, 103, 347–349, 490, 491, 534, 535, 546, 553
Dorsal trunk system, 535
Drinking, 467
and osmotic regulation, 568
Drugs (see also specific drugs), effects on:
autotomy, 289
central nervous system, 273–275
chromatophores, 146, 147
neuromuscular systems, 231–233, 273, 286
Dyes (see also Histological stains), basic, 289

E

Eccentric cells, see under Retinular cells
Ecdyses (see also Intermolts, Molting, and Molts), 542, 549, 559, 562, 566
Ecdysones, 536, 542
Effectors, central nervous system connections, 252, 496
independent, retinal pigments, 152, 153, 157, 158, 161, 162
pigmentary, 133–169
Efferent axons, see under Axons, Inhibitory axons, Motor axons
Egg laying, 117, 465, 484–486
Eggs, 321, 352, 354, 443
care and cleaning (see also Behavior patterns, maternal), 485, 486
Elastic receptors, 74–77, 101
Electrodes, capillary, see Microelectrodes
Electrodes, external, 215, 222, 225
internal (intracellular) (see also Microelectrodes), 71, 73, 208, 210–215, 223, 224, 226, 230, 233, 234, 257
Electron transfer system (see also Cytochromes), 528, 563
Electrolytes, 120, 179, 221
Electron micrography, of rhabdoms, 14, 26
of sinus glands, 300, 301
Electrophoresis, 144, 163, 181
paper, 141, 144, 145, 161, 298, 299

Rc values in, 200, 229, 234, 335
Electrophysiology, 66, 98, 99, 112, 114–116, 122, 124, 551
neuromuscular system, 199, 206–216
Electroretinograms (ERG's), 27, 33, 36, 43, 52, 543
and adaptation, 33, 34
components, 33, 34, 36, 37
origins, 26, 34, 37
and polarized light, 49
vertebrate, 37
Embryology (see also under Development, Growth, etc.), 558
Embryos, 321, 352, 498, 573
Emission spectra, 175, 177, 178, 180, 185
Endocrine organs (see also Androgenic glands, Y-Organs, etc.), 138, 153, 160, 163, 535
classical criteria, 138
Endocrine regulation, see Regulation, endocrine, and Regulation, hormonal
Endocrine systems, effects of light, 6
Endoparasites (see also under Parasites), 542
Endopodites (endopods), 322, 347
Endoskeleton, 220, 315
End-sacs, 548
Energy metabolism, 522, 563
Enteramine, see 5-Hydroxytryptamine
Enteroceptors, 502, 554
Environmental fitness (see also Acclimation, Habitat, Temperature, etc.), 562
Enzymes (see also specific enzymes, e.g. Choline esterases), 216, 529, 545, 547, 552, 557, 570
activation, 547
development, 558
functional centers, 563
hydrolytic, 216
Enzyme systems, molecular patterns, 524
Ephaptic transmission, 232, 253, 260, 533
Epicuticle, see under Cuticle
Epidermis (see also under Integument), 9, 135, 144, 159, 177, 292, 293
Epinephrine, see Adrenaline

Epineurium, 193
Epithelium, sensory, 533, 544
Equilibrium, 488–491
  gravitational, 389, 392
  receptors, see Statocysts
  spatial, 77, 103, 104
ERG's, see Electroretinograms
Ergotoxin, 274
α-Erythroidin, 232
Erythrophores (see also Chromato-
    phores), 133, 136, 137, 140–147,
    298, 299, 403
Escape, 40, 103, 255, 256, 264, 347, 379,
    476, 477, 500, 503, 504, 508
  mechanisms, 336, 342, 353, 354
  methods, 473, 474
  orientation, 380, 381, 492
Escape reactions, 100, 115, 255, 256, 353,
    355, 372, 382, 383, 504, 533
  effect of age, 264
  as klinokineses, 367
  to low salinity, 385
Escape reflexes, 261, 474, 539
Eserine, 274, 289
Esophageal commissures, see under
    Commissures
Estradiol, 147
Ethanol, see Ethyl alcohol
Ether, 181, 297, 298
Ethology (see also Behavior), 487, 512,
    578, 580, 581
  comparative, 529, 576
Ethyl alcohol (ethanol), 121, 124, 140,
    297, 298
Euphotic zone, 445
Euryhalinity, and riboflavin, 567
e-Vector (plane of polarization), see
    under Polarized light, etc.
Evolution (see also Phylogeny), 174,
    314, 540, 570–583
  and behavior, 512–514, 580
  bioluminescence, 174
  brine-living forms, 575
  chromosomal, 572
  compound eyes, 16, 17, 581, 582
  control of color changes, 162
  convergent, 16, 556, 572, 575–577, 581
  direction, 572
  excretory patterns, 574

fresh-water forms, 574, 575
  lobus osphradicus, 111
  mandibles, 581, 582
  marine forms, 574
  migrations, 445, 575
  and paleontology, 572
  parallel, 572, 575, 577, 580
  pereiopods, 581, 582
  phosphagens, 573
  proprioceptors, 77, 576
  rates, 572, 577
  regressive, 572
  serological evidence, 578
  statocysts, 103
  terrestrialness, 574
Evolutionary explanations, 523, 561,
    570–583
Evolutionary integration, 524
Excitability (see also Thresholds), 233,
    529, 532, 533, 545, 546
Excitation, 30, 177, 210, 212, 228, 231
Excitatory potentials, 212, 213, 218, 229,
    230
Excitatory systems, 228
Excitatory transmitters, 219
Excretion (see also under Nitrogen me-
    tabolism), ammonotelic, 542, 548,
    573
  of ions, 548
  selective, 548
  by storage, 542
Excretory organs (see also Antennal
    glands, Malpighian tubules, etc.),
    542, 567, 575
Excretory patterns, 548, 574
Excretory tubules, 548
Exognaths, 175
Exopodites (exopods), 313, 336, 339,
    340, 347, 352
  thoracic, 319, 323, 334, 335, 342, 343
Exoskeleton (see also Carapace and In-
    tegument), 65, 118, 133, 135, 219,
    314, 315, 331, 354
  joints, 66, 220, 314
  physiological influences, 549
  and sound production, see Sound pro-
    duction
Expantin, 137, 138
Explanations, scientific, 522, 526, 555

adaptive, 523, 555, 560–570, 583
causal, 514, 522, 562
developmental, 555, 558–560, 583
evolutionary, 523, 561, 570–583
genetic, 498, 555–558, 561, 562, 583
mnemic, 522, 562
phylogenetic, 561, 570–583
teleological, 465, 514, 522, 561
time scale for, 555
Extension receptors, 75
Extension reflexes, see under Reflexes, appendage
Extensor muscles, 75, *202*, 227, 265, *315*
Exteroceptors, 554
Extinction, of pigment solutions, *45*
Extract effects, 139, 144, 160
 from: cerebral ganglia (brain), 153, 232
  eyestalks, see under Eyestalk extracts
  optic ganglia, 140, 153
  pituitaries, see Pituitary extracts
  sinus glands, see Sinus gland extracts
  tritocerebral commissures, 156
  ventral nerve cord, 139
Eye chambers, 4
Eye movements (see also Eyestalk reflexes and Nystagmus), 43, 494
Eye muscles, 4, 6, 347, 348
Eye papilla, 139, 293
Eye reflexes, 41, 347–349
Eyes (see also Compound and Median eyes), 1–64, 175, 254, *267*, 268, 467, 488, *489*
 absence of, see Blind forms
 accessory, 16
 camera, 16, 17, 23, 52, 522, 550
 "caudal," 2, 3, 259, 268
 compared with statocysts, 534
 compound (lateral), see Compound eyes
 effects of: darkening, 348, 494, 495
  removal, 376, 511
 frontal, *24*
 larval (see also under Median eyes), 1, 4–6
 lateral (see also Compound eyes), 6, 272

and luminous organs, 569
median (naupliar), see Median eyes
microstructure, comparative 549
occurrence, 4–6
photochemical mechanisms, comparative, 549
physiological optics, comparative, 549, 550
and spatial orientation, 546
and special habitats, 569
tremor, 22, 23, 550
types, 4–6, 8, 16, 17, 24, 44
vertebrate, 26
Eyestalk extracts, *137*, 138–145, *146*, 153, *154*
 effects of, 139, 140, 143, 146, 156, 157, 297–299, 409
 effects of sinus-glandless, 140
 properties, 142
Eyestalk hormones, 321, 403
Eyestalk position, effects of: gravity and light, 491, *492*, 497, 498
 rotation, see Nystagmus
 statocysts, 68, 497, 498
Eyestalk reflexes, 41, 69, *81*, *82*, 84, 254
 compensatory, 69, *81*, *82*, 85, 91, 93, 94, 96, 104
Eyestalks, *10*, *11*, 26, 29, 30, 137–142, 153, 154, 254, 291, *292*, 552
 control of growth, 549
 effect of immobilizing, 378, 379, 553
 nervous inhibition by, 409
 neurosecretory cells in, 293, 295
 and orientation, 378, 379
 storage of vitamin A, 529, 565
Eyestalk removal, effects of: 68, *137*, 138, 403, 414
 on molting, 414
 on physiological rhythms, 402, 409, 412, 414

F

Facets, see Corneal facets
Facilitation, 192, 195, 198, 208, 212, *213*, 214, 216, *217*, 223–227, 230, 235, 261, 273, 275, 318
 of action potentials, 199
 of contraction, 199

of inhibition, 200, 201, 218, 267, 316, 552

synaptic, 288

Factor I, neurohumoral, 290

and γ-aminobutyric acid, 290

Fast and slow systems (see also under Motor systems), abdominal stretch receptors, 70, 71, 73, 74, 220, 551

innervation, 576

Fat absorption, 547, 548

Fatigue, 196, 199 201, 231, 261, 503

and synaptic transmission, 264, 273, 288, 317

Feathers, 527

Feedback mechanisms (see also Cybernetics), control of orientation, *491*

hormonal, 536

nervous, 503, 514, 536, 554

peripheral, 264

reflex, 252

Feeding (see also under Food), 115, 117, 118, 121, 124, 125, 258, 547

central nervous system center, 256

by filtering, 342, 466, 469, 546, 547

larval, 504, 505

and migrations, 445, 446, 449, 451, 452, 454

by parasites, 569, 570

relation to swimming, 342, 343

and specific gravity, 439

and swarming, 474, 475

Feeding behavior, 113, 115–118, 124, 466, 467, 476, 499, 506, 508, *510*

as displacement activity, 503, 513

effects of central nervous system surgery on, 495, 496, 502

effects on metabolic steady state, 515, 559

ritual, 513

Feeding currents, 342, 343, 469

Feeding habits, bulk, 449

carnivorous, 41, 42

omnivorous, 449, 466

Fertilization, 558

self-fertilization, 570

Fighting, see under Behavior patterns

Filter feeding, see under Feeding

Flagella, antennal, *110*, 111, 113, 114, 255, 272

Flavin mononucleotide (FMN) (riboflavin 5′-phosphate), 179

Flexion receptors, 76

Flexion reflexes, see under Reflexes, appendage

Flexor muscles, *75, 197, 202*, 203, 204, *209*, 215, *227*, 229, 230, 242, 258, *315*

Flexor tension, effects of central nervous system surgery on, 495

Flicker, see Critical flicker fusion frequency (*cff*)

Fluid resistance, and locomotion, 345, 346, 348

Fluorescence, and bioluminescence, 180, 181

of tissues, 2

FMN, see Flavin mononucleotide

f-Numbers, 19–21

Food (see also under Feeding), 113, 122, 343, 449, 476, 496

detritus as, 449

fruit as, 466, 487

phytoplankton as, 46

Food chains, 304

Food seeking (see also Prey catching), 113, 118, 125, 385, *386*, 391, 446, 502, 507

effect of light on, 504

methods, 466, 467

Form discrimination, 7, 23, 35–42, 550

Formic acid, 122, 385

Fossils (see also Paleontology), 572, *582*

Fovea, 13

Frequency discrimination, 102

Funnel canals, 109, *110, 111,* 116

Furca, 187

Furcilia larvae, 5

G

GABA, see γ-Aminobutyric acid

Gaits, see Walking patterns

Galvanotaxes, 391

Ganglia, 154, 193, 242, *243*, 244, *248*, 252, 259, 260, 266, 276, 319

abdominal, *243, 245, 246, 250*, 252, 261, *265*, 268, 285, 288, 318

choline esterase in, 284

structure, 249, 261, *262*, 264
acetylcholine content, 283
autonomic, 284, 288
cardiac, 241, 266, 273, 287, 529, 532, 533
cerebral (see also Brain), blood supply, 531
choline esterase in, 284
extracts of, 153, 232
cheliped, 254
commissural (paraesophageal), *243*, 249, *292*, 294, 295
optic (see also under Lamina ganglionaris, Medulla externa, etc.), 27, 139, 150, 155, *292*, 294, 318
effects on electroretinogram, 37
effects of extracts, 140, 153
number, 29, 140, 141
protocerebral connections, 26
oral, effects of removal, 494, 495
sixth abdominal (caudal photoreceptor), 2, 3, 244, 259
structure, 242, 244, *248*, 249
subesophageal, 160, *243*, *246*, 247–249, 259, 266, 268, 318, 539
effect of implantation, 159
effect of removal, 258
functions, 258, 493
supraesophageal (SEG) (see also Brain), 140, 160, 318, *496*, 497
effects of surgery, 493–497
telson, *243*, 247, 259, 261, 268
thoracic, 140, 160, *243*, *246*, 249, 254, 258, 261, 268, 294, 295, 318
ventral (see also Ventral nerve cord), 242, 246, *248*, 249, 250, 261, *292*
blood supply, 531
Ganglion cells, 111, 191, 242, 287, 529, 532
Gastric mill, *571*
Gastroliths, effect of eyestalk removal, 414
Gelatin, 112
Generator potentials, 26, *27*, 71–73, 532, 534, 551
Genes, 555–557, 576
Genetic explanations, 498, 555–558, 561, 562, 583

Genetic homologies, see under Homology
Genetics, 526, 537, 549, 555–558
and phylogeny, 572
Genital orifice, 484
Genotypes, *555–557*, 561, 562, 576
Geology, and evolution, 572
Geotaxes, 389, 390, 441–443
Giant fibers (in central nervous system), 194, 206, 242, 244, 245, 247–251, 255, 260–266, 268, 269, 272, 275, 353, 533
lateral, 245, 247, *248*, *249*, 255, 260, 261, *262*, 265, 272, 275
medial, 245, 247, *249*, *250*, 251, 255, 260, 261, *262*, 263, 265, 268
motor, 244, *245*, *249*, *250*, 276
occurrence and structure, 247, 539
segmental, 255, 260, 265
systems, *248*, 250, 260–265
transmission, *251*, 260, 261, *262*, 263–265, 288
Gill area, factors affecting, 547, 568
Gills, 289, 295, 296, 508, 541, 542, *571*
function in ionic and osmotic regulation, 533, 541, 561
Glands, endocrine, see Endocrine organs
Glial elements, 249
Gliding, see under Locomotion types
Globins, 564
Globuli, effects of removal, 257, 494–496
Glucose, 119, 222, 548
Glutamic acid, *115*, 231
Glycerol, 119
Glycine, *114*, 122, *123*, 124
Glycogen, 222
Glycolysis, 563
Gnathobases, *123*
Gnathopods, 323, 334, 484, 559
Golgi apparatus, 244
Gonads, 506, 530, 535, 549, 554
Gonopods, in copulation, 482, 483
Gravitation, diurnal variations, 401
Gravity, 77, 80, 83, 103, 127, 389, 414, 534, 553
center of, 103, 321, 322, 325, 345, 346, 349, 447

effects on: diurnal vertical migrations, 439–441, 444
  eyestalk and leg positions, 491, *497*, 498
  locomotion, 323, 345, 346, 348, 349, *390*, 447
Gravity receptors, 389, 504, 534, 544
Gravity responses, and orientation, 127, *488*, *490*, 491, 496–498, 504, 534, 535, 544
  tactic, 389, 393
Green glands, see Antennal glands
Growth (see also Development, Differentiation, and Relative Growth), 537, 542, 543, 549, 559, 561
  control, 549
  cycles, 537, 549
  equilibrium constant, 537
Growth index, initial, 537
Guanidines, 146
Guanine, 150
Guanophores (see also Chromatophores), 133, 135, *137*, 141, 144, *416*
Gustation, 116, 117, 385
Gustatory receptors, 116, 117, 124
Gut (intestine) (see also Mid-gut, etc.), 231, 273, 290

H

Habitats, abyssal, 447
  abyssopelagic, 569
  aerial, 431
  amphibious, 116, 117
  on anemones, 472
  anthills, 385
  aquatic, 111, 116, 117, 121, 314, 321, 355, 574
Habitats, bathypelagic, 21, 25, 29, 30, 44, 319, 538, 568
  and migrations, 433, 436, 437, 447
  and vision, 6, 7, 16, 17, *24*, 565, 569
  beaches, 333, 335, 379, 451, 493, 504
  benthic, 16, 314, 373, 431, 436, 437, 447, 449–454, 493, 547, 565, 569
  brackish-water, 548, 566, 567
  brine, 349, 548, 566, 567, 575
  burrows, see Burrows
  cavernicolous, see Habitats, troglodytic

cryptozoic, 568
deep-sea, 9, 15, 171, 186, 437, 444, 569
desert, 561
eurybathic, 569
euryhaline, 567
Habitats, fresh-water, 221, 341, 349, 540, 548, 566, 567
  evolution, 574, 575
  and migrations, 432, 436, 444
  hadopelagic, 569
  humus, 333
Habitats, littoral, 9, 25, 113, 122, 380, 468, 480, 565
  and migrations, 447, 449, 454, 486
  marine, 207, 221, 389, 446, 540, 548, 574
  mesopelagic, 565, 569
  mud, 333, 334
  nektonic, see Systematic Index
  neritic, 446, 574
  parasitic, see under Parasites
Habitats, pelagic, 16, 314, 341, 388, 529, 565, 567–569
  and migrations, 431–449, 454, 504
  planktonic, see Systematic Index
  riparian, 468
  sand, 323, 333, 451
  semiterrestrial, 574, 575
  stenobathic, 569
  subterranean, 9, 21
Habitats, terrestrial, 9, 111, 116, 117, 127, 383, 431, 467, 468, 486, 493, 539–542, 566, 568
  and evolution, 574, 575
  and locomotion, 314, 322, 325, 327, 328
  and migrations, 451–453
  tidal, 404, 469, 473
  trees, 451
  troglodytic, 15, 16, 29, 409, 568, 569
  wood, 451
Habits, crepuscular, 9, 29, 412
  diurnal, 9, 402
  nocturnal, 9, 402, 412
  sessile, 16, 546, 569
Haidinger's brushes, 49
Hair sensilla, 114, 115
Hairs, sensory (see also Statocyst hairs), 254, 267–269, *270*, *271*, 272

Halteres, 103
Hatching, 485, 486, 558, *571*
Hb, see Hemoglobins
HCy, see Hemocyanins
Head, 113, 122, 160, 255
Hearing, 78, 100–102, 104
Hearing organs, 67, 68, 100, 101, 488, 544
Heart rate (see also under Pacemakers)
  effects of chemicals and drugs, 231, 273, 283, 286, 287, 289, 290
  regulation, 2, 266, 267, 300, 319, 410, 537
    comparisons, 541, 547
    hormonal, 303, 535
Hearts, 283, 296, 300, 502
  accessory, 541
  innervation, 191, 267, 273
  structure, 287, 541, 547
Hemocoele, 290
Hemocyanins (HCy), 529, 541, 564, 577
Hemoglobins (Hb), 540, 541, 557, 564, 566
  molecular weight, 546, 564
  prosthetic group, 563
  synthesis, 536, 546, 568
Hemolymph (see also Blood), 284, 291, 294, 529
Hendersonian adaptedness, 562, 563
Hepatopancreas, 144, 176, 284, 285, 523, 547
Hermaphrodites, 559, 570
Heterogamety, 557
Heterologous reactions, 577, 578
Hexyldimethylamine, 274
Hiding, see under Behavior patterns and Shelter seeking
Histidine, 296
Histological stains, acid fuchsin, 294
  azan, *10, 11*, 294, 295
  chrome-hematoxylin, 296, 297
  Gomori method, 296
  Janus green B, 294
  Mallory's triple, *10, 11*
  methylene blue, 196, *197*, 202, 203, 244, *246*
  neutral red, 294
  phloxin, 296

Histology, central nervous system, 241–251, 297
  eyes, 549
  neuromuscular system, 214, 219, 220, 286
  neurosecretory systems, 293–296
Histones, 297
Homeostatic mechanisms (see also under Regulation), 530, 536, 561, 569
Homing (see also Orientation), 379, *450*, 451, 470
Homology, 224, 293, 525–528, 542, 583
  and analogy, 565, 566
  behavioral, 578
  chemical, 120, 121, 526
  criteria for, 540, 556, 558
    auxiliary, 527
    basic, 527
  Darwinian, 573
  definitions, 525, 526
  descriptive, 527, 530, 536, 540–542, 566, 572, 578
  developmental, 526, 558
  explanatory, 526
  general, 525, 526
  genetic, 526, 555, 556
  phylogenetic, see under Phylogeny
  physiological, 528
  serial, 525, 526, 530
  serological, 526, 577
  special, 525, 526, 527
  in visual structures, 16
Homology bridges, *571*
Hormonal control, see Regulation, hormonal
Hormones (see also Neurosecretion), 136, 142, 291, 295–299, 302, 403, 530, 552
  androgenic gland, 535, 539, 549, 554
  bioassays of, 298, 299
  in brain cells, 545
  dark-adapting, 155, 156, 407, 408
  darkening, 297, 299, 404
  effects on behavior and morphology, 502, 505, 506
  eyestalk, 321, 403
  functional centers, 563
  light-adapting, 407
  lightening, 297, 404

melanophore-stimulating, 566
molting (see also under Molting), 536,
    542, 561
numbers, 140, 141, 161, 536
precursors, 144
production, 403, 407
red pigment-concentrating, 298, 299
secretion, 142, 147, 403, 407–409
sex, 549, 554
sinus gland, 407, *419*, 545
sources, 138, 140, 141, 153–155, 545
specificity, 138, 146, 147, 161
storage, 302, 408
and target tissues, 163, 536
X-organ, 138, 295
Y-organ (ecdysones), 536, 542
Hosts, see Parasites
5-HT, see 5-Hydroxytryptamine
Humidity, diurnal variations, 401
effects on: color change, 159, 160
    locomotion (see also Hygrokineses),
        383, *384*, 504
    migrations, 451, 453
    thigmokineses, 388, 389
optimum, 391
preferendum, 122
relative (R. H.), 372, *384*
Humidity gradients, 383, 384
Humidity receptors, see Hygroreceptors
Hunger, 124, 467, 500
Hydrastinine, 232
Hydrochloric acid, 118, 119, 297, 299,
    443
Hydrogen ion (H⁺), 121
Hydrogen ion concentration (*p*H), 116,
    119, 221, 298, 544, 545
diurnal fluctuations, 410
effects on geotaxes and phototaxes, 372,
    443
Hydroquinone-quinone system, 181
Hydrostatic pressures, environmental,
    346, 350, 448
and deep-sea adaptation, 569
relation to diurnal vertical migrations,
    414, 442
Hydrotropism, 380
Hydroxylamine, *45*

5-Hydroxytryptamine (5-HT, serotonin,
    enteramine), 533
action on: erythrophores, 147
    hearts, 289
    proprioceptors, 289, 290
    sensory fibers, 232
distribution, 290, 304
as neurohumor, 281, 289, 290
Hygrokineses, 122, 383, 391, 453, 504
Hygroreceptors, 113, 160, 384
Hygrotaxes, 122
Hyoscine hydrobromide, 146
Hypothalamic-neurohypophyseal system,
    291, 304
Hypotheses, scientific, 555, 583

I

Illuminance, units, 8
Illumination, see Light
Image fixation, 42, 550
Image formation (see also Physiological
    optics)
compound eyes, 8, 17–26, 38, 39
    apposition, 17–19, 21
    ommatidial, 19, 20
    superposition, 19, 20, 25, 26
vertebrate eyes, 550
Image perception, 41
Image persistence, 23
Immunological reactions, see Antibodies,
    Antigens, Serology, comparative, etc.
Incubation, 450, 549
Indole alkylamine, 289
Induction, 558
Infrared radiation, sensitivity to, 1, 3
α-Inhibition, see Inhibition, peripheral,
    supplemented
β-Inhibition, see Inhibition, peripheral,
    simple
Inhibition (see also Regulation, nerv-
    ous), cardiac, 266
central, 206, 256, 258, 272–275, 317,
    318
    of rhythmic centers, *419*
locomotor, 34, 442, 444, 453
peripheral (neuromuscular), 206, 210–
    213, 218, 229, 231, 235, 236, 273,
    316, 317, 532, 545, 552

discovery, 192
effects of drugs and ions, 232, 234, 288
electrical effects, *210–213*, 230, 231
facilitation, 200, 201, 218, 267, 316
by factor I, 290
fatigue, 201
interaction with excitation, 212
mechanical effects, 230, 231
mechanisms, 72–74, 218, 228
and membrane permeability, 235
as model of central nervous system, 534
and molting, 204
simple, 213, *217*, 218, 230
slow and fast systems compared, 228
supplemented, 213, *217*, 218, 229–231
reciprocal, 204, 236, 317
Inhibitory axons (inhibitors), *197, 198,* 200, 201, *203,* 204, *205,* 210, 211, 235, 241, 246, 267, 290, 506
action potentials, 210, 212, 213, *217*
occurrence, 192, 204, 228
types, 204, 205, 228–230
Inhibitory mechanism, of abdominal stretch receptors, 550
peripheral, 531
of supraesophageal ganglia, 496, 497
Inhibitory neuron patterns, 539
Inhibitory potentials, *73, 210–213,* 230
Inhibitory systems, peripheral, 200, 201, 228–231
Innervation, efferent (see also under Inhibitory and Motor axons), 191, 193–206, 213–215, *217,* 222–231, 235, 530, 531
double, 162, 202–204, 213–215, 218, 222–224
multiterminal, *198,* 235, 531, 552
polyneuronal, 192, 196, 213–216, 228, 235, 316, 317, 552
quadruple, 202, 203, 215, 216
quintuple, *197*
reciprocal, 206
single, 215
triple, *197,* 204, 215, *217*
Insecticides, 304
Insulin, 557

Integrating mechanisms (see also Cybernetics, Feedback mechanisms, Regulation, etc.), 530, 547
Integration, by central nervous system, 66, 67, 83, 91, 206, 269, 576
motor (see also Locomotion, coordination), 74
Integument (see also Cuticle and Exoskeleton), 133, 134, *160,* 541
pigments in, 2, 159, *160,* 163, 403, 425
waterproof, 542, 568, 575
Intensity of light, see Light intensity
Intensity discrimination, visual, see under Light intensity
Interference microscopy, 19
Intermediate lobe, see under Pituitary
Intermedin, 147, 162, 299, 552
Intermolts (see also Ecdyses, Molting, and Molts), 297, 303
Interneurons, 242, *246,* 247–252, 255, 256, 259, 260, 265–269, *270, 271,* 272–276
comparison with mammalian reticular formation, 275
functions, 252, 260, 266, 276, 317
motor relations, 265–267
sensory fields, 267–273, 533, 534, 554
types, 246, 247, 251, 265, 266, 269
Intersegmental membranes, 353
Interstitial cells, gonadal, 549
Intestinal microfauna and flora, 570
Intestine, see Gut
Ionic indexes, 541, 548
Ionic movements, and neuromuscular transmission, see under Neuromuscular transmission
between neurons, 261
Ionic regulation, see under Regulation
Ionic substitution, 233
Ions, 113, 221, 528, 529, 541
absorption of, 541, 548
in blood, 541, 545–548, 561, 562
effects on: central nervous system, 195, 259, 273–275
neuromuscular systems, 218, 233–235, 286, 545
excretion, 548
loss in fresh water, 567
in muscles, 221

Iridescence, 134
IRM, see Releasing mechanisms, innate
Iron-filings, as statoliths, 78, 80
Iron porphyrin, 563
Ischiopodites (ischia), 253, 254, 273
Islets of Langerhans, 296, 549

J

Jnd, see Just noticeable difference
Joint receptors (see also under Propio-
    ceptors), 544
Joints, 269, 273, 314, *315*, 333
Jumping, see under Locomotion types
Junctional potentials, 207, 208, *209*, 210,
    214–216, *217*, 223, 224
  and excitation, 212, 213, 218
  fast, *209*, 214, 215, 219, 226, 227
  and inhibition, 212, 213, *217*, 218
  localized, 226
  relations to contractions, 218
    slow, 214, 215, 219, 226, 227
    summation, 215, 226
Just noticeable difference (jnd), 8, *31*,
    47

K

Kidneys, vertebrate, 548
Kineses (see also Hygrokineses, Photo-
    kineses, etc.), 117, 125, 365–399
  effects of central nervous system, 366,
    367, 392, 554
  fundamental mechanisms, 366–369
  in migrations, 439, 453
Klinokineses, 127, 128, 366, 367, 375,
    383, 384, 390, 392
  paths, *366*, 387
Krebs cycle, 528, 563

L

Labyrinth, vertebrate, 77, 93, 98, 99, 103
  and statocysts compared, 551
Lactic acid, 222
Lamellar bodies (onion bodies), 293
Lamina ganglionaris, *10*, *11*, 29, 37, 139
Larvae (see also specific larval types),
    1, 4–6, 42, 127, 159, 160, 370–374,
    387, 388, 540, 541, 559, 560, 568

absence in crayfish, 567
feeding, 504, 505
locomotion, 313, 316, 334, 336, 342,
    345, 352, 354
migrations, 431, 438, 448–452, 454, 504
median eyes, see under Median eyes
planktonic, 431, 437, 572
Latencies, receptor, 3, 125, *262*
Latent addition, 192
Leander units, *146*
  definition, 298
Learning, 276, 467, 487, 497, 499, 500,
    505–512, 514, 554, 562
  associative, 506–512
  conditioned, 498, 506–509
  curves, *507*
  habituation, 124, 497, 506, *507*, 510
  motor, 506, 508
  punishment, 507–509
  training, 120, 499, 506, 508, 509, *510*,
    511
  trial-and-error, 506, *507*
Le Chatelier's principle, 561
Legs, see Appendages and Pereiopods
Lens cylinders, 18, 19, 23, *24*, 25
Lenses, in photophores, 175, *176*, *177*
  in eyes, physiological optics, 6, 8, 19–
    21, 44
Ligaments, 541
Light, effects on: antennae, 348, 374
    body position, 347–349, 470, *492*, 505
    central nervous system, 6, 267, 268,
    550
    color change, 135–137, 417–420
    endocrine systems, 6, 408
    eye reflexes, 347–349
    food seeking, 504
    growth, 549
    heart rate, 2
    locomotion, 34, 321, 373, 374, 409,
    410, 453
    migration, 7, 373, 374, 389, 391,
    433, 439–445, 452, 453, 504
    orientation, 1, 127, *370*, 375, 377,
    379, 387, 392, 491, 495
    photokineses, 442
    phototaxes, 370–375
    physiological rhythms, 373, 401–406,
    415, *416*, 417–421, 426

retinal pigment migrations, 21, 31, 35, 43, 151, 155, 157–159, 405–407, *408*

rheotaxis, 387

swarming, 375, 433

vertical distribution, 433, 437, 438, 443, 445, 448

as stimulus (see also Stimuli, visual), 21, 346, 472, 491, 504

Light adaptation, 8, *12, 13,* 19–21, 29, *148, 149,* 150–153, 155–158, 348, 372

components, 33

electroretinogram measurements, 33, 34

factors inducing, 161

hormonal control, 407

optomotor measurements, 33

sustained responses, 34

Light-collecting power, optic, 17, 23, *24*

Light compass reactions, see under Menotaxes

Light fields, 369, 374, 392

Light gradients, 369, 374, 375

Light intensity (*I*) (see also Light), effects of, 321, 347, 370–375, 409, 417–420, 433, 440–445, 448, 453, 504

optimal, 375, 433, 440, 445

visual discrimination, *31,* 32, 33, 35, 46, *47, 550*

visual effects, 30, *31,* 32–35, *36,* 38

Light organs, see Luminous organs

Light production, see Bioluminescence

Light receptors, see Eyes, Photoreceptors, etc.

Light responses (see also Electroretinograms, Eyestalk reflexes, Phototaxes, etc.), 2, 3, 21, 30, 35, 43, 268, 269, 365, 376, 453, 553

effects of: age, 372, 374, 391

blinding, 376

external factors, 370–374, 444

internal factors, 369–373

ontogenetic changes, 373

polyphasic, 373

reaction time, 373, 374

Light sensitivity, 1–64

central nervous system, 550

general (dermal), 1–3, 6, 7, 32, 33, 43, 47, 48, 52, 369

Linkage, genetic, 556

Lipoproteins, 286

Lithium chloride, 122, 146

Liver, see Hepatopancreas

Lobus osphradicus, *110,* 111

Loci, genetic, 526

Locomotion (see also Escape, Swimming, etc.), *77,* 103, 122, 313–366, 373, 374, 443, 447, 554, 572

central nervous system regulation, 317–319, 321

ciliary, 354

circus movements, see Circus movements

coordination, 269–273, 320, 499, 502, 554

effects of: gravity, see under Gravity

humidity, 383, *384, 504*

light, 34, 321, 373, 374, 409, 410, 442, 444, 453

molting, 315, 316, 331

surgery, 320, 322, 350, 377, 499

general features, 314–321

integration and control, 266, 313, 316–321, 345, 353, 355, 492, 493

and optomotor responses, 383

orientation in, 43, 347, 348, 366–369, 431, 439, 440, 443, 446, 449

patterns (see also Walking patterns), 316, 317, 327, 328, *329,* 546, 554

plasticity in, 320, 321, 323, 355, 546

propulsion, 265, 322–325, *326, 329,* 330, 331, 336–342, 345–350, 572

rates, *3,* 319–322, 326, 327, 330–332, 351–356, 374, 383, *384,* 473

reflexes, 91, 316, 320, 345–349, 356

rhythms (see also Phase differences), 272, 275, *411*

spontaneous activity, 409, 410, 425

Locomotion types (see also Swimming and Walking), 322–354

burrowing, 29, 314, 334, 335, 354, 355, 488

climbing, 314, 327, 332, 333, 342, 354

digging, 334, 335, 473, 488, 503

floating, 347

flying, 353, 355

gliding, 331, 332, *336, 337,* 338, 339, 342, 344, 351, 352, 354

hop and sink, see Plankton navigation
hopping, 328
hovering, 339
jumping, 314, 335, 344, 347, 348, 351, 354, 355
leaping, 338, 351, 353
plowing, 333, 334
running, 257, 330, 332, 354, 473, 493, 498
stepping, 322, 327, 328, *329*, 332
Luciferase, 175, 178–181, *182*, 183, 184
chemical nature, 180–184
dehydrogenase, 184
isoelectric points, 184
purification, 178, 183
species specificity, 179
Luciferin, 174, 178–181, *182*, *183*, 529
absorption spectrum, 180, 181, *182*
chemical nature, 179–184
fluorescence, 181
hydrolysis, 181
light emission, *183*
oxidation, 180–182
purification, 178
species specificity, 179
Luminance, 8
Luminous (photogenic) cells, 172, *174*, *176*, *177*, 184
Luminous (photogenic) glands (see also Luminous organs), *174*, 187
Luminous granules, 174, 175, 185
Luminous organs (see also Luminous glands and Photophores), 173–177, 529, 569
development, 175
types, 174–177
Luminous (photogenic) secretions, 173, 175, 178, 184, 185
Luminous tubules, 176
Lunar cycles, see under Cycles and under Rhythms
Lung cavity, 467, 486

M

Magnesium, 221, 234, 235, 545–547, 561, 562
Magnesium chloride, 146

Magnesium ion (Mg^{++}), effect on tonus and excitability, 545, 546
Malpighian tubules, 542
Mandibles, 175, 336, 340, 344, 581, 582
Manège movements, see Circus movements
Marsupium, see Brood pouch
Masking, see under Behavior patterns, camouflage
Maternal behavior, see under Behavior patterns
Mating behavior, 117, *173*, 186, 187, *483*, 484, 500, 513, 539, 560, 580
color change in, 480
development, 505, 506
factors controlling, 554
and molting, 465, 480, 484
Mating migrations, see under Migrations
Maxillae, 112, 175
Maxillary glands, 542, 548, *571*
Maxillipeds, 203, 204, 256, 258, 270, 271, 485
function in locomotion, 313, 334, 335, 343, 344
Maxillules, 340, 344
Meat juice, as stimulus, 113, 116, *123*, 124
Mechanoreceptors (see also Propriceptors, Stretch receptors, etc.), 65–108, 288, 319, 529, 544, 551, 576
Mecholyl, see Acetyl-β-methylcholine
Median connectives, 535
Median (naupliar) eyes, 1, 2, 4–8, 23, 32, 33, 47, 48, 52, 161, 530, 535, 550, 559
color vision, 47, 48
development, 559
form discrimination, 7
innervation, 6, 7
larval, 1, 2, 4–7, 47, 48, 52
movement perception, 7
polarized light sensitivity, 7
retinal pigments, 6
specialized, 6
Medulla externa, 27, 139, 291
Medulla interna, 139, 291
Medulla terminalis, 29, 139, 153, 292, 293
Medulla terminalis ganglionic X-organ (MTGX), see under X-Organs

Megalopa larvae, 313, 352, 442

Melanins, 150, 538

Melanoid pigments, red, 557

Melanophores (see also Chromatophores), 133, 135, 136, 139–147, 159, 162, 298, *302*, 405, 538, 566
    control of physiological rhythms, 403, 405, *416*, *418*, *423*

Membrane conductance, 289, 532, 533

Membrane permeability, 142, 235, 286–288

Membrane potentials, in muscle, 206–209, *210*, *211*, 212–215, 223, 234, 236
    resting, see Resting potentials

Membrane transport, 529

Memory, visual, 51

Menotaxes, 367, 368
    astronomical, 51, 377, 379, 380, 391, 453, 492, 546
    to gravity, 481–491
    to light (light compass reactions), 377–380

Meropodites (merus), *75*, 192, 253, 474

Metabolic rate, 321, 426, 530, 537, 569
    and blood supply, 531
    effect on light responses, 372
    persistent rhythms, 410–414
    and size, 524

Metabolic regulation, 535, 536, 546, 561

Metabolic steady state, 515, 559

Metabolic work, 529, 567

Metabolism, 45, 127, 321, 557, 569, 570
    and behavior, 128, 515
    development, 558
    diurnal cycles, 412, 424
    of muscle fibers, 221, 222
    neurohumoral, 303
    and relative growth, 558, 559

Metabolites, 443, 529, 530, 558

Metachronal rhythms (see also Rhythms, physiological), 318, 324, 329, 343, 344

Metachrosis, see Chromatophores and Color changes

Metamorphosis, 5, 33, 387, 470, 559

Metanauplius larvae, 438

Methyl alcohol (methanol), 297

Methyl butyrate, 284

Microelectrodes (see also Electrodes), 114, 206, 208, 210, 215, 261, 262

Microsomes, 522

Microvilli, in rhabdoms, 14

Midbrain, photosensitivity, 550

Mid-gut, *571*

Migrations, 125, 431–463, 504, 553
    effects of light, see under Light
    and endocrine control, 553
    evolution, 445, 575
    and feeding, 445, 446, 449, 451, 452, 454
    osmotic factors, 553
    and rheotaxis, 450–454

Migration types: benthic, 449–454
    catadromous, 553
    diurnal, vertical, see Diurnal vertical migrations
    feeding, see under Feeding
    group, *475*
    horizontal, 443, 446–449, 454
    inshore, 446
    mating, 437, 446, 449–452, 454, 503, 553
    molting, 449, 452, 453
    ontogenetic, 432, 436, 437, 444, 448, 454, 560
    pelagic, 431–449, 454, 504
    seasonal, 127, 432, 437, 439, 444, 446–451
    spawning, see mating, above
    swarming, 448, 449
    terrestrial, 451–453
    tidal, 426, 448, 451, 453
    vertical, 389, 432–446, 504
        diurnal, see Diurnal vertical migrations

Mimesis, behavioral, 472

Mitochondria, 244, 286, 294, *300*, *301*, 302, 522, 523, 528

Mitosis, see Cell division

Modalities, chemoreceptor, see under Chemoreceptors
    taste, see under Taste

Models, biological, 500, 501, 525, 534

Moisture responses, see under Humidity and Hygrokineses

Molecules, and the limits of biology, 528

Molting (see also Ecdyses, Intermolts, and Molts), 141, 204, *292*, 295–297
  hormonal control, 542
    acceleration, 414
    inhibition, 291, 295, 303
  larval, 559
  and locomotion, 315, 316, 331
  and mating, 465, 480, 484
  and migrations, 449, 452, 453
  and peripheral inhibition, 204
  physiological rhythms, 414, 415
  and social behavior, 477, 479
  and statolith replacement, 467, 468
  and swarming, 415
  and turgor, 315
Molting cycles, 537, 549
  endocrine control, 535, 542
Molts (see also Ecdyses), 316, 543, 559, 567
  puberty, 480, 482
Moon (see also under Cycles and Orientation, astronomical), as menotactic reference, 51, 377
Morphology, and behavior, 505, 506, 512, 513
  chemical, 529
  comparative, see under Comparisons
  and phylogeny, 572
  typological, 526
Mosaic vision, 17, 18, 21, 23, 38
Motor axons (see also Axons), 191, 192, *198, 202–205,* 207–210, *227,* 232, 235, 241, 244, 247, *248, 250,* 261–265, 295, 316, 317
  fast, 195, *197, 214,* 215, 216, *217, 219,* 227, 228
  slow, *197,* 208, 215, 216, *217,* 218, *219,* 223, 228
Motor end plate, 216
Motor responses, 198–201, 203, *227,* 258, 531
Motor systems, 198–201
  fast, 199, 200, *209,* 214–219, 222–229, 576
  comparisons, 224–228
  slow, 74, 199, 200, 203, 214–219, 222, *223,* 224, 226, 229, 233
Motor units, 192, 235, 316, 552

Mouth parts, 111–115, 124, 242, 256, 258, 570
Movement, in isolated segments, 317, 318
Movement after-images, 41
Movement mechanoreceptors, see Proprioceptors, phasic
Movement perception, visual, 28, 38–41
  kinematoscopic, 39–41
  by median eyes, 7
  peripheral and central components, 39
MRO's, see Muscle receptor organs
MTGX (Medulla terminalis ganglionic X-organ), see under X-Organs
Mucus, 443
Multiterminal innervation, see under Innervation, efferent
Muscarine, 232
Muscle fibers, 196, *198,* 206–208, *209,* 211, *212,* 213, 214, 219–224, 226, 235, 286
  anatomy and histology, 214, 215, 219, 220, 315
  chemical components, 221, 222
  electrical responses, 209, 233, 235
  functional units, 206, 207
  heterogeneity, 235
  innervation, 213–215, 532
  mechanical responses, 220, 235
  membrane potentials, 206, 207
  metabolism, 221, 222
  origins and insertions, 219, 220
  sheath, 196
  slow, 552
  striated, 206, 314
Muscle receptor organs (MRO's) (see also under Stretch receptors), 66, 69–74, 102, 103
  adaptation, 69, 70
  fast and slow, 70, 71, 73, 74, 220
  inhibition, 72–74
  innervation and structure, 69, *70,* 72
  and muscle spindle similarity, 77, 576
  physiology, 69–74
Muscle receptors, abdominal (of Alexandrowicz), see Muscle receptor organs and under Stretch receptors
Muscle receptors, coxal, 74, 244

Muscles (see also Motor systems, Neuromuscular systems, specific muscles, etc.), *203*, 210, 219–230, 251, 254, 284, 522, 523, 529
 action potentials, see under Action potentials
 activation mechanisms, 221
 antagonistic, 236
 contraction, see Contractions, muscular
 cross-striated, 235, 316, 531
 efferent innervation, see under Innervation, Motor, Inhibitory, etc.
 electrolyte content, 221
 extrinsic and intrinsic, 314
 heat production, 222
 locomotor, 315, 316, 354
 membrane potentials, see under Membrane potentials
 membrane properties, 207
 metabolism, 221, 222
 neurohumors in, 283, 284
 ocular, see Eye muscles
 origins and insertions, *315*
 postural, 317
 receptor, 69, *70*, 220, 544, 576
 responses, local, 194, 195, 206, 209, *225*
  regulation, 316, 317
 resting potentials, see under Resting potentials
 smooth, innervation, 552
Muscle spindle, vertebrate, *77*, 103, 550, 551, 576
Muscle tonus, see Contractions, muscular and Tonus
Muscle twitch, see under Contractions, muscular
Mutations, 556, 557
Myelin, 193, 194, 539
Myochordotonal organs, *76*, 544
Myofibrils, 196, 198
Myosin, 221, 529, 563
Myrmecophilous forms, 375, 385

N

Natural laws, 555
Natural philosophy, 525
Natural selection, 558, 561, 565

Naupliar eyes, see Median eyes
Nauplius larvae, fresh-water, 567
 light responses, 370, 373, 374, 558
 locomotion, 336, 340, 342, 352
 phototaxes, 372, 443, 560
Navigation, see Orientation, Plankton navigation, Steering, etc.
Nekton, see Systematic Index
Nematocysts, 472, 528
Nephron, vertebrate, 548
Nerve fibers, see Axons and Giant fibers
Nerve nets, 253, 261
Nerve rings, 245, *246*, 252, 258
Nerves (see also specific nerves), 193–196, 207, 231–233, 254, 295
 action potentials, see under Action potentials
 cells, see Neurons
 degeneration, 258
 effects of cutting, 195
 fatigue, 196
 heat production, 195
 hyperexcitability, 233
 optic, 29, 30, 265, *496*
 peripheral, 253, 259
 vertebrate, 284
Nerve terminals, 286, 291, 293, 294, 296, 302, 303
Nervous centers, see under Central nervous system
Nervous integration, see Regulation, nervous
Nervous system (see also Central nervous system, Neurons, etc.), 160, 529, 547
 effects of surgery, 258
 effects of temperature, 127, 259
 neurohumors in, 283, 284, 552
 peripheral, neuron parsimony, 533, 545
Nests, for brooding, 487
Neurilemma (nerve sheath), *110, 111,* 193, 194
Neuroblasts, 293
Neuroendocrines, in central nervous system, 155, 281
Neuroendocrine structures, 535
Neurofibrils, 242, *300, 301*
Neurohemal organs, 291

Neurohormones (see also Neurohumors and Neurosecretory substances), 281–291, *292*, 293–311, 552
  carriers, 297
  precursors, 297
  release, 302, 303
Neurohumoral receptors, inhibitory, 232
Neurohumoral transmission, cholinergic, 552
  polyneuronal, 562
Neurohumors (see also Acetylcholine, Neurohormones, Neuromuscular transmitters, etc.), 281–291, 294, 303, 304, 532, 535
  destruction, 303
  effects on membrane conductance, 264, 532, 533
  Factor I, 290
  metabolism, 303
  and neuromuscular transmission, 304
  number, 536
  storage, 300
  synthesis, 303
Neurommatidia, *10, 11,* 29, 30
Neuromuscular junctions, 196–206, 281, 286, 316, 317, 532, 562
Neuromuscular systems, 191–240, 355, 531–534, 550, 552
  comparisons, 191, 192, 222–231
  early study, 192, 193
  effects of drugs and ions, 218, 231–235, 273, 286
  effects of motor stimulation, 207–210
  electrophysiology, 199, 206–216
  factors in locomotion, 316, 317, 321
  graded responses, 205
  histology, 214, 219, 220, 286
  inhibition, see Inhibition, peripheral
  inhibitory innervation, 228–231
  innervation patterns, 193–231
    motor, 193–206, 213–216, 222–228
Neuromuscular transmission, 216, *217,* 218, 219, 231–235
  and acetylcholine, 231, 273, 286, 545
  cholinergic, 231, 232, 545
  effects of drugs and ions, 218, 231–235, 545
  inhibition, see Inhibition, peripheral
  mechanisms, 216, *217,* 218, 219, 236

Neuromuscular transmitters (see also Adrenaline, Neurohumors, etc.), 216, 218, 231, 232
  cholinergic, 231, 232, 552
  enzymatic destruction, 216
  specific, 216, *217,* 218, 219, 232
Neurons (see also Axons, Innervation, etc.), 242, 244, 245, *246,* 261, 281, 282, 288, 291, 297, 304, 531–535, 539, 550–553
  cell bodies in central nervous system, 74, 244, 246, 247, 258
  conduction velocity, 194
  efferent, 244–246
  functional localization, 529
  inhibitory, 290, 539
  motor, *246,* 260, 266
  optic, 27–30
  secretory, 294
  sensory, 71, 72, *73,* 253, 533
    bipolar, 74, 76, 111
    mechanoreceptor, 74, 76, 102
  sheath, 194, 250, *251*
  slow potentials, 259
  somata, 71, 72
  types, 195, 244
Neuron-to-neuron interaction, peripheral, 550
Neuropiles, 244, 247, *248,* 250, 251, 268, 295, 496
Neurosecretion, 154, 155, 250, 281, 282, 291–305
  cytology, 529
  and molt control, 542
  and regeneration, 543
  release, 155
  storage, 155
Neurosecretory cells, 139, 281, 291, *292,* 293–296, 304, 305, 539
Neurosecretory substances (see also Neurohormones, etc.), 282, 296–303, 529, 536
  diversity, 296–299
  functions, 303
  histochemistry, 296, 297
  isolation, 297–299
  storage and release, 299–303
Neurosecretory systems, 291–296, 304, 535, 552

cytology and histology, 293–297, 529
pericardial organs, 295, 296
postcommissural organs, 295, 296
sinus gland system, 291–296
Neurosensory cells, photoreceptor (see also Retinular cells, Rods, and Cones), 6, 8, 9, 26–28, 42, 53, 550
Niches, ecological, 365, 391, 562
Nicotine, 146, 232, 287, 288
    effect on synaptic transmission, 263, 273, 274
Nissl substance, 242, 244
Nitric acid, 119
Nitrogen metabolism (see also under Excretion)
    adaptive reduction, 542, 568
    waste products, 542, 548, 568
Nitrogen, nonprotein, 221
Nodes of Ranvier, 193, 194, 539
Nonelectrolytes, 120, 121
Noradrenaline (norepinephrine), 281, 303, 304
    effects on: autotomy, 289
    chromatophores, 147
    heart, 289
Nucleoproteins, see under Protein complexes
Nucleotides, 548
Nutrition, 321, 372, 546, 549
Nystagmus (see also Eyestalk reflexes), 36, 40, 48, 91, 93, 382

O

Ocelli, see Median eyes
Octapeptides, vertebrate, 304
Oculomotor nerves, 86, 496
Odorous substances, 117, 118, 120
Off-effects, electroretinograms, 36
    in central nervous system visual responses, 267
    sixth abdominal ganglia, 3
Olfaction, 116–118, 384, 385, 488
Olfactory nerve, 110
Olfactory organs, 466
Olfactory receptors, 116–118
Olfactory spindles, 110
Ommatidia, 9, 10–13, 16–23, 30, 38, 52, 148, 149, 150, 151, 154, 157, 543
    axial angles, 15, 21, 22, 378

effect of histological fixation, 12, 13
in menotaxis, 378
number, 15, 17, 47
pigments, 20–22, 134, 135
specialized, 13, 17, 23, 24
structure, 9, 12, 13, 14, 134
as visual units, 26–28
Ommatidial optics (see also Physiological optics), 18–22
    reflection, 20–22
    refraction, 18–20, 25
    visual fields, see under Visual fields
Ommochromes, 150, 538
On-effects, 3, 33, 34, 36, 37, 49
    sixth abdominal ganglia, 3
Onion bodies (lamellar bodies), 293
Ontogeny, 373, 558, 560
    behavioral changes, 504–512
    and migrations, 432, 436, 437, 444, 448, 454, 560
Oöstegites, 571
Opener muscles, 202, 203, 204, 206, 210, 211, 212, 213, 218, 220, 222–224, 228–230, 232
    of chelipeds, 193, 506
    of dactylopodites, 290
Opener muscle systems, 195, 222–224, 229
Opening reflexes, see under Reflexes, appendage
Opening response, of barnacles, 119, 120, 124
Ophthalmic artery, 9
Opsins, 44, 564
Optic ganglia, see under Ganglia
Optic nerve axons, see under Axons
Optic peduncles (see also Eyestalks), 29, 51, 295
    action potentials, 30
Optic tracts (see also under Axons, Ganglia, etc.), 9, 29, 30, 51, 142, 160, 161
    differentiation, 559–566
Optomotor mechanisms, and steering, 492, 493
Optomotor responses, 28, 36, 40, 48, 51, 52, 382, 383, 387, 393, 543
    and acuity, 34, 38
    and adaptation, 33, 34

and locomotion, 383
and rheotaxis, 387
and visual fields, 40, 382
Oral ganglia, see under Ganglia
Order, and scientific explanation, 555
Organelles, 528
Organisms, fitness, 562
  multicellular, 529
  single-celled, 529
Organs of Pesta, 176
Orientation (see also under Body axes
    and Body orientation), 52, 365–369,
    378, 379, 387, 390, 448, 454, 470,
    487
  astronomical (see also under Moon,
    Polarized light orientation, and
    Sun), 41, 51, 375, 377, 379, *380,
    381*, 382, 392, 546
  chemical, see Chemoreception
  directional, 367, 376–378, *380, 381*,
    488, *489–491*, 492, 493
  effects of surgery on, 368, 376–379
  and gravity, see under Gravity re-
    sponses
  to light, see under Light
  locomotor, see under Locomotion
  negative, 346
  non-tactic, 385
  phototactic, see Phototaxes
  to polarized light, see Polarized light
    orientation
  spatial, see Spatial orientation
  with statocysts, see under Statocysts
  tactile, 511
  thermal, 125, 127
  transverse, 367–369, 377–380
  visual (see also under Light), 488,
    496, 504, 553
Orienting mechanisms, 367, 451, 487–
    504, 511, 515
Orthohygrokinesis, 453
Orthokineses, 127, 128, 366, 373–375, 383
Osmium tetroxide, 302
Osmoreceptors, 113, 115, 122, 385
Osmotic equilibrium, 541
Osmotic pressures, 115, 221
  blood, 575
Osmotic regulation, 533, 536, 541, 548,
    566–569, 575

Osmotic relations, 553, 574
Osmotic tolerance, 567, 568
Osmotic work, 529, 567 ˙
Ostia, 541
Otocysts, 78
Otoliths, 78
Ovaries, see Gonads
Oxidation, photochemical, 181
Oxygen, and bioluminescence, 179–181
  effects on central nervous system ac-
    tivity, 259
  effects on phototactic and geotactic re-
    sponses, 443
Oxygen consumption (Q_{o_2}), 424
  and body weight, 537
  and persistent rhythms, 411, 412, *413*,
    414, 424
Oxygen deficiency, effects of, 152, 260,
    274, 372, 385, 387, 401, 536, 546,
    568
Oxygen uptake (see also Oxygen con-
    sumption), efficiency, 546, 547
Oxytocin, vertebrate, 281, 299, 304
Ozone, *182*

P

Pacemakers, of hearts, vagus action, 550,
    551
  locomotor, 318, 319
  persistent diurnal rhythms, 423, 424
Pacinian corpuscles, 551
Paleontology (see also Fossils), 527, 575
Palps, 117
Pancreas, 547, 549
Papain, 144
Paradox, neuromuscular, 218, *219*, 227
Paraesophageal ganglia, see Ganglia,
    commissural
Parapodia, 313
Parasites, 16, 124, 127, 431, 436, 504,
    570
  feeding habits, 569, 570
  locomotion, 334, 352
Parasitic castration, 539, 542
Parasitism (see also Symbioses), 538–
    540, 542, 570
Pars intercerebralis-corpus cardiacum sys-
    tem, 304

Parthenogenesis, 557

Peduncles, of barnacles, 570

optic, see Eyestalks and Optic peduncles

Penises, 483

Pepsins, 547

Peptides, 299

Pereiopods (walking legs) (see also Appendages), 74, 76, 101, *110*, *111*, 112, 113, *114*, 115, 116, *123*, 124, 225, 226, 257, 273

effects of light on, 374

evolution, 581, 582

fifth, see Swimming paddles

innervation, 202, *203*, 246, 531, 539

locomotor functions, 315, 316, 319, 320, 322, 323, 327, 330–335, 339, 340, 344, 350–352, 355, 356

specialized functions, 467, 471, 479, 482, 486

Perfusion fluids, 233

Pericardial cavities, 295, 296

Pericardial organs, 290, 291, 295, 296, 302, 535

Pericardium, 541

Permanganate, potassium, 180

Permeability, 533

axonal, 194

membrane, 235, 286

regulation, 548

Peroxidases, 563

Peroxides, 180

Persistent rhythms, see under Rhythms

*p*H, see Hydrogen ion concentration

Pharmacology, see Drugs and specific drugs

Phase contrast microscopy, 19

Phase differences, appendages, 320, 324, *325*, *326*, 327, 328, *329*, 330, 331, 353

metachronal, see Metachronal rhythms

Phase shifts, in rhythms, 417–420

Phenotypes, 555, 556, 570

Phlorizin, 548

Phobotaxes, see Klinokineses

Phosphagens, 222, 573

Phosphorylation, 522

Photic zone (see also Euphotic zone), 446, 569

Photochemistry, 181, 441

visual (see also Rhodopsin, Visual pigments, etc.), 20, 26, 27, 28, 43–45, 549

Photogenic, see under Luminous

Photokineses, 1–3, 34, 321, 373–375, 442

and diurnal vertical migrations, 439, 445

negative and positive, 348

reversal, 348

Photoklinokineses, 375, 392

Photons, 30, 42

Photo-orthokineses, 374, 375, 392

Photophores (see also Bioluminescence, Luciferin, etc.), *176*, *177*, 178, 184–187, 538

control, 175–177

and eye size, 186

lenses, 175, *176*, *177*

reflectors, *176*, *177*

Photopic vision, 9, 22, 46, 47

Photoreceptors (see also Compound eyes, Eyes, etc.), 1–64, 134, 376, 529

caudal, 2, 3, 244, 259

dermal, 1, 2, 32, 33, 47, 48, 52

Photosensitivity, 1–64, 550, 543

Photospheres, see Photophores

Phototactic sign, alternating, 370, 373

effects of light intensity, 372, 374

effects on locomotion, 373

negative, 369–373, 375, 376, 560

positive, 369–373, 375–377, 391, 560

Phototaxes (see also Light responses), 2, 34, 35, 42, 43, 52, 352, 369–383, 391, 392, 441–443, 492

effects of temperature, 444

and migrations, 439, 441, 443, 445, 453

and persistent rhythms, 415

polarized light, see under Polarized light

two-light experiments, 31, 33, 46, 47, 49, 376, 377

and wavelength, 43, 46

Phyllopodia, 314, 315

Phyllosoma larvae, 454

Phylogenetic explanations, 561, 570–583

Phylogeny (see also under Evolution), 525, 526, 570–578, *579*
  of arthropods, 17, 581, *582*
  based on ethology, 512
  evidence for, 572, 573, 577
  and homologies, 526, 570, *571*, 573, 574, 578, 581
  physiological, 573, 576, 578
  serological, 577
Physiological optics, 8, 15, 17–23, *24*, 25, 26, 28, 38–40, 51, 549, 550, 562
  lens parameters, 19–21, 44
Physiological rhythms, see Rhythms, physiological
Physiology, and adaptation, 561
  comparative, *77*, 99, 103, 117, 354, 521–593
    definition, 523, 540, 583
    and evolution, 581, 583
    levels, 583
    nature, 521–523, 528, 555
  general, 522, 523
  nature of variables, 521–525
  and systematics, 537, 538
Physiotypes, 525
Physostigmine, 147, 232, 284, 285, 287, 288
Picrotoxin, 232, 290
Pigmentary effectors, 133–169
Pigmentation, adaptive, 569
  genetic variations, 557
  and speciation, 557, 558
Pigment cells, see Chromatophores and Retinal pigment cells
  control, nervous, 551, 552
Pigment control, see under Chromatophores and Retinal pigments
Pigment granules, 134, 135, 148, 159
Pigment migrations, see Retinal pigment migrations
Pigments (see also Cytochromes, Melanins, etc.), 133, 135, *137*, 138, *160*, 162, 179
  chromatophoral, see under Chromatophores, Melanophores, etc.
  diurnal changes, 402
  integumentary, 2, 159, *160*, 163, 403, 425
  retinal, see Retinal pigments

sixth abdominal ganglion, 3
  synthesis and destruction, 545
  and systematics, 576
Pilocarpine, 232
Pituitary, control of growth, 549
  intermediate lobe, 162, 552
  pars tuberalis, 162
  posterior, 297, 305
Pituitary extracts, 147
Plankton, see Systematic Index
Plankton exclusion theory, 442, 443, 446
Plankton navigation, 437, 440–448, 455
Plankton wheel, 440, 441, 448
Plasma, 564
Plasma membrane, 196
Pleiotropic effects, 556
Pleopods (swimmerets, swimming legs), 313, 317–319, 323, 333–336, 340, 344, 352
  in copulation, 483, 484
  egg-carrying, 486
  feeding currents, 469
  respiratory functions, 343
Poikilothermal forms, 162, 549
Polarized light, apparent brightness, 49
  linear, 49, 380
  natural occurrence, blue sky, 41, 48, 51, 382, 453
    underwater, 48, 382
  orientation, induced, 7, 41, 49, *50*, 51, 52, 380, 382, 392, 448, 453
  phototactic responses, 380, 382, 392
  plane of polarization (*e*-vector), 380, 382
  as stimulus, 543
Polarized light sensitivity, compound eyes, 13, 48–53
  median eyes, 7
Polarizing potentials, 211, 212, 529
Polymorphism, balanced, 557
Polyneuronal innervation, see under Innervation, efferent
Polypeptides, chromatophorotropins, 144
  as hormones, 552
  luciferin, 181
Polyphenol oxidase, 541, 542
Pore canals, *80*
Position, spatial, see Position receptors and Spatial orientation

Position receptors (see also Mechanoreceptors, Proprioceptors, Statocysts, etc.), 74, 76, 77, 80–91, 94, 97, 103, 551
  and gravity (see also Gravity receptors), 77, 80
  Type I, 87–91, 99
  Type II, *90*, 91, 99
Postcommissural organs, 291, 295, 296, 298, 535
Postlarvae, 334
Potassium, 119, 122, 221, 235, 274, 546
  effects on free acetylcholine, 285
  effects on neuromuscular transmission, 234
Potassium ferricyanide, 180, 181, *182*
Potentials, bioelectric, see Action potentials, Generator potentials, etc.
Predators, 445, 449, 466, 473, 474, 562
  crustaceans as, 438
Predictions, scientific, 555
Preferenda, chemical, 112
  humidity, 122
  thermal, 125, 127, 128, 390
Prey catching (see also Food seeking), 35, 42, 186, 445, 466, 506
Pressures, hydrostatic, see Hydrostatic pressures
Primitive forms, 314, 503, 514, 574, 578, *579*, 580, 581
Proecdysis (see also Ecdysis, Molts, etc.), 535
Prolactin, 566
Propionic acid, 122
Propodite, see Protopodites
Proprioception, 68–77, 273, 347–349
Proprioceptors (see also Chordotonal organs, Stretch receptors, etc.), 66, 68–77, 102, 103, 355, 550, 553, 575, 576
  amine action on, 289, 290
  in appendages, 74–76, 91, 289, 349, 554
  evolution, 77, 576
  phasic (movement receptors), 74, 349
  tonic, see Position receptors
Prostigmine, 147, 274, 287–289
Protein complexes (see also Hemocyanins and Hemoglobins), 538, 563
  with amino acids, 556, 557, 576

with bile pigments, 548
  with carotenoids, 543, 564, 565
  with nucleic acids, 522, 528, 556, 576
Protein similarities, and relationship, 577
Protein specificity, 576, 577
Proteins, 183, 286, 297, 522, 528, 529, 542, 556, 557, 564, 576
  antigenic, 577
  digestion, 547
  functional centers, 557, 563
  non-basic, 296
  structural, 529
Prothoracic glands, 542
Protocerebral neurosecretory cell-corpus cardiacum system, 542
Protocerebrum, 26, 29
Protoheme, 564
Protoplasm, 528
  synthesis, 558
  viscosity, 321
Protoplasmic streaming, 135
Protopodites (propodites, propodus, protopods), *75*, *202*, *203*, 204, 228–230, 254, 270, 272
Protozoea larvae, 5, 336, 343
Pseudo-ocelli, 17
Pseudotracheae, 540
Pseudozoea larvae, 5
Pteridines, 150
Pterins, 45, 175
Puberty, 480, 482, 537, 559, 560
Pupae, 540
Purines, 45, 150
Purkinje shift, 35
Pyloric funnel, *571*

Q

Quaternary amines, 233
Quaternary ammonium compounds, 233, 287, 289
Quinine, 112, 113, 118
Quinone tanning, 542

R

Races, 537
Radiations, cosmic-ray, 425
  ionizing, diurnal variations, 401

Radioactive tracers, CO₂, 222
  glucose, 222
Raptorial claws, 41, 42, 466, 467, 512
Recapitulation, behavioral, 580
  biochemical, 573
Reafferenzprinzip, 41, 382
Recent forms, *582*, 615
Receptor muscles, 69, *70*, 220, 544, 576
Receptors (see also Chemoreceptors,
    Eyes, Statocysts, etc.)
  cells, 534, 543
  distance, 488
  functional units, 26–28, 32, 52, 98, 99,
    114, 115, 125
  kinetic and tactic, 366–369, 488
  local, 488
  turning, see under Rotation
Receptor sensitivity, central nervous sys-
    tem control, 496, 576
Red, color discrimination, 43, 373, 374,
    543
Redox potential, 181
Reflecting pigments, see under Retinal
    pigments
Reflection-refraction mechanism, 51
Reflex arcs, 153, 532
Reflexes (see also Dorsal light reflex,
    Eyestalk reflexes, etc.), 67, 115–117,
    251–258, 275, 356, 533, 534, 554
  appendage, 554
    extension and flexion, *81*, 253, 272
    grasping, 113, 115–117, 254
  autotomy, 289
  axon, 252, 253, 532
  behavioral, see under Behavior pat-
    terns
  chain, 316, 502
  compensatory, see Compensatory re-
    flexes
  complex, 256, 257, 266
  conditioning, 41, 506
  effects of surgery, 257, 258
  equilibrium, 490, 491
  eye, see Eye reflexes
  eyestalk, see Eyestalk reflexes
  gravity, see Gravity responses
  heterolateral, 252
  homolateral, 252

light, see Dorsal light reflex, Photo-
    taxes, etc.
  local, 266
  locomotor, see under Locomotion
  monosynaptic, 252
  prey-catching, 35
  righting, 256, 257
  to rotation, 94
  segmental, 247
  simple, 253–256
  thresholds, 120, 269
  turning (see also Rotation and Turn-
    ing movements), 83, 84, 367, 368,
    376
Refractive indexes, optic, 18, 19, 25
Refractory period, neuromuscular, 232,
    233
Regeneration, 538, 539, 549, 559
  control, 535, 536, 543
Regressive forms, 580, 581
Regulation (see also Homeostatic mech-
    anisms), 515, 524, 558
  allometric, 536
  automatic, 490, 514, 515
  behavioral, 502, 505, 506, 536
  directional orientation, *491*
  endocrine (see also hormonal, below),
    281, 522, 535, 542, 543, 553, 554
  of growth, 549
  hormonal, bioluminescence, 175, 186
    cardiac, 303, 535
    chromatophores, see under Chro-
      matophore control
    color changes, see Chromatophoro-
      tropins
    feedback mechanisms, 536
    molting, 291, 295, 303, 414, 542
    physiological rhythms, 321, 403,
      404, 407, 410
    regeneration, 535, 536
    relative growth, 559
    reproductive cycles, 535
    retinal pigments, 153–156, 163,
      303, 404, 407, 408, 535, 543
    sex determination, 549
    sexual differentiation, 535, 539, 549,
      557
  ionic, 536, 541, 548, 549, 561, 566
  metabolic, 535, 536, 546, 561

nervous (see also Compensation, central), 281, 317–319, 321, 409, 522, 534, 551, 552
  feedback mechanisms, 503, 514, 536, 554
  osmotic, see under Osmotic regulation
  physiological rhythms, 421–425
  pigmentary, see under Chromatophores and Retinal pigments
  reflex, see Compensatory reflexes
  respiratory, 536
  temperature compensation, 126, 128
Relationship, biological, 570–572, 578, 579
Relative growth (allometry), 524, 536, 537, 543, 559
  equilibrium constant, 537
  hormonal control, 559
  and metabolism, 558, 559
Relative humidity, 372, 384
Relaxation, 200, 229
Releasing mechanisms (RM), 500, 501, 504, 506–508, 511, 513–515
  innate (IRM), 500, 513, 514
Renal organs (see also Antennal glands, Excretory organs, etc.), 548
Repellents, see under Stimuli, chemical
Repetitive discharges, 212, 233, 256, 264, 265, 266
Reproduction (see also Breeding, Mating, etc.), 505, 535, 537, 549, 566, 570
  cycles, 505, 535, 537, 549
Resolution, optic, 17, 20, 40
Respiration, 342, 343, 387, 401, 469, 540, 568, 570
  rate, 529
  regulation, 536
  transport, 540
  ventilation, 116, 259, 319, 502, 568
Respiratory currents, 116, 342, 343
  and chemoreception, 385, 386
Respiratory organs (see also Gills, Lungs, Pseudotracheae, etc.), 467, 575
Respiratory pigments (see also Hemocyanins, Hemoglobins, etc.), 540, 541, 563, 564
  and phylogeny, 577
Respiratory quotients (R.Q.), 530
Resting position, 448, 494

Resting potentials, 561
  in muscle, 71, 72, 207, 210, 211, 212, 214, 234, 532
    peripheral inhibition, 210–213, 230
  in nerve, 71, 72
Reticular system, 553
Retina, 135, 142, 148, 150–152, 158, 378, 534, 538, 550
  blood supply, 153
  development, 560
  functional units, 550
Retinal grain, 17, 18, 38, 39
Retinal photochemistry (see also Rhodopsins and Visual pigments), 562
Retinal pigment cells, 8, 9
  accessory, 161
  distal, 149, 150, 161
  reflecting, 148, 150
Retinal pigment migrations, 21–23, 25, 33–35, 151–159, 161, 405–407, 408, 425
  and adaptation, 34
  compound eye significance, 35
  control, 151–159, 161, 163
    hormonal, 153–156, 163, 303, 404, 407, 408, 535, 543
    nervous, 153, 157, 161, 163, 543
    vascular, 153
  diurnal rhythms, 158, 159, 408, 415
  effects on: acuity, 21, 34, 151
    critical flicker fusion frequency, 34
    thresholds, 21
  effects of light, 31, 35, 43, 151, 155, 157–159, 405
  functions, 21, 34, 151
  interrelationship of the eyes, 151, 152
  persistent rhythms, 405–408
Retinal pigments, 6, 10–13, 18–21, 28, 44, 134, 135, 148–159, 161, 162
  distal, 12, 13, 20, 21, 25, 31, 135, 151–153, 154, 155, 158, 292
    control, 153–156
    dark adaptation, 156
    daytime position, 405
    light adaptation, 156
    light sensitivity rhythm, 407, 408
    nocturnal position, 405
  and eye structure, 148–150, 154

hormonal control, see under Regulation, hormonal, and under Retinal pigment migrations
in insects, 161
in median eyes, 6
occurrence, 21, 22
persistent rhythms, in constant darkness and light, 405, 406
proximal, *10–13*, 20, 21, 25, 33, 135, *149*, 151–153, *154*, 156–159
  absence of persistent rhythms, 405
  control, 156, 163
  reflecting (tapetal), 6, *10*, *11*, 18, 20–22, 135, 148, 150–155, 157, 158
  migrations, 406
Retinas, 9, *10*, *11*, 15–17, 23, *24*, 26–29
  functional specialization, 15, 16
  neural layers, 27
  vertebrate, 18
Retinene (vitamin A aldehyde), 44, 529, 543, 564, 565
Retinular cells, 20, 23, 28, 38, 134, *148*, 153
  accessory, *149*, 150
  arrangement, 9, *10–13*
  axons, *12*, *13*, 28
  basal, *12*, *13*, 14
  eccentric, 13, 14, 27, 157
  as functional units, 26, 27, 52
  numbers, 4, 5, 9–13, 47, 543
  photomechanical responses, 22
  rudimentary, *149*
  types, 9, 10, *12*, *13*, 37
Retinulas, 8, 9, *10*, *11*, 12, *13*, 16, 19–23, *24*, 26–28
  as functional units, 27
  localization of photosensitivity, 26, *27*
R.H., see Humidity, relative
Rhabdomeres, 14, 27
Rhabdoms, *10–13*, 21, 134, *148*, *149*, 150, 151, *154*
  apparent absence, 14
  chemical nature, 13, 14
  dioptric effects, 20, 26
  in median eyes, 6
  microstructure, 14, 20, *27*, 543
  occurrence, 13–15
  origin, 13, 14
  photomechanical responses, 22

as photosensitive elements, *10*, *11*, 14, 15, 20, 26–28
pigments in, 20, 28, 44
types, 14, 25, 543
Rheotaxes, 68, 387, 388, 450–454
Rhodopsins, 543, 564, 565
  bleaching, 44
  function, 44
  localization, 20, 28, 44
  occurrence, 28, 44
  spectral characteristics, 44, *45*
Rhythms, environmental (see also Cycles and Diurnal rhythms), 401, 422, 437
Rhythms, physiological (see also Diurnal rhythms and Metachronal rhythms), 401–430
  color changes, see under Color changes
  control centers, see under Central nervous system
  and diurnal vertical migrations, see under Diurnal vertical migrations
  effects of: eyestalk removal, see under Eyestalk removal
    light, see under Light
    temperature, 406, 415–417
  endogenous, 379, 417, 422, 502
  frequency regulation, 421–425
  heart, 319
  hormonal, see under Regulation, hormonal
  lunar, 401, 402, 413–415
  mechanisms of, 415–421
  persistent, 402–426
    centers for, 402, 403, 418
    chromatophores, see under Chromatophore control
    in constant darkness or light, 404, 405, 415, *416*, 426
    effects of temperature, 406, 415, 417
    frequency stability, 425, 426
    melanophores, see under Melanophore control
    metabolic rate, 410–414
    molting, see under Molting
    oxygen needs, see under Oxygen consumption
    phase shifts, 415, 417, 425, 426
    retinal pigments, see under Retinal pigment migrations

phase shifts, 417–420
plasticity, 422
  solar, 401, 415
  tidal, 401, *403*, 404, 405, *411*, 412, 415
  predominance of 24-hour rhythmicity, 422, 425
  relation to environmental rhythms, 401, 404, 405, 406, 410, 413
  retinal pigments, see under Retinal pigment migrations
  swarming, 414, 415
  swimming, 319, 343, 344
  ventilation, 319
  walking, 319, 323–329
Riboflavin, 538, 567, 568
Riboflavin 5'-phosphate, see Flavin mononucleotide
Ribosomes, 528
Righting movements, 256, 257, 494, 495
Ritual behavior, see under Behavior patterns
RM, see Releasing mechanisms
RM1, RM2, see Receptor muscles
Rods, vertebrate, 18, 28, 31, 32, 35, 37
Rostrum, 137, 138, 254
Rotation (angular displacement) (see also Turning), 77, 81, *82*, 83, 84, 89, 91–99, 103, 345, 367, 492, 493
Rotation receptors, 80, *88*, 91–99, 102, 103, 551
Rotator muscles, *203*, 204, 220
Running, see under Locomotion types
Ryanodine, 147

S

Saccharin, 118, 120
Salinity, effects on behavior, 372, 385
Saliva, 547
Sapid substances, 112–114, 117, 118, 120, 124
Sarcoplasm, 316
Saturations, color, 48
Scaphognathites, 116, 502
Schreckreaktionen, 367
Schwann's cells, 193, 194, 251
Scientific explanation, see under Explanations

Scolopale, 76
Scolopophorous organs, 66
Scopolamine, 147
Scotopic vision, 9, 23, 44, 46, 47
Scototaxes, 377
Screening pigments, in ommatidia, 20–22
Searching behavior, see under Behavior patterns and Shelter seeking
Seasonal variations (see also under Cycles), 186, 211, 283, 506
  in migrations, see under Migrations
Sea water, 115, 122, 565
SEG, see Ganglia, supraesophageal
Segmentation, see Body segments
Semicircular canals, vertebrate, 93, 98, 99, 103, 551
Semipermeable membrane, 142
Sense organs (see also Eyes, Hygroreceptors, Mechanoreceptors, etc.), 252, 269, 543, 553
  bimodal output, 91
  comparisons, 534, 535
  as compasses, 489
  effects of removal, 368
  gyroscopic, 103
  operating range, 33
  phasic responses, 551
  sensitivity regulation, 8, 77, 496, 576
  tonic responses, 320, 551
Sensilla, 112, 117
Sensilla basiconica, 109, 112
Sensilla, peg, 112
Sensory and behavioral correlations, 85
Sensory cells (see also Neurosensory cells), 26, 138, 210, 259, 533
Sensory cushion, 85, *87*
Sensory discrimination, 46–48, 67, 102, 122, 124, 535
  scales, 535
Sensory fibers, 232, 244, 247, 248, 252, 265, 272
Sensory fields, 117, 125, 269–273, 276
Sensory hairs (see also Statocyst hairs, Tactile hairs, etc.), 65, *80*, *110*, 111, 489
Sensory papilla X-organs (SPX), 139
Sensory pores, 293
Sensory stimuli, see under Stimuli
Sensory thresholds, see under Thresholds

Serology, comparative, 526, 577, 578, *579*
Serotonin, see 5-Hydroxytryptamine
Setae, 65, 319, 323, 340, 343, 351, 356
Settling, of barnacles, 470, 502, 505
Setules, 65
Sex characteristics, secondary (see also
    Gnathopods, Oöstegites, etc.), 535
Sex chromosomes, 557
Sex determination, genetic, 549, 557
    hormonal, 549
    phenotypic, 570
Sex hormones, 549, 554
Sexual behavior, 479–484
    attraction, 186, 187, 480
    discrimination, 7, 186, 496, 501
    play, 482, *483*
    pursuit, 476, 481, 484
    rejection, 480, 481
Sexual cycles, 372, 537
Sexual differentiation, 542, 559
    genetic, 557
    hormonal control, 535, 539, 549, 557
Sexual dimorphism, physiological, 111
Sexual selection, 514
Shadow, responses to, 7, 275
Shear, as sensory stimulus, 389, 390, 489,
    491, 551
Shelters, burrows, see Burrows
    plant stems, 469
    shells, 48, 388, 470, 496, 500, 501, *507*,
        511, *512*
Shelter seeking (see also under Behavior
    patterns), 466, 468–470, 473, 474,
    502, 505, 509
Sherrington's fiber, 272, 273, 544
Sibling species, 580
Sickle cell anemia, 557
Signal reaction, visual, 40
Silica, 299
Sinking, by plankton, 345–349, 440–444
Sinus gland extracts, *137*, 139, 140, 142–
    144, *145*, 153, 154, *302*
    effects on retinal pigments, 407
    properties, *137*, 139, 143, 144, *145*
Sinus gland nerves, 139
Sinus glands, 139–144, 153–155, 159, 291,
    292, 293–299, *300–302*, 305
    effects on molting, 141, 296

effects of removal, *137*, 139, 141, 155,
    157
functions, 535
granules, 298, 300, 302
histology and cytology, 293–296
hormones, 407, *419*, 545
and retinal pigment control, 155
Sinus gland systems, 291, *292*, 293–296
    general plan, 291–293
Sinus plates, see Postcommissural organs
Sinus venosus, 551
Sky polarization, see under Polarized
    light
Slow systems, see under Motor systems
Smell, see Olfaction
Snapping claws, 474, 477, 479
Social behavior, see under Behavior pat-
    terns
Sodium, 221, 233
    external, 235
    internal, 221
    relation to action potentials, 194, 233
    replacement, 233, *234*
Sodium acetate, 285
Sodium bisulfate, 146
Sodium chloride, 146, 179
    as chemical stimulus, 112, 113, 118,
        120, 122, 124
Sodium fluoride, 285
Sodium hydroxide, 297
Sodium taurocholate, 147
Somites, 242
Sound production, 101, 102, 104, 473,
    474, 477, 501
Sound receptors, see Hearing organs
Sound, as stimulus, 100, 104
Space perception, visual, 35–42
Spatial orientation, 103, 273, 350, 383,
    544
    and dorsal light reflex, 534, 535, 546
    and eyes, 546
    factors controlling, 345, 347–349, 368,
        392, 453, 546
    and gravity reflex, see under Gravity
        responses
    reflex mechanisms, 546
    sensory mechanisms, 546
    by statocysts, 392, 546
    and touch, 67, 68

Spatial relations, 555
Spawning, 449, 467, 479, 483–486
  migrations, see Migrations, mating
Speciation, 572, 580
  and pigmentation, 557, 558
Species, communal, 476
  numbers, *582*, 615–617
Species specificity, amino acids, 221
  behavior, 481, 498, 500, 501, 505, 513,
    546, 578, 580
  luciferase and luciferin, 179
Specific gravity, 321, 345, 346, 348, 349,
  439
Specificity, biochemical, 297, 540, 556,
  576, 577
  hormonal, see under Hormones
  immunological, 577
Spectra, see Absorption spectra, Differ-
  ence spectra, Emission spectra
Spectral sensitivity, 2, 8, 35, 42–46, 564
  adaptation to environment, 44, 543,
    564, 565
Speeds, locomotor, see under Locomotion
Spermatophores, *483*, 484
Spermatozoa (spermatozoids), 465, 483–
  485
Sperm receptacles, female, 482, 483
Spikes, see Action potentials
Spinal cord, 265, 276
Spinal motor neurons, 210
Spines, *123*, 346, 351
Spontaneous activity, 233, 253, 258–260,
  270, 271, 276, 319, 493
  appendages, 502
  appetence, 501, 502, 581, 582
  cardiac ganglia, 532
  in constant darkness or light, 409
  effects of: drugs and ions, 274, 287,
    546
    oxygen deficiency, 274
    supraesophageal gland removal, 496
  interneurons, 274
  motor, 408–410, 412, 425
  nutritional control, 546
  rhythmic components, 426
  sensory, 99, 551, 553
  statocysts, 74, 83–86, 98, 99
SPX, see Sensory papilla X-organs
Station-keeping, 441, 442, 444, 446, 448

Statocyst hairs, 66, 79, 80, *81,* 86, *95, 97,*
  389, 503, 532
  free hook hairs, 96
  functions, 81, 85, 86, 94, 98, 102
  group hairs, 96
  hook hairs, *92, 93, 95,* 96, *97*
  statolith hairs, 79, 85, *92, 93,* 94, *95,*
    96, *97*
  thread hairs, 79, 85, *87, 92, 93,* 94, *95,*
    96, 97, 99
  functions, 93, 94, 96–98
Statocyst receptors, types, 86–91, 100
Statocysts, *79,* 80–85, *86–90,* 91, *92, 93,*
  94–104, 349, 529, 532, 534, 535, 544,
  551, 553
  action potentials, 85
  asymmetry, 553
  compared with eyes, 534
  control of orientation, 349, 389, 390,
    392, 453, 491–493, 546
  cyst fluid, 85, 93, 102, 103
    movements, 78, 80, 94, 96, 103
  effects of: damage, 320
    removal, 68, 91, 98, 99, 101, 256,
      257, 349, 389, 488, 494, 495, 497
  effects on: behavior, 68, 98, 488, 489,
    490–492
    eyestalk position, 497, 498
    leg position, *497,* 498
    walking, 320
  evolution, 103
  innervation, 66
  location, *79, 92, 93*
  mechanisms, 83–85, 488
  occurrence, 78–80, 103, 493, 544
  physiology, 68, 78, 80–99
  sensory cushion, 85, *87*
  spontaneous activity, 74, 83–86, 98, 99
  and statolith replacement, 467, 468
  structure, 78–80, 87, *92, 93, 95*
  tegumental glands, 85
Statoliths, 78–86, *87, 92, 93, 95,* 96, 102,
  489
  effects of removal, 82–84, 86, 497, 551
  iron filings as, 78, 80
  nature, 78–80, 85, *95,* 447
  replacement after molting, 467, 468
  shearing force, 389, 390, 491
Steady state, metabolic, 515, 559

Steady state systems, 523
Steering (see also Orientation), 251, 255, 323, 338, 341, 346–351, 356, 448, 453, 491–493, 554
Stereoscopic vision, 41, 42
Stereotropism, 388
Sternites, 333
Stiftchensäume, 14
Stimulation frequencies, 200, 224
Stimuli, chemical, 112–114, *115*, 116–122, *123*, 124, 125, 254, 286, 365, 383–387
    attractants, 122, 124, 385, 443
    kinetic effect, 383, 385, *386*
    repellents, 122, 124, 443
    tactic effect, 383
  electrical, 254, 391
    direct current, 195
    intercalated shocks, 223, 224, *227*, 228
    repetitive, 212, 216, 223, *227*
  mechanical, 365, 372, 387–390
  for mechanoreceptors (see also Gravity), 91
  nonspecific, 502
  noxious, 255
  orienting (see also Kineses and Taxes), 504
  photic, see under Light
  punitive, 509
  releasing, see Releasing mechanisms
  rotation, 93
  sensory, 255, 268, 269, 346, 489, 491, 534, 551
  sign, 500, 501, 507, 508, 515
  sound, 100, 104
  static or phasic, 102
  tactile (see also Touch), 67, 68, 388, 393, 474, 475, 501
  thermal, 365, 390
  visual (see also under Light), 7, 8, 13, 31, 33, 41, 268, 385, 474, 475, 496, 543
Stimulus field, directionality, 365, 369
Stimulus gradient, 365, 366
Stomach, 256
Stomatogastric system, *243*
Strength-duration curves, *7*, 33

Stress, osmotic, 568, 569
  thermal, 568, 569
Stretch, effect on sensory neurons, 71, 72, *73*, 253
Stretcher muscles, *202*, 203, 204, 206, 213, 223, 229
Stretcher muscle systems, 224, 228, 229
Stretch receptors, 208, 210, 259, 268, 529, 533, 576
  abdominal (of Alexandrowicz) (see also Muscle receptor organs), 220, 255, 273, 532, 534, 543, 544, 550, 576
    fast (phasic) and slow (tonic), 551
  action of acetylcholine and drugs on, 288, 290
  dermal, 551
Stridulation, see Sound production
Stroboscopes, 336
Strontium, 233
Strychnine, 100, 146, 372
Stylopization, and parasitic castration, 542
Subesophageal ganglia, see under Ganglia
Subphotic zone (see also Photic zone), 16
Substance A, see A-Substance
Substrate, 319, 320, 323, 327, 331, 333, 342, 355, 389, 470, 504
Sucrose, 112, 113, 124, 146, *302*
Sugars, as chemical stimuli, 112, 118, 121, 124
Sulfuric acid (H_2SO_4), 119
Summation, 199, 208, *209*, 212, 215, 224, *226*, 254, 263, 267
Sun, as menotactic reference (see also Orientation, astronomical), 51, 377, 379, *380*, *381*, 453, 492
Sunlight, harmful effects, 445
Superposition eyes, see under Compound eyes
Supraesophageal ganglia (SEG), see under Ganglia
Surface active substances, 548
Surgery, effects on: behavior, 494, 495, 509, 511
    brain, 159, 256, 493–497
    central nervous system, see under Central nervous system
    ganglia, 159, 258, 493–497

locomotion, 320, 322, 350, 377, 499
orientation, 368, 376–379
Survival, and adaptation, 560–562
Swallowing, 256, 548
Swarming (see also under Migrations),
187, 414, 415, 446–449, 474, 475
effects of light, 375, 433
Sweat glands, 561
Swimmerets, see Pleopods
Swimming (see also under Locomotion),
103, 251, 255, 256, 258, 268, 313,
314, 330, 335–356, 498
abdomen in, 452
appendages (see also Pereiopods and
Pleopods), 112, 341, 349, 350, 355,
499
control, 318, 319, 345
currents, 336, 337, 339, 342, 343, 349,
356
effects of light intensity on, 374
and migrations, 438–441, 443, 447, 452,
455
relation to feeding and respiration,
342, 343
rhythms, see under Rhythms
in sine wave, 448
speed, 319, 321, 351–353, 439, 440
types of propulsion, 265, 336, 337, 338–
342
Swimming orientation, 345–350, 447,
448, 488, 489, 490, 491, 504
backward, 255, 339, 341, 344, 350, 351,
473, 539
circular, 493
dorsal side down, 344, 345, 538
dorsal side up, 344
downward, 440
forward, 339, 342, 346
horizontal, 348, 447
oblique, 553
sideways, 313, 339, 341, 343, 344, 350,
356
surface, 351
vertical, 345, 439, 440
Swimming paddles (fifth pereiopods),
313, 319, 323, 333, 336, 337, 339–
341, 344, 350, 351, 356
compared with fins or wings, 354, 546

Symbioses (see also Parasitism), 124,
470–473, 504, 569, 570
Sympatol, 147
Synapses, 244, 245, 247, 248, 249, 250–
252, 261–266, 275, 281, 553
complex branching, 533
of optic nerve fibers, 29, 30
structure, 251
types, 245, 275
axonal, 275, 533
commissural, 248, 261
dendritic, 275, 533
lateral, 244, 250, 251, 264, 273, 275
multiplying, 264, 266
somatic, 275, 533
Synaptic connections, 251, 257
Synaptic delays, 262–265
Synaptic potentials, 263
Synaptic transmission, 250, 260–264, 273,
274, 288, 304, 317
action of drugs and chemicals on, 288,
289
aminergic, 304
cholinergic, 304
one-to-one, 261, 264
rectifying effect, 262
Syncytia, chromatophores, 133
Systematics, 537, 538, 576
of Crustacea, 615–617

T

Tactile hairs, 65, 67
Tactile receptors (see also Stimuli, tac-
tile), 68, 488
Tail fans, 318, 354
Tails (see also Telson), 255, 265, 266,
272, 353
Tapetal cells, 12, 13
Tapetal pigment, see under Retinal pig-
ments
Target tissues, see under Hormones
Tarsal chemoreceptors, 121
Taste, 116–118, 124, 256, 488
Taste modalities, 116–120, 545
Taste receptors, 500
Taxes (see also Geotaxes, Hygrotaxes,
etc.), 117, 125, 346, 365–399, 491
definition, 365–367

effects of central nervous system, 367–369, 392, 554
fundamental mechanisms, 366–369
in migrations, 439, 450–454
Taxonomic affinity, 524, 526, 581
estimation, 571, 572
and ethology, 578
Taxonomic characters, adaptive importance, 526
Tegumental glands, in statocysts, 85
Tegumental nerves, *496*
Teleology, 465, 514, 522, 561
Telotaxes, 367, 377
Telson (see also Tails), 141, *243*, 247, 259, 261, 268, 334
Temperature (see also under Stimuli and Thermoreception), 125–128, 321
adaptation, see under Adaptation
diurnal variations, 401
effects on: growth, 549
light responses, 161, 371, 374, 444
metabolism, 127
migrations, 443, 444, 451–453
nervous system, 127, 259
retinal pigment migration, 152, 161
rheotaxis, 387
optimal, 321, 566
and physiological rhythms, 406, 415–417
Temperature gradients, 125, 217, 390
Temperature preferendum, 390
Temporal resolution, visual, 40
Tendons, 315
Tergum, 470
Terrestrial migrations, see under Migrations
Terrestrialness, see under Adaptation and under Habitats
Territoriality, 470, 477
Tetani, 198, 200, 223, 224
Tetrabutyl ammonium, 233
Tetraethyl ammonium, 233
Thermocline, effect on vertical distribution, 444
Thermoreception, 125–128
Thermoreceptors, 545
phasic, 126
tonic, 126
Thermotaxes, 127

Thiamine, 570
Thigmokineses, effect of humidity, 388, 389
Thigmotaxes, 388
Thoracic appendages, 112, 113, 124, *202*, 224, 229, 244, 270
use in locomotion, 270, 318, 323, 329, 331, 333, 336, 338, 340, 342–344, 350, 353, 356
Thoracic ganglia, see under Ganglia
Thorax, 122, 160, *205*, 266, 270
Thread hairs, see under Statocyst hairs
Thresholds, *31, 72, 75,* 76, 99, 102, 318
absolute, 31, 122, 125, 535
autotomy, 254, 255
behavioral, 120, 122, 264
behavioral vs. sensory, 38
chemoreceptor, 116–122, *123,* 545
effect of boiling point, 120
effect of carbon chain length, 121, 122
effect of oil-water distribution coefficient, 120
for homologous aliphatic series, 121, 545
difference (jnd), *47*
electrophysiological, 122
mechanoreceptor, angular acceleration, 98
rotation, 89
neuromuscular system, 195, 233
relation to membrane conductance, 532, 533
psychophysical, 32
reflex, 120, 269
sensory, 8, *77,* 535
synapses, 263
visual, 3, 7, 21, 31, 33, 38, *47,* 151
acuity, 33–35, 38, 40
and adaptation, 33
compound eyes, 21, 28, 30, 31
effects of intensity, 38
effects of wavelength, 38, 42, 43
optomotor, *36*
Thrombin, 547
Tidal cycles, see under Cycles
Tidal migrations, see under Migration types

Tonus, 200, 258, 273, 317, 318, 320, 474, 495, 534, 545, 546, 551
  maintenance, 99, 553
  relaxation, 317
Touch (see also Stimuli, tactile), 67, 68, 77, 102, 253, 268–272, 511
  distant, 68
Touch receptors, 551
Tracheal systems, 540
Training, see under Learning
Transmission, chemical, 263, 281, 287, 290
  electrical, 262–264
  ephaptic, see Ephaptic transmission
  neuromuscular, see Neuromuscular transmission
  nonpolarized, 261
  polarized, 261, 262
  synaptic, see Synaptic transmission
Transmission mechanisms, 262
  blocking agents, 262, 263
  facilitating agents, 262, 263, 290
Transmitter substances, see Acetylcholine, Neurohumors, etc.
Transparency, as protective coloration, 445
Transpiration, 542
Triethylamine, 274
Tritocerebral commissure, extracts of, 156
Tropotaxes, 367–369, 377
Trypsin, 144, 299
Tryptophan, 296, 297
Tubocurarine, 147
Tubular maximum, 548
Turbidity, effect on polarized light sensitivity, 49, 52
Turbulence, and locomotor movements, 341, 343
Turgor, influence on locomotion, 314, 315, 338
Turning movements (see also Rotation), 366, 491–493, 535, 553
  control, 488, 491–493, 496
Turning reflexes, see under Reflexes
Twitch, see under Contractions
Tyndall scattering, polarized light, 51
Typology, 525, 526

Tyrosinase, 542
Tyrosine, 297

U

Ultraviolet (UV) cut-off, 44
Ultraviolet radiation, fluorescence in, 180, 181
  sensitivity to, 1, 2, 6, 7, 43, 48, 543
Ultraviolet vision, 44, 47
Urea, 119, 183
Uric acid, 548
Uricotely, 542, 548
Urine, flow rate, 567
  hyperosmotic, 542
  hyposmotic, 548, 567, 575
  hypotonic, as adaptation, 567
  isosmotic, 548, 567, 575
  mechanism of formation, 548
Uropods, 141, 251, 255, 271, 334
  use in locomotion, 323, 335, 350
Utriculi, teleost, 553

V

Vacuoles, 244
Vanillin, as chemical stimulus, 113, 118, 120, 124
Vapor pressure, 120
Vasopressin, 281, 299, 304
Velocity, angular, 366
Velocity constants, luciferin oxidation, 183
Ventilation, 116, 259, 319, 502, 568
Ventral ganglia, see under Ganglia
Ventral light reflex, 43, 346, 349
Ventral nerve cord (see also under Central nervous system and Ganglia, ventral), 136, 246, 247, 249, 256, 268, 272, 283, 287, 288, 317, 318
  acetylcholine synthesis, 285
  action of picrotoxin on, 290
  choline esterase in, 284
  extracts, 139
Ventral nerve cord sheath, permeability, 287, 288
Veratrine, 232
Veritol, 147

Vertical migrations, see Diurnal vertical migrations and under Migration types
Vibration receptors, 100, 101, 488
Vibration responses, 67, 68, 75, 100, 101, 275, 501
Vision, 1–64, 514, 543, 549
  binocular, 42
  color, see Color vision
  form, see Form discrimination
  related to equilibrium, 77, 104
Visual acuity, 28, 33–39, 550
  effects of retinal pigments, 21, 151
  factors affecting, 21, 22, 25, 34, 38
  and intensity discrimination, 35
  minimum separable, 33, 34, 36, 38, 39
  minimum visible, 38, 39, 543
  and mosaic vision, 21, 38
  thresholds, see under Thresholds
  vernier, 38
Visual fields, 18, 26, 40, 41
  effects of displacement (see also Optomotor responses), 40, 382, 383
  of median eyes, 23
  neural organization, 29, 33
  of ommatidia, 18, 21, 22, 28, 40, 543
  overlap, 21, 22, 28, 38–40
Visual fixation, 42, 550
Visual pigments (see also under Photochemistry, Rhodopsin, etc.), 1, 6, 8, 10–13, 18–22, 28, 30, 31, 33–35, 43–45
  absorption spectra, 43, 44, 45, 565
  bleaching, 28
  localization, 20, 26, 27, 28
  natural selection, 565
  steady state, 33
Visual purple, see Rhodopsin
Visual responses, in central nervous system, 267, 268, 496
  photomechanical, 22, 135, 150–152, 157, 158
Visual stimulation (see also Stimuli, visual), 255, 385
Visual systems, neurology (see also under Axons, Ganglia, Optic tracts, etc.), 30
Vitamin A, in vision, 44, 529, 565
Vitamin A aldehyde, see under Retinene

W

Walking (see also Locomotion), 314, 320, 322–333, 354, 355, 447
  central nervous system control, 206, 493, 494, 539
  and eyestalk movements, 41
  forestroke-backstroke ratios, 324, 325, 326, 328, 329, 330, 344
  mechanics of, 322–324
  and migrations, 452
  rhythms, see under Rhythms
Walking legs, see Pereiopods
Walking patterns (gaits), 324, 325, 326, 327, 328, 329, 330, 331
  adaptive changes, 276, 546, 554
  backward, 331
  forward, 318, 324–329
  sideways, 313, 318, 323, 329–331, 378, 493
Water, as chemoreceptor stimulus, 113, 114, 115
  conservation, 541, 542, 561, 568
  currents, 67, 68, 336, 346, 355, 385, 387, 393, 505
  viscosity, effects on locomotion, 321, 345, 346, 348
    effects on plankton migrations, 439, 443
Waveguide effects, visual, 3, 18, 25, 26
Wavelength, effect on directional swimming, 448
  effect on visual thresholds, 38, 42, 43
  maximum penetration in sea, 31, 565
Wavelength functions, and compound eyes, 31, 42–48
Weber-Fechner law, 374
Weber fraction $(\Delta I/I)$, 8, 31, 32, 38, 46
Wind tunnel experiments, 336
Wings, 354, 546, 566

X

Xanthophores (see also Chromatophores), 133, 136, 137, 143, 144, 298
X-Organs (medulla terminalis ganglionic X-organ, MTGX), 291, 292, 293, 295, 296, 559
  control of hormone release, 295
  extracts, 139

homologies, 293
hormones produced, 138, 295
pars ganglionaris, 293, 295
X-Organs (Sensory papilla X-organs,
    SPX), 139
X-Organ-sinus gland complex, 303, 304,
    529, 535, 542
X-Rays, ocellar sensitivity, 8

Y

Yellow, color discrimination, 48
Yohimbine, 232

Y-Organs (molting glands), *292*, 535,
    536, 542, 559
degeneration, 559
Young-Helmholtz trichromatic theory, 47

Z

Z-Bands, in muscle, 198
Zoea larvae, 111, 127, 313, 321, 323, 352,
    371, 440, 442, 448, 559
Zygotes, 558